## DATE DUE

| | | |
|---|---|---|
| NO1 89 | JUN 01 2011 | |
| JY 2 70 | | |
| NO 3 70 | | |
| No 20 | JUN 0 6 70M | |
| DEC 15 1970 | | |
| JUN 2 1976  1993 NOV | | |
| NOV 1 7 1993 | | |
| NOV 1 8 RECD | | |
| JUN 0 5 1993 | | |
| MAY 3 0 RECD | | |
| | | |
| UL 3 0 1992 | | |
| JUL 1 6 RECD | | |
| OCT 2 8 2003 | | |
| OCT 1 6 2003 | | |
| | | |

# PLATE I.

## SPHINX-MOTHS.

1 = Pholus pandorus.
2 = Smerinthus geminatus.
3 = Ampelophaga versicolor.
4 = Marumba modesta.
5 = Hemaris thysbe.
6 = Thyreus abbotti.

**American Nature Series**
Group I.   Classification of Nature

# AMERICAN INSECTS

BY

## VERNON L. KELLOGG

*Professor of Entomology and Lecturer on Bionomics
in Leland Stanford Jr. University*

*WITH MANY ORIGINAL ILLUSTRATIONS*

BY

MARY WELLMAN

*SECOND EDITION, REVISED*

NEW YORK

**HENRY HOLT AND COMPANY**

1908

ROBERT DRUMMOND COMPANY, PRINTERS, NEW YORK

TO

JOHN HENRY COMSTOCK

# PREFATORY NOTE
## TO SECOND EDITION, REVISED

In this new and revised edition of American Insects a detailed analytical table of contents has been substituted for the simple list of chapter titles used in the first edition, and an additional chapter (Chapter XIX) on the subject of insect behavior and psychology has been added. While descriptive accounts of the reflexes and instincts of insects are to be found on almost every page of the book—insect instinct is indeed one of the primary subjects of the book—the author has believed that a special discussion and attempt at analysis of the springs and control of insect behavior would be of interest to the reader. This special though necessarily all too condensed and brief treatment of the subject has therefore been introduced into the present edition.                                                V. L. K.

STANFORD UNIVERSITY,
   March 26, 1908.

# PREFATORY NOTE

IF man were not the dominant animal in the world, this would be the Age of Insects. Outnumbering in kinds the members of all other groups of animals combined, and showing a wealth of individuals and a degree of prolificness excelled only by the fishes among larger animals, and among smaller animals by the Protozoa, the insects have an indisputable claim on the attention of students of natural history by sheer force of numbers. But their claim to our interest rests on securer ground. Their immediate and important relation to man as enemies of his crops, and, as we have come to know only to-day, as it were, as a grim menace to his own health and life—this capacity of insects to destroy annually hundreds of millions of dollars' worth of grains and fruits and vegetables, and to be solely responsible for the dissemination of some of the most serious diseases that make man to suffer and die, forces our attention whether we will or not. Finally, the amazing variety and specialization of habit and appearance, the extraordinary adaptations and "shifts for a living" which insects show, make a claim on the attention of all who harbor the smallest trace of that "scientific curiosity" which leads men to observe and ponder the ways and seeming of Nature. Some of the most attractive and important problems which modern biological study is attacking, such as the significance of color and pattern, the reality of mechanism and automatism in the action and behavior of animals as contrasted with intelligent and discriminating performances, the statistical and experimental study of variation and heredity, and other subjects of present-day biological investigation, are finding their most available material and data among the insects.

This book is written in the endeavor to foster an interest in insect biology on the part of students of natural history, of nature observers, and of general readers; it provides in a single volume a general systematic account of all the principal groups of insects as they occur in America, together with special accounts of the structure, physiology, development and metamorphoses, and of certain particularly interesting and important ecological relations of insects with the world around them. Systematic entomology, economic entomology, and what may be called the bionomics of insects are the special subjects of the matter and illustration of the book. An effort has been made to put the matter at the easy command of the average intelligent reader; but it has been felt that a little demand on his attention will accomplish the result more satisfactorily than could be done with that utter freedom from effort

with which some Nature-books try to disseminate knowledge. The few
technical terms used are all explained in the text in connection with their
first use, and besides are inserted in the Index with a specific reference, in
black-faced type, to the explanation. So that the tyro reading casually in
the book and meeting any of these terms apart from their explanation has
only to refer to the Index for assistance. Readers more interested in accounts
of the habits and kinds of insects than in their structure and physiology
will be inclined to skip the first three chapters, and may do so and still find
the rest of the book "easy reading" and, it is hoped, not devoid of entertain-
ment and advantage. But the reader is earnestly advised not to spare the
little attention especially needed for understanding these first chapters, and
thus to ensure for his later reading some of that quality which is among
the most valued possessions of the best minds.

In preparing such a book as this an author is under a host of obligations
to previous writers and students which must perforce go unacknowledged.
Some formal recognition, however, for aid and courtesies directly tendered
by J. H. Comstock of Cornell University, whose entomological text-books
have been for years the chief sources of knowledge of the insects of this
country, I am able and glad to make. To my artist, Miss Mary Wellman,
for her constant interest in a work that must often have been laborious and
wearying, and for her persistently faithful endeavor toward accuracy, I extend
sincere thanks. To Mrs. David Starr Jordan, who read all of the manuscript
as a "general reader" critic, and to President Jordan for numerous suggestions I am particularly indebted. For special courtesies in the matter of
illustrations (permission to have electrotypes made from original blocks)
I am obliged to Prof. F. L. Washburn, State Entomologist of Minnesota (for
nearly one hundred and fifty figures), Prof. M. V. Slingerland of Cornell
University, Dr. E. P. Felt, State Entomologist of New York, Mr. Wm.
Beutenmüller, editor of the Journal of the New York Entomological Society,
and Dr. Henry Skinner, editor of the Entomological News.

VERNON L. KELLOGG.

STANFORD UNIVERSITY, CALIFORNIA,
    June 1, 1904.

# CONTENTS

## CHAPTER I

## CHAPTER II

## CHAPTER III

## CHAPTER IV

## CHAPTER V

# Contents

# Contents

# Contents

## APPENDIX

# AMERICAN INSECTS

## CHAPTER I

### THE STRUCTURE AND SPECIAL PHYSIOLOGY OF INSECTS

ERHAPS no more uninteresting matter, for the general reader or entomological amateur, can be written about insects than a descriptive catalogue of the parts and pieces of the insect body. And such matter is practically useless because it doesn't stick in the reader's mind. If it is worth while knowing the intimate make-up of a house-fly's animated little body, it is worth getting this knowledge in the only way that will make it real, that is, by patient and eye-straining work with dissecting-needles and microscope. This book, anyway, is to try to convey some information about the kinds and ways of insects, and to stimulate interest in insect life, rather than to be a treatise on insect organs and their particular functions. Life is, to be sure, only the sum of the organic functions, but this sum or combination has an interest disproportionate to that of any of its component parts, and has an aspect and character which cannot be foretold in any completeness from ever so careful a disjoined study of the particular functions. And so with the body, the sum of the organs: it is the manner and seeming of the body as a whole, its symmetry and exquisite adaptation to the special habit of life, the fine delicacy of its colors and pattern, or, at the other extreme, their amazing contrasts and *bizarrerie*, on which depend our first interest in the insect body. A second interest, although to the collector and amateur perhaps the dominant one, comes from that recognition of the differences and resemblances among the various insects which is simply the appreciation of kinds, i.e., of species. This interest expanded by opportunity and observation and controlled by reason and the habit of order and arrangement is, when extreme, that ardent and much misunderstood and scoffed at but ever-impelling mainspring of the collector and classifier.

Of all entomologists, students of insects, the very large majority are collectors and classifiers, and of amateurs apart from the few who have "crawleries" and aquaria for keeping alive and rearing " worms " and water-bugs and the few bee-keepers who are more interested in bees than honey, practically all are collectors and arrangers. So, as collecting depends on a knowledge of the life of the insect as a whole, and classifying (apart from certain primary distinctions) on only the external structural character of the body, any detailed disquisition on the intimate character of the insectean insides would certainly not be welcome to most of the users of this book.

That insects agree among themselves in some important characteristics and differ from all other animals in the possession of these characteristics is implied in the segregation of insects into a single great class of animals. Class here is used with the technical meaning of the systematic zoologist. He says that the animal kingdom is separable into, or, better, is composed of several primary groups of animals, the members of each group possessing in common certain important and fundamental characteristics of structure and function which are lacking, at any rate in similar combination, in all other animals. These primary groups are called phyla or branches. All the minute one-celled animals, for example, compose the phylum Protozoa (the simplest animals); all the starfishes, sea-urchins, sea-cucumbers, and feather-stars, which have the body built on a radiate plan and have no backbone, and have and do not have certain various other important things, compose the phylum or branch Echinodermata; all the back-boned animals and some few others with a cartilaginous rod instead of a bony column along the back compose the class Chordata; all the animals which have the body composed of a series of successive rings or segments, and have pairs of jointed appendages used as feet, mouth-parts, feelers, etc., arising from these segments, compose the phylum Arthropoda. There are still other phyla—but I am not writing a zoology. The insects are Arthropoda; and any one may readily see—it is most plainly seen in such forms as a locust, or dragon-fly, or butterfly, and less plainly in the concentrated knobby little body of a house-fly or bee—that an insect's body shows the characteristic arthropod structure; it is made up of rings or segments, and the appendages, legs for easiest example, are jointed. An earthworm's body is made up of rings, but it has no jointed appendages. A worm is therefore not an arthropod. A crayfish, however, is made up of distinct successive body-rings, and its legs and other appendages are jointed. And so with crabs and lobsters and shrimps. And the same is true of thousand-legged worms and centipeds and scorpions and spiders. All these creatures, then, are Arthropods. But they are not insects. So all the back-boned animals, fishes, amphibians, reptiles, birds, and mammals are Chordates, but they are not all birds.  The phylum Chordata is subdivided into or composed of the various classes Pisces (fishes), Aves (birds), etc.  And similarly the phylum Arthropoda is composed of several distinct classes, viz.: the Crustacea, including the crayfishes, crabs, shrimps, lobsters, water-fleas, and barnacles; the Onychophora, containing a single genus (Peripatus) of worm-like creatures; the Myriapoda, including the thousand-legged worms and centipeds; the Arachnida, including the scorpions, spiders, mites, and ticks; and finally the class Insecta (or Hexapoda, as it is some-times called), whose members are distinguished from the other Arthro-

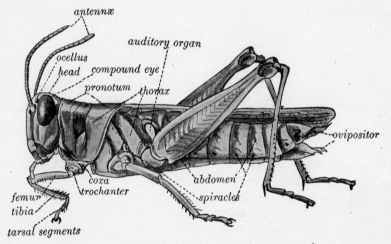

FIG. 1.—Locust (enlarged) with external parts named.

pods by having the body-rings or segments grouped into three regions, called head, thorax, and abdomen, by having jointed appendages only on the body-rings composing the head and thorax (one or two pairs of appendages may occur on the terminal segments of the abdomen), and by breathing by means of air-tubes (tracheæ) which ramify the whole interior of the body and open on its surface through paired openings (spiracles).  The insects also have three pairs of legs, never more, and less only in cases of degeneration, and by this obvious character can be readily distinguished from the Myria-pods, which have many pairs, and the Arachnids, which have four pairs. Centipeds are not insects, nor are spiders and mites and ticks.  What *are* insects most of this book is given to showing.

To proceed to the classifying of insects into orders and families and genera and species inside of the all-including class is the next work of the collector and classifier.  And for this—if for no other reason—some further knowledge of insect structure is indispensable.  The classification rests mostly on resemblances and differences in corresponding parts of the body, apparent in the various insect kinds. What these parts are, with their names and general characters, and what their particular use and significance' are, may be got partly from the following brief general account, and partly from the special accounts given in connection with special groups of insects elsewhere in this book. A little patience and concentration of attention in the reading of the next few pages will make the reader's attention to the rest of the book much simpler, and his understanding of it much more effective.

The outer layer of the skin or body-wall of an insect is called the cuticle, and in most insects the cuticle of most of the body is firm and horny in char-

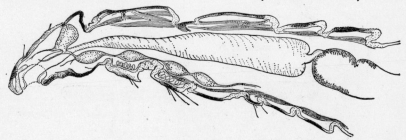

FIG. 2.—Longitudinal section of anterior half of an insect, *Menopon titan*, to show chitinized exoskeleton, with muscles attached to the inner surface. (Much enlarged.)

acter, due to the deposition in it, by the cells of the skin, of a substance called chitin. This firm external chitinized * cuticle (Fig. 2) forms an enclosing exoskeleton which serves at once to protect the inner soft parts from injury

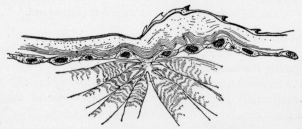

FIG. 3.—Bit of body-wall, greatly magnified, of larva of blow-fly, *Calliphora erythrocephala*, to show attachment of muscles to inner surface.

and to afford rigid points of attachment (Figs. 2, 3 and 4) for the many small but strong muscles which compose the insect's complex muscular system. Insects have no internal skeleton, although in many cases small processes project internally from the exoskeleton, particularly in the thorax or part

* It is not certainly known whether the cuticle is wholly secreted by the skin cells, or is in part composed of the modified external ends of the cells themselves.

of the body bearing the wings and legs. Where the cuticle is not strongly
chitinized it is flexible (Fig. 6), thus permitting
the necessary movement or play of the rings
of the body, the segments of the legs, antennæ
and mouth-parts, and other parts. The small
portions of chitinized cuticle thus isolated or
made separate by the thin interspaces or sutures

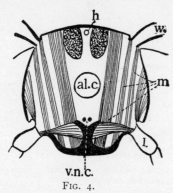

FIG. 4.                            FIG. 5.

FIG. 4.—Diagram of cross-section through the thorax of an insect to show leg and wing
   muscles and their attachment to body-wall. *h.*, heart; *al.c.*, alimentary canal; *v.n.c.*
   ventral nerve-cord; *w.*, wing; *l.*, leg; *m.*, muscles. (Much enlarged; after Graber.)
FIG. 5.—Left middle leg of cockroach with exoskeleton partly removed, showing muscles.
   (Much enlarged; after Miall and Denny.)

are called sclerites, and many of them have received specific names, while
their varying shape and character are made use of in distinguishing and
classifying insects.

FIG. 6.—Chitinized cuticle from dorsal wall of two body segments of an insect, showing
   sutures (the bent places) between segmental sclerites. Note that the cuticle is not
   less thick in the sutures than in the sclerites, but is less strongly chitinized (indicated by its paler color).

The whole body is composed fundamentally of successive segments
(Figs. 1 and 7), which may be pretty distinct and similar, as in a caterpillar
or termite or locust, or fused together, and strongly modified, and hence
dissimilar, as in a house-fly or honey-bee. The segments, originally five
or six, composing the head, are in all insects wholly fused to form a single
box-like cranium, while the three segments which compose the thorax are
in most forms so fused and modified as to be only with difficulty distinguished
as originally independent body-rings. On the other hand, in most insects

the segments of the abdomen retain their independence and are more or

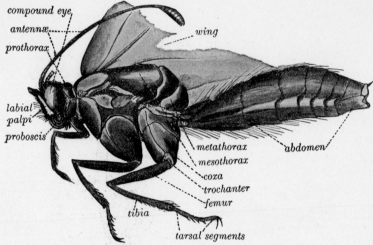

FIG. 7.—Body of the monarch butterfly, *Anosia plexippus*, with scales removed to show external parts. (Much enlarged.)

less similar, thus preserving a generalized or ancestral condition. On the head are usually four pairs of jointed appendages (Fig. 8), viz., the

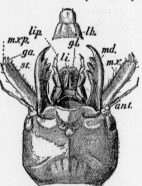

FIG. 8.—Dorsal aspect of head of dobson-fly, *Corydalis cornuta*, female, showing mouth-parts. *lb.*, labrum, removed; *md.*, mandible; *mx.*, maxilla; *li.*, labium; *gl*, glossæ of labium; *st.*, stipes of maxilla; *mxp.*, palpus of maxilla; *ant.*, antenna.

antennæ and three pairs of mouth-parts, known as mandibles, maxillæ, and labium or under-lip. Of these the mandibles in most cases are only one-segmented, while the two members of the labial pair have fused along their inner edges to form the single lip-like labium. The so-called upper lip or labrum, closing the mouth above, is simply a fold of the skin, and is not homologous, as a true appendage or pair of appendages, with the other mouth-parts. In some insects with highly modified mouth structure certain of the parts may be wholly lost, as is true of the mandibles in the case of all the butterflies. The head bears also the large compound eyes and the smaller simple eyes or ocelli (for an account of the eyes see p. 30). Attached to the thorax are three pairs of legs, which are jointed appendages, homologous in origin and fundamental structure with the mouth-parts and antennæ, and two pairs of wings (one or both pairs may be wanting) which are expansions of the dorso-lateral skin or body-wall, and are not homologous with the jointed ventral appendages. The thorax usually has its first or most anterior segment, the prothorax, distinct from the other two and freely movable, while the hinder two, called meso- and meta-thoracic segments, are usually enlarged and firmly fused to form a box for holding and giving attachment to the numerous strong muscles which move the wings and legs. The abdomen usually includes ten or eleven segments without appendages or projecting processes except in the case of the last two or three, which bear in the female the parts composing the egg-laying organ or ovipositor, or

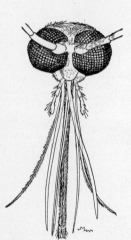

FIG. 9.              FIG. 10.

FIG. 9.—Head, much enlarged, of mosquito, *Culex* sp., showing piercing and sucking mouth-parts. (After Jordan and Kellogg.)

FIG. 10.—Head and mouth-parts of honey-bee, much enlarged. Note the short, trowel-like mandibles for moulding wax when building comb, and the extended proboscis for sucking flower-nectar. (Much enlarged.)

in certain insects the sting, and in the male the parts called claspers, cerci, etc., which are used in mating. On the abdomen are usually specially notice-able, as minute paired openings on the lateral aspects of the segments, the breathing-pores or spiracles, which admit air into the elaborate system of tracheæ or air-tubes, which ramify the whole internal body (see p. 19).

Of all these external parts two groups are particularly used in schemes of classification because of their structural and physiological importance in connection with the special habits and functions of insect life, and because of the pronounced modifications and differences in their condition: these are the mouth-parts and the wings.

Insects exhibit an amazing variety in food-habit: the female mosquito likes blood, the honey-bee and butterfly drink flower-nectar, the chinch-bug sucks the sap from corn-leaves, the elm-leaf beetle and maple-worm bite and chew the leaves of our finest shade-trees, the carrion-beetles devour decaying animal matter, the house-fly laps up sirup or rasps off and dissolves loaf-sugar, the nut- and grain-weevils nibble the dry starchy food of these seeds, while the apple-tree borer and timber-beetles find sustenance in the dry wood of the tree-trunks. The biting bird-lice are content with bits of hair and feathers, the clothes-moths and carpet-beetles feast on our rugs and woolens, while the cigarette-beetle has the depraved taste of our modern youth.

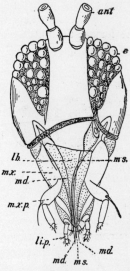

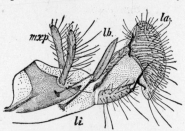

FIG. 11.                    FIG. 12.

FIG. 11.—Mouth-parts, much enlarged, of the house-fly, *Musca domestica*. *mx.p.*, maxillary palpi; *lb.*, labrum; *li.*, labium; *la.*, labellum.

FIG. 12.—Head and mouth-parts, much enlarged, of thrips. *ant.*, antenna; *lb.*, labrum; *md.*, mandible; *mx.*, maxilla; *mx.p.*, maxillary palpus; *li.p.*, labial palpus; *m.s.*, mouth-stylet. (After Uzel; much enlarged.)

With all this variety of food, it is obvious that the food-taking parts must show many differences; one insect needs strong biting jaws (Fig. 8), another a sharp piercing beak (Figs. 9, 13, and 14), another a long flexible sucking proboscis (Figs. 10 and 16), and another a broad lapping tongue (Fig. 11). Just this variety of structure actually exists, and in it the classific entomologist has found a basis for much of his modern classification.

Throughout all this range of mouth structure the insect morphologists and students of homology, beginning with Savigny in 1816, have been able to trace the fundamental three pairs of oral jointed appendages, the mandibles, maxillæ, and labium. Each pair appears in widely differing conditions; the mandibles may be large strong jaws for biting and crushing, as with the locust, or trowel-like, for moulding wax, as with the honey-bee, or long, flat, slender, and saw-toothed, as with the scorpion-flies, or needle-like, as in all the sucking bugs, or reduced to mere rudiments or wholly lacking, as in the moths and butterflies. Similarly with the other parts. But by careful study of the comparative anatomy of the mouth structure, and particularly by tracing its development in typical species representing the various types of biting, sucking, and lapping mouths, all the various kinds of mouth structure can be compared and the homologies or structural correspondences of the component parts determined. Figs. 8 to 16 illustrate

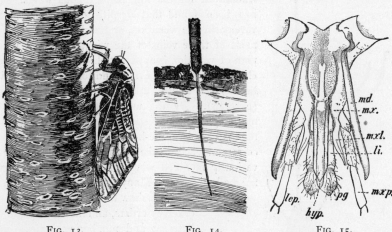

md.
mx.
mxl.
li.
lep.
pg
mxp.
hyp.

FIG. 13.          FIG. 14.          FIG. 15.

FIG. 13.—Seventeen-year cicada, *Cicada septendecim*, sucking sap from twig. (After Quaintance; natural size.)

FIG. 14.—Section of twig of Carolina poplar showing beak of cicada in position when sucking. (After Quaintance; much enlarged.)

FIG. 15.—Mouth-parts, much enlarged, of net-winged midge, *Bibicocephala doanei*, female. *md.*, mandible; *mx.*, maxilla; *mx.l.*, maxillary lobe; *mx.p.*, maxillary palpus; *li.*, labium; *hyp.*, hypopharynx; *pg.*, paraglossa of labium; *l.ep.*, labrum and epipharynx.

examples of different mouth structures, with the corresponding parts similarly lettered.

The most conspicuous structural characteristic of insects is their possession of wings. And the wings undoubtedly account for much of the success of the insect type. Insects are the dominant animal group of this age, as far as number of species constitutes dominance, their total largely surpassing that of the species of all the other kinds of living animals. Flight is an extremely effective mode of locomotion, being swift, unimpeded by obstacles, and hence direct and distance-saving, and an animal in flight is safe from most of its enemies. The wings of insects are not modified true appendages of the body, but arise as simple sac-like expansions (Fig. 17) of the body-wall or skin much flattened and supported by a framework of strongly chitinized lines called veins.  These veins are corresponding cuticular thickenings, in the upper and lower walls of the flattened wing-sac, which protect, while the wing is forming, certain main tracheal trunks that carry air to the wing-tissue.  After the wing is expanded and dry, the tracheæ mostly die out, and the veins are left as firm thick-walled branching tubes which serve admirably as a skeleton or framework for the thin membranous wings.   It has been found that despite the obvious great variety in the venation, or number and arrangement of these veins of the wing, a general type-plan of venation is apparent throughout the insect class.  The more important and constant veins have been given names, and their branches numbers (Fig. 18).  By the use of the same name or number for the corresponding vein throughout all the insect orders, the homologies or morphological correspondences of the veins as they appear in the variously modified wings of the different insects are made apparent.  Many figures scattered through this book show the venation of insects of different orders, and the corresponding lettering and numbering indicate the homologies of the veins.  As the wing venation presents differing conditions readily noted and described, much use is made of it in classification.

The differences in the wings themselves, that is, in number, relative size of fore and hind wings, and in structure, i.e., whether membranous and delicate, or horny and firm, etc., have always been used to distinguish the larger groups, as orders, of insects, and the first classification, that of Linnæus (1750 app.), divides the class into orders almost solely on a basis of wing characters.  The ordinal names expressed, to some degree, the differences, as Diptera,* two-winged; Lepidoptera, scale-winged; Coleoptera, sheath-winged, and so on.  As a matter of fact, there may be much differ-

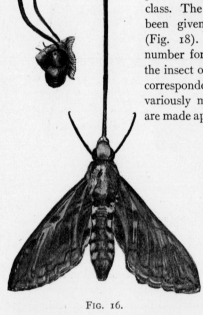

FIG. 16.

FIG. 16.—Sphinx moth, showing proboscis; at left the proboscis is shown coiled up on the under side of the head, the normal position when not in use.  (Large figure, one-half natural size; small figure, natural size.)

* The derivation of the Linnæan ordinal names is given on p. 223.

ence in the wings within a single order; most beetles, for example, have four wings, but some have two and some none. There are indeed wingless species in almost every insect order. But a typical beetle has quite distinctive and commonly recognized wing characters; that is, it has two pairs of wings, the fore pair being greatly thickened, and developed to serve as sheaths for the larger, membranous under-pair, which are the true flight wings. Similarly, practically all moths and butterflies have two pairs of

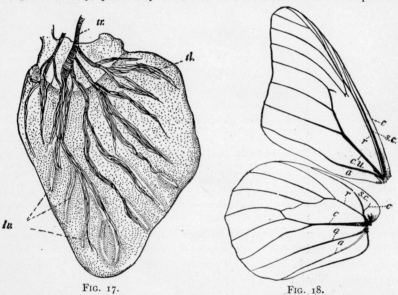

FIG. 17.                                    FIG. 18.

FIG. 17.—Wing of cabbage-butterfly, *Pieris rapæ*, in early sac-like stage. *tr.*, trachea; *tl.*, tracheoles; *l.v.*, lines of future veins. (After Mercer; greatly magnified.)

FIG. 18.—Diagram of wings of monarch butterfly, *Anosia plexippus*, showing venation. *c.*, costal vein; *s.c.*, subcostal vein; *r.*, radial vein; *cu.*, cubital vein; *a.*, anal veins. In addition, most insects have a vein lying between the subcostal and radial veins, called the median vein. (Natural size.)

membranous wings completely covered above and below by small scales, which give them their distinctive color and pattern.

The exoskeleton, or cuticle, of the insect body is sometimes nearly smooth and naked, but usually it is sculptured by grooves and ridges, punctures or projections, and clothed with hairs or those modified flattened hairs known as scales (especially characteristic of butterflies and moths). This clothing of hairs or scales, or the skin itself, is variously colored and patterned, often with the obvious use of producing protective resemblance or mimicry, but often without apparent significance. (For an account of the colors and patterns of insects and their uses see Chapter XVII.) The hairs may serve for protection, or may be tactile organs, or even organs of hearing (see p. 26). The projecting processes may be spines or thorns or curious and inexplicable knobs and horns. The rhinoceros-beetle (Dynastes) (Fig. 19) and the sacred scarabeus are familiar examples of insects with such prominent processes.

The insect body, as a whole, appears in great variety of form and range of size, as our knowledge of the variety of habit and habitat of insects would lead us to expect. In size they vary from the tiny four-winged chalcids which emerge, after their parasitic immature life, from the eggs of other insects, and measure less than a millimeter in length, to the giant Phasmids

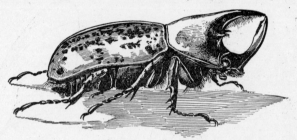

Fig. 19.—Rhinoceros-beetle, *Dynastes tityrus*, showing chitinous horns.

(walking-sticks) of the tropics, with their ten or twelve inches of body length, and the great Formosan dragon-flies with an expanse of wing of ten inches. A Carboniferous insect like a dragon-fly, known from fossils found at Commentry, France, had a wing expanse of more than two feet. Insects show a plasticity as to general body shape and appearance that results in extreme modifications corresponding with the extremely various habits of life that obtain in the class. Compare the delicate fragility of the gauzy-winged May-fly with the rigid exoskeleton and horny wings of the water-beetle; the long-winged, slender-bodied flying-machine we call a dragon-fly with the shovel-footed, half-blind, burrowing mole-cricket; the plump, toothsome white ant that defends itself by simple prolificness with the spare, angular, twig-like body of the walking-stick with its effective protective resemblance to the dry branches among which it lives. Compare the legless, eyeless, antennaless, wingless, sac-like degraded body of the orange-scale with the marvelous specialization of structure of that compact exponent of the strenuous insect life, the honey-bee; contrast the dull colors of the lowly tumble-bug with the flashing radiance of the painted lady-butterfly. But through all this variety of shape and pattern, complexity and degeneration, one can see the simple fundamental insect body-plan; the successive segments, their grouping into three body-regions, the presence of segmented appendages on head and thorax and their absence on abdomen (except perhaps in the terminal segments), and the modification of these appendages into antennæ and mouth-parts on the head, legs on the thorax, and ovipositor, sting, or claspers in the abdomen.

In the character of the structure and functions of the internal organs or systems of organs of insects, a special interest attaches to the conditions shown by the circulatory and respiratory systems, and by the special sense-

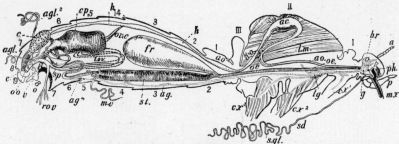

FIG. 20.—Diagram of lateral interior view of monarch butterfly, *Anosia plexippus*, showing the internal organs in their natural arrangement, after the removal of the right half of the body-wall together with the tracheæ and fat body; I to III, segments of the thorax; 1 to 9, segments of the abdomen. Alimentary Canal and Appendages: *ph.*, pharynx; *sd.* and *sgl.*, salivary duct and gland of the right side; *oe.*, œsophagus; *f.r.*, food-reservoir; *st.*, stomach; *i.*, small intestine; *c.*, colon; *r.*, rectum; *a.*, anus; *m.v.*, Malpighian tube. Hæmal System: *h.*, heart or dorsal vessel; *ao.*, aorta; *a.c.*, aortal chamber; Nervous System (dotted in figure): *br.*, brain; *g.*, subœsophageal ganglion; *l.g.*, compound thoracic ganglia; *ag.*₁, *ag.*₄, first and fourth abdominal ganglia. Female Reproductive Organs: *cp.*, copulatory pouch; *v.*, vagina; *o.*, oviduct, and *oo.*, its external opening; *r.ov.*, base of the right ovarian tubes turned down to expose the underlying organs; *l.ov.*, left ovarian tubes in position, and *ov.c.*, their termination and four cords; *sp.*, spermatheca; *a.gl.*₁, part of the single accessory gland; *a.gl.*₂, one of the paired accessory glands; only the base of its mate is shown. Head: *a.*, antenna; *mx.*, proboscis; *p.*, labial palpus. (After Burgess; three times natural size.)

organs and their manner of functioning. The muscular system varies from the simple worm-like arrangement of segmentally disposed longitudinal and ring muscles possessed by the caterpillars, grubs, and other worm-like larvæ,

to the complicated system of such specialized and active forms as the honey-bee and house-fly. Lyonnet describes about two thousand distinct muscles in the caterpillar of the goat-moth. Insect muscles are similar, in their finer structure, to those of other animals, most of them being composed of finely

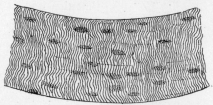

FIG. 21.—Bit of muscle of a biting bird-louse, *Eurymetopus taurus*. (Greatly magnified.)

cross-striated fibers (Figs. 21 and 22) held together in larger or smaller masses and attaching to the rugosities of the inner surface of the exoskeleton. The muscle substance, when fresh, is peculiarly transparent and delicate-looking, but it has great contractile power.

The alimentary canal (Figs. 23–27), like that of other animals, is a tube but little longer than the body in flesh-eating forms, and much longer in plant-feeders; it runs, more or less curving and coiled, through the body from mouth to anal opening, which lies in the last segment of the abdomen.

This tube is expanded variously to form crop, gizzard, or stomach, and

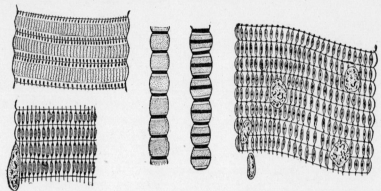

FIG. 22.—Diagrammatic figures of bits of insect muscle, variously treated. (After Van Gehuchten; greatly magnified.)

FIG. 23. — Alimentary canal of a locust. At upper end the œsophagus, then the expanded crop, then several large gastric cœca, then the true stomach, the thread-like Malpighian tubules, the bent intestine, and the expanded rectum. (After Snodgrass; enlarged.)

contracted elsewhere to be œsophagus or intestine. One or two pairs of salivary glands pour their fluid into the mouth, while the digesting stomach or ventriculus usually possesses two or more pairs of diverticula known as gastric cœca, which are lined with glands believed to secrete special digestive fluids. Neither liver nor kidneys are present in the insect body, but the secretory function of the latter are undertaken by a number of usually long thread-like tubular diverticula of the intestine known as Malpighian tubules. The intestine itself is usually obviously made up of three successive parts, a large intestine, small intestine, and rectum. There are also present not infrequently intestinal cœca.

Two striking peculiarities about the reproductive system of insects are the possession by the female of one or more spermathecæ (Fig. 66, *r.s.*) in which the male fertilizing cells, the spermatozoa, are received and held, and the completion of all the envelopes of the egg, including the outer hard shell, before its specific fertilization takes place. Fer-

FIG. 24. — Dissection of cockroach to show (*al.c.*) alimentary canal. (After Hatschek and Cori; twice natural size.)

tilization is itself accomplished in the lower end of the egg-duct just before the egg is laid, by the escape of spermatozoa from the spermatheca (the female

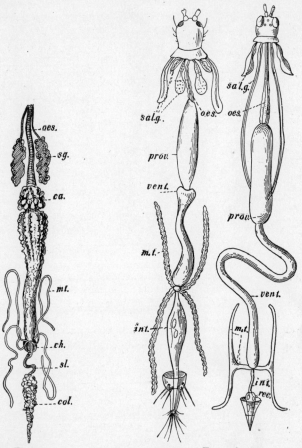

FIG. 25.

FIG. 26.

FIG. 25.—Alimentary canal of larva of harlequin-fly (*Chironomus* sp.). *oes.*, œsophagus; *s.g.*, salivary gland; *ca.*, cardiac chamber of stomach; *mt.*, Malpighian tubules; *ch.*, intestinal chamber; *sl.*, small intestine; *col.*, colon. (After Miall and Hammond; much enlarged.)

FIG. 26.—Alimentary canal of two species of thrips; at left *Trichothrips copiosa*, male, at right *Aelothrips fasciata*. *sal.g.*, salivary gland; *oes.*, œsophagus; *prov.*, proventriculus; *vent.*, ventriculus; *m.t.*, Malpighian tubules; *int.*, intestine; *rec.*, rectum. (After Uzel; greatly enlarged.)

having of course previously mated) and their entrance into the egg through a tiny opening, the micropyle (Fig. 67), in the egg-shell and inner envelopes. A queen bee mates but once, but she may live for four or five years after this and continue to lay fertilized eggs during all this time. She must receive several million spermatozoa at mating, and retain them alive in the spermatheca during these after-years.

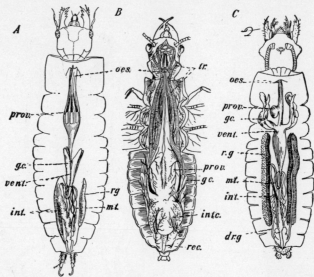

FIG. 27.—Alimentary canal of dobson-fly, *Corydalis cornuta*. *A*, larva; *B*, adult; *C*, pupa; *oes.*, œsophagus; *prov.*, proventriculus; *g.c.*, gastric cœca; *vent.*, ventriculus; *r.g.*, reproductive gland; *m.t.*, Malpighian tubules; *int.*, intestine; *int.c.*, intestinal cœcum; *rec.*, rectum; *drg.*, oviduct. (After Leidy; twice natural size.)

The circulatory system of insects presents two particular features of interest in that the blood does not, as in our bodies, carry oxygen to the tissues, and

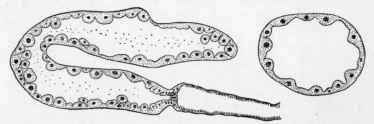

FIG. 28.—Cross-section and longitudinal section of salivary gland of giant crane-fly, *Holorusia rubiginosa*. (Greatly magnified.)

that there is a contractile pulsating heart-like organ, but no arteries or veins. The so-called heart is a delicate-walled, narrow, subcylindrical vessel composed of a series of most commonly from three to eight successive chambers lying longitudinally along the median line just underneath the dorsal wall of the abdomen and thorax (Figs. 30 and 31). Each chamber opens, guarded by a simple valvular arrangement (Fig. 33), into the chambers behind and before it, the posterior one being closed behind and the anterior

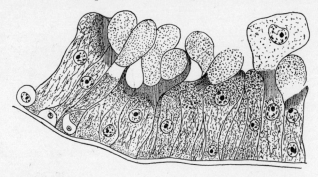

FIG. 29.—Cells of digestive epithelium of stomach (ventriculus) of crane-fly, *Ptychoptera* sp., showing secretion of digestive fluids, or expulsion of cell-content. (After Van Gehuchten; greatly magnified.)

one extending forward into or near the head as a narrowed tubular anterior portion, which is sometimes called the aorta. From the anterior open end of this aorta the blood, forced by pulsations of the heart-chambers, which proceed rhythmically from the posterior one forward, pours out into the body-cavity, proceeding in more or less regular currents or paths, but never enclosed in arterial vessels, bathing all the tissues, and carrying food to them. Finally taking up fresh supplies of food by bathing the food-absorbing walls of the alimentary canal, it enters the chambers of the heart through lateral openings in these (either at the middle or anterior end of each), which thus establish communication between the body-cavity and heart. The blood receives no more oxygen than it needs for its own use, and thus does not play nearly so complex a function in the insect's body as in ours. And this simplicity of function probably explains in some degree the extreme primitiveness of the make-up of the circulatory system. It will be seen that the respiratory

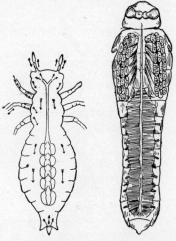

FIG. 30.          FIG. 31.

FIG. 30.—Diagram of circulatory system of a young dragon-fly; in middle is the chambered dorsal vessel, or heart, with single artery. Arrows indicate direction of blood-currents. (After Kolbe.)

FIG. 31.—Dissection showing dorsal vessel, or heart, of locust, *Dissosteira carolina*. (After Snodgrass; twice natural size.)

system, on the other hand, is particularly highly developed, as it devolves

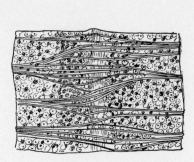

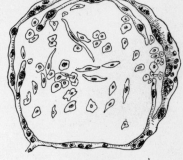

FIG. 32.                                    FIG. 33.

FIG. 32.—Portion of dorsal vessel and pericardial membrane of locust, *Dissosteira carolina*.  (After Snodgrass; greatly magnified.)

FIG. 33.—Cross-section of dorsal vessel or heart in pupa of tussock-moth, *Hemerocampa
leucostigma*, showing valves.  (Greatly magnified.)

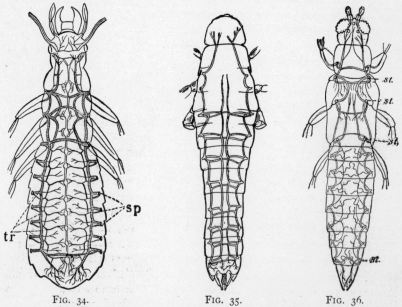

FIG. 34.                    FIG. 35.                    FIG. 36.

FIG. 34.—Diagram of tracheal system in body of beetle.  *sp.*, spiracles; *tr.*, tracheæ.
(After Kolbe.)

FIG. 35.—Diagram showing main tracheæ in respiratory system of locust, *Dissosteira
carolina*.  (After Snodgrass; twice natural size.)

FIG. 36.—Diagram showing respiratory system in thrips.  *st.*, spiracles.  (After Uzel;
much enlarged.)

on it not merely to take up oxgyen from the outer air and give up the waste carbon dioxide of the body, but also to convey these gases to and from all the tissues of the body.  The blood is not red, but pale yellowish or greenish, and is really more like the lymph of the vertebrate body than like its blood

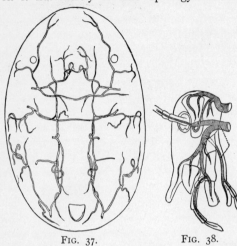

FIG. 37.          FIG. 38.

FIG. 37.—Diagram showing respiratory system of pupa of mealy-winged fly, *Aleyrodes* sp.; only two pairs of spiracles are present. (After Bemis; much enlarged.)

FIG. 38.—Diagram of tracheæ in head of cockroach. Note branches to all mouth-parts, and the antennæ.   *t.*, tracheæ, or air-tubes. (After Miall and Denny.)

Insects do not breathe through the mouth or any openings on the head, but have a varying number (usually from two to ten pairs) of small paired openings on the sides of the thorax and abdomen.  These openings, called spiracles, or stigmata, are arranged segmentally and in most insects are to be found on two of the thoracic segments and on all the abdominal segments except the last two or three.  The openings are guarded by fine hairs or even little valvular lids to prevent the ingress of dust, and are the entrances to an extended system of delicate air-tubes or tracheæ which branch and subdivide until the whole of the internal body is reached and ramified by fine capillary vessels bringing fresh air to all the tissues and carrying off the waste carbon dioxide made by the metabolism of these tissues.  The usual general arrangement of this elaborate respiratory system is shown in Figs. 34, 35, and 36.  Short broad trunks lead from each spiracle to a main longitudinal trunk on each side of the body, from which numerous branches arise, these going to particular regions of the body (Fig. 38) and there branching repeatedly until even individual cells get special tiny

FIG. 39.—Piece of trachea (air-tube), greatly magnified, showing spiral thread (tænidia). (Photomicrograph by George O. Mitchell.)

respiratory capillaries. The tracheæ are readily recognized under the microscope by their finely transversely ringed or striated appearance (Fig. 39). These transverse "rings" are really spirally arranged short chitinized thread-like thickenings on the inner wall of the tube, which by their elasticity keep the delicate air-tubes open. The tubes are filled and emptied by a rhythmic alternately contracting and expanding movement of the abdomen, called the respiratory movement. When the ring-muscles contract, the walls of the abdomen are squeezed in against the viscera, which, compressing the soft air-tubes, force the air out of them through the spiracles; when the body-walls are allowed to spring back to normal position fresh air rushes in through the spiracles and fills up the air-tubes, which expand because of the elastic spiral thickenings in their walls. Insects which live in water either come up to the surface to breathe and in some cases to take down a supply of air held on the outside of the body by a fine pubescence like the pile of velvet, or they are provided with tracheal gills (Fig. 40) which enable them to breathe the air mixed with, or dissolved in, the water. Gilled insects do not, of course, have to come to the surface to breathe. The gills may be thin plate-like flaps on the sides or posterior tip of the body, or may be tufts of short thread-like tubes variously arranged over the body. Or they

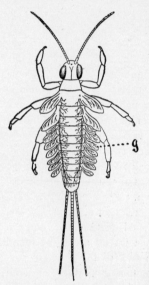

FIG. 40.—Young (nymph) of May-fly showing (*g.*) tracheal gills. (After Jenkins and Kellogg.)

may be, as in the dragon-fly nymphs, thin folds along the inner wall of the rectum, the water necessary to bathe them being taken in and ejected again through the anal opening. In all cases these insect gills differ from those of other animals, as crabs and fishes, in that they are not organs for the purification of the blood, i.e., effecting an exchange of carbon dioxide and oxygen carried by it, but are means for an osmotic exchange of the fresh air dissolved in water for carbon-dioxide-laden air from air-tubes or tracheæ which run out into the gills. Probably no more blood enters these gills than is necessary to bring food to them. Impure air is brought to them by air-tubes, and exchanged by osmosis through the thin walls of air-tube and gill-membrane for fresh air, which passes from these gill air-tubes to the rest of the respiratory system of the body.

The nervous system of insects shows the fundamentally segmental make-up of the body better than any of the other systems of internal organs, although probably in the successive chambers of the dorsal vessel or heart, and certainly in the paired arrangement of the spiracles and tracheal trunks leading from them, a segmental condition is obvious.  The central nervous system consists

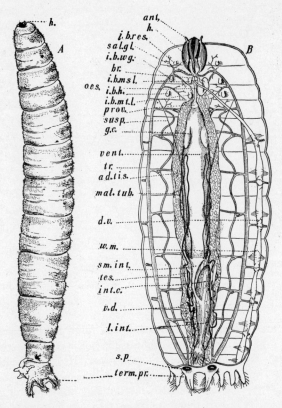

Fig. 41.—Larva of giant crane-fly, *Holorusia rubiginosa.*  *A*, entire; *B*, dissected, showing all organs except the muscles and ventral nerve-chain.  *h.*, head; *ant.*, antenna; *i.b.res.*, imaginal bud of pupal respiratory tube; *i.b.wg.*, imaginal bud of wing; *i.b.ms.l.*, imaginal bud of mesothoracic leg; *i.b.h.*, imaginal bud of balancer; *i.b.mt.l.*, imaginal bud of metathoracic leg (the imaginal buds of fore legs are concealed by head-capsule); *sal.gl.*, salivary gland (the other salivary gland is removed); *br.*, brain; *œs.*, œsophagus; *prov.*, proventriculus; *susp.*, suspensorium; *g.c.*, gastric cœcum; *vent.*, ventriculus; *tr.*, trachea; *ad.tis.*, adipose tissue; *mal.tub.*, Malpighian tubule; *d.v.*, dorsal vessel; *w.m.*, wing-muscles of pericardium; *sm.int.*, small intestine; *tes.*, testis; *int.c.*, intestinal cœcum; *v.d.*, vas deferens; *l.int.*, large intestine; *sp.*, spiracle; *term.pr.*, terminal processes.  (Twice natural size.)

of a brain and a ventral chain of pairs of ganglia segmentally arranged and connected by a pair of longitudinal cords or commissures (Figs. 42, 43, 44). The two members of each of the pairs of ganglia as well as of the pair of

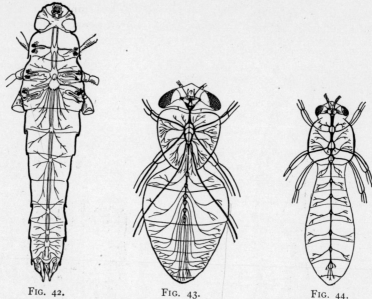

FIG. 42.          FIG. 43.          FIG. 44.

FIG. 42.—Diagram of ventral nerve-cord of locust, *Dissosteira carolina*. (After Snodgrass; twice natural size.)

FIG. 43.—Diagram of the nervous system of the house-fly. (After Brandt; much enlarged.)

FIG. 44.—Nervous system of a midge, *Chironomus* sp. (After Brandt, much enlarged.)

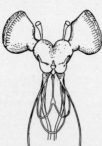

FIG. 45.—Brain, compound eyes, and part of sympathetic nervous system of locust, *Dissosteira carolina*. (After Snodgrass; greatly magnified.)

commissures are in most insects more or less fused to form single ganglia and a single commissure, but in others the commissures, at least, are quite distinct. In the simpler or more generalized condition of the nervous system as seen in the simpler insects and the larvæ of the higher ones there are from three or four to seven or eight abdominal ganglion pairs, one pair to a segment, a pair in each of the three thoracic segments, and one in the head just under the œsophagus. From this ganglion (or fused pair) circumœsophageal commissures run up around the œsophagus to an important ganglion (also composed of the fused members of a pair) lying just above the œsophagus and called the brain, or supraœsophageal ganglion (Figs. 45, 46, and 47). From this proceed the nerves to those important organs of special sense situated on the head, the antennæ and eyes. From the subœsophageal ganglion nerves run to the mouth-parts, from the thoracic ganglia to the wings and legs and the complex thoracic muscular system, while from the abdominal ganglia are innervated the abdominal muscles and sting, ovipositor, or male claspers. In addition to this main or ventral nervous system there is a small and considerably varying sympathetic system (Figs. 46 and 48) to which belong a few minute ganglia sending nerves to those viscera which act automatically or by reflexes, as the alimentary canal and heart. This sympathetic system is connected with the central or principal

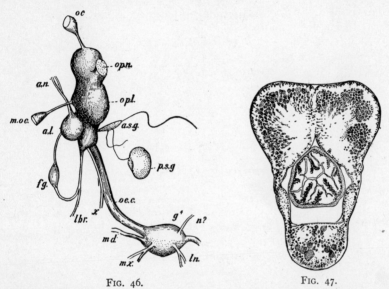

FIG. 46.                                    FIG. 47.

FIG. 46.—Brain, circumœsophageal commissures, and subœsophageal ganglion of the red-legged locust, *Melanoplus femur-rubrum*. *oc.*, ocellus; *op.n.*, optic nerve; *a.n.*, antennal nerve; *m.oc.*, middle ocellus; *op.l.*, optic lobe; *a.l.*, olfactory lobe; *a.s.g.*, anterior sympathetic ganglion; *p.s.g.*, posterior sympathetic ganglion; *f.g.*, frontal sympathetic ganglion; *lbr.*, nerve to labrum; *oe.c.*, circumœsophageal commissure; *g⁴*, subœsophageal ganglion; *md.*, nerve to mandible; *mx.*, nerve to maxilla; *l.n.*, nerve to labium; *n.*, unknown nerve, perhaps salivary. (After Burgess; greatly magnified.)

FIG. 47.—Cross-section of brain, œsophagus, circumœsophageal commissures, and subœsophageal ganglion of larva of the giant crane-fly, *Holorusia rubiginosa*.

nervous system by commissures which meet the brain just at the origin from it of the circumœsophageal commissures.

The specialization of the ventral nerve-chain is always of the nature of a concentration, and especially cephalization of its ganglia (Figs. 49 and 50). The abdominal ganglia may be fused into two or three or even into one compound ganglion; or indeed all of them may migrate forward and fuse with the hindmost thoracic ganglion, thus leaving the whole abdomen to be innervated by long nerves running from the thorax. The thoracic ganglia may fuse to form one, and in extreme cases all the abdominal and thoracic ganglia may be fused into one large mid-thoracic center.

In tracing the development of the nervous system during the ontogeny of one of the specialized insects, the changes from generalized condition, i.e., presence of numerous distinct ganglia segmentally disposed, shown in the newly hatched

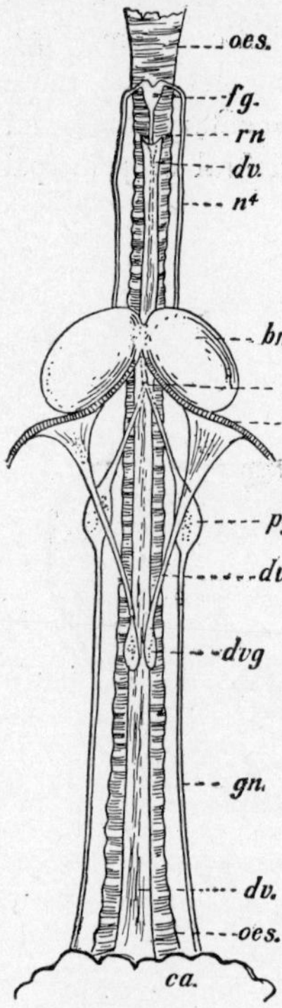

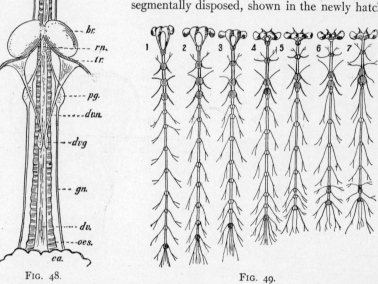

FIG. 48.      FIG. 49.

FIG. 48.—Part of sympathetic nervous system of larva of harlequin-fly, *Chironomus dorsalis*. *oes.*, œsophagus; *f.g.*, frontal ganglion; *r.n.*, recurrent nerve; *d.v.*, dorsal vessel; *n⁴*, nerve passing from brain to frontal ganglion (Newport's fourth nerve); *br.*, brain; *rn.*, point of division of recurrent nerve; *tr.*, tracheæ; *pg.*, paired ganglia; *d.v.n.*, nerve of dorsal vessel; *d.v.g.*, ganglia of dorsal vessel; *g.n.*, gastric nerve to cardiac chamber. The course of the recurrent nerve beneath the dorsal vessel is dotted. (After Miall and Hammond; greatly magnified.)

FIG. 49.—Stages in the development of the nervous system of the honey-bee, *Apis mellifica;* 1 showing the ventral nerve-cord in the youngest larval stage, and 7 the system in the adult. (After Brandt; much enlarged.)

larva, to specialized condition, i.e., extreme concentration and cephalization, that is, migration forward and fusion of the ganglia, shown in the adult, are readily followed (Figs. 49 and 50).

The special senses of insects and the sense-organs are of particular interest because of the marked unusualness of the character of the specialization of both the organs and senses, as compared with the more familiar conditions of the corresponding organs and functions of our body. The world is known to animals only by the impressions made by it on the sense-organs, and the particular condition of functioning of these organs, therefore, is of unique importance in the life of any particular animal. If the senses vary much in their capacities among different animals, the world will have a different seeming to different creatures. It will be chiefly known to any particular species through the dominant sense of that species. To the congenitally blind the world is an experience of touched things, of heard things, and of smelled and tasted things. To the bloodhound it is known chiefly by the scent of things. It is a world of odors; the scent of anything determines its dangerousness, its desirableness, its interestingness. As insects know it, then, the world depends largely upon the particular character and capacity of their sense-organs, and we realize on even the most superficial examination of the structure of these organs, and casual observation of the

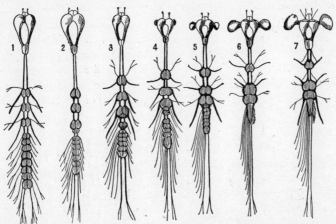

FIG. 50.—Stages in the development of the nervous system of the water-beetle, *Æcilius sulcatus;* 1 showing the ventral nerve-cord in the earliest larval stage, and 7 the system in the adult. (After Brandt; much enlarged.)

responses of insects to those stimuli, like sound-waves, light-waves, dissolved and vaporized substances, which affect the sense-organs, that the insects have some remarkable special sense-conditions. But the difficulties in the way of understanding the psychology of any of the lower animals are obvious when it is recalled that our only knowledge of the character of sense-perceptions has to depend solely on our experience of our own perceptions, and on the basis of comparison with this. We do not know if hearing is the same phenomenon or experience with insects as with us. But a comparison of the morphology of the insect sense-organs with that of ours, and a course of experimentation with the sight, hearing, smelling, etc., of insects, based on similar experimentation with our own senses, leads us to what we believe is some real knowledge of the special sense-conditions of insects.

Insects certainly have the senses of touch, hearing, taste, smell, and sight. If they have others, we do not know it, and probably cannot, as we have

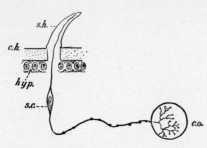

no criteria for recognizing others. The tactile sense resides especially in so-called "tactile hairs," scattered more or less abundantly or regularly over the body. Each of these hairs has at its base a ganglionic nerve-cell from which a fine nerve runs to some body ganglion (Fig. 51). They are specially numerous and conspicuous on the antennæ or "feelers," and often on certain processes called cerci, projecting from the tip of the abdomen. They may occur, however, on any part of the body, and are usually recognizable by their length and semi-spinous nature. The sense of taste resides in certain small papillæ, usually two-segmented, or in certain pits, which

FIG. 51.—Diagram showing innervation of a tactile hair. *sh.*, tactile hair; *ch.*, chitinized cuticle; *hyp.*, hypoderm, or cellular layer of the skin; *s.c.*, ganglion cell; *c.o.*, ganglion of the central nervous system. (After vom Rath.)

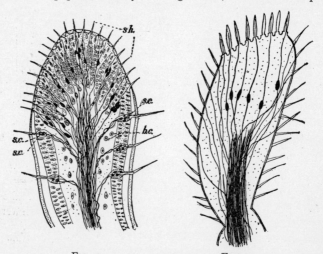

FIG. 52.               FIG. 53.

FIG. 52.—Nerve-endings in tip of maxillary palpus of *Locusta viridissima*. *s.h.*, sense-hairs; *s.c.*, sense-cells; *b.c.*, blood-cells.   (After vom Rath; greatly magnified.)
FIG. 53.—Nerve-endings in tip of labial palpus of *Machilis polypoda*. (After vom Rath; greatly magnified.)

occur on the upper wall of the mouth (epipharynx) and on the mouth-parts, especially the tips of the maxillary and labial palpi, or mouth-feelers. As substances to be tasted have to be dissolved, and have to

come into actual contact with the special taste nerves, it is obvious
that insects, to taste solid foods, have first to dissolve particles of these
foods in the mouth-fluids, and that the taste-organs have to be situated
in the mouth or so that they can be brought into it to explore the food, as
are the movable, feeler-like palpi.   What experimentation on the sense of
taste in insects has been carried on shows that certain insects certainly taste
food substances, and indicates that the sense is a common attribute of all
insects.   Lubbock's many experiments with ants, bees, and wasps present
convincing proof of the exercise of the taste sense by these insects.   Forel
mixed morphine and strychnine with honey, which ants, attracted by the
honey smell, tasted and refused.   Will's experiments show that wasps
recognize alum and quinine by taste.   He found bees and wasps to have
a more delicate gustatory sense than flies.

Smell is probably the dominant special sense among insects.   It exists
at least in a degree of refinement among certain forms that is hardly
equalled elsewhere in the animal kingdom.   The smelling organs are microscopic pits and minute papillæ seated usually and especially abundantly
on the antennæ, but probably also occurring to
some extent on certain of the mouth-parts.   The
fact that the antennæ are the principal, and in
many insects the exclusive, seat of the olfactory
organs has been proved by many experiments in
removing the antennæ or coating them with par-
affine.   Insects thus treated do not find food or
each other.   As substances to be smelled must
actually come into contact, in finely divided condition, with the olfactory nerve-element, these
pits and papillæ are arranged so as to expose
the nerve-end and yet protect it from the
ruder contact with obstacles against which the
antennæ may strike.   It is certain that most
insects find their food by the sense of smell, and
the antenna of a carrion-beetle (Fig. 54) shows
plainly the special adaptation to make this sense
highly effective.   On the "leaves" of each antenna
of June-beetles nearly 40,000 olfactory pits occur.
Some of the results of experimentation on smell
indicate a delicacy and specialization of this sense
hardly conceivable.   A few examples will illustrate
this.   It is believed that ants find their way back
to their nests by the sense of smell, and that
they can recognize by scent among hundreds of individuals taken from

FIG. 54.—Antenna of a
carrion-beetle with the
terminal three segments
enlarged and flattened,
and bearing many smell-
ing-pits.   (Photomicro-
graph by George O. Mit-
chell; much enlarged.)

various communities the members of their own community. Miss Fielde's experiments show that the recognition of ants by each other depends on the existence of a sense of smell of remarkable differentiative capacity. The odors of the nest, of the species, of the female parent, and of the individual are all distinct and perceivable by the smelling-organs, situated on distinct particular antennal segments. In the insectary at Cornell University a few years ago a few females of the beautiful large promethea moth were put into a covered box which was kept inside of the insectary building. No males of this moth species had been seen about the insectary nor in

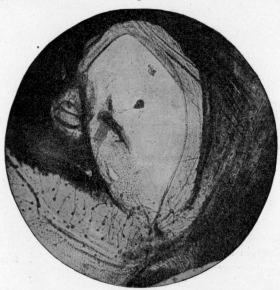

its immediate vicinity for several days, although they had been specially sought for by collectors. Yet in a few hours after the female moths were first confined nearly fifty m a l e prometheas were fluttering about outside over the glass roof of the insectary. They could not see the females, but undoubtedly discovered them by the sense of smell. These promethea moths have elaborately branched or feathered antennæ, affording area for very many smelling-pits.

Fig. 55.—Auditory organ of a locust, *Melanoplus* sp. The large clear part in the center of the figure is the thin tympanum with the auditory vesicle (small, black, pear-shaped spot) and auditory ganglion (at left of vesicle and connected with it by a nerve) on its inner surface. (Photomicrograph by George O. Mitchell; greatly magnified.)

Mayer's experiments with promethea also reveal the high specialization of the sense of smell. This investigator carried 450 promethea cocoons from Massachusetts to the Florida keys. Here on separated small islands the moths issued from the cocoons, hundreds of miles south of their natural habitat. This isolation insured that no other individuals than those controlled by the experimenter could confuse the observations. Female moths were confined in glass jars with the mouth closed by netting. Other females were confined in smaller glass jars turned upside down and the mouth buried in sand. Males being released at various distances soon found their way to the jar (containing females) which had its mouth open to the air, but no male came to the jar with its mouth hermetically sealed. Through the glass sides of both jars the females were plainly visible. The antennæ of certain males were covered with shellac. These males, when released, never found the females, and often paid no attention to them when brought within an inch of their bodies. Of other males the eyes were covered with pitch; but these males had no difficulty whatever in finding the females. It is plainly obvious from these experiments that the males found the females wholly by scent and not at all by sight.

FIG. 56.—Male mosquito, showing (*a.h.*) antennal hairs. (After Jordan and Kellogg; three times natural size.)

That some insects hear is proved by their possession of auditory organs, and has also been demonstrated by experiment. The fact, too, that many insects have special sound-making apparatus and do make characteristic sounds is a kind of proof that they can also hear. The auditory organs of insects, curiously enough, are of several kinds and are situated on different parts of the body, in various species. Among the locusts, katydids, and crickets, the most conspicuous of all the sound-making insects except the cicada, the ears are small tympanic membranes on the base of the abdomen in the locusts (Fig. 55), and on the tibiæ of the fore legs in the katydids and crickets. Associated with each tympanum is a small liquid-filled vesicle and a special auditory ganglion from which an auditory nerve runs to one of the ganglia of the thorax. Among the midges and mosquitoes the antennæ— those all-important sensitive structures —are abundantly provided with certain fine long hairs, the auditory hairs (Fig. 56), which take up the sound-waves and transmit the vibrations to an

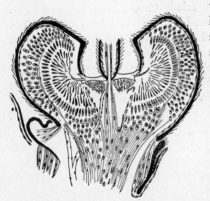

FIG. 57.—Diagram of longitudinal section through first and second antennal segments of a mosquito, *Mochlonyx culiciformis*, male, showing complex auditory organ composed of fine chitinous rods, nerve-fibers, and nerve-cells. (After Child; greatly magnified.)

elaborate percipient structure composed of many fine chitin-rods and ganglionated nerves contained in the next to basal antennal segment (Fig. 57). From this segment runs a principal auditory nerve to the brain. Many other insects besides the midges and mosquitoes possess this type of auditory organ; in fact such an organ, more or less well developed, has been found in almost every order except the Orthoptera (the order of locusts, crickets, katydids, etc.) in which the tympanic auditory organs occur.

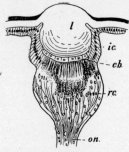

Special isolated hairs scattered sparsely over the body, connected with a special peripheral nervous arrangement, are believed by some entomologists to be a third kind of auditory structure, and are called chordotonal organs. Experimentally the sense of hearing has been surely determined for certain insects. A single striking example of this experimentation must here suffice. Mayer fastened a live male mosquito to a glass slide, put it under a microscope, and had a series of tuning-forks of different pitch sounded. When the $Ut_4$ fork of 512 vibrations per second was sounded many of the antennal hairs were set, sympathetically, into strong vibration. Tuning-forks of pitch an octave lower and an octave higher also caused more vibration than any intermediate notes. The male

FIG. 58.—Longitudinal section through ocellus of the honey-bee, *Apis mellifica*. *l.*, cuticular lens; *i.c.*, cellular layer of skin; *c.b.*, crystalline layer; *r.c.*, retinal cells; *o.n.*, optic nerve. (After Redikorzew; greatly magnified.)

mosquito's auditory hairs, then, are specially fitted to respond to, i.e., be stimulated by, notes of a pitch produced by 512 vibrations. Other, but fewer, hairs of different length vibrated in response to other tones. Those auditory hairs are most affected which are at right angles to the direction from which the sound comes. From this it is obvious that, from the position of the antennæ and the hairs, a sound will be loudest or most intense if it is directly in front of the head. If the mosquito is attracted by sound, it will thus be brought straight head end on toward the source of the sound. As a

FIG. 59.—Ocellar lens of larva of a saw-fly, *Cimbex* sp., showing its continuity with the chitinized cuticle. (After Redikorzew; greatly magnified.)

matter of fact, Mayer found the female mosquito's song to correspond nearly to $Ut_4$, and that her song set the male's auditory hairs into vibration. With little doubt, the male mosquitoes find the females by their sense of hearing.

Insects have two kinds of eyes, simple and compound. On most species both kinds are found, on some either kind alone, and in a few no eyes at all. Blind insects have lost the eyes by degeneration. The most primitive living insects, Campodea and others, have eyes, although only simple ones. The larvæ of the specialized insects, i.e., those with complete metamorphosis, also have only simple eyes. The compound eyes are not complex or specialized derivations of the simple ones, but are of independent origin and of obviously distinct structural character. The simple eyes, also called ocelli (Fig. 58), which usually occur to the number of three in a little triangle on top of the head, are small and inconspicuous,

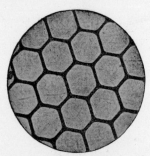

FIG. 60.—Part of corneal cuticle, showing facets, of the compound eye of a horse-fly, *Therioplectes* sp. (Photomicrograph by George O. Mitchell; greatly magnified.)

and consist each of a lens, this being simply a small convexly thickened clear part of the chitinized cuticle of the head-wall (Fig. 59) and a group of modified skin-cells behind it specially provided with absorbent pigment and capable of acting as a simple light-sensitive or retinal surface. The ocellus is supplied with a special nerve from the brain. The compound eyes are always paired and situated usually on the dorso-lateral parts of the head; they are usually large and conspicuous, sometimes, as in the dragon-flies and horse-flies, even forming two-thirds or more of the mass of the head. Externally each compound eye presents a number (which varies all the way from a score to thirty thousand) of facets or microscopic polygonal cuticular windows (Fig. 60). These are the cornea of the eye. Behind each facet is a distinct and independent subcylindrical eye-element or ommatidium composed of a crystalline cone, (wanting in many insects) enveloping pigment (which presumably excludes all light-rays except those which fall perpendicularly or nearly so to the corneal lens of that particular ommatidium), and a slender tapering part including or composed of the nervous or retinal element called rhabdom (Fig. 61). Each of these ommatidia perceives that bit of the external object which is directly in front of it; i.e., from which light is reflected perpendicularly to its corneal facet. All of these microscopic images, each of a small part of the external object, form a mosaic of the whole object, and thus give the familiar name mosaic

FIG. 61.—Longitudinal section through a few facets and eye-elements (ommatidia) of the compound eye of a moth. *f.*, corneal facets; *cc.*, crystalline cones; *p.*, pigment; *r.*, retinal parts; *o.n.*, optic nerve. (After Exner; greatly magnified.)

vision to the particular kind of seeing accomplished by the compound eye.

The character or degree of excellence of sight by the two kinds of eyes obviously varies much.   The fixed focus of the ocelli is extremely short,

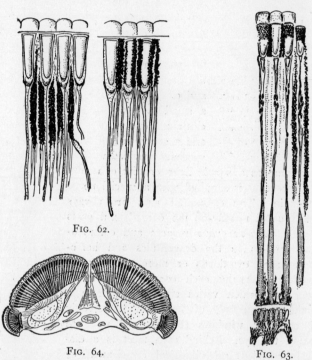

FIG. 62.

FIG. 64.                              FIG. 63.

FIG. 62.—Longitudinal sections through outer part of eye-elements (ommatidia) of compound eyes of *Lasiocampia quercifolia;* ommatidia at left showing disposition of pigment in eyes in the light, at right, in the dark.   (After Exner; greatly magnified.)

FIG. 63.—Longitudinal section through a few eye-elements of the compound eye of *Catocola nupta;* left ommatidia taken from an insect killed in the dark, right ommatidium taken from insect killed in the light.   (After Exner; greatly magnified.)

FIG. 64.—Section through the compound eyes of a male May-fly, showing division of each compound eye into two parts, an upper part containing large eye-elements (ommatidia), and a lower part containing small eye-elements (ommatidia).   (After Zimmerman; greatly magnified.)

and probably the range of vision of these eyes is restricted to an inch or two in front of the insect's head.   Indeed entomologists commonly believe that the ocelli avail little beyond distinguishing between light and darkness. With the compound eyes the focus is also fixed, but is longer and the range of vision must extend to two or three yards.   It is obvious that the larger and more convex the eyes the wider will be the extent of the visual field, while the smaller and more abundant the facets the sharper and more distinct will be the image. Although no change in focus can be effected, certain accommodation or flexibility of the seeing function is obtained by the movements of the pigment (Figs. 62 and 63) tending to regulate the amount of light admitted into the eye (as shown by Exner), and by a difference in size and pigmental character of the ommatidia (Fig. 64) composing the compound eyes of certain insects tending to make part of the eye especially

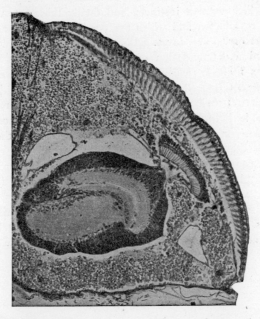

FIG. 65.—A section through the compound eye, in late pupal stage, of a blow-fly, *Calliphora sarraceniæ*. In the center is the brain with optic lobe, and on the right-hand margin are the many eye-elements (ommatidia) in longitudinal section. (Photomicrograph by George O. Mitchell; greatly magnified.)

adapted for seeing objects in motion or in poor light, and another part for seeing in bright light and for making a sharper image (as shown by Zimmerman for male May-flies, and by myself for certain true flies (see p. 318)). Our careful studies of the structure of the insect eye, and the experimentation which we have been able to carry on, indicate that, at best, the sight of insects cannot be exact or of much range.

The psychology of insects, that is, their activities and behavior as determined by their reflexes, instincts, and intelligence, is a subject of great interest and attractiveness, but obviously one difficult to study exactly. The elaborateness of many insect instincts, such as those of the ants, wasps, and bees, to choose examples at once familiar and extreme in their complexity, makes it very difficult to analyze the trains of reactions into individual ones, and to determine, if it is indeed at all determinable, the particular stimuli which act as the springs for these various reactions. The attitude of the modern biologist in this matter would be to keep first in mind the theory of reflexes, to look keenly for physico-chemical explanations of the reactions, and only when forced from this position by the impossibility of finding mechanical explanations for the phenomena to recognize those complex reflexes which we call instincts, and finally those acts which we call intelligent, or reasonable, and which are possible only to the possessors of associative memory. The investigations, mostly recent, which have been directed toward a determination of the immediate springs or stimuli of insect reactions indicate clearly that many of these responses, even some which were formerly looked on as surely indicative of considerable intelligence on the part of their performers, are explicable as rigid reflex (mechanical) reactions to light, gravity, the proximity of substances of certain chemical composition, contact with solid bodies, etc. On the other hand the position of the extreme upholders (Bethe, Uexkull, and others) of the purely reflex explanation of all insect behavior will certainly prove untenable. As one of the phases of insect biology to which this book is particularly devoted is that which includes the study of habits, activities, or behavior, we may dispense with any special discussion of instinct in this introductory chapter. It is sufficient to say that no other class of invertebrate animals presents such an interesting and instructive psychology as the insects.

# CHAPTER II

## DEVELOPMENT AND META-MORPHOSIS

THAT animals are born or hatch from eggs in an immature condition is such familiar natural history that we are likely to overlook the significance and consequences of the fact unless our attention is particularly called to them. This condition of immaturity makes it necessary that part of the free life of the organism has to be devoted to growth and development and has to be undergone in an imperfect condition, a condition of structure and physiology, indeed, which may be very different from that of the parents or of maturity. While most animals that are born alive resemble the parents in most respects, always excepting that of size, many of those animals which hatch from eggs deposited outside the body of the mother issue from the egg with few indeed of the characteristics of the parents and may be so dissimilar from them that only our knowledge of the life-history of the animal enables us to recognize these young individuals as of the same species as the parent. The butterfly hatching as the worm-like caterpillar, and the frog as the fish-like tadpole, are the classic examples of this phenomenon. The mammals, our most familiar examples of animals which give birth to their young alive and free, nourish, for weeks or months before birth, the developing growing young. But with egg-laying animals usually only such nourishment is furnished the young as can be enclosed as food-yolk within the egg-shell. As a matter of fact, some young which hatch from eggs, as, for example, chickens, quail, etc., hatch in well-developed condition; and some young mammals, nourished by the mother's body until birth, are in a conspicuously undeveloped state, as a young kangaroo or opossum. But nevertheless it is generally true that an animal hatched from an egg has still a larger amount of development to undergo before it comes to the stature and capacity of its parents than one which is

35

born alive, after having passed a considerable time growing and developing
in the body of the mother.   And this difference in degree of development at
birth is largely due simply to the difference in amount of nourishment
which can be afforded the young.   The embryo in the egg uses up its food
early in its developmental career and before it has reached the stage of
likeness to its parents.   It issues in a condition picturing some far-distant
ancestor of its species, or more frequently, perhaps, in a modified, adapted
condition, fit to make of this tender unready creature thus thrust before
its time into the struggle for living an organism capable of caring for itself,
although not yet endowed with capacities as effective as, or even similar to,
those of the parent.

It is familiar to us, then, that development is not wholly postnatal or
postembryonic; that before birth or hatching a greater or less amount of
development, requiring a longer or shorter
period of time, has already been undergone.
Every animal begins life as a simple cell; all
animals except the Protozoa (the simplest animals, those whose whole body for its whole
life is but a single cell) finish life, if red
Nature permits them to come through myriad
dangers safely to maturity, as a complex of
thousands or millions of cells united into
great variety of tissues and organs.   This
great change from most simple to most complex
condition constitutes *development:* the actual
increase of body-matter and extension of
dimensions is *growth.*

Fig. 66.—Ovaries and oviducts
of a thrips. *o.t.,* ovarial tubes;
*o.d.,* oviduct; *r.s.,* seminal
receptacle, or spermatheca;
*d.r.s.,* duct of the seminal receptacle. (After Uzel; much
enlarged.)

Most insects hatch from eggs; being born
alive is the exceptional experience of the young
of but few kinds, and even this is a sort of
pseudo-birth.   Such hatch alive, one may better
say, for they begin life in eggs, not laid outside the mother body to be sure, but held in
the egg-duct until hatching-time.   With very few exceptions, young insects
are not nourished by the mother except in so far as she stores a supply of
yolk around or by the side of each embryo inside the egg-shell.   The forming of the egg is a matter which does not lend itself readily to the observation and study of amateurs, but is a phenomenon of unusual interest to
whomever is privileged to discover it.   The insect ovaries consist of a pair
of little compact groups of short tapering tubes (Fig. 66).   In the anterior or
beginning end of each tube is a microscopic space or chamber from whose
walls cells loosen themselves and escape into the cavity.   These cells become

either the germinal or the food part of the eggs. There seems to exist no differentiation among these cells at first, but soon certain ones begin to move slowly down through the egg-tube in single file, each becoming surrounded and enclosed by yolk, i.e., reserve foodstuff. This gathering of yolk increases the size of the forming eggs, so that they appear as a short string of beads of varying size enclosed in the elastic egg-tube. When of considerable size each egg in the lower end of the tube becomes enclosed

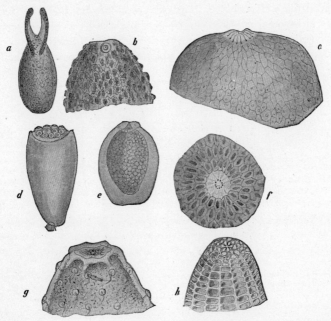

FIG. 67.—Insect eggs and parts of eggs, showing micropyle. *a*, egg of *Drosophila cellaris; b*, upper pole of egg of robber-fly, *Asilus crabriformis; c*, upper pole of egg of hawk-moth, *Sphinx populi; d*, egg of head-louse, *Pediculus capitis; e*, egg of dragon-fly, *Libellula depressa; f*, upper surface of egg of harpy-moth, *Harpyia vinula; g*, upper pole of egg of *Hammalicherus cerdo; h*, upper pole of egg of sulphur-butterfly, *Colias hyale.* (After Leuckart; much enlarged.)

in two envelopes, a membranous inner one (yolk or vitelline membrane) and an outer horny one, the chorion or egg-shell. But both of these envelopes are pierced at one pole by a tiny opening, the micropyle (Fig. 67), and through this opening the fertilizing spermatozoa enter the egg from the seminal receptacle just before the egg is extruded from the body.

The development of the embryo within the egg is also securely sealed away from the eyes of most amateurs. The study of insect embryology requires a knowledge of microscopic technic, and facilities for fixing and imbedding and section-cutting which are not often found outside the college laboratory. But the particularly interesting and suggestive stages in this development may be outlined and illustrated in brief space. First, the germinal cell near the center of the egg divides repeatedly (Fig. 68 *A*) and the resulting new cells migrate outward against the inner envelope of the egg and arrange themselves here in a single peripheral layer, called the blastoderm (Fig. 68 *D*, *bl*). On what is going to be the ventral side of the egg the cells of the blastoderm begin to divide and mass themselves to form the ventral plate (Fig. 69 *C*). The embryo is forming here; the rest of the blastoderm becomes modified and folded to serve as a double membranous envelope (called amnion and serosa) for the embryo. Stretching nearly from pole to pole as a narrow streak along the ventral aspect of the egg, the

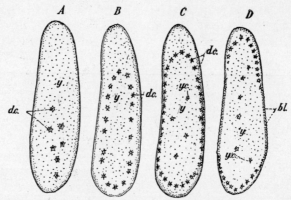

Fig. 68.—Early stage in development of egg of water-scavenger beetle, *Hydrophilus* sp. *A*, first division of nucleus; *B*, migration of cleavage-cells outward; *C*, beginning of blastoderm; *D*, blastoderm; *y.*, yolk; *dc.*, cleavage-cells; *yc.*, yolk-cells; *bl.*, blastoderm. (After Heider; greatly magnified.)

developing embryo begins soon to show that fundamental structural characteristic of insects, a segmental condition (Fig. 69 *D*). One can now make out the forming body-rings or segments, and each soon shows the beginnings or rudiments of a pair of appendages (Fig. 69 *E*). The appendages of the head and thoracic segments continue to develop and begin soon to assume their definitive character of antennæ, mouth-parts, and legs, but those of the abdominal segments never get farther than a first appearance and indeed soon disappear. In the mean time the internal systems of organs are gradually developing, the ventral nerve-chain first, then the alimentary canal, and later the muscles, tracheæ, and the heart. All the time the yolk is being gradually used up, fed on, by the cells of the developing and growing embryo, until finally comes the disappearance of all the stored food, and the time for hatching.

The eggs have been laid, because of the remarkable instinct of the mother, in a situation determined chiefly by the interests of the young which are to hatch from them. The young of many kinds of insects take very different food from that of the mother—a caterpillar feeds on green leaves, the butterfly on flower-nectar—or live under very different circumstances—young dragon-flies and May-flies live under water, the adults in the air. A monarch butterfly, which does not feed on leaves, nor has ever before produced young, seeks out a milkweed to lay its eggs upon. The young monarchs, tiny black-and-white-banded caterpillars, feed on the

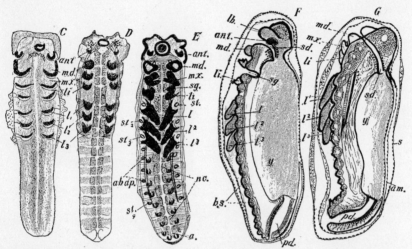

FIG. 69.—Early stages in the development of the egg of saw-fly, *Hylotoma beriberidis*. *C*, ventral plate removed from egg; *D*, ventral plate, showing segmentation of body; *E*, embryo, showing developing appendages; *F*, same stage, lateral aspect; *G*, older stage, lateral aspect. *ant.*, antenna; *md.*, mandible; *mx.*, maxilla; *li.*, labium; $l^1$, $l^2$, $l^3$, legs; *sg.*, salivary glands; *st.*, spiracles; *ab.ap.*, abdominal appendages; *n.c.*, nerve-centers; *a.*, anal opening; *lb.*, labrum; *sd.*, œsophageal invagination; *y.*, yolk; *b.s.*, abdominal segments; *pd.*, intestinal invagination; *am.*, amnion; *s.*, serosa. (After Graber; greatly magnified.)

green milkweed leaf-tissue; indeed they starve to death if they cannot have leaves of precisely this kind of plant! The reason that the butterfly, whose only food is the nectar of almost any kind of flower, ranges wide to find a milkweed for its eggs, is one not founded on experience or teaching or reason, but on an inherited instinct, which is as truly and as importantly an attribute of this particular species of butterfly as its characteristic color pattern or body structure. And the female of the great flashing strong-winged dragon-fly, queen insect of the air, when egg-laying time comes, feels a strange irresistible demand to get these eggs into water, dropping them in from its airy height, or swooping down to touch the tip of the abdo-

men to the water's surface, there releasing them, or even crawling down
some water-plant beneath the surface and with arduous labor thrusting the
eggs into the heart of this submerged plant-stem.   From the eggs hatch
wingless dwarf-dragons of the pond bottom, with terrible extensile, clutching mouth-parts and an insatiable hunger for living prey.

So our young insects, after completing their embryonic development,
come to the time of their appearance as free individuals compelled to find
their own food and no longer sheltered by a firm egg-shell from the strenu-

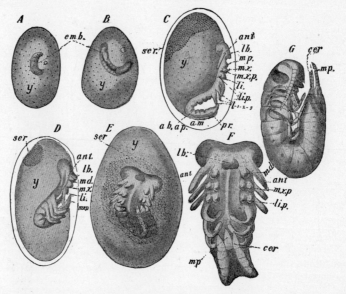

FIG. 70.—Series of stages in development of egg of fish-moth, *Lepisma* sp.   *A*, beginning embryo; *B*, embryo showing segmentation; *C*, embryo showing appendages;
*D*, embryo more advanced; *E*, embryo still more advanced; *F*, embryo still older
and removed from egg; *G*, embryo removed from egg at time of readiness to hatch.
*y.*, yolk; *emb.*, embryo; *ser.*, serosa; *am.*, amnion; *ant.*, antenna; *lb.*, labrum;
*md.*, mandible; *mx.*, maxilla; *mx.p.*, maxillary palpus; *li.*, labium; *li.p.*, labial
palpus; *l¹, l², l³*, legs; *pr.*, proctodæum, or intestinal invagination; *cer.*, cerci; *mp.*,
middle posterior process.   (After Heymons; greatly magnified.)

ous fighting and hiding of the open road.   Now these young insects, depending upon how far they have carried their developmental course in the egg,
hatch either almost wholly like their parents (excepting always in size), or
in a condition fairly resembling the parents, but lacking all traces of wings
and showing other less conspicuous dissimilarities, or finally they may appear
in guise wholly unlike that of their parents, in such a condition indeed that
they would not be recognized as insects of the same kind as the parents.
But in all cases the young are certain, if they live their allotted days or weeks

or months, to attain finally the parent structure and appearance. This attainment is a matter of further development, of postembryonic development, and the amount or degree of this development or change is obviously determined by the remoteness or nearness of the young at the time of hatching to the adult or parental condition. The young of many of our most familiar insects, as beetles, flies, moths and butterflies, and ants, bees, and wasps, hatch out extremely unlike their parents in appearance: the well-known worm-like caterpillars of butterflies and moths are striking examples of this unlikeness. The changes necessarily undergone in the development from caterpillar to butterfly are so great that there actually results a very considerable degree of making over, or metamorphosis of the insect, and for convenience of roughly classifying insects according to their development, entomologists have adopted the terms complete metamorphosis, incomplete metamorphosis, and no metamorphosis to indicate three not very sharply distinguished kinds or degrees of postembryonic development.

In the latter category are comparatively few species, because most insects have wings, and no insect is winged at birth. But the members of the simplest order (Aptera) are all primitively wingless, and their young are, in practically all particulars except body size and the maturity of the reproductive glands, like the adults (Fig. 71); their development may fairly be said to take place without metamorphosis. In addition to these primitively simple insects there are certain degenerate wingless species like the biting bird-lice, for example, whose young also reach the parental stature and character without metamorphosis.

In the next category, that of development with incomplete metamorphosis, are included two large orders of insects and several smaller ones. All the sucking-bugs (order Hemiptera) and all the locusts, katydids, crickets, and cockroaches (composing the order Orthoptera), as well as the May-flies, dragon-flies, white ants, and several other small groups of unfamiliar forms, agree in having their young hatched in a condition strongly resembling the parents, although lacking wings, and in some cases, particu-

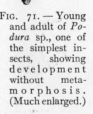

FIG. 71. — Young and adult of *Podura* sp., one of the simplest insects, showing development without metamorphosis. (Much enlarged.)

larly those in which the young live on different food and in a different habitat from the adults, differing rather markedly in several superficial characters. Such is the case, for example, with the dragon-flies, whose young are aquatic and breathe by means of tracheal gills, and are provided with specially constructed seizing and biting mouth-parts. But in such essential characteristics as number of legs, character of eyes and antennæ, and, usually, character of mouth-parts, the young and parent agree. During postembryonic

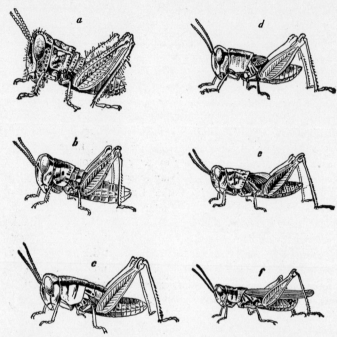

FIG. 72.—Developing stages, after hatching, of a locust, *Melanoplus femur-rubrum,* *a*, just hatched, without wing-pads; *b*, after first moulting; *c*, after second moulting. showing beginning wing-pads; *d*, after third moulting; *e*, after fourth moulting, *f*, adult with fully developed wings. (After Emerton; younger stages enlarged; adult stage, natural size.)

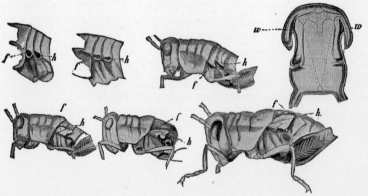

FIG. 73.—Stages in development of the wings of a locust. *f.*, developing rudiment of fore wing; *h.*, developing rudiment of hind wing; *w.*, wing-pad. (After Graber; twice natural size.)

development the young have to develop wings and make what other change is necessary to reach the adult type, but the life is continually free and active and the change is only a simple gradual transformation of the various parts in which differences exist. A common locust is an excellent example of an insect with such incomplete metamorphosis. Fig. 72 shows the developing locust at different successive ages, or stages, as these periods are called because of their separation from each other by the phenomenon, common to all insects, of moulting. As the insect grows it finds its increase of girth and length restrained by the firm inelastic external chitinized cuticle, or exoskeleton. So at fixed periods (varying with the various species both in number and duration) this cuticle is cast or moulted. From a median longitudinal rent along the dorsum of the thorax and head, the insect, soft and dangerously helpless, struggles out of the old skin, enclosed in a new cuticle which, however, requires some little time to harden and assume its proper colors (often protective). After each moulting the young locust appears markedly larger and with its wing-pads better developed (Fig. 73). But not until the final moulting—in the case of the locust

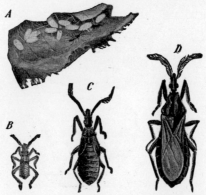

FIG. 74.—Metamorphosis, incomplete, of an assassin-bug (family Reduviidæ, order Hemiptera). *A*, young just hatching from eggs; *B*, young after first moulting, showing beginning wing-pads; *C*, older stage with complex wing-pads; *D*, adult with fully developed wings. (One-half larger than natural size.)

this is the fifth—are the wings usable as organs of flight. So that there is after all likely to be a rather marked difference between the habits of the young and those of the adult of an insect with incomplete metamorphosis, that difference being primarily due to structural differences. The young are confined to the ground, and their locomotion is limited to walking or hopping. The adults can live, if they like, a life in the air, and they have a means of locomotion of greatly extended capability.

The insects with complete metamorphosis are the beetles, the two-winged flies, the butterflies and moths, the ichneumons, gall-flies, ants, bees, and wasps, the fleas, the ant-lions, and several other small groups of insects with less familiar names. In the case of all the thousands of species in these groups, the young when hatched from the egg differ very much in structure and appearance, and also in habits and general economy, from the parents. Familiar examples of such young are the caterpillars and "worms" of the moths and butterflies, the grubs of beetles, the maggots of the flesh- and house-flies, and the helpless soft white grubs in the cells of bees and wasps. These strange young, so unlike their parents, have the generic name larvæ, and the stage or life of the insect passed as a larva is known as the larval stage. In almost all cases these larvæ have mouth-parts fitted for biting and chewing, while most of the adults have sucking-mouth parts; the larvæ have only simple eyes and small inconspicu-

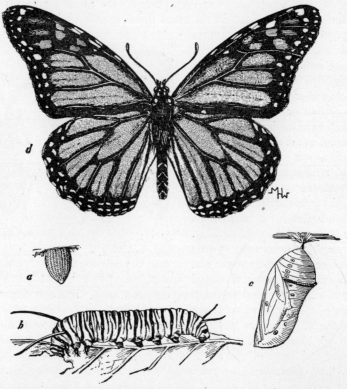

FIG. 75.—Metamorphosis, complete, of monarch butterfly, *Anosia plexippus*. *a*, egg (greatly magnified); *b*, caterpillar or larva; *c*, chrysalid or pupa; *d*, adult or imago. (After Jordan and Kellogg. Natural size.)

ous antennæ; the adults have both simple and compound eyes and well-developed conspicuous antennæ; the larvæ may have no legs, or one pair or two or any number up to eight or ten pairs; the adults have always three pairs; the larvæ are wholly wingless, nor do external wing-pads (i.e., developing wings) appear outside the body during the larval stage; the adults have usually two pairs (sometimes one or none) of fully developed wings. Internally the differences are also great. The musculation of the larva is like that of a worm, to accomplish wriggling, crawling, worm-like locomotion; in the adult it is very different, particularly in head and thorax; the alimentary canal is usually adapted in the larva for manipulating and digesting solid foods; in the adult, usually (except with the beetles and a few other groups), for liquid food; there may be large silk-glands in the larva, which are rarely present in the adult; the respiratory system of the larvæ of some flies and Neuroptera is adapted for breathing under water; this is only rarely true of the adults. The heart and the nervous system show lesser differences, but even here there is no identity: the ventral nerve chain of the larvæ may contain twice as many distinct ganglia as in the adult.

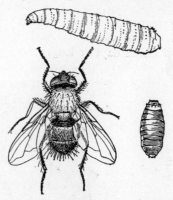

FIG. 76.—Larva, pupa, and adult of the flesh-fly, *Calliphora erythrocephala*, with complete metamorphosis. (Two times natural size.)

The larva lives its particular kind of life: it grows and moults several times; but externally it shows at no time any more likeness to the adult than it did at hatching. But after its last moult it appears suddenly in the guise of a partially formed adult in (usually) quiescent mummy-like form, with the antennæ, legs, and wings of the adult folded compactly on the under side of the body, and the only sign of life a feeble bending of the hind-body in response to the stimulus of a touch. This is the insect of complete metamorphosis in its characteristic second stage (or third if the egg stage is called first), the pupal stage. The mummy is called pupa or chrysalid. As the insect cannot, in this stage, fight or run away from its enemies, its defence lies in the instinctive care with which the larva, just before pupation, has spun a protecting silken cocoon about itself, or has burrowed below the surface of the ground, or has concealed itself in crack or crevice. Or the defence may lie in the fine harmonizing of the color and pattern of the naked exposed chrysalid with the bark or twig on which it rests; it may be visible but indistinguishable. The insect as pupa takes no food; but the insect as larva has provided for this. By its greed and overeating it has laid up a reserve or food-store in the body which is drawn on during the pupal stage and carries the insect through these days or weeks or months of waiting for the final change, the transformation to the renewed

FIG. 77.—Adult worker (*a*) and larva (*b*) of honey-bee. (Adult natural size; larva twice natural size.)

active food-getting life of the adult or imaginal stage. Familiar examples of this kind of metamorphosis, the real metamorphosis, are provided by the life of the monarch butterfly, the honey-bee, and the blow-fly. The great red-brown monarch lays its eggs on the leaves of a milkweed; from the eggs hatch in four days the tiny tiger-caterpillars (larvæ) (Fig. 75) with biting mouth-parts, simple eyes, short antennæ, and eight pairs of legs on its elongate cylindrical wingless body. The caterpillars bite off and eat voraciously bits of milkweed-leaf; they grow rapidly, moult four times, and at the end of eleven days or longer hang themselves head downward from a stem or

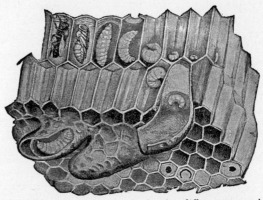

Fig. 78.—Brood-cells from honey-bee comb showing different stages in the metamorphosis of the honey-bee; worker brood at top and three queen-cells below; beginning at right end of upper row of cells and going to left, note egg, young larva, old larva, pupa, and adult ready to issue; of the large curving queen-cells, two are cut open to show larva within. (After Benton; natural size.)

leaf and pupate, i.e., moult again, appearing now not as caterpillars, but as the beautiful green chrysalids dotted with gold and black spots. The forming antennæ legs and wings of the adult show faintly through the pupal cuticle, but motionless and mummy-like each chrysalid hangs for about twelve days, when through a rent in the cuticle issues the splendid butterfly with its coiled-up sucking proboscis, its compound eyes, long antennæ, its three pairs of slender legs (the foremost pair rudimentary), and its four great red-brown wings. The queen honey-bee lays her eggs, one in each of the scores of hexagonal cells of the brood-comb (Fig. 78). From the egg there hatches in three days a tiny footless, helpless white grub, with biting mouth-parts and a pair of tiny simple eyes. The nurses come and feed this larva steadily for five days; then put a mass of food by it and "cap" the cell; the larva has grown by this time so as nearly to fill the cell. It uses up the stored food, and "changes" to the pupa, with the incomplete lineaments of the adult bee. It takes no more food, but lies like a sleeping prisoner in its closed cell for thirteen days, and then it awakens to active life, gnaws its way through the cell-cap and issues into the hive-space a definitive honey-bee with all the wonderful special structures that make the honey-bee body such an effective little insectean machine. The blow-fly (Fig. 76) lays a hundred or more little white eggs on exposed meat. From these eggs come in twenty or thirty hours the tiny white wriggling larvæ (maggots), footless, eyeless, wingless, nearly headless, with a single pair of curious extensile hooks for mouth-parts. For ten to fourteen days these larvæ squirm and feed and grow, moulting twice in this time; they then pupate inside of the larval cuticle, which becomes thicker, firmer, and brown, so as to enclose the delicate pupa in a stout protective shell. The blow-fly now looks like a small thick spindle-shaped seed or bean, and this stage lasts for twelve or fourteen

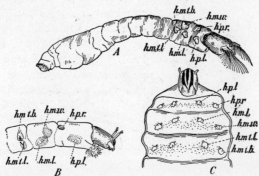

Fig. 79.—Dipterous larvæ showing (through skin) the imaginal discs or buds of wings, these buds being just inside the skin. *A*, larva of black fly, *Simulium* sp.; *B*, anterior end of larva of midge, *Chironomus* sp.; *C*, anterior end, cut open, of larva of giant crane-fly, *Holorusia rubiginosa*; *h.pr.*, bud of prothoracic respiratory tube; *h.pl.*, bud of prothoracic leg; *h.mw.*, bud of mesothoracic wing; *h.ml.*, bud of mesothoracic leg; *h.mtb.*, bud of metathoracic balancer; *h.mtl.*, bud of metathoracic leg. (Much enlarged.)

days. Then the winged imago, the buzzing blow-fly, as we best know it, breaks its way out. In the house-fly the same kind of life-history, with complete metamorphosis of the extremest type, is completed in ten days. Nor do we realize how really extreme and extraordinary this metamorphosis is until we study the changes which take place inside the body, as well as those superficial ones we have already noted.

The natural question occurs to the thoughtful reader: "Is the metamorphosis or transformation in the postembryonal development of such insects as the butterfly, bee, and blow-fly as sudden or discontinuous and as radical as the superficial phenomena indicate?" The answer is no, and yes; the metamorphosis is not so discontinuous or saltatory and yet is even more radical and fundamental than the external changes suggest. To take a single example, the case of the blow-fly (admittedly an extreme one), the phenomena of internal change are, put briefly, as follows: The imaginal wings, legs, and head-parts begin to develop as deeply invaginated little buds of the cell-layer of the larval skin early in larval life. This development is gradual and continuous until pupation, when the wing and leg rudi-

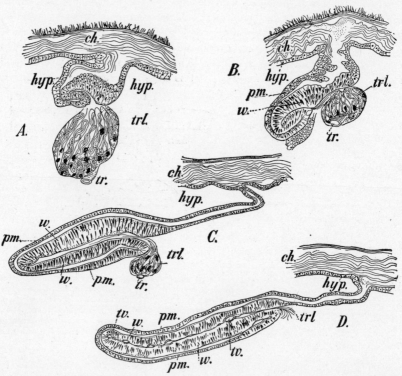

Fig. 80.—Stages in development of wing-buds in the larva of the giant crane-fly, *Holorusia rubiginosa* (the wing-buds have been dissected out and sectioned, so as to show their intimate anatomy). *A, B, C, D*, four stages successively older. *ch.*, chitinized cuticle; *hyp.*, hypoderm or cellular layer of skin; *tr.*, trachea; *trl.*, tracheoles; *p.m.*, peritrophic membrane; *w.*, developing wing; *t.v.*, tracheal branch indicating position of future wing-vein. (Greatly magnified.)

ments and the new head are pulled out upon the exterior of the body. Just before pupation, when the larva has given up its locomotion and feeding, the larval muscles, tracheæ, salivary glands, alimentary canal, and some other tissues begin to disintegrate, and rapidly break wholly down, so that in the pupa there appear to be no internal organs except the nervous system, reproductive glands, and perhaps the heart, but the whole interior of the body is filled with a thick fluid in which float bits of degenerating larval tissue. At the same time with this radical histolysis or breaking down of tissue a rapid histogenesis or developing of imaginal parts from certain groups of undifferentiated primitive cells, derived probably mostly from the larval skin-cells, is going on. Thus many of the larval organs and tissues, instead of going over into the corresponding imaginal ones, wholly disintegrate and disappear, and the imaginal parts are newly and independently derived. In connection with the breaking down of the larval tissues phagocytes or freely moving, tissue-eating, amœboid blood-cells play an important part, although one not yet fully understood. They are either the causal agents of the histolysis, or are assisting agents in it, the tissue disintegration beginning independently, or—a recent suggestion—they are perhaps more truly to be looked on as trophocytes, that is, carriers of food, namely, disintegrating tissue, to the developing centers of the imaginal parts. Much investigation remains to be done on this interesting subject of histolysis and histogenesis in insects with complete metamorphosis,

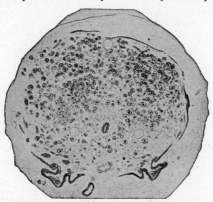

Fig. 81.—A cross section of the body of the pupa of a honey-bee, showing the body-cavity filled with disintegrated tissues and phagocytes, and (at the bottom) a budding pair of legs of the adult, the larvæ being wholly legless. Photomicrograph by George O. Mitchell; greatly magnified.)

but enough has been already accomplished to show the basic and extreme character of the transformation from larva to adult.

If we ask for the meaning of such unusual and radical changes in the development of insects, we confront at once an important biological problem. Most biologists believe that in a large and general way the development of animals is a swift and condensed recapitulation of their evolution; meaning by development the life-history or ontogeny of an individual, and by evolution the ancestral history or phylogeny of the species. According to this "biogenetic law" the interpretation of the significance of the various stages and characters assumed by an animal in the course of its development from single fertilized egg-cell to the complex many-celled definitive adult stage is simple: These stages correspond to various ancestral ones in the long genealogical history of the species. Every vertebrate, for example, is at some period in its development more like a fish than any other living kind of animal; it has gill-slits in its throat, is tailed, and is indeed a fish-like creature. This is its particular developmental stage, corresponding to the ancestral fish-like ancestors of all vertebrates. Do then the larvæ and pupæ of insects with complete metamorphosis represent ancestral stages in insect evolutionary history? In some degree the larval stage does, but in no degree does the pupal. Insects are certainly not descended from an animal that, like a pupa, could neither move nor eat and which had no internal organs except a nervous system, heart, and rudimentary reproductive glands. Biologists

FIG. 82.—A bit of degenerate muscle from tussock-moth, *Hemerocampa leucostigma*. Note phago-cytic cells attacking muscle at the margins. (Greatly magnified.)

recognize that the exigencies of life during adolescence may profoundly modify what might be termed the normal course of development. As long as the developing animal is shielded from the struggle for existence, is provided with a store of food and protected from enemies by lying in an egg-shell or in the body of the mother, it may pursue fairly steadily its recapitulatory course of development; but once emerged and forced to shift for

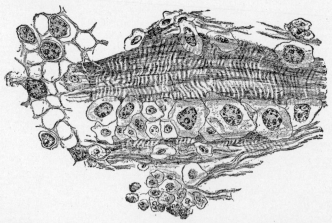

FIG. 83.—Degenerating muscle from pupa of giant crane-fly, *Holorusia rubiginosa*, showing phagocytic cells penetrating and disintegrating the muscle-tissue. (Greatly magnified.)

itself, it must be, at whatever tender age it is turned out, or whatever ancient ancestor it is in stage of simulating, adapted to live successfully under the present-day and immediate conditions of life. If the butterfly gets hatched long before it has reached its definitive butterfly stage, and while it is in a stage roughly corresponding to some worm-like ancestors—and from such ancestors insects have undoubtedly descended—it must be fitted to live successfully a crawling, squirming, worm-like life. That those insects which hatch as worm-like larvæ do in fact owe their wingless, worm-like body condition partly to being born in a stage simulating a worm-like ancestor is proba-

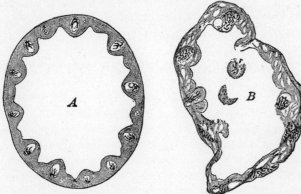

FIG. 84.—Degeneration, without phagocytosis, of salivary glands in old larva of giant crane-fly, *Holorusia rubiginosa*. *A*, cross-section of salivary gland before degeneration has begun; *B*, cross-section of salivary gland after degeneration has set in. (Greatly magnified.)

bly true. But to be a successful worm demands very different bodily adaptations from those of a successful butterfly. And so far does the larval butterfly go, or so far has it been carried, in meeting these demands that nature finds it more economical—to get into figurative language— or easier to break down almost wholly the larval body—after a new food-supply for further development has been got and stored away, and to build up from primitive undifferentiated cell beginnings the final definitive butterfly body, than to make over these very unlike larval parts into the adult ones. The pupal stage, quiescent, non-food taking, and defended by a thick chitinous wall, often enclosed in a silken cocoon, buried in the ground or crevice, or harmonizing so perfectly with its environment as to be indistinguishable from it, is the chief period of this radical and marvelous breaking down and building anew. It is an interpolated stage in the development of the butterfly corresponding to nothing in the phyletic history; an adaptation to meet the necessities of its life-conditions. To my mind, this is the interpretation of the phenomena of complete metamorphosis.

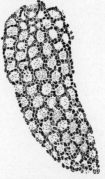

FIG. 85.—Cross-section of newly developing muscle in pupa of honey-bee, *Apis mellifica*. (Greatly magnified.)

# CHAPTER III

## THE CLASSIFICATION OF INSECTS

As has been explained in the preceding chapter, insects are primarily classified on the basis of their postembryonic development. Insects with incomplete metamorphosis, that is, those which do not undergo a non-feeding, usually quiescent, pupal stage in their development are believed to be more nearly related to each other than to any of the insects which undergo a so-called complete metamorphosis. So they are spoken of collectively as the Hemimetabola, while all the insects with a distinct pupal stage are called the Holometabola. But when one has collected an adult insect, as a fly or moth or grasshopper, and wishes to classify it, this primary classification based on character of development often cannot be made for lack of information regarding the life-history of the particular insect in hand. The next grouping is into orders, and this grouping is based chiefly on structural characters, and corresponds to one's already more or less familiar knowledge of insect classification. Thus all the beetles with their horny fore wings constitute one order, the Coleoptera; the moths and butterflies with their scale-covered wings another order, the Lepidoptera; the two-winged flies the order Diptera, the ants, bees, wasps, and four-winged parasitic flies the order Hymenoptera, and so on. So that the first step in a beginner's attempt to classify his collected insects is to refer them to their proper orders.

Now while entomologists are mostly agreed with regard to the make-up of the larger and best represented orders, that is, those orders containing the more abundant and familiar insects, there are certain usually small, obscure, strangely formed and more or less imperfectly known insects with regard to whose ordinal classification the agreement is not so uniform. While some entomologists incline to look on them simply as modified and aberrant members of the various large and familiar orders, others prefer to indicate the structural differences and the classific importance of these differences by establishing new orders for each of these small aberrant groups. Most entomologists of the present incline toward this latter position, so that whereas Linnæus, the first great classifier of animals, divided all insects into but seven orders, the principal modern American * text-book of systematic ento-

* Comstock, J. H., A Manual of Insects, 1898.

52

mology recognizes nineteen distinct ones. This does not mean, of course, that twelve new orders of insects have been found since Linnæus's time, although two or three of the orders are in fact founded on insects unknown to him, but means that certain small groups classified by Linnæus simply as families in his large orders have been given the rank of distinct orders by modern systematists. And as our knowledge of insects and their relationship to each other is certainly much larger now than it was one hundred and fifty years ago, we may feel confident that the many-order system of classification is more nearly a true expression of the natural interrelationships of insects than was the old seven-order system. But not all entomologists agree on the nineteen-order system. Few, indeed, still use the Linnæan system, but many believe that the division of the insect class into nineteen orders gives too much importance to certain very small groups and to some others which are not markedly aberrant, and these entomologists recognize a lesser number of orders, varying with different authors from nine to about a dozen. In this book we shall adopt the nineteen-order system as used in Comstock's Manual. In the first place the author believes that this classification best represents our present knowledge of insect taxonomy; in the second place this is the classification taught by nearly all the teachers of entomology in America.

To determine the order to which an insect belongs we make use of a classifying table or key. In the Key to Orders which follows this paragraph, all the insect orders are characterized by means of brief statements of structural features more or less readily recognized by simple inspection of the superficies of the body; to determine some of the conditions a simple lens or hand-magnifier will be needed. The orders are so arranged in the key that by choosing among two or more contrasting statements the student may "trace" his specimen to its proper order. Inspection of the Key with an attempt or two at tracing some familiar insect, as a house-fly, moth, or wasp whose order is already known, will make the method of use apparent. It must be borne in mind that young insects, such as caterpillars of moths, grubs of beetles, and the wingless nymphs of locusts, dragon-flies, etc., cannot be classified by this key. Indeed the young stages of most of the insects which we know well as adults are unknown to us, and there is, besides, such manifold adaptive variety in the external structure of those forms which we do know that no key for the classification into orders of immature insects can now be made.

### KEY TO THE ORDERS OF INSECTS.

#### (Arranged by Prof. H. E. Summers.)

(For adult insects only. If in any paragraph all the italicized characters agree with the specimen in hand, the remaining characters need not be read; these latter are for use in doubtful cases, or where the organs characterized in italics are rudimentary or absent. The technical terms used in this Key have all been defined in Chapter I.)

A.   *Primitive wingless insects; mouth-parts well developed, but all except the apices of the mandibles and maxillæ withdrawn into a cavity in the head;* tarsi (feet) always one- or two-clawed; body sometimes centiped-like, with well-developed abdominal legs, in this case tarsi two-clawed..................(The simplest insects.) Aptera.

AA. Normally *winged insects*, wings sometimes rudimentary or absent; mouth-parts not withdrawn into a cavity in the head.

    B.   *Mouth-parts, when developed, with both mandibles and maxillæ fitted for biting; abdomen broadly joined to thorax; tarsi never bladder-shaped;* when mouth-parts are rudimentary, if the wings are two, there are no halteres (p. 303); if the wings are four or absent, the body is not *densely* clothed with scales.

        C.   *Posterior end of abdomen with a pair of prominent unjointed forceps-like appendages; fore wings, when present, short, veinless, horny or leathery.*
                                       (Earwigs.) Euplexoptera.

        CC. *Posterior end of abdomen usually without prominent unjointed forceps-like appendages;* when these are present the fore wings are always developed, veined.

           D.   *Fore wings, when present, veined and membranous, parchment-like or leathery;* when absent, the labium (under-lip) either cleft in the middle, or the mouth-parts prolonged into a distinct beak.

               E.   *Fore wings, when present, thicker than hind wings, somewhat leathery or parchment-like; hind wings folded several times lengthwise, like a fan, in repose;* when wings are absent, prothorax large.
                     (Locusts, crickets, cockroaches, etc.) Orthoptera.

              EE. *Fore wings membranous, of same structure as hind wings; hind wings usually not folded, but occasionally folded like a fan;* when wings are absent, prothorax small.

                  F.   *Antennæ inconspicuous.*

                      G.   *Hind wings smaller than fore or absent; posterior end of abdomen with two or three many-jointed filaments.*
                                 (May-flies.) Ephemerida.

                      GG. *Hind wings not smaller than fore; posterior end of abdomen without many-jointed filaments.*
                     (Dragon-flies and damsel-flies.) Odonata.

                FF. *Antennæ conspicuous.*

                  G.   *Tarsi less than five-jointed; labium cleft in the middle.*

                      H.   *Wings always present, although sometimes very small; hind wings broader .than fore wings, folded in repose; prothorax large,* nearly flat on dorsal surface.

                                    (Stone-flies.) Plecoptera.

HH. *Hind wings, when present, not broader than fore wings, not folded in repose; prothorax small, collar-like.*

    I. *Tarsi four-jointed; wings, when present, equal in size......*(Termites.) ISOPTERA.

    II. *Tarsi one- to three-jointed.*

       J. *Tarsi one- or two-jointed; always wingless.*

          (Biting bird-lice.) MALLOPHAGA.

       JJ. *Tarsi usually three-jointed; occasionally two-jointed, in which case wings always present, fore wings larger than hind wings.* (Book-lice, etc.) CORRODENTIA.

GG. *Tarsi five-jointed, but with one joint sometimes difficult to distinguish; labium usually entire in middle, sometimes slightly emarginate.*

    H. *Wings, when present, naked or slightly hairy; hind wings with or without folded anal space; in former case prothorax large and nearly flat on dorsal surface; in wingless forms* mouth prolonged into a distinct beak.

       I. *Mouth-parts not prolonged into a distinct beak, at most slightly conical.*

          (Dobsons, ant-lions, etc.) NEUROPTERA.

       II. *Mouth-parts prolonged into a distinct beak.*

          (Scorpion-flies, etc.) MECOPTERA.

    HH. *Wings, when present, thickly covered with hairs; hind wings usually with folded anal space; prothorax small, collar-like;* mouth not prolonged into a beak. (Caddis-flies.) TRICHOPTERA.

DD. *Fore wings, when present, veinless; horny or leathery;* when absent, labium entire, and mouth-parts not prolonged into a distinct beak. (Beetles.) COLEOPTERA.

BB. *Mouth-parts, when developed, more or less fitted for sucking; sometimes also fitted in part* (the mandibles) *for biting: in this case either* (1) *base of abdomen usually strongly constricted, joined to thorax by a narrow peduncle, or* (2) *the tarsi bladder-shaped, without claws;* when mouth is rudimentary either the wings are two and halteres are present, or the wings are four or none and the body (and wings if present) are densely clothed with scales.

    C. *Prothorax free; body (and wings if present) never densely clothed with scales;* maxillary palpi usually absent; when present, tarsi bladder-shaped, without claws.

    D. *Tarsi bladder-shaped, without claws; wings four (sometimes absent), narrow, fringed with long hairs;* maxillæ triangular, with palpi. (Thrips.) THYSANOPTERA.

    DD. *Tarsi not bladder-shaped, usually clawed; wings not fringed with long hairs; maxilla (when mouth is developed) bristle-like, without palpi.* (Bugs.) HEMIPTERA.

CC. *Prothorax not free;* maxillary palpi present, sometimes rudimentary and difficult to see, in which case body (and wings if present) densely clothed with scales; tarsi never bladder-shaped, usually clawed.

D.  *Mandibles often rudimentary, when present bristle-like.*
   E.  *Wings four (sometimes wanting), clothed with scales; body covered thickly with scales or hairs; mouth, when developed, a slender sucking proboscis, closely coiled under head.*
       (Moths and butterflies.)  LEPIDOPTERA.
   EE.  *Wings two (or wanting), naked or with scattered hairs; hind wings in winged forms represented by halteres; body either naked or with scattering hairs; mouth a soft or horny beak, not coiled under head.*
      F.  *Prothorax poorly developed, scarcely visible from dorsal side* ..............................(Flies.)  DIPTERA.
      FF.  *Prothorax well developed, distinctly visible from dorsal side;* wings never present.......(Fleas.)  SIPHONAPTERA.
DD.  *Mandibles well developed, fitted for biting; wings four (sometimes two or none), naked or with scattered hairs.*
   (Ichneumon-flies, gall-flies, wasps, bees, and ants.)  HYMENOPTERA.

After one has classified an insect in its proper order there remains, first, the determination of the family (each order being composed of from one to many families), then of the genus (each family comprising one to many genera), and finally of the particular species of the genus (each genus including one to many species). This ultimate classification to species, however, will be possible to the amateur in comparatively few cases. There are so many species of insects (about 300,000 are known) that it would require many shelves of books to contain the descriptions of them all. As a matter of fact, in only a few orders have the descriptions of the species been brought together in manuals available for general students. For the most part the descriptions are scattered in scientific journals printed in various languages and wholly inaccessible to the amateur. There are less than 1000 different species of birds in North America; there are more than 10,000 known species of beetles. Now when one recalls the size of the systematic manuals of North American birds, and realizes that ten such volumes would include only the insects of one order, it is apparent that complete manuals of North American insects are out of the question. Except in the case of the most familiar, wide-spread, and readily recognizable insect species we must content ourselves with learning the genus, or the family, or with the more obscure, slightly marked, and difficult members of certain large groups, as the beetles and moths, simply the order of our insect specimens.

When one has determined the order of an insect by means of the above key he should turn to the account of this particular order in the book (see index for page) and find the keys and aids to the further classification of the specimen which the author has thought could be used by the general student. Comparison with the figures and brief descriptions of particular species which are given in each order may enable the amateur to identify the exact species of some of his specimens. But the specific determination

of most of the insects in an amateur's cabinet (or in a professional entomologist's either, for that matter) will have to be done by systematic
specialists in the various insect groups. Few professional entomologists
undertake to classify their specimens to species in more than the one or
two orders which they make their special study. Duplicate specimens should
be given numbers corresponding to those on specimens kept in the cabinet,
and be sent to specialists for naming. Such specialists, whose names can
be learned from any professional entomologist, have the privilege of retaining for their own collections any of the specimens sent them.

# CHAPTER IV

## THE SIMPLEST INSECTS (Order Aptera)

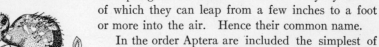

**C**ERTAIN household pests which are not moths and do not look like fish, but which are commonly called "fish-moths" (Fig. 86), are our most familiar representatives of the order of "simplest insects." The "fish" part of the name comes from the covering of minute scales which gives the body a silvery appearance, and the "moth" part is derived from our habit of calling most household insect pests "moths." Thus we speak of "buffalo-moths" when we refer to the carpet-feeding hairy larvæ of certain beetles. When we say clothes-moths we are really using the word moth accurately, for in their adult condition these pests are true moths, although the injury to clothing is wholly done by the moth in its young or caterpillar stage.

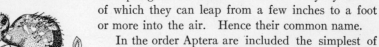

FIG. 86.—The fish-moth, *Lepisma saccharina*. (After Howard and Marlatt: twice natural size.)

Besides the fish-moths other not unfamiliar Aptera are the tiny "springtails" (Fig. 87), which sometimes occur in large numbers on the surface of pools of water or on snow in the spring. Others may be easily found in damp decaying vegetable matter, as discarded straw or old toadstools. They are provided with an odd little spring on the under side of the body by means of which they can leap from a few inches to a foot or more into the air. Hence their common name.

FIG. 87.—The pond-surface springtail, *Smynthurus aquaticus*. (After Schött; much enlarged.)

In the order Aptera are included the simplest of living insects. By "simplest" is meant most primitive, most nearly related to the ancestors of the whole insect class. Also, as might be expected, these most primitive insects are simplest in point of bodily structure; but in this respect they are nearly approached by simple-bodied members of several other orders. These latter forms, however, have a simple body-structure due to the degradation or degeneration of a more complex type.

58

It is familiar knowledge that animals which live parasitically on others, or which adopt a very sedentary life, show a marked degeneration of body structure, an acquired simplicity due to the loss of certain parts, such as organs of locomotion (wings, legs), and of orientation (eyes, ears, feelers, etc.). Thus the parasitic biting bird-lice (order Mallophaga, see p. 113), which live their whole lives through on the bodies of birds, feeding on the feathers, are all wingless and of generally simple superficial structure. They are nearly as simple externally perhaps as the Aptera, but we believe that they are the degenerate descendants of winged and in other ways more complexly formed ancestors.

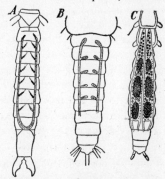

Fig. 88. — Diagrammatic figures showing the segmental disposition of the ovarial tubes in three Apteran genera. *A, Japyx; B, Lepisma; C, Campodea.* (After Targioni-Tozzetti; much enlarged.)

Similarly certain species of insects in nearly all orders have adopted a life-habit which renders flight unnecessary, and these insects having lost their wings are in this character simpler than the winged kinds. Examples of such insects are the worker ants and worker termites, many household insects, as the bedbugs and fleas, and many ground-haunting forms, as some of the crickets, cockroaches, and beetles.

The Aptera, however, owe their simplicity to genuine primitiveness; among all living insects they are the nearest representatives of the insectean ancestors. But not all the Aptera are "simplest." That is, within the limits of this small order a considerable complexity or specialization of structure is attained, although all the Aptera are primitively wingless, as the name of the order indicates.

These insects develop "without metamorphosis"; that is, the young (Figs. 90 and 94) are almost exactly like the parents except in size. They have simply to grow larger and to become mature. In internal structure the simpler Aptera show some most interesting conditions. Their internal

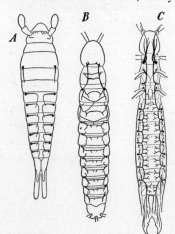

Fig. 89.—Diagrammatic figures showing the respiratory system in three Apteran genera. *A, Machilis; B, Nicoletia; C, Japyx.* (After Targioni-Tozzetti; much enlarged.)

systems of organs have a segmental character corresponding to the external segmentation of the body. The ovarial tubes, which are gathered into two groups or masses, one on each side of the body, in all other insects (Fig. 66), are separate and arranged segmentally in Japyx (Fig. 88), and less markedly so in Machilis; the respiratory system of Machilis (Fig. 89) consists of nine pairs of distinct, segmentally arranged groups of tracheæ (air-tubes), while the ventral nerve-cord has a ganglion in almost every segment of the body. As insects are certainly descended from ancestors whose bodies were composed of segments much less interdependent and coordinated than those of the average living insect, those present-day insects which have the body both externally and internally most strongly segmented are believed to be the most generalized or primitive of living forms. In addition to the segmented character of the internal organs we have also another strong evidence of the primitiveness of the order in the possession by several Aptera of rudimentary but distinct external pairs of appendages on the abdominal segments, appendages undoubtedly homologous with the thoracic legs, and probably well developed in the insect ancestors as abdominal legs like those of the centipeds.

The order Aptera is composed of two suborders, which may be distinguished as follows:

Abdomen elongate, composed of ten segments, and bearing long bristle-like or shorter forceps-like appendages at its tip; no sucker on ventral side of first abdominal segment; antennæ many-segmented...............Thysanura.

Abdomen short and robust, composed of six segments, and usually with a forked spring at tip (usually folded underneath the body), and with a ventral sucker on first abdominal segment; antennæ 4- to 8-segmented.......Collembola.

Thysanura.—This suborder includes three families (a problematical fourth family is found in Europe), as follows:

Body covered with scales.....................................Lepismidæ.

Body not covered with scales.

Tip of abdomen with forceps-like appendages..................Japygidæ.

Tip of abdomen with slender many-segmented appendages......Campodeidæ.

To the last family in the above key belongs the interesting creature *Campodea staphylinus* (Fig. 90), which zoologists regard as the most primitive living insect. It is small, white, flattened, wingless, and so soft-bodied and delicate that it can hardly be picked up uninjured with the most delicate forceps. It is about $\frac{1}{4}$ inch long (exclusive of caudal appendages), and is to be looked for under stones and bits of wood. I have found it in Germany, in New York, and in California, which indicates its wide distribution. Other collectors have taken it in Italy, England, and in the Pyrenees. It is said to live also in East India. Is it not a little surprising that this most primitive, wholly defenceless, and ancient insect should be able to live successfully the world over in the face of, and presumably in competition with, thousands of highly developed specialized modern insect forms? It is a striking proof that Nature does not inevitably crush out all of her first trials in favor of her later results!

The Campodeidæ contain another genus, Nicoletia (Fig. 91), one species of which, *N. texensis*, has been found in California and Texas, and which may be distinguished from Campodea by its possession of three caudal appendages instead of two as in the latter form.

The Japygidæ include but a single genus, Japyx, represented in this country by two described species and several as yet undescribed forms found at Stanford University. *Japyx subterraneus* is a species first found under stones at the mouth of a small grotto near the Mammoth Cave (Kentucky). Japyx (Fig. 92) is larger than Campodea, being about one-half inch long, and is readily recognized by its caudal forceps. Like Campodea its body is white and soft.

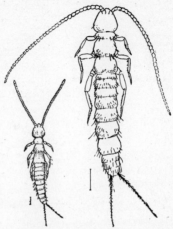

FIG. 90.—Young and adult of *Campodea staphylinus* (from California), the simplest living insect. (Natural size indicated by line.)

The Lepismidæ include the familiar household fish-moths and a number of similar forms which live under stones and logs in soft soil at the bases of tree-trunks, under dead leaves in woods, and sometimes on the damp sand of seashores. Three genera of this family occur in North America, which may be distinguished as follows:

Caudal appendages short; prothorax very wide and body behind it tapering rapidly..............LEPISMINA.
Caudal appendages long; body elongate and tapering gradually backward.
Eyes large and close together..............MACHILIS.
Eyes small and far apart....................LEPISMA.

FIG. 91.—*Nicoletia texensis*, from California. (Eight times natural size.)

Lepisma is best known by the species *L. saccharina* (Fig. 86), which is the silverfish or fish-moth of the house. It is silvery white, with a yellowish tinge on the antennæ and legs, and is from one-third to two-fifths of an inch long. The three long caudal appendages, characteristic of the genus, are conspicuous. It feeds chiefly on sweet or starchy materials, sometimes doing much damage in libraries, where it attacks the bindings. It attacks starched clothing, eats the paste off the wall-paper, causing it to loosen, and infests dry starchy foods. It runs swiftly and avoids the light. It can be fought by sprinkling fresh pyrethrum powder in bookcases, wardrobes, and pantries. Another species, *L. domestica* (Fig. 93), called the bake-house silverfish, is often common about fireplaces and ovens, running over the hot metal and bricks with surprising immunity from the effects of the heat. This habit has gained for it in England, according to Marlatt, the name of "fire-brat." It can be distinguished from the species *saccharina* by the presence of dark markings on the back. Both *saccharina* and *domestica* are common in England, and *saccharina* probably came to this country from there.

FIG. 92.—*Japyx* sp., from California. (Five times natural size.)

Machilis (Fig. 95) does not occur in houses, but is more common than Lepisma outdoors. It is to be found under stones, in the soil around the base of tree-trunks, among dead leaves and fallen pine-needles, and at least one species occurs in the sand of sea-beaches.

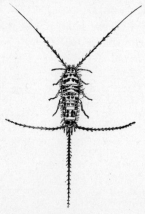
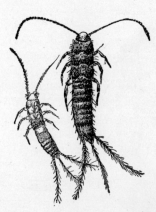

FIG. 93.                    FIG. 94.

FIG. 93.—The fish-moth, *Lepisma domestica*. (After Howard and Marlatt; a little larger than natural size.)
FIG. 94.—Young and adult of *Lepisma* sp., from California. (Twice natural size.)

COLLEMBOLA.—The springtails, mostly of microscopic size, and wholly unfamiliar to any but persistent explorers of nature, comprise many more species than the Thysanura. Their most distinctive character is the possession, by most of them, of the forked spring (Figs. 96 and 97), by means of which they leap vigorously when disturbed. This spring is attached to the next to last body segment or to the antepenultimate one. It consists of a basal part and of two terminal processes. It is carried bent forward under the body, with the bipartite tip held in a little catch on the third abdominal segment. In some species the catch is lacking. The springtails also possess a curious organ on the ventral aspect of the first abdominal segment which appears to be a small projecting sucker or tube. This sucker is often more or less divided into two parts, in one family consisting plainly of two elongate, delicate tubes (Figs. 96 and 97). The use of this peculiar structure has not been definitely determined. Some entomologists think that it serves as a clinging organ, enabling the insect to attach its body firmly to the object upon which it rests. Others believe that the sucker serves in some way to take up moisture, while still others believe it to aid in respiration. The Collembola as well as the Thysanura cannot live in a dry atmosphere. This suborder is divided into five families, as follows (MacGillivray):

A. Spring wanting ........................APHORURIDÆ.
AA. Spring present.

FIG. 95.—*Machilis* sp., from California. (Three times natural size.)

B. Spring arising from ventral side of antepenultimate abdominal segment. PODURIDÆ.
BB. Spring arising from ventral side of penultimate abdominal segment.
    C. Abdomen elongate, cylindrical, much longer than broad........................ENTOMOBRYIDÆ.
    CC. Abdomen globular, but little larger than broad.
        D. Terminal segment of antennæ long, ringed. SMYNTHURIDÆ.
        DD. Terminal segment of the antennæ short, with a whorl of hairs..............PAPIRIIDÆ.

FIG. 96.—The spotted springtail, *Papirius maculosus*, with spring folded underneath body. (Natural length, 2 mm.)

Of these five families the members of one, the Aphoruridæ, in which the spring is wanting, are non-saltatorial. In all of the others leaping is a characteristic habit. The Smynthuridæ and the Papiriidæ are represented by but one genus each, viz., Smynthurus and Papirius. *Smynthurus hortensis* is a common form in gardens, and may be called the "garden-flea." It is found in the Eastern States in May and June "upon the leaves of young cabbage, turnip, cucumber, and various other plants, and also on the ground. It

FIG. 97.—The spotted springtail, *Papirius maculosus*, with spring extended. (Natural length, 2 mm.)

is dull black, with head, legs, and bases of the antennæ rust-color." *Smynthurus aquaticus* (Fig. 87) often occurs in great numbers on the surface of pools. The insects look like tiny black spots on the water surface, but a little observation soon reveals their lively character.

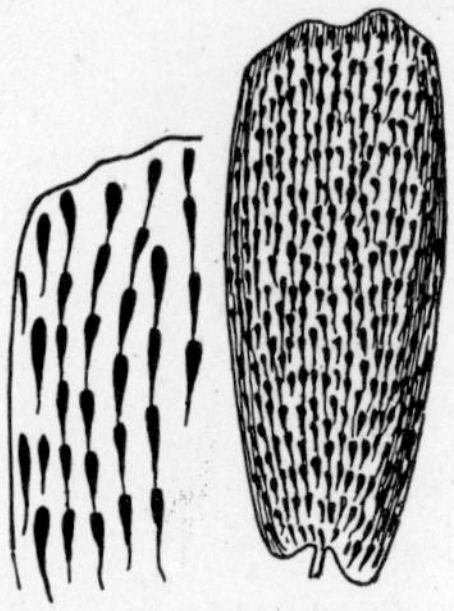

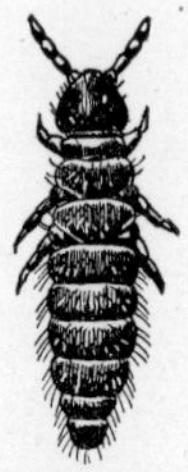

The Poduridæ and Entomobryidæ are represented in North America by twelve and fourteen genera respectively. Many of the Podurids are covered with scales and are often prettily colored and patterned. The scales (Fig. 98) are very minute and bear many fine lines and cross-lines, regularly arranged. On this account they are much used as test objects for microscopes, the quality of the lens being determined by its capacity to reveal their extremely fine mark-

FIG. 98. FIG. 99.

FIG. 98.—Scales from a springtail. (After Murray; greatly magnified.)

FIG. 99.—The snow-flea, *Achorutes nivicola.* (After Folsom; much enlarged.)

ings. One of the most interesting Podurids is the snow-flea, *Achorutes nivicola* (Fig. 99), which gathers in large numbers on the surface of snow in the late spring. Comstock says that the snow-flea is sometimes a pest where maple-sugar is made, the insects collecting in large quantities in the sap.

An interesting representative of the Entomobryidæ is the house springtail, *Lepidocyrtus americanus* (Fig. 100), said by Marlatt to be "not infrequently found in dwellings in Washington." It is about one-tenth of an inch long, silvery gray, with purple or violet markings. In Europe also one species of springtail is common in houses. As these insects live on decaying vegetable matter, they probably do no special harm in the house. They especially frequent rather moist places, and may often be found in window-plant boxes and conservatories.

FIG. 100. — The American springtail, *Lepidocyrtus americanus*, ventral aspect, showing spring folded underneath body. (After Howard and Marlatt; much enlarged.)

# CHAPTER V

## THE MAY-FLIES (Order Ephemerida) and STONE-FLIES (Order Plecoptera)

AY-FLIES, lake-flies, or shad-flies, common names for the insects of the order Ephemerida, are familiar to people who live on the shores of lakes or large rivers, but are among the unknown insects to most high-and-dry dwellers.

Travelling down the St. Lawrence River from Lake Ontario to Quebec one summer, I had hosts of day-long companions in little May-flies that clung to my clothing or walked totteringly across my open book. The summer residents of the Thousand Islands get tired of this too-constant companionship, and look resentfully on the feeble shad-fly as an insect pest. One evening in August, 1897, my attention, with that of other strollers along the shore promenade at Lucerne, was called to a dense, whirling, tossing haze about a large arc light suspended in front of the great Schweizerhof. Scores of thousands of May-flies, just issued from the still lake, were in violent circling flight about the blinding light, while other thousands were steadily dropping, dying or dead, from the dancing swarm to the ground. Similar sights are familiar in summer-time in this country about the lights of bridges, or lake piers and shore roads. This flying dance is the most conspicuous event in the life of the fully developed, winged May-fly, and indeed makes up nearly all of it. With most species of May-flies the winged adult lives but a few hours. In the early twilight the young May-fly floats from the bottom of the lake to the surface, or crawls up on the bank, the skin splits, the fly comes forth full-fledged, joins its thousands of issuing companions, whirls and dances, mates, drops its masses of eggs on to the the lake's surface, and soon flutters and falls after the eggs. It takes no food, and dies without seeing a sunrise. Sometimes the winds carry dense clouds of May-flies inland, and their bodies are scattered through the streets of lakeside villages, or in the fields and woods. Sometimes the great swarms

65

fall to the water's surface and there are swept along by wind and wave, until finally cast up in thick winrows, miles long, on the lake beach. Millions of dead May-flies are thus piled up on the shores of the Great Lakes.

We call the May-flies the Ephemerida, after the Ephemerides of Grecian mythology, and the name truly expresses their brief existence—above water. But they have lived for a year at least before this, or for two or even three years, as wingless, aquatic creatures, clinging concealed to the under side of stones in the lake or stream bottom, or actively crawling about after their food, which consists of minute aquatic plants and animals or bits of dead organic matter. In this stage their whole environment, habits, and general appearance are radically different from those of the brief adult life. We can only guess, if our curiosity compels us to attempt some explanation, at the manner and the cause of such a strange life-history. What advantage is there in such a specialized condition that Nature could not have arrived at by less indirect means? What is indeed the utility of the whole modification? The quick answer "utility," which is to account for all such strange structural and physiological conditions on the basis of useful adaptations brought about by the slow but persistent action of natural selection, leaves us, confessedly, answered simply on a basis of belief. In hundreds of cases that may come under our observation, in how few are we really able to perceive a reason-satisfying course of adaptive development based on the selection of useful small fluctuating variations?

The eggs of the May-fly fall from the body of the mother to the water's surface in two packets, which, however, break up while sinking, so that the released

FIG. 101.—May-flies about an electric lamp.

eggs reach the bottom separately. From each egg hatches soon a tiny flattened, soft-bodied, six-legged creature called a nymph, without wings or wing-pads, and looking very much like a Campodea (the simplest living insect, see p. 61). This nymph crawls about, feeds, grows, moults, grows, moults again and again (in a species observed by Lubbock there were twenty-one moultings), and finally at the end of a year, or of two or three years, depending on the species, is ready to issue as a winged adult. During the nymphal life wings have been slowly developing, visible as short pads projecting from the dorsal margins of the meso- and meta-thorax, and appearing visibly larger after each moulting (Fig. 102). Respiration is accomplished by flat, leaf-like gills (Fig. 102) (these do not appear in some species until after one or two moultings), arranged segmentally along the sides of the abdomen. The mouth-parts are well developed for biting and chewing, with sharp-pointed jaws (mandibles). During its aquatic life at the bottom of stream or pond the May-fly has to undergo all the vicissitudes of an exposed and protracted life; it is eagerly sought after by larger, fierce, predaceous insects, stronger of jaw and swifter than itself; it is the prized food of many kinds of fishes, and it has to struggle with its own kind for food and place.

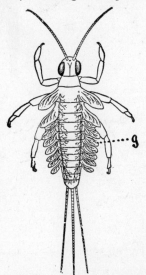

FIG. 102.—Young (nymph) of May-fly, showing (g) tracheal gills. (After Jenkins and Kellogg; three times natural size.)

At the end of the immature life the nymphs rise to the surface, and after floating there a short time suddenly split open the cuticle along the back and after hardly a second's pause expand the delicate wings and fly away. Some nymphs brought into the laboratory from a watering-trough at Stanford University emerged one after another from the aquarium with amazing quickness. Almost all other insects require some little time after the final moulting for the gradual unfolding of the wings, and drying and strengthening of the body-wall, before flight or other locomotion. Most of the May-fly species go through another moulting after acquiring wings, a phenomenon not known to occur in the case of any other insect. The stage between the first issuance from the water with expanded wings and the final moulting is called the subimago stage, and may last, in various species, from but a few minutes to twenty-four hours. Such is, in general, the life-history of the May-flies. As a matter of fact, the life-history of no single May-fly species has yet been followed completely through. And here is an opportunity for some keen-eyed amateur ento-mologist to add needed facts to our knowledge of insect life.

The breathing-organs of the nymph are of interest, as special adaptations to enable them to take up oxygen and give off carbon dioxide without com-ing to the surface, as do the water-beetles, water-bugs, mosquito-wrigglers, and many other familiar aquatic insects. Each plate-like gill (Fig. 102) is a flattened sac, with upper and lower membranous walls which run into each other all around the free margin. Inside this sac is an air-tube (tracheal trunk) with numer-ous fine branches. By osmosis an interchange of gases takes place through the walls of the tracheæ and of the sac—car-bonic dioxide passing out, and air from that held in solution in the water passing in. If a nymph held in a watch-glass of water be watched, at times all the gills will be seen rap-idly vibrating, thus setting up currents and bringing fresh aerated water to bathe the gills.

In the adult winged stage (Fig. 103) the May-flies are extremely frail and delicate-bodied. The wings are fine and gauzy, consisting of the thinnest of membranes stretched over a perfect net-work of veins. The fore

FIG. 103.—May-fly, from California.   (Natural size.)

wings are always markedly larger than the hind wings; in some species the latter are very small indeed, or even wanting altogether (Fig. 104). The body-wall is weakly chitinized, and collected specimens almost always shrivel and collapse badly in drying. The abdomen usually bears two or three long filaments on its tip; the head is provided with compound eyes and short awl-like antennæ. The often-repeated statement in text-books that adult May-flies have no mouth nor mouth-parts is not literally true of all species, as weakly developed jaws and lips are present in some. But they are in such weak and atrophied condition that they can hardly be func-tional. It is probable, therefore, that no adult May-fly takes food. In the males of some species the compound eyes present a very interesting condition, being divided, each into two parts, by a narrow impressed line or by a broader space (Fig. 105). The two parts differ in the size of the facets of the ommatidia, i.e., eye-elements, and it has been ascertained (Zimmerman, 1897) that this difference in size of facets is accompanied by other and more important structural differences, which make it certain that the two parts of the eye have different powers of seeing. One part is especially adapted for seeing in the dark, or for detecting slight differences in intensity of light, but is ill-fitted for exact sight, while the other part is adapted for seeing in daylight, and for making a more exact picture of outline. As the mating flights occur usually at twilight or in the evening, Zimmerman believes that this modification of the eyes of the males is to enable them to discover the females in the whirling shadow-dances. Chun has recorded a similar division and difference in the eye of certain ocean crustaceans and believes that the "dark eyes" are used for seeing in the dimly lighted water below the surface, while the "light eyes" are for special use at the brilliantly lighted

FIG. 104.—May-fly, *Cænis dimidiata*, possessing only one pair of wings. (Much enlarged.)

surface. I have noted similar conditions in the eyes of both male and female net-winged midges (Blepharoceridæ), small, two-winged flies of particularly interesting life (see p. 319). It is unusual to find such parallel adaptations in forms so unrelated.

The May-flies show an anatomical condition of much interest to entomologists in the paired openings for the issuance of the eggs. Insects have their organs arranged in pairs, one on each side of the middle line of the body, as the legs, wings, mouth-parts, antennæ, eyes, spiracles, etc., or exactly on the middle line, as the heart, alimentary canal, and ventral nerve-cord. That is, the typical insect body is bilaterally symmetrical, and the more apparent this symmetry is the simpler and more generalized the insect

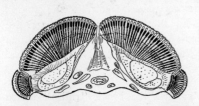

FIG. 105.—Section through head of male May-fly, *Potamanthus brunneus*, showing composition of compound eye and two sizes of eye-elements (ommatidia). (After Zimmer; greatly magnified.)

is believed to be. All other insects but the May-flies have the two egg-ducts, one from each egg-gland, fused inside the body, so as to form a short, single, common duct on the median line. But the May-flies have the ducts separate; that is, paired and bilateral for their whole course. This is taken to be an indication of the primitiveness and antiquity of the order.

If the May-flies are an ancient group of insects, and there is little doubt of this, we have in them another example (we have previously noted one in the case of Campodea, see p. 60) of primitive insects of excessively frail and defenceless character persisting in the face of the strenuous struggle for existence and of the competition, in this struggle, of highly developed, specialized insect forms. Perhaps the solution of this problem in the case of the May-flies is to be found in their extreme prolificness and in the ephemeral character of their adult lives. It is only in the adult condition that May-flies are so ill-fitted to defend themselves; so they simply make no attempt to do so. They lay their eggs immediately on coming of age, and thus accomplish the purpose of their adult stage. In their immature form they are not so handicapped in the struggle for existence, although they seem by no means in position to compete with some of their neighbors, like the nymphs of the stone-fly and dragon-fly.

About 300 species of Ephemerida are known, of which 85 occur in North America. Their classification has been comparatively little studied and is a difficult matter for beginners. The differences among the adults are so slight, and the preserved specimens are so uniformly misshapen and dried up, that most of us will have to be satisfied with knowing that we have in hand a May-fly, without being able to assign it to its genus. Keys to the North American tribes and genera of May-flies may be found by the student who may wish to attempt the generic determination of his specimens, in a paper by Banks in the Transactions of the American Entomological Society, v. 26, 1894, pp. 239–259.

There are better defined differences among the nymphs than among the adults, but unfortunately the nymphs have been as yet too little studied for the making out of a comprehensive key to the genera. Needham and Betten give an analytical table of genera of Ephemerid nymphs as far as known in the Eastern United States, in Bulletin 47 of the New York State Museum, 1901.

ON THE under side of the same stones in the brook "riffles" where the May-fly nymphs may be found, one can almost certainly find the very similar nymphs (Fig. 106) of the stone-flies, an order of insects called Plecoptera. More flattened and usually darker, or tiger-striped with black and white, the stone-fly nymphs live side by side with the young May-flies. But they are only to be certainly distinguished from them by careful examination. The gills of the immature stone-flies usually consist of single short filaments or tufts of short filaments rising from the thoracic segments, one tuft just behind each leg (Fig. 106), and not flat plates attached to the sides of the abdomen as in the May-fly nymphs. The feet of the stone-flies have two claws, while those of the young May-flies have but one. The stone-fly nymph has a pair of large compound eyes, as well as three small simple eyes, strong jaws for biting and chewing (perhaps for chewing heir nearest neighbors, the soft-bodied, smaller May-fly nymphs!), and two slender backward-projecting processes on the tip of the abdomen. The legs are usually fringed with hairs, which makes them good swimming as well as running organs. The nymphs can run swiftly, and quickly conceal themselves when disturbed.

FIG. 106.—Young(nymph) of stone-fly, from California. (Twice natural size.)

All stone-fly nymphs, as far as known, require well aerated water; they cannot live in stagnant pools or foul streams. Needham says that a large number of the smaller species are wholly destitute of gills absorbing the air directly through the skin. Nymphs brought in from a brook and placed in a vessel of still water will be seen with claws affixed, vigorously swinging the body up and down, trying to get a breath under the difficult conditions into which they have been brought. The food-habits are not at all well known: some entomologists assert that small May-fly nymphs and other soft-bodied aquatic creatures are eaten, while others say that the food consists of decaying organic matter.

Here is another opportunity for some exact observation by the interested amateur. On the other hand it is perfectly certain that the nymphs themselves serve as food for fishes.

The fully worked-out life-history of no stone-fly seems to have been recorded. The eggs, of which 5000 or 6000 may be deposited by a single female, are probably dropped on the surface of the water, and sink to the bottom after being, however, well distributed by the swift current. Sometimes the eggs are carried about for a while by the female, enclosed in a capsule attached to the abdomen. The young moult several times in their growth, but probably not nearly as many times as is common among May-flies. When ready for the final moulting, the nymph crawls out on a rock or on a tree-root or trunk on the bank, and splitting its cuticle along the back, issues as a winged adult. The cast exuviæ (Fig. 107) are common objects along swift brooks.

FIG. 107.—Exuvia of nymph of stone-fly. (Natural size.)

The adults (Fig. 108) vary much in size and color, the smallest being less than one-fifth of an inch long, while the largest reach a length of two inches. Some are pale green, some grayish, others brownish to black. There are four rather large membranous, many-veined wings without pattern, the hind wings being larger than the front ones. When at rest, the fore wings lie flat on the back, covering the much-folded hind wings. The mouth-parts are present and are fitted for biting, although the food-habits are not known. It is asserted that some species take no food. The antennæ are long and slender. The abdomen usually bears a pair of long, many-segmented, terminal filaments. The body is rather broad and flattened, and there is no constriction between the thorax and abdomen. On the ventral aspect of each thoracic segment there is a pair of small openings whose func-

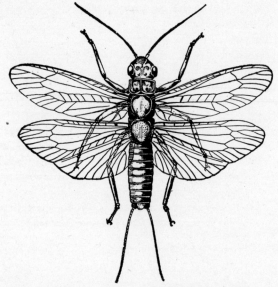

FIG. 108.—A stone-fly, *Perla* sp., common about brooks in California. (After Jenkins and Kellogg; twice natural size.)

tion is unknown. The adults of certain species retain, although in shriveled and probably functionless condition, the filamentous gills. This fact is of importance in connection with the question as to whether insects are descended from aquatic or terrestrial ancestors. Those who believe in the aquatic ancestry have found a simple origin for the spiracles (breathing-pores) by imagining them to be the openings left when the gills, used in aquatic life, were lost. But the adult stone-flies which retain their gills also have wholly independent spiracles.

About 100 species of stone-flies are known in North America. The adults are to be found flying over or near streams, though sometimes straying far away. They rest on trees and bushes along the banks. The green ones usually keep to the green foliage, while the dark ones perch on the trunk and branches. The various species are included in ten genera, which may be determined by the following table:

### TABLE OF NORTH AMERICAN GENERA OF PLECOPTERA.

The following technical terms not heretofore defined are used in this key: *cerci*, slender processes projecting from the tip of the abdomen; *radial sector, cubital vein,* and other names of veins in the wings may be understood by reference to Fig. 109.

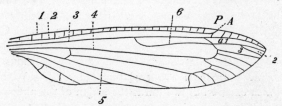

FIG. 109.—Diagram of venation of wing of a stone-fly; *1*, costal vein; *2*, subcostal vein; *3*, radial vein; *4*, medial vein; *5*, first anal vein; *6*, radial sector; *P*, pterostigma; *A*, arculus: $a_1, a_2, a_3$, apical cells. Between the medial and first anal vein is the cubital vein, not numbered. Cell *M* is the cell behind the medial vein; cell *Sc* is the cell behind the subcostal vein.

A.   With two long, many-jointed cerci.
   B.   Radial sector not reduced, i.e., with four or more branches.
      C.   Wings strengthened throughout by many cross-veins, there being many cross-veins between the branches of the media, between the accessory cubital veins, and in the anal areas of both pairs of wings..PTERONARCYS.
      CC. Wings with few or no cross-veins between the branches of the media, between the branches of the cubital veins, and in the anal area.
         D.   Radial area of the fore wings with an irregular network of veins·
                          DICTYOPTERYX.
         DD. Radial area of the fore wing with no cross-veins except the radial cross-veins, or with a few regular cross-veins....PERLA (in part).
   BB. Radial sector reduced, i.e., with less than four branches.
      C.   Hind wings much broader than the fore wings.
         D.   With several cross-veins in cell *M* of the fore wings.
            E.   Cell *Sc* of the fore wings with at least three cross-veins.
               F.   With three ocelli....................PERLA (in part).
               FF. With only two ocelli.....................PSEUDOPERLA.
            EE. Cell *Sc* of the fore wings with only one or two cross-veins. Small species of a green or yellow color........CHLOROPERLA.
         DD. With only one cross-vein in cell *M* of the fore wings between the arculus and the medio–cubital cross-vein.................CAPNIA.
      CC. Hind wings of the same width as the fore wings; the anal area of the hind wings not expanded....................................ISOPTERYX.
AA. With the cerci rudimentary or wanting.
   B.   Second segment of the tarsi equal in length to the others; rudimentary cerci present..............................................................TÆNIOPTERYX.

BB. Second segment of the tarsi small, shorter than the others, cerci absent.
   C.   Veins radiating from the ends of the radial cross-vein forming an X.
                                   NEMOURA.
   CC. Veins radiating from the ends of the radial cross-vein not forming an X.
                                   LEUCTRA.

The genus Perla (Fig. 108) includes more species than any other. The species of Pteronarcys retain gills in the adult condition. The species of Chloroperla are small, delicate, and pale green. Leuctra includes the slenderest of the stone-flies; they are small and brownish. Comstock says that there are several species of stone-flies that appear on the snow on warm days in late winter. They become more numerous in early spring, and often find their way into houses. The most common one in Central New York is the small snow-fly, *Capnia pygmæa*, which is grayish black. The female is 9 mm. (about $\frac{2}{5}$ in.) long, with an expanse of wings of 16 mm. (about $\frac{3}{5}$ in.), while the male is but $4\frac{1}{2}$ mm. (about $\frac{1}{5}$ in.) long, and has short wings which extend but two-thirds the length of the abdomen.

# CHAPTER VI

## DRAGON-FLIES AND DAM-SEL-FLIES (Order Odonata)

WHEN it is high noon on the mill-pond,— when leaves droop, and sun glares upon the water, and the air is hot and still, when other creatures seek the shade, and even the swallows that skim the air morning and evening are resting,—then those other swallows of the insect world, the dragon-flies, are all abroad. . . . One may stand by the side of a small pond, and follow for hours with his eye the evolutions of one of the large dragon-flies skim-

ming over the surface in zigzag lines or sweeping curves, stopping still in midair, and starting again, seeming never to rest, nor even to tire. Poised in the air, with the sunlight dancing on its trembling wings, it is indeed a beautiful sight.

"'Dragon-flies? Folks call 'em devil's-darnin'-needles in our parts, and they say they will sew up your ears.' Yes; and in some localities they

FIG. 110.—A dragon-fly (from life).

are called 'snake-doctors,' and are said to bring dead snakes to life; and other meaningless names are given them, such as 'snake-feeders,' 'horse-stingers,' 'mule-killers,' etc.; but in spite of all these silly names and the silly superstitions they represent, dragon-flies are entirely harmless to man — are indeed to be counted as friends, for they destroy vast numbers of mosquitoes and gnats and pestiferous little flies. To such creatures they must seem real dragons of the air. While one is standing by the pond let him follow awhile the actions of a dragon-fly that is making short dashes in different directions close to the bank. Let him fix his eye on a little fly hovering in the air, and note that after the dragon-fly has made a dart toward it, it is gone. Let him repeat the observation as the dragon-fly goes darting hither and thither. It will be hard to see the flies captured, so quickly it is done, but one can see that ' the place that once knew them knows them no more.' And the usefulness of the dragon-fly in taking off such water-haunting pests will be appreciated."

Thus entertainingly and truthfully writes Professor Needham of the strong-winged, brilliantly colored, graceful insects of our present chapter. If one could see through muddy water and would fix his gaze on the weed-choked slimy depths of the pond, he would see the dragon-flies in another stage of their life, under very different

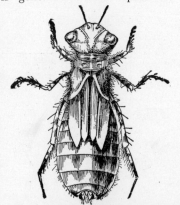

FIG. 111.—The young (nymph) of a dragon-fly. (From Jenkins and Kellogg; twice natural size.)

conditions of existence, and in very different guise. Crawling awkwardly about over and through the decaying weeds and leaves and mud of the bottom or lying in ambush, half concealed by coverings of slime, would be seen certain strange big-headed, thick-bodied, dirty gray-green, wingless creatures from half an inch to two inches long. Occasionally one of these creatures suddenly darts forward by spurting water from the hinder tip of its body; occasionally one quickly thrusts out from its head a vicious pincer-like organ which is more slowly withdrawn, or rather folded up, with an unfortunate tiny water-animal squirming in the toothed pincers. Still dragons, though now dragons of the deep instead of flying dragons, these are our insects in their immature or larval life. Their

FIG. 112.—Young (nymph) dragon-fly, showing lower lip folded and extended. (From Jenkins and Kellogg; twice natural size.)

prey, consisting of water-bugs, May-fly larvæ, small crustaceans, mollusks, and any of the numerous aquatic insect larvæ, including other young dragon-flies, is probably always caught alive. Not by active pursuit, as in the air above, but by lying in wait in the murky depths of the pond until the unsuspecting insect comes within reach of the extensible lower lip with its pair of broad spiny, jaw-like flaps at the clutching tip. The fierce face of the young dragon, with its great mouth and sharp jaws, is all concealed by this lip when folded up, and there is little in the appearance of the dirty, sprawling, smooth-faced creature to betray its dragon-like character. But appearances in the insect world may be as deceptive as in our own, and too late the careless water-bug out on a foraging swim for lesser prey finds himself in range of a masked battery and becomes the preyer preyed upon.

About three hundred different species of dragon- and damsel-flies (damsel-flies are the smaller, slender-bodied, narrow-winged kinds, see Fig. 113) are known in North America, about two thousand having been found in all the world. In any single locality where conditions are at all favorable to dragon-fly life, that is, where there are live streams and ponds, from a score to two or three times as many different dragon-flies can be found. One hundred species occur in Ohio, and one hundred and twenty in New York, states offering specially favorable natural conditions for them, while only about fifty species have been found in California, a much larger but more arid region. The young of no dragon-fly species is known to live in salt water, although nymphs have been found in brackish water and in streams impregnated with sulphur from sulphur springs.  Nor do dragon-flies like cold weather.  Although a few species are found in the far North (recorded at 70° N. in Norway, 65° N. in Alaska, and 63° N. in Siberia) and a few at high cold altitudes (as high as 10,000 feet) on mountain flanks, the great majority of them need considerable temperature for growth and development and even for activity during adult life.   Calvert says that but one species is known which regularly passes the winter in adult stage, and

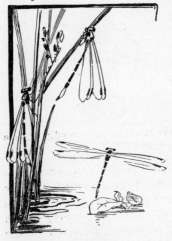

that most dragon-flies live as adults from but twenty-five to forty-five days, and these in the summer.  In California, where the winter temperature at sea-level only occasionally falls to 32° F., adult dragon-flies can be found in most of the months of the year.

The adult dragon-flies are to be seen pursuing their prey, like hawks, with swift darting flights over ponds, along streams, and even scattered widely inland over fields and in woods.  A few kinds have a liking for the vicinity of houses.  Needham, a careful student of these insects, has found that the hunting region above and along the shores of a pond may be imaginarily divided into zones one above the other, each zone characterized by the presence of a few particular

FIG. 113. — Damsel-flies (narrow-winged dragon-flies).  (Natural size; from life.)

dragon-fly species.   "So, in fact," he writes, "we find the smaller damsel-flies flying over the water in a straight course an inch or less above the surface, and rarely venturing higher; the larger damsel-flies a little higher; the amber wings at an average of about six inches; the larger skimmers a foot or more from the surface, and upland skimmers and darters still higher.  One has only to stand a little while by some small area of water where all these are flying to see that each keeps rather closely to his proper altitude.  Why do damsel-flies keep so close to water?   The reason is not far to seek.   Dragon-flies eat one another—the strong destroy the weak.  If to venture up into the altitude of the larger species means to run the risk of being eaten, we can readily see why the damsel-flies should stay down below.  The hawk may roam the air at will, but sparrows must keep to the bushes."

We think of dragon-flies, as of albatrosses and Mother Carey's chickens, as being always on the wing.  They catch their prey while flying, eat it while flying, mate while flying, and some of them deposit their eggs while on the wing. But of course all dragon-flies rest sometimes, and some of them, especially the damsel-flies, are at rest most of the time, clinging to stems or leaves by the water's edge. The larger kinds may be found occasionally perched on the tips of tall swaying reeds, or on a stump or projecting dead limb. From these coigns of vantage they swoop like a hawk on any rash midge that ventures awing in the neighborhood. Cold or cloudy weather, or a strong wind, will drive most dragon-flies to shelter.

The Odonata are unexcelled among insects for swiftness, straightness, and quick angular changes in direction of flight. The successful maintenance of their predatory life depends upon this finely developed flight function together with certain structural and functional body conditions which might be said to be accessory or auxiliary to it. And this may be an appropriate place to describe briefly a few of their salient structural characteristics.

All dragon-flies have four well-developed wings, and all show such a similar general bodily make-up and appearance, that from an acquaintanceship with two or three familiar species any member of the order can be recognized as really belonging to the group. The body in all is long, smooth, and subcylindrical or gently tapering. This clean, slender body offers little resistance to the air in flight, and serves as an effective steering-oar. The wings are long and comparatively narrow, fore and hind wings being much alike, almost exactly alike indeed in the damsel-flies. The venation is of the general type known as net-veining (Fig. 114b), the few strong longitudinal veins being connected by many short cross-veins. The fore wings are greatly strengthened along their costal (front) margin by having the first longitudinal (subcostal) vein behind the margin placed at the bottom of a groove, and the cross-veins in that groove so enlarged vertically as to take on the character of flat, plate-like braces or buttresses. As, in the figure-of-eight movement of the wing in flight, the front margin first meets the resistance of the air, it is necessary that swiftly and strongly beating wings should be especially strengthened along this edge, and this is just what the peculiar folding and bracing of the costal region of the dragon-fly's fore wing accomplishes.

The head is unusually large and is more than two-thirds composed of the pair of great compound eyes. More than 30,000 facets have been counted in the cornea of certain dragon-fly species, and this means that each eye is made up of more than 30,000 distinct eye-elements or ommatidia, each capable of seeing a small part or point of any object in range of vision. Thus an image of a near-by object is made in fine mosaic, and the finer the mosaic the more definite and precise is the vision by means of compound eyes. These great eyes, too, have facets directed up and down and sidewise as well as forward, and by a special sort of articulation of the head on the thorax it can be rotated readily through 180°, so that the principal part of each eye can be directed sidewise or even straight down. For accurate flight and successful pursuit of flying prey the dragon-fly has full need of good eyes. It is to be noted, too, that the eyes are relatively largest in those particular dragon-fly kinds which have the most powerful flight. On the head, also, are three simple eyes (ocelli), the pair of very small awl-like antennæ, and the great mouth. The mouth is overhung as by a curtain by the large flap-like upper lip (labrum). The jaws (mandibles) are strong and toothed, and obviously well adapted for tearing and crushing the captured prey.

When the prey is come up with, however, it is caught not by the mouth but by the "leg-basket." The thorax is so modified, and the insertion of the legs such, that all the legs are brought close together and far forward, so that they can be clasped together like six slender, spiny grasping arms just below the head. Although the catching and eating is all done in the air and very quickly, observers have been able to see that the prey is caught in this "leg-basket" and then held in the fore legs while being bitten and devoured. These slender legs are used only very slightly for locomotion, but they serve well for the light unstable perching which is characteristic of the dragon-flies.

The internal anatomy is specially characterized, as might well be imagined, by a finely developed system of thoracic muscles for the rapid and powerful motion of the wings and the delicate and accurate movements of the legs. The respiratory system is also unusually well developed, such active insects needing a large quantity of oxygen, and generating a large amount of carbon dioxide. The respiratory movements, according to Calvert, consist in an alternate expansion (inspiration through the ten pairs of breathing-holes, or spiracles, arranged segmentally on thorax and abdomen) and contraction (expiration) of the abdomen. The rate of movement varies greatly at different times owing to unknown causes, but is always quickened by exercise, increased temperature, or mechanical irritation. In different dragon-flies the inspirations have been noted to be from 73 to 118 a minute.

The dragon-flies are famous for their beautiful metallic colors. As they dart through the air one gets glimpses of iridescent blue and green and copper, of tawny red and violet and purple reflections that are most fascinating and tantalizing. Seen close at hand in the collections, however, they are mostly dull-colored and, except for their "pictured" wings and the symmetry and trim outline of their body, rather unattractive "specimens." But a freshly caught dragon-fly shows the real glory of the coloring: delicate changing shades of green and violet and copper quiver in the great eyes;

the thorax is translucent green or blue, and the long symmetrical body is warm red or deep blue or purple or green.  It is often covered with a soft whitish "bloom," that tones down the brilliant metallic iridescence.    But as the body dries, the colors fade.  They are due not so much to pigment as to the interference in reflection of the various color-rays, this interference being caused by the structure of the body-wall.  Just as soap-bubbles or weathered plates of glass or mica produce brilliant colors by interference effects, so does the semi-transparent laminate outer body-wall of the dragon-fly produce its fleeting color glories.  While the wings of many kinds are clear, unmarked by blotches or line, the wings of others bear a definite "picture" or pattern, usually light or dark brown or even blackish, reddish, thin yellow, or whitish.  These wing-patterns make the determination of many of the dragon-fly species a very simple matter.

When the dragon-flies go winging about over ponds and streams they are engaged in one of three things: in eating, in mating, or in egg-laying. The prey of the dragon-fly may be almost any flying insect smaller than itself, although midges, mosquitoes, and larger flies constitute the majority of the victims.  Howard says that the voracity of a dragon-fly may easily be tested by capturing one, holding it by its wings folded together over its back, and then feeding it on live house-flies.  Beutenmüller found that one of the large ones would eat forty house-flies inside of two hours.  Howard says that a dragon-fly will eat its own body when offered to it (query, to its head?) and that a collected dragon-fly, if insufficiently chloroformed and pinned, will when it revives cease all efforts to escape if fed with house-flies, the satisfying of its appetite making it apparently oblivious to the discomfort or possible pain of a big pin through its thorax.  That dragon-flies are sometimes cannibalistic has been repeatedly confirmed by observation. The nymphs have been seen to devour nymphs of their own and other species; the nymphs of a European form have been observed to come out of water at night and attack and devour newly transformed imagoes of the same species, while several instances are recorded of the capture and devouring of an imago of one species by an imago of another.

The good that is done by dragon-flies through their insatiable appetite for mosquitoes is very great.  Now that we recognize in mosquitoes not only irritating tormentors and destroyers of our peace of mind, but alarmingly dangerous disseminators of serious diseases (malaria, yellow fever, filariasis), any enemy of them must be called a friend of ours.  A prize was once offered for the best suggestions looking toward practicable means of artificially utilizing dragon-flies for the destruction of mosquitoes and house-flies, but no very efficient improvement on the dragon-fly's natural tastes and practices were brought out by this essay competition.

In Honolulu, the principal city of our mid-Pacific territory, the mosquitoes are so abundant that no one neglects to enclose his bed carefully each night in mosquito-netting, and all bedrooms are equipped with an ingenious canopy which can be folded closely in the daytime and readily spread over the bed at night. The continuous and abundant presence of mosquitoes is such a matter of fact that it has dictated certain particular habits of life to the inhabitants of Honolulu. But in the daytime one is singularly free from mosquito attack. Coincidentally with this one notes the surprising abundance and strangely domestic habits of great dragon-flies. I have watched dozens of dragon-flies hawking about a hotel *lanai* (porch) in the heart of the town. No pond or stream is nearer than the city's outskirts. Dragon-flies are in the main streets, in all the gardens, and they are chiefly engaged in the laudable business of hunting the hordes of "day" mosquitoes to their death. The most conspicuous features of insect life in Hawaii are the hosts of dragon-flies by day and the hordes of mosquitoes by night. As the dragon-flies unfortunately are not night flyers (although some forms keep up the hunting until it is really dark), it is by night that one realizes what a plague the mosquito is in the islands. Were it not for the dragon-flies, life in the islands would be nearly intolerable. The rice-swamps and taro-marshes and the heavily irrigated banana and sugar plantations offer most favorable breeding-grounds for the mosquitoes, but also fortunately for the dragon-flies as well. The mosquitoes of Hawaii are not indigenous; they were introduced with white civilization. It is told, and is not improbable, that the skipper of a trading schooner in early days, to revenge himself for some slight put on him by the natives, purposely put ashore a cask of water swarming with mosquito wrigglers. It needed no more than that to colonize this fascinating tropic land with the mosquito plague. How the saving dragon-flies came is not yet come to be tradition; indeed, few Hawaiians understand how important a part the dragon-fly plays in their life. They do appreciate the mosquito.

In the Samoan Islands, too, where we have another tropical colony, the mosquitoes are a great plague. Here the matter is made more serious. The Samoan mosquitoes are carriers and disseminators of a dreadful disease known as elephantiasis from the enormous enlargement of the legs and arms of sufferers from it. This disease is the great scourge of these islands, more than 30% (from my own observation; 40% and 50% are estimates given by other observers) of the natives having it. (For an account of the rôle of mosquitoes in the dissemination of malaria, yellow fever, and elephantiasis, see Chapter XVIII of this book.) The dragon-flies are, in Samoa as in Hawaii, conspicuous by their abundance and variety, and they do much to keep in check the quickly breeding mosquitoes.

Watching the flying dragon-flies over a pond, you may occasionally see one poising just over the surface of the water, and striking it with the tip of the abdomen; or another kind may be seen to swoop swiftly down to the surface occasionally in its back-and-forth flight, and to dip the tip of

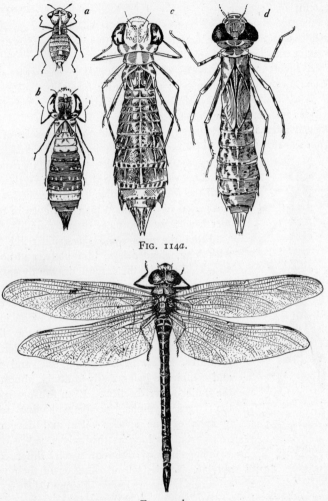

FIG. 114*a*.

FIG. 114*b*.

Stages in the development of the giant dragon-fly, *Anax junius*. *a*, youngest stage; *b*, *c*, and *d*, older stages, showing gradual development of the wings. (Young stage, slightly enlarged after Needham; adult three-fourths natural size.)

the body for a moment into the water. These are females engaged in laying their eggs. The eggs issue in small masses, usually held together by a gelatinous substance. From several hundred to several thousand eggs are laid by each female. Needham counted 110,000 eggs in a single egg-mass of Libellula. Sometimes the eggs may be laid on wet mud or attached to moist water- or shore-plants. The damsel-flies and a few of the dragon-flies insert the eggs in the stems of dead or living water-plants below the surface of the water. To do this they have to cling to the stem, with the abdomen or sometimes the whole body under water, and cut slits in it with the sharp ovipositor. The eggs are sometimes laid on submerged timbers and moss- or alga-covered stones. Kellicott observed females of *Argia putrida* (a damsel-fly abundant along Lake Erie) to remain wholly under water for from five to fifty-five minutes at a time. These females were accompanied by males which also stayed under for similar lengths of time.

The eggs hatch after various periods, depending on the species of dragon-fly and on the time of year of oviposition. In midsummer Needham found the eggs of some species to hatch in from six to ten days, while others laid in autumn did not hatch until the following spring. In the same lot of eggs the period of incubation may vary even in midsummer from a week to more than a month.

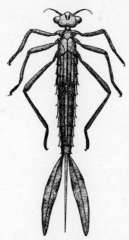

Fig. 115.— The young (nymph) of a damsel-fly (narrow-winged dragon-fly), *Lestes* sp. The three leaf-like processes at the tip of the abdomen are gills (Twice natural size.)

From the eggs come tiny, spider-like nymphs with long, slender legs, thin body, and no sign of wings. Even in the largest dragon-fly species the just-hatched young are only about one-twelfth of an inch long, while the nymphs of the common Libellulas are only one-twenty-fifth of an inch long at hatching. They begin their predatory life, confining their attention at first to the smaller aquatic creatures, but with increasing size and strength and confidence being ready to attack almost any of the under-water dwellers. Even fish are seized by the larger nymphs, Needham having seen the nymphs of one species seize and devour young brook-trout as long as themselves.

The young of different species differ considerably in size, shape, and duration of their nymphal existence. The nymphs of some species require more than a year to develop into adults, while those of some others are ready to transform in a few months, not a few dragon-fly species having two generations a year. The one-year life cycle, however, is usual among the more familiar dragon-flies, the eggs laid during midsummer hatching in late summer, the nymphs hibernating and being ready to emerge the following summer. Needham thinks that the damsel-flies have a number of broods in a season, the processes of transformation and oviposition beginning as soon as the weather permits, and continuing industriously to the close of the season.

The nymphs cast the skin repeatedly during their growth and development, although the exact number of moultings is not known for any species. After two or three moults the wing-pads appear and with each successive moult increase in size. Immediately after moulting the nymphs are light greenish or gray, and their characteristic color pattern is distinct, but they gradually darken, the pattern becoming more and more obscure until by the time for another moulting the body is uniformly dark and dingy. The nymphs (Fig. 115) of the damsel-flies are elongate and slender, and have three long conspicuous gill-plates at the tip of the abdomen, which they can also use as sculls for swimming. The dragon-fly nymphs are robust-bodied, some of them indeed having the abdomen nearly as wide as long and much flattened. All the nymphs are provided with the long grasping lower lip, which can be folded mask-like over the face when not engaged in seizing prey. The mandibles are strong and sharp and the whole mouth is well fitted for its deplorable but necessary business.

The true dragon-fly nymphs do not have plate-like gills, like those of the damsel-flies, nor any other external kind, but have the posterior third of the intestine lined with so-called internal gills. These internal or rectal gills are in six longitudinal bands, each consisting of two thin rows of small plates or tufts of short slender papillæ. Water is taken into the intestine through its posterior opening and, after bathing the gills, giving up its dissolved oxygen, and taking up carbon dioxide, it is ejected through the same opening. When this water is ejected violently it serves to propel the nymph forward. It is also apparently occasionally used for defence.

Just as the adult flying dragon-flies keep to certain regions above or in the neighborhood of the pond, so Needham has found the nymphs to have various preferred lurking-places in the pond. The damsel-fly nymphs and a few of the more active dragon-fly nymphs clamber among submerged vegetation or inhabit driftwood and submerged roots or brush. The heavier sprawling Libellulid nymphs usually crawl over the bottom or climb over fallen rubbish, while certain other Libellulids and some similar forms occupy the mud or sand of the bottom. The nymphs of one of these latter kinds is described as each scratching a hole for itself and descending into it like a chicken into a dust-bath, kicking the sand over its back and burrowing until all but hidden, only the tops of its eyes, the tips of its treacherous labium, and the respiratory aperture at the end of the abdomen reaching the surface.

After the few weeks or month or year which the nymph requires for its full growth and development it is ready to transform. If in early summer, when the dragon-flies are beginning to appear, one will go out to the dragon-fly pond a little after daylight, he will see this transforming or issuance of the winged imagoes busily going on. The nymphs crawl out of the water, and up on stones or projecting sticks, or on bridge-piles or the sides of boats, or on the stems of weeds growing by the water's edge. Here they cling quietly,

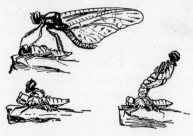

awaiting the moment when the chitinous body-wall shall split lengthwise along the back of the thorax, and the made-over body inside with its damp, compressed wings, its delicate transparent skin, and changed mouth-parts and legs shall slowly work its way out of the old nymphal coat. The nymphs of some dragon-flies and damsel-flies crawl out among the weeds and grass of the shore for some distance before choosing a resting-place, and none of

FIG. 116.—The issuance of an adult white tail, *Plathemis trimaculata*. (After Needham; natural size.)

these will be very readily seen. But careful searching in a place from which winged individuals are occasionally arising will soon reveal the transforming in all of its stages (Fig. 116). It takes some time for the emergence of the damp, soft imago from the nymphal skin, and some further time for the slow expanding and drying of the wings, and the hardening of the body-wall so that the muscles can safely pull against it. When all this has come about the imago can fly away. But even yet the colors are not fully acquired

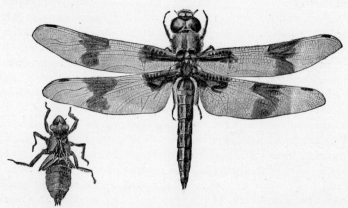

FIG. 117.—Adult and last exuvia of the whitetail, *Plathemis trimaculata*. (Natural size.)

and fixed, and these fresh imagoes have an unmistakably new and shiny appearance. They are called teneral specimens. Usually the emergence of nymphs from the pond and the subsequent transforming cease by the middle of the forenoon, and after that one can find only the frail, drying cast nymphal skins or exuviæ, clinging here and there to stones and plant-stems. Attached to these exuviæ there may be often noted two or three short, white, thread-like processes. These are the dry chitinous inner linings of the main tracheal trunks of the dragon-fly which were moulted with the outer body-wall. As the main tracheal tubes are really invaginations of the outer skin, it is obvious that the inner lining of the trachea is continuous with the outer coat (chitinized cuticle) of the body-wall and so is naturally cast off with it.

Fig. 118.—Adult and last exuvia of the damsel-fly, *Lestes uncata*. (Natural size.)

Although the habits of the adult dragon-flies must be studied out of doors, the nymphs can be brought indoors and kept alive so that their walking and swimming and hiding and capturing of prey, and often their transformation into winged imagoes, can be readily observed. In their natural habitat some of these observations are nearly impossible, and for school-room or private-study aquaria hardly any other animals can be found of more interest to the observer, whether child or grown-up, than the dragon-fly nymphs.

Professor Needham, who has done more and better work in the study of the immature life of dragon-flies than anybody else, gives the following directions for collecting and rearing the nymphs:

"If one wishes to collect the nymphs which lie sprawling amid fallen trash, a garden-rake with which to draw the trash aside, fingers not too dainty to pick them up when they make themselves conspicuous by their active efforts to get back into the water, and a pail of water in which to carry them home, are all the apparatus required.

Fig. 119.—A home-made water-net for collecting dragon-fly nymphs. (After Needham.)

"A rake will bring ashore those other nymphs which burrow shallowly under the sediment that lies on the bottom, and also a few of those that cling to vegetation near the surface; but for getting these latter a net is better. Fig. 119

shows the construction of a good water-net that can be made at home out of a piece of grass-cloth, two sizes of wire, and a stick.

"The best places to search for dragon-fly nymphs in general are the reedy borders of ponds and the places where trash falls in the eddies of creeks. The smaller the body of water, if permanent, the more likely it is to yield good collecting. The nymphs may be kept in any reasonably clean vessel that will hold water. Some clean sand should be placed in the bottom, especially for burrowers, and water-plants for damsel-fly nymphs to rest on. They may be fed occasionally upon such small insects (smaller than themselves) as a water-net or a sieve will catch in any pond. Their habits can be studied at leisure in a dish of water on one's desk or table.

"The best season for collecting them is spring and early summer. April and May are the best months of the year, because at this time most nymphs are nearly grown, and, if taken then, will need to be kept but a short time before transforming into adults. And this transformation every one should see; it will be worth a week's work at the desk; and as it can be appreciated only by being seen, some simple directions are here given for bringing the nymphs to maturity. Place them in a wooden pail or tub (Fig. 120). If

FIG. 120.—A simple aquarium for rearing dragon-fly nymphs. (After Needham.)

the sides are so smooth that they cannot crawl up to transform, put some sticks in the water for them to crawl out on. Tie mosquito-netting tightly over the top, or, better, make a screen cover; leave three or four inches of air between the water and the netting; feed at least once a week; set them where the sun will reach them; and after the advent of warm spring weather look in on them early every morning to see what is going on."

Elsewhere Professor Needham says that nymphs may be fed bits of fresh meat in lieu of live insects. If meat is fed, it must be kept in motion before them, as they will refuse anything that does not seem alive. Some nymphs will take earthworms. Care must be taken to keep cannibalistic kinds apart from others. When the nymphs transform the freshly issued imagoes should be transferred each with its cast skin (exuvia) to dry boxes for a short time, till their body-wall and wings gain firmness and the colors are matured. The imago and its exuvia should always be kept together.

Specimens of the adults for the cabinet should have the wings spread like butterflies and moths (for directions for spreading see the Appendix). The slender and brittle dried abdomen breaks off very easily, and a bristle or fine non-corrosive wire should therefore be passed lengthwise through the body as far as the tip of the abdomen. A couple of insect-pins, inserted lengthwise one at each end of the body, are used by some. Specimens intended for exchange should not be pinned up, but "papered," i.e., put with folded wings into an enclosing little triangular paper envelope made by folding an oblong paper sheet once diagonally and then folding over slightly the two margins.

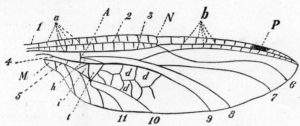

FIG. 121.—Diagram of venation of wing of dragon-fly. *a*, antecubitals; *b*, postcubitals; *N*, nodus; *P*, pterostigma; *A*, arculus; *t*, triangle. (After Banks.)

### TABLES FOR CLASSIFICATION.

#### KEY TO SUBORDERS (IMAGOES).

Front and hind wings nearly similar in outline, and held vertically over the back when at rest; head wide and with eyes projecting and constricted at base. (Damsel-flies.) Suborder ZYGOPTERA.

Front and hind wings dissimilar, hind wings usually being much wider at base, and both pairs held horizontally outstretched when at rest; eyes not projecting and constricted at base............(Dragon-flies.) Suborder ANISOPTERA.

#### KEY TO SUBORDERS (NYMPHS).

Posterior tip of abdomen bearing three, usually long, leaf-like tracheal gills. (Damsel-flies.) Suborder ZYGOPTERA.

Posterior tip of abdomen with five, converging, short, spine-like appendages. (Dragon-flies.) Suborder ANISOPTERA.

### SUBORDER ZYGOPTERA.

#### KEY TO FAMILIES (IMAGOES).

Wings with not less than five antecubital cross-veins (Fig. 121).
Family CALOPTERYGIDÆ.

Wings with not more than three, usually two, antecubitals (Fig. 121).
Family AGRIONIDÆ.

#### KEY TO FAMILIES (NYMPHS).

Basal segment of the antennæ extremely elongate......Family CALOPTERYGIDÆ.
Basal segment of the antennæ short, subrotund.............Family AGRIONIDÆ.

The family Calopterygidæ includes but two genera, Calopteryx, in which the basilar space of the wings is open and the wings themselves are rather broad near the tip, and Hetærina, in which the basilar space is net-veined and the wings narrow.

*Calopteryx maculata* (Fig. 122), the most familiar representative in the Eastern States of the first genus, has velvety black spoon-shaped wings, (brownish in freshly moulted, or teneral specimens), and a long, slender body, of striking metallic blue or green. The females can be distinguished from the males by their possession of a milk-white pterostigma (Fig. 121). These beautiful "black wings" are found in gentle fluttering flight, usually along small streams in woods or meadows. The female lays her eggs "among

FIG. 122.—The black wing, *Calopteryx maculata.*

the rubbish and mud along the borders of ditches," and the nymphs found in the ditches and streamlets have the middle one of the three caudal gills flat and shorter than the other two. Kellicott has seen the males of this species fight fiercely with each other. "Two will fly about each other, evidently with consuming rage, when one finally appears to have secured a position of advantage and darts at his enemy, attempting, often successfully, to tear and damage his wings."

The best known representative of the other genus is a perfect masterpiece of insect beauty and grace. Entomologists know it as *Hetærina americana* (Fig. 123); I suggest that we call it the "ruby-spot," although only the males bear the gem. The head and thorax of the males are coppery red, the abdomen metallic green to coppery, and the basal fourth of each of the long, slender, and otherwise clear wings is bright blood-red. In the females the whole body is metallic green, with the basal third of the wings pale yellowish brown. These damsel-fly beauties are shy and retiring, rarely venturing more than a few feet away from the willow-overhung bank of their favorite swift-running stream. Sometimes hundreds of them come together and cling in

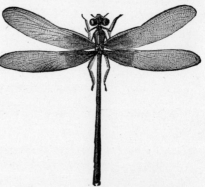

FIG. 123.—The ruby-spot, *Hetærina americana.*

graceful festoons to the drooping willow branches. Then they look like strings of rubies, or of warm red flowers or seeds.

The family Agrionidæ includes the host of slender-bodied, narrow- and clear-winged true damsel-flies. Most of them are small, and many keep so closely in low herbage or shrubby woodland that they attract little attention. A few of the longer-bodied and longer-winged forms, however, fly in the open along the stream-banks or over the ponds. Some are strikingly varied with black and orange or yellow, and all, whether brightly colored or dull, are graceful and charming. There are at least a dozen genera of Agrionids in this country, comprising about seventy-five species, but their classification is too difficult to be undertaken by general students. Damsel-flies deposit their eggs in the tissue of aquatic plants by cutting slits in the stems with their sharp ovipositor. The nymphs are slender and elongate, and can readily be known by the three caudal leaf-like tracheal gills. The nymph stage of these forms is much shorter than with the true dragon-flies, lasting usually probably but a few weeks, or at most two or three months. When ready to transform the nymphs crawl out of the water and into the low herbage on the stream or pond bank. I have seen scores of freshly emerged damsel-flies rising from a few square yards of tall grass near a pond, although it required close search to discover the nymphs, so well concealed were they in the dense tangle.

## SUBORDER ANISOPTERA.

### KEY TO FAMILIES (IMAGOES).

Antecubitals of the first and second rows mostly meeting each other; triangle of fore wings with long axis at right angles to the length of the wings, triangle of hind wing with long axis in direction of the length of the wing.
LIBELLULIDÆ.

Antecubitals of the first and second rows not meeting (or running into each other) except the first and another thick one; triangles of fore and hind wings of similar shape (Fig. 121).

Eyes meeting above on middle line of head; abdomen with lateral ridges.
ÆSCHNIDÆ.

Eyes just touching at a single point or barely apart; abdomen without lateral ridges........................................CORDULEGASTERIDÆ.

Eyes distinctly separated; abdomen without lateral ridges......GOMPHIDÆ.

### KEY TO FAMILIES (NYMPHS).

Under-lip (labium) flat, not concealing most of the face, with jaw-like or oblong side pieces (lateral lobes).

Antennæ 7-segmented, tarsi 3-segmented, climbing nymphs..ÆSCHNIDÆ.

Antennæ 4-segmented, the fourth segment rudimentary; fore tarsi 2-segmented; burrowing nymphs...........................GOMPHIDÆ.

Under-lip (labium) spoon-shaped, covering most of the face, when closed, with nearly triangular side pieces (lateral lobes).

Two stout teeth with a notch between them on the middle lobe of the under-lip (labium).................................CORDULEGASTERIDÆ.

A single median tooth on the middle lobe of the under-lip....LIBELLULIDÆ.

The family Cordulegasteridæ includes only seven species of dragon-flies found in the United States, all belonging to one genus, Cordulegaster. They are large, with eyes barely touching on top of the head, without metallic body-colors, and with clear wings. The nymphs burrow into the sand or vegetable silt on the bottom of shallow places. Thus buried, with only the top of the eyes and tip of the abdomen showing, they remain motionless for a long time, if prey does not come near. "In a dish of sand on my table," says Needham, "I have had a nymph remain without change of position for weeks, no food being offered it. Let any little insect walk or swim near the nymph's head, and a hidden labium springs from the sand with a mighty sweep and clutches it." The imagoes are strong flyers and have the habit of flying back and forth, as on a regular beat, over some small, clear stream.

The family Gomphidæ includes six genera, comprising about fifty species in our country. They are mostly large forms, clear-winged and with bodies striped with black and green or yellow. They are readily distinguished by the wide separation of the rather small eyes. The abdomen is stiff and spike-like. The eggs, held in a scanty envelope of gelatin, are deposited by the repeated descent of the flying female to the water of a clear pond or flowing stream, the tip of the abdomen first striking the surface. The gelatin dissolves and the eggs, scattering, sink to the bottom and become hidden in the silt. The nymphs are active burrowers, capturing their prey either on or beneath the surface of the bottom silt. The adults often alight on foliage, or on the surface of some log stretching across a stream, or on the bare soil of a path or roadway. They do not fly about in apparent sportiveness as the skimmers (Libellulidæ, p. 95) do, nor, like the skimmers, perch atop a slender twig. June is the best month in the East for these dragon-flies. The principal genus of the family is Gomphus, which includes one-third of all our Gomphidæ. Of these *Gomphus exilis* is probably the most common one in the Northeastern States. Its head is pale green, thorax brownish with two oblique green bands on each side, and abdomen blackish brown with a basal green spot or band on the back of each segment. The nymphs transform at the very edge of the water, seldom crawling more than an inch or two above it. *Hagenius brevistylus* is a large black-and-yellow species common in the East, South, and Middle West. The nymph has an unusually wide, flattened body.

The Æschnidæ include our largest, swiftest, and most voracious dragon-flies. Various species are flying through the whole season from early spring to late summer. Some roam far from water, being found over dry fields and roadways, and even in houses. Some forms fly until late in the evening, making life a burden for the mosquitoes gathering for their night's singing and feasting. The eggs are thrust into the stems of aquatic plants, in floating timbers, in the wood of piers, etc., at or near the surface of the

water. The nymphs are slender, clean creatures, with smooth bodies patterned with green and brown, and very active, strong, and brave. They
climb among green plants and roots or submerged driftwood along the border
of open water or the edge of a current. The imagoes of this family can be
recognized by the meeting of the eyes all along the top of the head. The
wings are long, broad, and clear, and the body-colors are mostly bright blue
and green. The family is represented in the United States by about twenty-five
species, belonging to six genera. *Anax junius*, one of the commonest dragon-
flies all over the United States, and found also from Alaska to Costa Rica,
in China, Siberia, and in various islands of the Pacific, notably the Hawaiian
group, is the most inveterate enemy that the mosquito has. It is conspicuously on the wing from early spring to
late fall, flying from daylight to dark,
and doing untold good by its ceaseless
warfare on the mosquito hosts. It
can be recognized by its clear wings,
large size (wings over two inches long),
and bright-green thorax and head, the
latter bearing on the upper front a
round black spot surrounded by yellow,
the yellow encircled by a dark-blue
ring (Fig. 124*a*). A still larger member
of this family is the great "hero"

Fig. 124*a*.    Fig. 124*b*.

Fig. 124*a*.—Top of head, showing characteristic mark in front of eyes, of *Anax
junius*. (Enlarged.)

Fig. 124*b*.—Top of head, showing characteristic mark in front of eyes, of *Æschna
constricta*. (Enlarged.)

dragon-fly, *Epiæschna heros*, which is like *Anax junius* in general appearance, but has wings two and one-half inches long, and abdomen nearly three
inches long. It has a black T spot on the upper face, instead of a round
one. Another similar, widely distributed and common form is *Æschna
constricta*, about the size of *Anax junius*, reddish brown marked with bright
green, and with a black T spot on the upper front of face (Fig. 124*b*). The
males have the abdomen marked with blue, with little or no green, while
the females have but little blue or none at all.

The members of the family Libellulidæ are called "skimmers." They
may be seen continually hovering over the surface of still water, or swiftly
foraging over fields. Many of them have the wings strongly marked with
large black or brown or milk-white blotches, and the abdomen is often
covered with a whitish powder or "bloom." They outnumber all the other
true dragon-flies in point of species, and except for *Anax junius*, *Æschna
constricta*, and perhaps the giant hero dragon-fly, include the most familiar
and wide-spread members of the order. One of the best known and most
beautiful of the skimmers is the pond-loving "ten-spot," *Libellula pulchella*
(Fig. 125), found all over the country. Each of its wings has a longitudinal
basal blotch, a median blotch (at the nodus), and an apical blotch of black-

ish brown. The males have the space between these blotches milky white. In old individuals the abdomen has a strong whitish bloom. Other familiar

FIG. 125.—The ten-spot dragon-fly, *Libellula pulchella*. (After Needham; nat. size.)

and well-marked species of Libellula are *L. basalis*, with blackish-brown body and with the basal third to half of the wings dark brown or black and the rest of the wing clear, or in the old males chalky white out as far as the

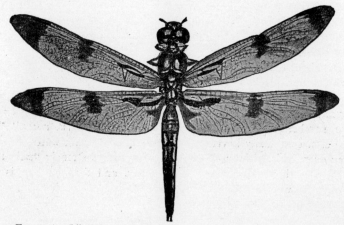

FIG. 126.—*Libellula semi-fasciata*. (After Needham; natural size.)

pterostigma, and in the females with brownish apices; *L. quadrimaculata*, with olive or yellowish body marked with black, front wings with more or less yellowish at base and along the front margin, and a small fuscous nodal spot, hind wings with a yellowish-black triangular basal spot and fuscous nodal spot; and *L. semi-fasciata*, whose complex wing-markings are

FIG. 127.—The water-prince, *Epicordulia princeps*, female.
(After Needham; natural size.)

shown in Fig. 126. Tramea is a genus of large swift dragon-flies whose hind wings have the base expanded and conspicuously colored. *Tramea lacerata* is a familiar species. The water-prince, *Epicordulia princeps* (Fig.

FIG. 128.—The amber wing, *Perithemis domitia*, male at left, female at right.
(After Needham; natural size.)

127), is a common large dragon-fly, but one hard to capture because of its fine flight. The wings show a basal patch, often nearly wanting on the front pair, a patch at the nodus, and a black apex. It likes "ponds or slug-

gish streams with muddy reed-grown banks, and seems absolutely tireless
in flight; very rarely indeed is one seen resting." One of the smallest of

Fig. 129.—The wind sprite. *Celithemis eponina.* (After Needham; natural size.)

Fig. 130.—*Tetragoneuria epinosa,* female. (After Needham; natural size.)

the true dragon-flies is the amber wing, *Perithemis domitia* (Fig. 128). The
wings are clear amber, unmarked in the male, but richly spotted with dark

brown in the female. It has a slow hovering flight and often rests on the tips of erect reeds with wings held perfectly horizontal. It is only on wing in quiet, warm sunshine; clouds or cold breezes send them quickly into hiding. Among the familiar Libellulids with unblotched wings is *Meso-themis simplicicollis*, an abundant species east of the Rockies. The females and young males have head, thorax, and front half of abdomen green, the hinder half blackish brown. In old males the body becomes grayish blue with a whitish bloom. Williamson says that sometimes two males will flutter motionless, one a few inches in front of the other, when suddenly the rear one will rise and pass over the other, which at the same time moves in a curve downwards, backwards, and then upwards, so that the former position of the two is just reversed. These motions kept up

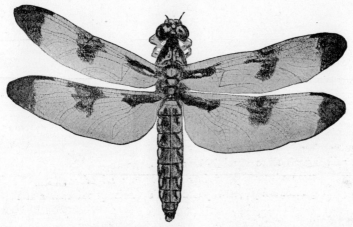

FIG. 131.—The whitetail, *Plathemis lydia*. (After Needham; natural size.)

with rapidity and regularity give the observer the impression of two inter-secting circles which roll along near the surface of the water.

The whitetail, *Plathemis lydia* (Fig. 131), resembles the ten-spot, but is one-fourth smaller. In the males also the apex of the wings is usually clear, not brown. The whitetail rather likes slow-flowing brooks and open ditches. When alight it has the habit of setting its wings aslant down-ward and forward with a succession of jerks. Needham thinks that the powdery whiteness of the body of the old males (in females and young males the body is brown marked with yellow) must render it more easily seen by its enemies, the king-birds and others, and thus be a disadvantage in the struggle for existence. He says, indeed, that the whitest ones avoid resting-places over a dark background and settle oftenest on white sticks, on bleached stumps, or on light-colored earth. Very frequently one will alight on a white insect-net when it is laid down, or even when still held in the hand.

# CHAPTER VII

## THE TERMITES, OR WHITE ANTS (Order Isoptera)

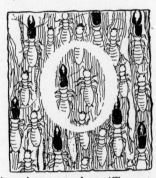

NCE when camping in the King's River Cañon, one of the great vertical-walled, flat-floored cañons of the Sierra Nevada, the boldest axeman of our party attacked the fallen trunk of a once towering yellow pine. The practical outcome of this attack was a sufficient supply of firewood for the cook's stone-built stove, but the great log yielded better things than chips and chunks. A few blows showed it to be the home of a thriving colony of the largest of the American termites (*Termopsis angusticollis*), and the thousands of individuals in this insect household were objects of interested observation the summer through. We had heard of the rarity of white-ant queens in collections, and saw in this isolated and apparently easily "rounded-up" community an easy chance to discover the egg-laying queen of this species. But we had not reckoned with the Californ'a manner of tree-trunk: it outlasted the summer's chopping by two score feet of log four feet thick. Yellow pines grow 250 feet high in the Sierran forests. But although no queen was found, the make-up of the buried termite city was revealed. Galleries and chambers, secret ways and narrow tunnels were all exposed, and the interesting communal life of these soft, white-bodied little creatures was made partly known to us.

We have in the United States but few kinds of termites, and these much less interesting in habit than those of tropic lands. The Amazons and Central Africa are the centers of termite life, and there, because of their great mounds, their serious ravages on all things wooden, and their enormous numbers, the white ants come to be nearly the most conspicuous of the insect class. Drummond's account, in his Tropical Africa, of the habits and life of the termites of the Central African region is simply a tale of marvels. And the scattered accounts of the Brazilian species are hardly less wonderful. In the South Sea, too, the termites play their part prominently. I have seen scores of cocoanut-palms in Samoa with their trunks traced over from ground to "feather-duster" top, a hundred feet above, by the laboriously builded wood-pulp tunnels of the termites. Each of these trees carried also on its trunk, about four feet from the ground, a termite "shed" or depot (Fig. 133), a foot thick, a foot wide, and two feet long, made, like the tunnels, of pellets of chewed wood, glued together with saliva, and filled with crowded galleries and chambers.

Fig. 132.—Giant hillock-nests of termites in tropical Africa.
(Adapted from Drummond.)

But in the United States our few species make their communal nests in dead and dying wood, or underground, and not being given to building great dome-like mound-nests, or making covered ways up all the trees of a great forest or plantation, are not as conspicuous as their tropical cousins. Still, few observers of insects have failed to notice the little, white, wingless worker termites, scurrying about when some dead stump is overturned or split open, or to see the winged males and females swarming out of the ground some sunny day, and, after a brief period of flight, pursued by birds and predaceous insects, settling to earth again and losing their wings.

Before proceeding to take up the incompletely known life-history of our American termites it will be advisable to describe their general structural characters and the composition of the termite communities. The body is always soft, and usually milky-whitish in color, though sometimes light or dark brown. It is plump, and slightly broader than thick. The abdomen is joined broadly to the thorax, not by a little stem or peduncle as in the ants, with which insects the name "white ants" (unfortunately too long and widely used to be done away with) confuses the ermites in the popular mind. The termites not only are not ants, but are neither nearly related to them nor of similar structure. The only resemblances between the two forms exist in the communal life and in the composition of the community by different kinds of individuals. The termites are either blind or have only simple eyes, have slender antennæ which look as if made up of tiny beads strung a-row, and have biting mouth-parts with strong jaws. They live in small or large communities, the individuals in any one of which, although belonging to the same species, being of from three to eight different kinds or castes. That is, each community is composed of winged and wingless individuals, the winged being males and females, while the wingless include immature individuals, sexually incomplete workers and soldiers, and also so-called complemental males and females which are individuals able to help in the increase of the community. In some species there are no workers, while in others the workers may be of two kinds. The soldiers differ from all the others in he extraordinary development of their jaws which are long and scissor-like; their heads are also much enlarged and strongly chitinized. The food of all consists mainly of dead wood, and of curious pellets excreted from the intestine and called "proctodeal

Fig. 133. — Termite shed on cocoanut-palm in Samoa. From the shed note numerous tunnels leading down to the ground, in which is the main nest of the community; a few tunnels (only one visible in the picture) lead up the trunk of the tree. (Photograph by the author.)

food." In addition some species attack live wood and even soft plants, and cloth, books, papers, etc., suffer from termite ravages. The serious nature of their attacks on wood will be referred to later.

The development of the termites is apparently simple; the wingless workers resemble closely, except in size, the just-hatched young; the soldiers have but to acquire their largeness of head and mandibles, and the perfect insects their wings. But there is a serious complexity in termite development in that at hatching all the young are alike, and the different castes or kinds of individuals become differentiated during the postembryonic development, i.e., after hatching. This matter is discussed later.

In the United States but seven species of this order of insects are known. They represent three genera, which may be distinguished by the following table:

KEY TO GENERA.

Simple eyes absent...............................................TERMOPSIS.
Simple eyes present.
    Tarsi with a pulvillus (little pad) between the claws; prothorax large and
        oblong; costal (anterior) area of the wings veined..CALOTERMES.
    Tarsi without terminal pulvillus; prothorax cordate; costal area of wings
        without veins..........................................TERMES.

Termopsis and Calotermes each include two species, all four limited to the Pacific Coast; while Termes includes three species, of which but one, *T. flavipes*, is found in the northeastern states. This has been introduced from America into Europe, and is well known there. The other two species, and *flavipes* also, are found in the southwestern and Pacific coast states. Thus *Termes flavipes* (Figs. 134 and 135) is the only representative of the order Isop-

tera which can be observed and studied in the East, but it is so commonly distributed that the student of insects in almost any locality can find its communities. Despite its abundance, however, the long time it has been known, and the very interesting nature of its habits, its life-history is not yet wholly worked out.

FIG. 134.—*T. flavipes*, worker. (After Marlatt; natural size indicated by line.)

It makes its nest in or under old logs and stumps. Sometimes it mines a nest in the beams and rafters of old houses. Howard records the serious injuries done to a handsome private residence in Baltimore through the mining of the first-floor timbers by the hidden termites. Comstock has found them in the southern states infesting living plants, particularly orange-trees, guava-bushes, and sugar-cane. According to Comstock, they attack that part of the living plant which is at or just below the surface of the ground. In the case of pampas-grass the base of the stalk is hollowed; with woody plants, as orange-trees and guava-bushes, the bark of the base of the trunk is eaten, and frequently the tree is completely girdled; with sugar-cane the most serious injury is the destruction of the seed-cane.

The workers of *T. flavipes* (Fig. 134) are, when full grown, about $\frac{1}{6}$ in. long, while the soldiers are a little larger. Both of these castes are whitish. But the winged males (Fig. 135*a*) and females which come from the nest and swarm in the air in late spring or early summer are chestnut-brown to blackish and measure about $\frac{1}{5}$ in. in length. The four wings are of about equal size, and when the insect is in flight expand about $\frac{3}{5}$ in. When at rest they lie lengthwise on the back, projecting beyond the tip of the abdomen. They have many veins and are pale brown in color. After flying some time and to some distance, the insects alight on the ground and shed their wings (Fig. 135*b*). This they are enabled to do because of a curious suture or line of weakness running across each wing near its base. All the wing beyond this suture falls off, leaving each now wingless male or female with four short wing-stumps. These swarming flights attract the birds. Hagen noted fifteen different species of birds following such a termite flight one May-day in Cambridge, Mass. "Besides the common robins, blue-birds, and sparrows," he says, "were others not seen before near the house. The birds caught the Termes partly in flight, partly on the ground, and the robins were finally so gorged in appearance that their bills stood open!"

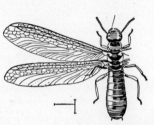
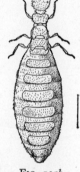

FIG. 135*a*.                    FIG. 135*b*.

FIG. 135*a*.—*T. flavipes*, winged male. (After Marlatt; natural size indicated by line.)
FIG. 135*b*.—*T. flavipes*, complementary queen. (After Marlatt; natural size indicated by line.)

After the swarming flight the few uneaten males and females pair, and each pair probably founds a new colony. Perhaps some of the pairs are found by workers, and taken possession of as the royal couple for a new community. Exactly how the new communities of *flavipes* begin is not known; and this is an excellent opportunity for some amateur observer to distinguish himself! The egg-laying queen mother of a *flavipes* colony also has yet to be discovered. There exist in many species of termites individuals called complemental males and females. These are forms which, in case of the loss of the real king or queen, can develop into substitute royalties. Whether such forms exist in all *flavipes* colonies does not seem to be certainly known. It is obvious that there is still much to learn about the interesting life of our commonest and most wide-spread termite species.

Of the other six species of our country, all of which are limited to the southern, southwestern, and Pacific states, three, representing all of the three genera, and found about Stanford University, have been recently studied by Professor Harold Heath. These are *Termopsis angusticollis*, the largest of the American termites, *Calotermes castaneus*, a small species with brown-bodied winged forms, and *Termes lucifugus*, a small white species common in Europe, and probably brought to this country from there. The following account of *Termopsis augusticollis* is based chiefly on Heath's * studies.

*Termopsis angusticollis* (Fig. 136) is the largest of the three species and the most abundant. In favorable localities colonies may be found in almost every stump and decaying log, and even in dead branches on otherwise healthy trees. The galleries are made in the deeper portions of the wood, and usually follow the grain. The colonies with the primary royal pair number usually from 50 to 1000 individuals, and include workers, soldiers, and immature forms. The full-grown workers (Fig. 136) are $\frac{3}{5}$ in. long, the soldiers (Fig. 136) $\frac{2}{3}$ in., and the kings and queen (Fig. 137) a little less, while the wings expand $1\frac{1}{2}$ in. After the death of the primary royalties and the development of several substitute royal forms the egg-laying and consequent increase of the colony are much more rapid. Heath counted 3221 individuals

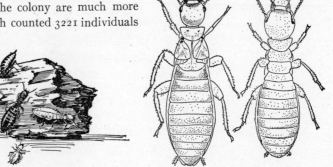

FIG. 136.                           FIG. 137.

FIG. 136.—The large termite of California, *Termopsis angusticollis;* workers, young, and a soldier. (From life; natural size.)
FIG. 137.—*A*, Dealated primary queen of *Termopsis angusticollis*, at least four years old; *B*, complemental queen. (After Heath; three times natural size.)

in one colony, in which were also thousands of eggs. The colony which we found in the yellow-pine log in the King's River Cañon certainly numbered many thousands. In the late summer or early autumn the nymphs (young stage, with visible wing-pads of perfect insects) that have developed during the year moult, the operation taking from ten to twenty minutes, after which they rest for two hours, while the wings expand, and the body-wall hardens and darkens; they take flight usually about dusk. Some

* Heath, H., The Habits of California Termites, Biological Bulletin, vol. 4, 1902, pp. 47–63.

soon fall to the ground, but others may fly a mile. The swarm is pursued by birds until dark, and then bats take a turn at the chase. The few termites that escape fly from tree to tree, seeking a spot of decaying wood. Heath has noted them dashing against door-knobs and nail-holes and against discolored spots on trees and logs, in their search for a place where decay has begun. After finding a suitable spot they usually shed their wings, not by biting them off, as said of some species, but by curving the abdomen until it rests across the wings of one side and then moving backwards and sidewise until the wing tips are brought against some obstruction, thus causing the wings to buckle and break along the transverse suture or line of weakness at the base. Sometimes the wings are not shed until after the nest is begun. The spot is usually selected by the female, and she begins the mining and does most of it. She is accompanied by one or more males, who may occasionally help in excavating. When the burrow is large enough for two, one male usually crowds in beside the queen and fights off the others. Sometimes two males may remain with the queen; Heath thinks that such a condition may last for a year or more. He has found a few cases where two, three, and even six pairs live in company. The actual mating does not take place, probably, until some time after the nest is begun. Heath has noted pairing from a week to a fortnight after swarming.

The egg-laying may be long postponed. Usually, however, about two weeks after pairing the first egg is laid, and from one to six are deposited daily until the total number amounts to from fifteen to thirty. When the habitat is unusually moist the royal pair may remain together for a year without producing young. Heath has found the Termopsis royalties to mate readily in captivity, and has had more than 500 pairs of primary kings and queens in excellent condition after a year of captivity. Royal pairs with small colonies are readily found by stripping off the bark of trees from three to nine months after the swarming period. Heath has been the first to find actual egg-laying queen termites in this country.

After from fifteen to thirty eggs are laid the laying ceases, and the parents give their time to enlarging the nest and to caring for the eggs, which are kept scrupulously clean, and frequently shifted from place to place in the nest. The young are all alike when first hatched. After three moults, one of them appears as a large-headed individual, and after three more moults develops into a perfectly formed soldier, although little more than one-half the size of the soldiers in old communities. Three months later another soldier appears, larger than the first, and later others still larger, until after a year the full-sized form appears. The first workers, too, are smaller than the later ones. Nymphs, i.e., young of the winged individuals, do not appear until after the first year, so that the swarm of winged individuals cannot leave a nest until the end of the second year of its existence. The life of these early, undersized individuals is short. They disappear, perhaps are killed, when the full-sized individuals appear. These latter, both workers and soldiers, live at least two years and perhaps longer.

The primary king and queen live for at least two years, and almost certainly longer. Heath believes he has evidence of five years of life. After the death of the royal pair from natural or other causes, the members of the orphaned colony develop from the young nymphs from ten to forty substitute royal forms. By some unknown process, perhaps peculiar feeding, these selected nymphs are quickly brought to sexual maturity, and the queens begin egg-laying. As they are fed and cleaned by the workers, their only business is to lay eggs. Heath observed some of the larger queens to lay from seven to twelve eggs a day continuously. In exceptional cases a worker, or even a soldier, may be developed into an egg-laying queen. One may also occasionally find a few winged soldiers.

In Africa forty-nine species of Termites are known * (Sjostedt), and it is on this continent that "the results of Termitid economy have reached their climax." More than a century ago an exploring Englishman, Smeathman, startled zoologists with his account of the marvelous termite communities

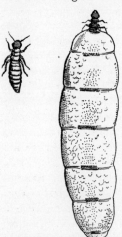

FIG. 138.—Worker and queen of *Termes red-mani*. (After Nassonow; natural size.)

of West Africa. He told of the great mound-nests of *Termes bellicosus*, twenty feet high, and so numerous that they had the appearance of native villages (Fig. 132). The soldiers are fifteen times as large as the workers, and the fertile queen has her abdomen so enlarged and stretched by the thousands of eggs forming inside that it comes to be "fifteen hundred or two thousand times the bulk of the rest of her body and twenty or thirty thousand times the bulk of a laborer." He describes the egg-laying as proceeding at the rate "of sixty a minute, or eighty thousand and upward in one day of twenty-four hours." In the South Kensington Museum at London there is such a prodigious queen resembling simply a cylindrical whitish sausage four inches long. A similar specimen is to be found in the natural-history museum of the University of Kansas.

The enormous number of individuals in a great village of nests cannot

* Sjostedt, Y., Monographie der Termiten Afrikas, Kongl. Svenska, Vetensk. Ak. Handl., v. 34, 1900, pp. 1–236, Stockholm.

even be imagined. But according to African travelers the direct results of the presence of such a population are very apparent. Drummond (Tropical Africa, 1891) writes: "You build your house, perhaps, and for a few months fancy you have pitched upon the one solitary site in the country where there are no white ants. But one day suddenly the door-post totters, and lintel and rafters come down together with a crash. You look at a section of the wrecked timbers, and discover that the whole inside is eaten clean away. The apparently solid logs of which the rest of the house is built are now mere cylinders of bark, and through the thickest of them you could push your little finger. Furniture, tables, chairs, chests of drawers, everything made of wood, is inevitably attacked, and in a single night a strong trunk is often riddled through and through, and turned into matchwood. There is no limit, in fact, to the depredation of these insects, and they will eat books, or leather, or cloth, or anything; and in many parts of Africa I believe if a man lay down to sleep with a wooden leg it would be a heap of sawdust in the morning! So much feared is this insect now that no one in certain parts of India and Africa ever attempts to travel with such a thing as a wooden trunk. On the Tanganyika plateau I have camped on ground which was as hard as adamant, and as innocent of white ants apparently as the pavement of St. Paul's, and awakened next morning to find a stout wooden box almost gnawed to pieces. Leather portmanteaus share the same fate, and the only substances which seem to defy the marauders are iron and tin."

But more impressive than this devastation of houses, tables, and boxes is the sight of millions of trees in some districts plastered over with tubes, galleries, and chambers of earth due to the amazing toil of the termites in their search for dead or dying wood for food. According to Drummond, these tunnels are made of pellets of soil brought from underground, and stuck together with saliva. The quantity of soil thus brought above ground is enormous, and Drummond sees in this phenomenon a result very similar to that accomplished by earthworms in other parts of the world, and made familiar to us by Darwin, namely, a natural tillage of the soil. As Drummond says: "Instead of an upper crust, moistened to a paste by the autumn rains and then baked hard as adamant in the sun, and an under soil hermetically sealed from the air and light, and inaccessible to all the natural manures derived from the decomposition of organic matters—these two layers being eternally fixed in their relations to one another—we have a slow and continued transference of the layers always taking place. Not only to cover their depredations, but to dispose of the earth excavated from the underground galleries, the termites are constantly transporting the deeper and exhausted soils to the surface. Thus there is, so to speak, a constant circulation of earth in the tropics, a ploughing and harrowing, not furrow by furrow and clod by clod, but pellet by pellet and grain by grain."

With a few references to certain special conditions and problems in the termite economy, we must finish our consideration of these highly interesting insects. Do the termite individuals of a community communicate with each other, or is the whole life of the colony so inexorably ruled by instinct that each individual works out its part without personal reference to any other individual, although with actual reference to *all* the others, that is, to the community as a whole? It is pretty certain that termites have a means of communication by sounds. The existence of a tympanal auditory organ in the tibiæ of the front leg, like that of the crickets and katydids, has been shown by Fritz Müller, and the individuals have a peculiar jerking motion which seems likely to be connected with the making of sounds by stridulation, sounds, however, that are not audible to us.

The spread of termites from one continent to another, as in the case of *Termes flavipes* from America to Europe, and *Termes lucifugus* from Europe to America, can be easily explained by involuntary migration in ships. In unpacking several cases of chemicals received from Germany at Stanford University, scores of termites were exposed when the wooden boxes were broken up. The insects, mining in the wood of the boxes, had protection, food, and free transportation on their long ocean journey from Hamburg around Cape Horn to California!

In termite nests are often found individuals of other insect orders. So often are such cases noted, and so many are the kinds of strangers likely to be present, that entomologists recognize a special sort of insect economy which they term termitophily, or love of termites! The strangers seem to be tolerated by the termites, and apparently live as guests or conmensals. More than 100 species of insects have been recorded as termitophiles. This curious guest-life exists on even a much larger scale in the nests of true ants, in which connection it is called myrmecophily (see p. 552).

The most important problem, and one whose solution will require much exact observation (and, if possible, experimentation), is that of the origin, or causes of production, of the different castes or kinds of individuals in the termite community. It has been determined by various observers that all the termites of a community are apparently alike at birth. That is, there is no apparent distinction of caste, no separation into workers, soldiers, and perfect insects. The soldiers and workers are not, as was formerly thought, the result of the arrested development of the reproductive organs. They are not restricted to one of the sexes. If then it is not arrested development, or sex, or embryonic (hereditary) differentiation, what is the causal factor? Grassi, an Italian student of the termites, thinks that it is food; that the feeding of the young with food variable in character brings about the differentiation of individuals. To understand this claim it is necessary to attend more closely to the feeding habits. The food of termites consists almost exclusively, as has already been said, of wood. But this wood may be taken directly from the walls of the burrow or secured indirectly from another individual. In this latter case it consists of disjecta of undigested material, which, while mostly wood, must be mixed with other organic material: because the termites keep their nests clean by eating their cast skins and the dead bodies of other individuals. This undigested material is called proctodeal food. In addition, a certain amount of evidently very different matter is regurgitated through the mouth from the anterior part of the alimentary canal. This is called stomodæal food. As the young receive all their food from the workers, it is apparent that there is opportunity for a choice, on the part of the nurses, in the kind of food given the young. And it is presumed by Grassi that such a choice is made, and that it results in the differentiation of the castes. As a matter of fact, such a differentiation of individuals is accomplished in the honey-bee community by feeding those larvæ which the workers wish to make fertile queens "royal jelly"—a rich food regurgitated through the mouth from the anterior part of the alimentary canal. This is done for the queens during the whole larval life, while larvæ which are fed royal jelly for only one or two days, and then mixed pollen and honey for the rest of larval life, develop into workers. With the honey-bee, however, the workers are to be looked on as probably only arrested females. But in the case of *Termopsis angusticollis* Heath has experimented by feeding members of various colonies, both with and without primary royal pairs, "on various kinds and amounts of food—proctodeal food dissected from workers, or in other cases from royal forms, stomodeal food from the same sources, sawdust to which different nutritious ingredients had been added—but in spite of all I cannot," he says, "feel perfectly sure that I have influenced in any unusual way the growth of a single individual."

FIG. 139.—*Embia texana*. (After Melander; enlarged.)

This is by all odds the most important and interesting problem in termite economy, and the solver of it will do much for zoological science.

A singular and primitive family of small insects, the Embiidæ, of doubtful affinities, is represented by not more than twenty living species, of which but four occur in this country. The individuals do not live in communities as the termites do, but in structural characters they probably more nearly resemble these insects than any others. Fig. 139 illustrates a typical Embiid. This species, *Embia texana*, is about one-quarter of an inch long, and of rufous color.  It was described from a few specimens found at Austin, Texas.  This insect seems to be very susceptible to differing degrees of humidity, and specimens were visible only after the ground had been moistened by rains.  As the sun dries the ground, the insects burrow into the soil.  They spin small silken webs in which they live singly. These webs are tunnels made in some crevice of the rock which shelters them, or are spun between grains of soil.  They are an inch or more in length and closed at one end, and probably serve simply for protection.  The spinning-organs of the insect are located in its fore feet, a condition unique among animals.  The food-habits of the Embiids are not yet known.

# CHAPTER VIII

## THE BOOK-LICE AND BARK-LICE (Order Corrodentia) AND THE BITING BIRD-LICE (Order Mallophaga)

SOMETIMES in taking from the shelves an old book, long untouched, there may be seen, on turning its leaves, numerous extremely minute, pale-colored, wingless insects, the book-lice, or dust-lice. So small are they, indeed, that a reading-glass or hand-lens will be needed to make out anything of their real appearance. They run about rather swiftly and seek to conceal their soft, defenceless little bodies somewhere in the binding. Under the lens they are seen to have a rather broad, flattened body (Fig. 140), six short legs, no wings (although sometimes tiny wing-pads are present), long, slender antennæ, and a pair of small black spots on the head, the simple eyes. There is a distinct neck, the head being free, and plainly wider than the prothorax. The abdomen is nearly oval in outline. There are no distinctive markings or pronounced chitinization of the soft body-wall. These book-lice can be found elsewhere than in old books; they feed on dry, dead organic matter, the paste of the book-bindings and the paper, and are common in birds' nests, where they feed on the cast-off feathers, in the crevices of bark, and on old splintered fences, where they feed on moulds and dead lichens.

Certain other insects closely related to the book-lice are not so small and simple, however, some having two pairs of wings and a plump, rounded body (Fig. 141); these look much like plant-lice (Aphids). These winged kinds do not live in libraries, moreover, and the name "book-lice" is a misnomer for them. They are rarely seen by persons not trained entomologists, and indeed are not at all familiar to professed students of insects.

The life-history of these obscure insects has been but little studied, but it is of a simple kind, the metamorphosis being incomplete, and in the case of the wingless forms certainly very slight. The young of the wingless forms "greatly resemble the old, but have no ocelli or wings, and sometimes the tarsi are of two joints, while in the adult they have three." The structure of the adults presents no points of particular interest except in the case of the mouth. The book-lice have biting mouth-parts, the jaws being strong and heavy for the successful mastication of the hard dry food. In the throat

III

there is a peculiar little chitinized structure, which may be called the œsophageal sclerite (Fig. 145). This structure is situated in the floor of the pharynx (forward end of the œsophagus), and has some special function in connection with the peculiar food-habits. It was first described by Bur-

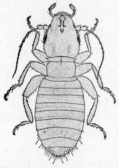

gess, and was for a long time supposed to be peculiar to the book-lice alone. But, in a study of the mouth structure of the biting bird-lice (Mallophaga), I found an almost identical œsophageal sclerite in thirteen out of the twenty-two genera of the Mallophaga. On the basis of this common possession of a curious and undoubtedly important mouth structure by the book-lice and the bird-lice (and on the basis of other strong similarities) it seems certain that these two groups of insects have a common ancestry not very remote, and probably should be included in a single order.

FIG. 140.—A wingless book-louse, *Atropos* sp. (Much enlarged.)

The order Corrodentia as at present known contains about two hundred described species, scattered over the world. The largest species occur in Brazil, and have an expanse of wing of nearly an inch. Ceylon and the Hawaiian Islands are said by Sharp to be specially rich in species.

The members of the order can be divided into two families as follows:

Wings well developed; ocelli present (in addition to compound eyes)...PSOCIDÆ.
Wings wanting or present as small scales or pads; ocelli absent ....ATROPIDÆ.

The winged Corrodentia or Psocidæ (which may be called bark-lice to distinguish them from the wingless book-lice) are too rarely seen to be at all familiar. They may most commonly be found in small clusters on bark, each cluster or colony being covered over by fine silken threads spun from the mouth. The wings are held roof-shape over the back (Fig. 141), and the body and wings are usually pale smoky in general color. The small white eggs are laid on the surface of the bark in small patches, and in a cluster

FIG. 141.—A winged bark-louse. (Thirteen times natural size.)

of bark-lice, individual in all stages, from very young to adult, may be seen.

Banks gives the following key to the North American genera:

The techinal terms *discoidal cell* and *posterior cell* may be understood by reference to Fig. 142.

1. Wings with scales and long hairs .........................AMPHIENTOMUM.
   Wings without hairs and scales, hyaline. . ......................................2.
2. Tarsi 3-jointed.................................................................3.
   Tarsi 2-jointed.................................................................4.

3. Discoidal cell closed............................................Myopsocus.
   Discoidal cell open...............................................Elipsocus.
4. Discoidal cell closed...........5.
   Discoidal cell open. ...........6.
5. Discoidal cell four-sided . Psocus.
   Discoidal cell five-sided.
           Amphigerontia.
6. Third posterior cell elliptical.
                Cæcilius.
   Third posterior cell elongated.
           Polypsocus.
   Third posterior cell absent.
       Peripsocus.

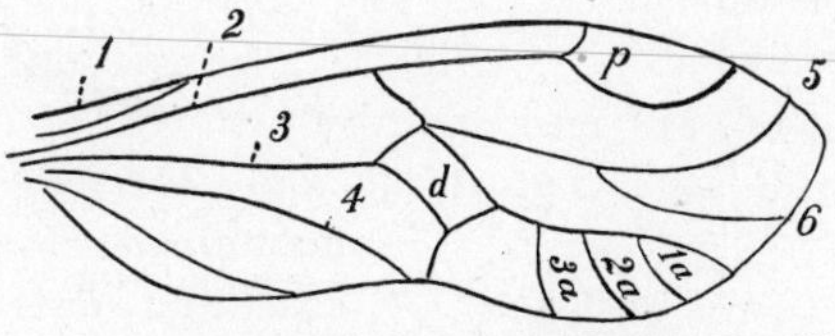

Fig. 142.—Diagram of venation of a Psocid. *d*, discoidal cell; *1a, 2a, 3a*, posterior cells. (After Banks.)

The few North American species of the true book-lice or Atropidæ are included in five genera, which may be distinguished as follows:

The technical terms, hitherto undefined, used in the following table are the following: *squamæ*, wings in the condition of small scales or pads; *hyaline*, clear, not colored.

1. Meso- and metathorax united, no wings...........................Atropos.
   Meso- and metathorax separate, rudimentary wings. ......................2.
2. Wings with veins...........................................Dorypteryx.
   Wings veinless, in form of squamæ or tubercles. ...........................3.
3. Squamæ small, hyaline .........................................Clothilla.
   Squamæ in the form of scars.................................Lepinotus.
   Small tubercles in the place of squamæ .......................Hyperetes.

The genera Atropos and Clothilla were named for two of the three Fates of mythology, and a third genus was named Lachesis for the third Fate, but unfortunately the last genus was not a valid one, so the book-lice have lost their third Fate, and by the rigid laws of zoological nomenclature can never regain her! The few species of these two Fate-named genera are the commonest of the book-lice. *Atropos divinatoria* is the species usually found in books. It is about 1 mm. long, is grayish-white, and the small eyes show as distinct black specks on the head. It does not limit its feeding to the paste of book-bindings, but does much damage to dried insects in collections. To this insect has long been attributed the power of producing a ticking noise known as the "death-watch," but McLachlan, an authority on the Corrodentia, does not believe that this minute insect "with a body so soft that the least touch annihilates it can in any way produce a noise sensible to human ears." A small beetle, called Anobium, is well known to make such a ticking (by knocking its head against the wood of door-casings, floors, etc., in which it lives) and probably the "death-watch" is always made by this beetle.

Bird-collectors are often annoyed by small, wingless, flat-bodied, swift-running insects which sometimes escape from the feathers of bird specimens to the hands and arms of the collector. Poultry-raisers are sometimes more seriously troubled by finding them so abundant on their fowls as to do considerable injury. They are called bird-lice, but they should not be confused, because of this name, with the true blood-sucking lice that infest many kinds of animals, particularly domestic mammals and uncleanly persons. The biting bird-lice (Fig. 143), constituting the order Mallophaga, never suck blood, but feed exclusively on bits of the dry feathers, which they bite off with small but strong and sharp-edged mandibles. The true lice have mouth-parts fitted for piercing and sucking, and constitute one of the numerous families of the order of sucking bugs, Hemiptera (see p. 217).

FIG. 143.—A biting bird-louse, *Nirmus præstans*, from a tern, *Sterna maxima*. (Photomicrograph by George E. Mitchell; natural size, one-twelfth inch.)

More than a thousand species of biting bird-lice, or Mallophaga, are known, of which about two hundred and fifty have been found on North American birds. Although by far the larger number of Mallophaga infest birds, numerous species are found on mammals. On these hosts the insect feeds on the hair or on epidermal scales. On both birds and mammals, therefore, the food consists of dry and nearly or quite dead cuticular substances, and never of blood or live flesh. Those species of Mallophaga which infest birds are never found on mammals, and vice versa.

The injury done to the hosts by these parasites consists not in the character of the food-habits, but chiefly in the irritation of the skin caused by the scratching of the sharp-clawed little feet of the insects in their migrations over the body. When, as happens sometimes in poultry-yards and dovecotes, a fowl or pigeon is infested by hundreds of these active little pests, the afflicted bird becomes so restless and excited that it takes too little food and gets too little rest and thus grows thin and weak. The dust-baths taken by fowls and other birds are chiefly to get rid of the bird-lice. The fine dust, getting into the breathing-pores (spiracles) of the insects, suffocates them. So that the best remedies for these pests of the barn-yard are to see that the fowls have plenty of dust to bathe in, and also to keep thoroughly clean their roosting- and breeding-places. By tightly closing up the hen-house and burning sulphur inside (the fowls, it is hardly necessary to say, first being excluded) most of the infesting parasites can be killed.

The life-history of the Mallophaga is very simple. The small elongate eggs are glued separately to the hair or feathers of the host, and from them young soon hatch (Fig. 144,3), which, except in size and, to some degree, in marking, closely resemble the parents. These young begin immediately their hair or feather diet, grow larger, moult a few times, and in a few weeks reach maturity. There is never, in young or old, any sign of wings or wing-pads. The body is flattened, so much so indeed that it is difficult to hold a live specimen securely between thumb and finger-tip. The body-wall is strongly chitinized, and is firm and smooth. The markings are often very distinct, and sometimes bizarre, but the coloration varies only from white to black through various shades of pale yellowish brown, tawny, reddish brown, and blackish brown. The antennæ are short and in one suborder (see classification key) are wholly concealed in pits or grooves on the under side of the

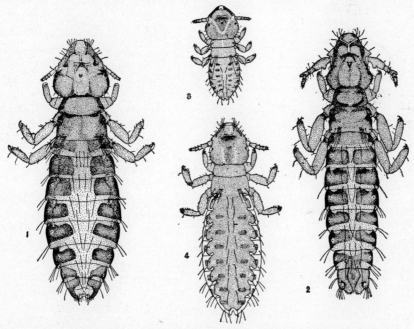

FIG. 144.—Immature and adult stages of the biting bird-louse, *Lipeurus forficulatus,* taken from a pelican. 1, adult female; 2, adult male; 3, very young stage; 4, older immature stage. (Natural size of adult specimens $\frac{1}{10}$ in.)

flattened head. The legs are strong, and each foot bears two claws. These small creatures run very swiftly.

Perhaps the oddest thing about the structure of the Mallophaga is the presence in the throat of the curious œsophageal or pharyngeal sclerite already referred to in the account of the Corrodentia. This sclerite is a sort of bonnet-shaped piece (Fig. 145) lying in the lower wall of the throat and seems to be an arrangement for starting the little bitten-off pieces of feather barbs straight, that is, lengthwise down the œsophagus! The bark-lice and book-lice, which have a similar œsophageal sclerite, also bite off and swallow small bits of hard, dry organic substance.

The most interesting thing in connection with the Mallophaga, excepting their parasitic life and strange food-habits, is the puzzling problem of their distribution. The problem in its largest phase is this: the species of Mallophaga are, in a majority of cases, peculiar (so far as recorded) each to some one host species. But the instances are many where a single parasite species is common to a few or even to many host species. How does this condition of commonness to several hosts come to exist?

As the Mallophaga are wingless, their power of migration from bird to bird is limited. Moreover, they can live for but a short time off the body of a warm-blooded host. After a bird is shot, the Mallophaga on it die in from two hours to three or four days: in rare cases living individuals are found on the drying bird-skin after a week. Although the parasites in a badly infested hen-house will be seen on the roosts and in the nests, in Nature the insects are rarely found off the host's body. On such a likely place as an ocean rock from which I had just frightened hundreds of perching pelicans, cormorants, and gulls no parasites could be found. Practically migration must be accomplished while the bodies of the hosts are in contact. Such cases occur during mating and nesting, and when gregarious birds roost or perch closely together. Occasional migration might occur from a bird of prey to its captured victim, or from victim to hawk.

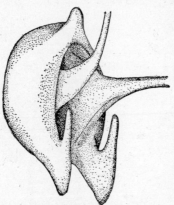

Fig. 145.—Bonnet-shaped pharyngeal sclerite, lateral aspect, from a biting bird-louse, *Eurymopetus taurus*, from an albatross. (Greatly magnified.)

The general character of the cases in which a single Mallophagan species is common to several host-species may now be considered. *Docophorus lari* has been found on thirteen species of sea-gulls, and *Nirmus lineolatus* on nine. Gulls are gregarious, perching together on large food-masses and on ocean rocks. But on these rocks gulls are closely associated with other coast birds, as cormorants, pelicans, murres, etc. And the gull-parasites might have opportunities to migrate to these other bird-species. *Docophorus icterodes* and *Trinoton luridum* are common to many duck species (each has been collected from nine), but ducks also are gregarious, and in addition are much given to hybridizing. But a parasite may be common to several host-species of non-gregarious habits. *Docophorus platystomus* is common to several hawk-species, *D. cursor* to several owl-species, *D. excisus* to several swallows, *D. californiensis* to several woodpeckers, and *D. communis* to several passerine birds. In the other genera of Mallophaga are similar cases, and in all these cases it is hard to see how actual migration of the parasite from host to host of different species could take place.   Indeed there are cases in which such migration is absolutely impossible.   Of the 262 species of Mallophaga taken from North American birds, 157 have been described as new species, while 105 are specifically identical with Mallophaga originally described from European and Asiatic birds; hosts, that is, not only of different species, but geographically widely separated from the North American hosts!   Eliminating the few cases of importations of living European birds to this country, and the few species of cicumpolar range, there remain to be accounted for about 100 cases in which a single species of Mallophaga is common to both Old World and New World hosts.

It will have been noted that in all the cases above mentioned of parasite species common to several North American host-species, the host-birds are closely allied forms, that is, species of the same genus or allied genera. This condition holds good also for practically all of the cases in which both European and American hosts have a common parasite.   For example, *Docophorus pertusus* is common to the European coot (*Fulica atra*) and the American coot (*Fulica americana*); *Nirmus pileus* is common to the European avocet (*Recurvirostra avocetta*), and to the American avocet (*Recurvirostra americana*); *Lipeurus forficulatus* is common to the European pelican (*Pelecanus onocrotalus*) and to the American pelicans (*Pelecanus erythrorhynchus* and *P. californicus*), and so on through the list.   From this fact of near relationship of hosts in all the cases of parasite species common to several host-species it seems almost certain that this common occurrence, under circumstances not admitting of migration of the parasites from host to host, is due to the persistence of the parasite species unchanged from the time of the common ancestor of the two or more now distinct but closely allied bird-species.   In ancient times geographical races arose within the limits of the ancestral host-species; these races or varieties have now come to be distinct species, distinguished by superficial differences in color and markings of plumage, etc.   But the parasites of the ancient hosts have remained unchanged; the plumage as food, the temperature of the body, practically the whole environment of the insect, have remained the same; there has been no external factor at work tending to modify the parasite species, and it exists to-day in its ancient form, common to the newly arisen descendants of the ancient host.

To classify Mallophaga the following keys to suborders, families, and genera may be used.   In these keys are included only genera which have been found in the United States.   Seven other genera of Mallophaga are known.

In the following tables the following technical terms are used which have not been previously defined: *clavate*, club-shaped; *capitate*, with the tip swollen like a ball; *tra-*

*beculæ*, triangular membranous processes projecting laterally from the head and situated one in front of each antenna; *temples*, the hinder lateral parts of the head; *ocular emargination*, a bending in of the lateral margins of the head just in front of the eyes; *labral lobes*, short blunt membranous processes projecting laterally from near the front angles of the head; *sternal markings*, blackish markings, bars or spots, on the ventral aspect of the thorax.

### Key to Suborders of Mallophaga.

With short slender 3- or 5-segmented, exposed antennæ; no palpi; mandibles vertical................................................................... Ischnocera.

With short clavate or capitate, 4-segmented antennæ concealed in shallow cavities on under side of head; 4-segmented palpi; mandibles horizontal.

Amblycera.

### Key to Genera of the Suborder Ischnocera.

A.   With 3-segmented antennæ; tarsi with one claw; infesting mammals only (family *Trichodectidæ*) ................................................................Trichodectes.

AA.  With 5-segmented antennæ; tarsi with two claws; infesting birds only (family *Philopteridæ*).

    B.   Antennæ alike in both sexes.

        C.   Front deeply angularly notched........................Akidoproctus.

        CC.  Front convex, truncate, and rarely with a curving emargination, but never angularly notched.

            D.   Body broad and short; head with large movable trabeculæ.

                E.   Forehead with a broad, transverse membranous flap, projecting beyond lateral margins of the head in the male, barely projecting in the female.........................Giebelia.

                EE. Without such membranous flap.............. Docophorus.

            DD. Body elongate, narrow; head with very small or no trabeculæ.

Nirmus.

    BB.  Antennæ differing in the two sexes.

        C.   Body wide, elongate oval to suborbicular.

            D.   Temples rounded; tip of abdomen with shallow, curving emargination; antennæ with no appendage; third segment unusually long.

Eurymetopus.

            DD. Temples usually angulated; tip of abdomen convex, rarely angularly emarginated with two points.

                E.   First antennal segment of male large, and sometimes with an appendage; third segment always with appendage.

Goniodes.

                EE. First antennal segment of male large, but always without appendage; third segment without appendage..Goniocotes.

        CC.  Body elongate, narrow, sides subparallel.

            D.   Antennæ and legs long; a semicircular depression in front of mouth .............................................................Lipeurus.

            DD. Antennæ and legs short; depression in front of mouth narrow and elongate, extending as a furrow to the anterior margin of the head.

Oncophorus.

### Key to Genera of the Suborder Amblycera.

A.   Tarsi with one claw; infesting mammals only (family *Gyropidæ*).........Gyropus.

AA.  Tarsi with two claws; infesting birds only (family *Liotheidæ*).

    B.   Ocular emargination distinct, more or less deep.

C.  Forehead evenly rounded, without lateral swellings; antennæ projecting slightly beyond border of the head....................COLPOCEPHALUM.
CC. Forehead with strong lateral swellings.
    D.  Mesothorax separated from metathorax by a suture....TRINOTON.
    DD. Meso- and metathorax fused; no suture........LÆMOBOTHRIUM.
BB. Ocular emargination absent or very slight.
  C.  Sides of the head straight or slightly concave, with two small laterally projecting labral lobes...............................PHYSOSTOMUM.
  CC. Sides of the head sinuous; forehead without labral lobes.
    D.  Ocular emargination filled by a strong swelling; sternal markings forming a quadrilateral without median blotches......NITZSCHIA.
    DD. Ocular emargination without swelling, hardly apparent or entirely lacking; median blotches on sternum.
      E.  Very large; with two-pointed appendages on ventral aspect of hind head; anterior coxæ with very long lobe-like appendages......................................... ANCISTRONA.
      EE. Small or medium; without bi-partite appendages of hind head. MENOPON.

The Mallophaga most likely to come under the observation of people not collectors of birds are the species which infest domestic fowls and mammals, and the following few descriptions and figures of particular species are therefore limited to such kinds.

The most notorious member of the order is the common chicken-louse, *Menopon pallidum* (Fig. 146). It is of a pale straw-yellow color, from 1 mm. ($\frac{1}{2.5}$ in.) to 1.5 mm. in length, and is an unusually swift and active little pest. Other Mallophaga infesting chickens are *Goniocotes hologaster*, recognized by its squarish head with angulated temples, and *Lipeurus variabilis*, 2 mm. ($\frac{1}{1.2}$ in.) long and slender, with distinct black markings on the otherwise smooth, white body.

Ducks are infested by several species. Common among them is the little *Docophorus icterodes* (Fig. 147), 1 mm. ($\frac{1}{2.5}$ in.) long, with head curiously expanded and rounded in front, darkish-red head, and thorax with darker

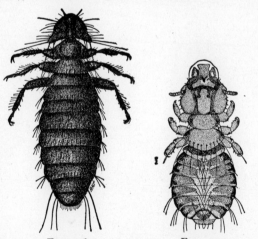

FIG. 146.                    FIG. 147.

FIG. 146.—The biting chicken-louse, *Menopon pallidum.* (After Piaget; natural size, 1 to 1.5 mm.)

FIG. 147.—The biting louse of wild ducks, *Docophorus icterodes.* (Natural size indicated by line.)

bands, and a white region in the middle of the abdomen. *Trinoton luridum* is another common duck-louse unusually large, being from 4 to 5 mm. (₅ in.) long and readily distinguished by the triangular head with lateral swellings, and the abdomen with pronounced blackish-brown transverse bands.

FIG. 150.

FIG. 149.

FIG. 151.

FIG. 148.

FIG. 152.

FIG. 148.—A biting louse of pigeons, *Lipeurus baculus*. (Natural size indicated by line.)

FIG. 149.—Biting louse of the dog, *Trichodectes latus*. (After Nitzsch; natural size, 1 to 1.5 mm.)

FIG. 150.—Biting louse of the horse, *Trichodectes parumpilosus*, male. (After Morse; natural size shown by line.)

FIG. 151.—Biting louse of cattle, *Trichodectes scalaris*. (After Lugger; natural size, 1.5 to 2 mm.)

FIG. 152.—Biting louse of fringilline birds, *Docophorus communis*. (Natural size indicated by line.)

Pigeons are almost always infested by a long and very slender louse, *Lipeurus baculus* (Fig. 148). The head and thorax are reddish brown, while the abdomen is dusky with darker segmental blotches. This bird-louse was described and named more than two hundred years ago.

All of the species infesting domestic mammals belong to the genus Trichodectes. Dogs are often infested by *Trichodectes latus* (Fig. 149), a short, wide-bodied species about 1 mm. long; while cats are less often infested by *T. subrostratus*, distinguishable by the rather pointed head with a short, longitudinal furrow on the under side. Horses and donkeys are troubled by two or three species, of which *T. pilosus*, a hairy form with antennæ rising near the front of the head, and *T. parumpilosus* (Fig. 150), a broader-bodied form with head larger and less flatly rounded in front, are most common. *Trichodectes scalaris* (Fig. 151) infests cattle the world over, while sheep and goats have species peculiar to themselves. Comparatively few species of Trichodectes have been recorded from wild mammals, but this is simply because they have not been sought with care. Species have

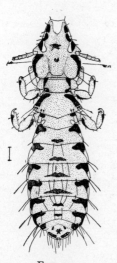

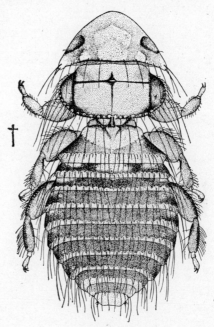

FIG. 153.                    FIG. 154.

FIG. 153.—A biting louse of gulls, *Nirmus felix*, male. (Natural size indicated by line.)
FIG. 154.—Giant bird-louse of the albatrosses, *Ancistrona gigas*, male. (Natural size indicated by line.)

been found on the bear, raccoon, fox, coyote, weasel, gopher, beaver, deer, skunk, and porcupine. Gyropus, the other mammal-infesting genus of

Mallophaga, has been found only on the guinea-pig. Washing the body of the infested animal with kerosene emulsion (see p. 190) is probably the most effective remedy for biting lice.

Of the nearly three hundred species of Mallophaga which I have recorded (Proc. Nat. Mus., v. 22, 1899, pp. 39–100) from wild North American birds, mention may be made of the largest, *Læmobothrium loomis*, taken from the Canada goose; of *Docophorus communis* (Fig. 152), the most abundant and widely distributed parasite of perching and song birds; of the pretty *Nirmus felix* (Fig. 153), with its clean white body and sharply marked black spots; of the fierce-looking *Lipeurus ferox*, found on albatrosses; and of *Ancistrona gigas* (Fig. 154), found on fulmars, the broadest of the Mallophaga.

As there are nearly one thousand different species of North American birds, and Mallophaga have been taken from but two hundred and fifty of them, it is obvious that the collector and student of these parasites has a profitable field open to him.

# CHAPTER IX

## THE COCKROACHES, CRICKETS, LOCUSTS, GRASS-HOPPERS, AND KATYDIDS
### (Order Orthoptera)

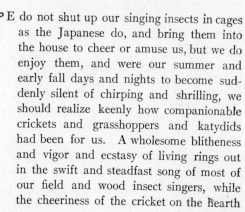

E do not shut up our singing insects in cages as the Japanese do, and bring them into the house to cheer or amuse us, but we do enjoy them, and were our summer and early fall days and nights to become suddenly silent of chirping and shrilling, we should realize keenly how companionable crickets and grasshoppers and katydids had been for us. A wholesome blitheness and vigor and ecstasy of living rings out in the swift and steadfast song of most of our field and wood insect singers, while the cheeriness of the cricket on the hearth is familiar poetry and proverb.

Almost all this insect music comes from the members of one order, the Orthoptera. Indeed there is but one famous insect *maestro*, the cicada (of the order Hemiptera), which does not belong to the group of crickets, locusts, green grasshoppers, and katydids. Besides being singers, too, the Orthoptera are the characteristic leapers of the insect world; crickets and locusts easily surpass the world's athletes for high jumping if the record takes into account the comparative size of the athletes. And, curiously, the singing Orthoptera are the leaping ones. Of the six families composing the order, three include insects which do not sing nor leap, while the other three are made up of singers and leapers.

As one tramps the roadways or dry pastures in summer and autumn, the steady shrilling of the locusts on the ground, or their sharp "clacking" as they spring into air, are most familiar sounds. When you ramble through the uncut meadows and lush low grounds the still shriller singing of the slender-bodied, thin-legged, meadow green grasshopper is heard, while in the orchards and woods the snowy tree-crickets and broad-winged katydids keep up the chorus.  At home, in house and garden, the domestic cricket offers its music to the already over-full ears.  All this choiring is done by singers without a voice; that is, without the production of sound from the throat and mouth by means of vocal cords set into vibration by air.  Insects are orchestral performers, using their legs and wings, for the most part, to make their music.  When the locust sings while at rest, it is rasping the inner surface of the broad hind thighs across the roughened outer surface of the folded fore wings; when it "clacks" in the air, it is striking the front margin of the hind wing back and forth past the hinder margin of the thickened fore wings.  When the cricket shrills on the hearth, or anywhere else, *he,* for only the male crickets have the musical gift, is holding his fore wings up over his body at an angle with it of about 45° and is rubbing together the upper surfaces of the basal region of the fore wings, which are specially modified for this purpose.  The tree-crickets, katydids, and meadow green grasshoppers have, in the males, the same general sort of music-making apparatus as the cricket, and sing by similarly rasping or rubbing together the modified parts of the fore wings.  This

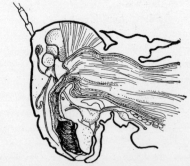

FIG. 155.—Longitudinal section through head and neck of locust, showing disposition of alimentary canal, brain, and suboesophageal ganglion.  (After Snodgrass; much enlarged.)

music-making by rasping is called stridulation, and for the most part insect stridulation is strictly strident, and sounds to better advantage in the field than it would from caged songsters in the parlor.

All the Orthoptera have biting mouth-parts, and bite off and chew their food, which is usually live vegetable matter, especially green leaves, although the members of one family are predaceous, preying on other insects, and those of another family prefer dried vegetable or animal matter. The metamorphosis is incomplete, the young, when hatched, resembling the parents except for small size and lack of wings. The young have the same feeding habits and same haunts as the adults, and by development and growth the

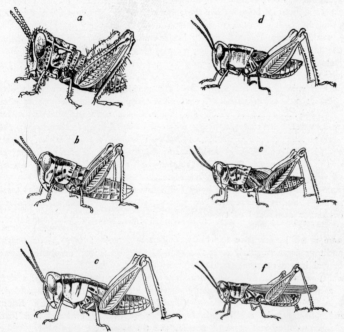

Fig. 156.—The immature stages of a locust, *Melanoplus femur-rubrum*. *a*, just hatched, without wing-pads; *b, c, d*, and *e* after first, second, third, and fourth moultings respectively, showing appearance and development of wings; *f*, adult, with fully developed wings. (After Emerton.)

wings and parental stature are soon acquired. The name of the order is derived from the straight-margined leathery fore wings, or elytra, whose chief function is to cover and protect the larger membranous hind wings on which the flight function depends. Among the leaping Orthoptera the hindmost legs are very large and long, and when at rest or in walking the "knee-joints" of these legs are much higher than the back of the insect.

The three singing and leaping families are the Acridiidæ, locusts and grasshoppers with short antennæ; Locustidæ, meadow green grasshoppers and katydids, all with long thread-like antennæ; and Gryllidæ, the crickets. The three silent and walking or running families are the Blattidæ, cockroaches; Mantidæ, praying-horses and soothsayers; and Phasmidæ, walking-sticks or twig-insects. These families can be distinguished by the following table:

### KEY TO FAMILIES OF ORTHOPTERA.

Non-leaping and mute; hind femora closely resembling those of the other legs and scarcely stouter or longer than the middle femora; tarsi 5-segmented; ovipositor concealed.

Body oval, depressed; head nearly horizontal and nearly or quite concealed by the flattish shield-like pronotum; quickly running....(Cockroaches.) BLATTIDÆ.

Body elongate, generally narrow; head free, often with constricted neck; pronotum elongate, never transverse; slowly walking.

Fore legs spined and fitted and held for grasping; antennæ usually shorter than body; pronotum usually longer than any other body segment; anal cerci jointed .....................................(Praying Mantes.) MANTIDÆ.

Fore legs not fitted for grasping; antennæ usually longer than body; pronotum short .....................(Leaf-insects and Walking-sticks.) PHASMIDÆ.

Leaping and usually capable of stridulation; hind femora stouter or longer, or both, than the other femora; the hind legs enlarged, for leaping; tarsi 4- or 3-segmented; head vertical; ovipositor usually visible.

Antennæ much shorter than the body (with few exceptions); ocelli three; tarsi 3-segmented; auditory organs, when present, situated on basal abdominal segment; ovipositor composed of two pairs of short, strong, slightly curving pieces.

(Locusts.) ACRIDIIDÆ.

Antennæ much longer than the body, delicately tapering; tarsi 3- or 4-segmented; auditory organs usually near the base of the fore tibiæ; ovipositor usually prolonged into a compressed blade, or needle, its parts compact.

Tarsi 4-segmented; ocelli usually absent; ovipositor usually exserted and forming a strongly compressed, usually curving, blade with tip not expanded.

(The long-horned grasshoppers.) LOCUSTIDÆ.

Tarsi 3-segmented; ocelli variable; ovipositor usually exserted and forming a nearly cylindrical straight needle, the tip somewhat expanded.

(Crickets.) GRYLLIDÆ.

Mrs. Smith takes it amiss when you ask permission to collect "roaches" in her house, and will prove to you any *day* the conspicuous absence of these unwelcome guests in the scrubbed and spotless pantry and kitchen. But with a candle go stocking-footed at night into the same kitchen and you will not unlikely find "good hunting." Although but few of the thousand different kinds of cockroaches known in the world are to be found in the United States, these few, and particularly three or four imported foreigners among them, are very abundant, and, after dark, very much in evidence in their favorite habitat. Their chosen abiding-place is in kitchens, pantries, laundries, restaurants, bakeshops, etc., where the atmosphere is warm and humid and the roach's table is well set with good things. Almost any sort of dry organic matter suits their taste; bread, crackers, miscellaneous cold-lunch delicacies, the paste of bookbindings and wall-paper, leather, woolens, and even their own egg-cases and cast skins making up the dietary. The fo'k'sel and galley of ships are the roaches' special joy; the hotels and restaurants of tropic and subtropic lands house swarms of these bill-evading guests. From Mazatlan, Mexico, a naturalist sent me quarts of large native American roaches (*Periplaneta americana*), which he readily scooped up from his bedroom floor. Ships come into San Francisco from their long half-year voyages around the Horn with the sailors wearing gloves on their hands when asleep in their bunks in a desperate effort to save their finger-nails from being gnawed off by the hordes of roaches which infest the whole ship. A few of our species still live outside under stones and old logs, but most of them have learned that an easier life awaits them in the kitchen.

The roaches compose the Orthopterous family Blattidæ, and are an ancient and persistent insect group. In Carboniferous times, before flies, butterflies, bees, and wasps had come into existence, cockroaches were the dominant insects. The body in all is flattened and slippery with the legs adapted for quick running, so that the insects are well fitted to escape safely into narrow cracks and crevices. The head is concealed from above by the expanded shield-shaped dorsal wall of the prothorax (pronotum). Wings are present in most species, the front pair leathery and serving, when the wings are folded, to cover and protect the larger, thin, membranous hind pair. In some forms the females are wingless, and the indoor habit may be held responsible for the lessened usefulness and resultant loss of the wings. The mouth-parts are fitted for biting hard dry substances, the jaws being strong and toothed.

Fig. 157.— Egg-case of cockroach. (Three times natural size.)

The eggs are laid in small purse-like, horny, brown cases (Fig. 157), which are usually carried about by the female until the young are ready to issue. The young grow slowly, requiring probably about a year, in most species, to become fully developed. From the beginning, the young can run about and take care of themselves, eating the same kind of food as the adults. They moult several times during growth, and at each moult the wing-pads are a little larger.

There are four common species of cockroaches found in dwellings in this country, only one of which is native. This is the large American roach, *Periplaneta americana*, about 1½ inches long (to tip of folded wings), light brown in color, and with the wings expanding nearly 3 inches. This species is abundant in the middle and western states, having gradually extended its range north from its native region in Mexico and Central America. The Australian roach, *Periplaneta australasia*, resembles *P. americana*, but is darker in ground color, a quarter of an inch shorter, and has a conspicuous yellow submarginal band running around the shield-shaped pronotum. Each fore wing has also a strong yellow tapering bar in the basal part of the costal region. It came originally from the Australian Pacific region, and is now spread widely over the world, being common in this country in Florida and other southern states. The most abundant and destructive house-roach in the eastern states is the small German cockroach, *Ectobia germanica* (Fig. 158), about half an inch long, and pale yellowish brownish with a pair of distinct black longitudinal stripes on the pro-

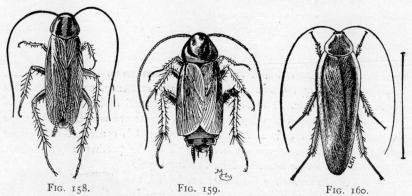

FIG. 158. FIG. 159. FIG. 160.

FIG. 158.—The croton-bug, or German cockroach, *Ectobia germanica*. (Twice natural size.)

FIG. 159.—The black beetle, or Oriental cockroach, *Periplaneta orientalis*. (One and one-half times natural size.)

FIG. 160.—The common wood cockroach, *Ischnoptera pennsylvanica*. (After Lugger; natural size indicated by line.)

notum. This roach is often called croton-bug, from its intimate association with the pipes of New York City's Croton-water system. It is an importation from Europe, where it is especially abundant in Germany. Its real nativity is unknown, but it is now of world-wide distribution. The fourth species is the black or Asiatic roach, or black beetle, as it is sometimes called, *Periplaneta orientalis* (Fig. 159). This roach is about one inch long, with brownish-black body; in the female the wings are rudimentary, and in the male the wings when folded do not quite reach the tip of the abdomen. This species is common in all the eastern and Mississippi Valley states and extends as far west as the great plains. It is the commonest cockroach in England and Europe. The native outdoor species most familiar in this country is the common wood-cockroach, *Ischnoptera pennsylvanica* (Fig. 160), with long, light-colored wing-covers, and wings which extend considerably beyond the tips of the abdomen. The margin of the pronotum is light, the disk being dark, and the front margins (lateral when folded) of the wing-covers are lighter than the discal parts. The body is an inch long and rather narrow and slender. This species is common in the woods and sometimes comes into houses in summer-time.

In the southern states and those of the Mississippi Valley a large insect may be not infrequently seen standing motionless in a corner of a window, in a striking attitude. This attitude may be taken as one of hopeful prayer, as those who gave the name praying-mantis to the insect seem to have taken it, or one of self-confident readiness to do violent work with those upraised, sharply spined, and very willing fore feet. This is the way the house-flies rightfully take the mantis's attitude. Watch an unwary bluebottle crawl or buzz into the fatal corner. Blundering buzziness is finished for that blue-

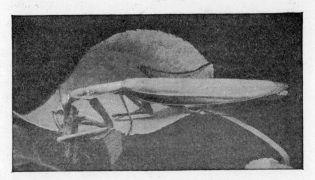

FIG. 161.—The praying-mantis, *Mantis religiosa*.   (After Slingerland; natural size.)

bottle; and the first course of a square meal has come to him who waits and watches. Other names, as rearhorse, camel-cricket, and soothsayer, have been given the mantis, all suggested by the attitude and curious body make-up of the creature. The prothorax is long and stem-like, the head broader than long, with protuberant eyes, and the fore legs are not used for locomotion, but are large, strongly spined, and fitted for seizing and holding the prey. The wings are short and broad and usually rather leaf-like in coloration and texture, the whole insect when at rest resembling somewhat a part of the plant on which the mantis ordinarily stands. The window-corner is a new and unnatural *locale* for the insects, but the abundance of prey here in summer-time makes it a good feeding-ground.

The family Mantidæ includes less than a score of species in this country, all of them southern in range, and only a few occurring north of the Rio

Grande and Gulf coast regions. All the species are carnivorous, and undoubtedly do much good in making away with many noxious insects. In 1899 some specimens of the common European praying-mantis, *Mantis*

*religiosa* (Fig. 161), were found in and near Rochester, N. Y. They had probably been accidentally imported into this country in nursery stocks from France. As this species seems able to live farther north than our native species, Professor Slingerland is laudably trying to establish it in our country. He takes care of a colony, and is distributing many of the egg-cases over the entire country. All the mantids lay their eggs in curious masses (Figs. 162 and 163), covered with a quickly drying tough mucus. These egg-cases are attached to branches and plant-stems in the fall, and the young hatch in the following summer and soon grow (moulting several times and developing wings) to full stature, which for our most common native species, *Stagmomantis carolina*, is about 2½ inches long.

FIG. 162.—Egg-cases of the praying-mantis, *Mantis religiosa*. (After Slingerland; natural size.)

Slingerland has collected a number of the old accounts of the European mantis which are of interest as proofs of the light and graceful fancy of some of the early author-naturalists. The ancient Greeks gave the insects the name *Mantis*, that is, "prophet." Mouffet, writing over three hundred years ago, says: "They are called *Mantes*, that is, *foretellers*, either because by their coming (for they first of all appear) they do show the spring to be at hand, so Anacreon the poet sang; or else they foretell death and famine, as Cælius the Scoliast of Theocritus has observed; or, lastly,

FIG. 163.—Egg-case of praying-mantis, *Mantis religiosa*, cut open, showing arrangement of eggs inside. (Natural size.)

because it always holds up its fore feet like hands praying as it were, after the manner of their Diviners, who in that gesture did pour out their supplications to their Gods." And he says again: "They resemble the Diviners in the elevation of their hands, so also in likeness of motion; for they do not sport themselves as others do, nor leap, nor play, but walking softly, they retain their modesty, and shewes forth a kind of mature gravity. . . . So divine a creature is this esteemed, that if a childe aske the way to such a place, she will stretch out one of her feet, and shew him the right way, and seldome or never misse." Piso in his works states that mantids "change into a green and tender plant, which is of two hands' breadth. The feet are fixed into the ground first; from these, when necessary, humidity is attracted, roots grow out and strike into the ground; thus they change by degrees, and in a short time become a perfect plant."

Almost everywhere that mantids occur, strange superstitions are held concerning them. Most of these ascribe some degree of sanctity to them, and to kill them maliciously is considered sinful. Cowan says that "the Turks and other Moslems have been much impressed by the actions of the common *Mantis religiosa*, which greatly resemble some of their own attitudes of prayer. They readily recognize intelligence and pious intentions in its actions, and accordingly treat it with respect and attention, not indeed as in itself an object of reverence or superstition, but as a fellow worshipper of God, whom they believe that all creatures praise with more or less consciousness and intelligence. Other superstitions with respect to the Mantis are current: when it kneels it sees an angel in the way, or hears the rustle of its wings; when it alights on your hand you are about to make the acquaintance of a distinguished person; if it alights on your head, a great honor will shortly be conferred upon you. If it injures you in any way, which it does but seldom, you will lose a valued friend by calumny. Never kill a Mantis, as it bears charm against evil." Finally, monkish legends tell us, says Slingerland, that St. Francis Xavier, seeing a Mantis moving

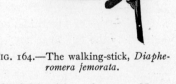

Fig. 164.—The walking-stick, *Diapheromera femorata*.

along in its solemn way, holding up its two fore legs as in the act of devotion, desired it to sing the praise of God, whereupon the insect carolled forth a fine canticle!

More amazing than the Mantids for modification of form and appearance away from the usual insect type are the members of the family Phasmidæ. The only representatives of this family in the United States are the walking-sticks, or twig insects (Fig. 164), of which half a dozen genera, with from one to three species each, have been recorded. The only one of these genera which is found in the East is Diapheromera, of which *D. femorata* is the common species. Our other Phasmids are found in the West or extreme South. All of our species are wingless and are generally sluggish in movement, and depend for protection largely on their amazingly faithful resemblance in shape and color to twigs, and on their capacity to emit an ill-smelling fluid from certain glands on their prothorax. *Diapheromera femorata* (Fig. 164) feeds on the leaves of oaks, walnuts, and probably other trees. It drops its hundred seed-like eggs loosely and singly on the ground, where they lie through the winter, hatching irregularly through the following summer. Some may even go over a second winter before hatching. *Femorata* may be either brown or green; so it frequents dead or leafless, or live and green-leaved parts, according to the correspondence of its body color with the one or the other of these environments. The long, slender, wingless body, the thin, long legs held angularly, and the harmonizing body color, all serve to make the walking-stick well-nigh indistinguishable when at rest on the twigs.

In tropic and subtropic countries the Phasmids are numerous (over 600 species are known) and present other striking resemblances to the details of their habitual environment. A conspicuous and perfect example of resemblance is the green leaf-insect Phyllium (Pl. XIII, Fig. 2), whose wings, flattened body, and expanded plate-like legs, head, and prothorax, all bright green and flecked irregularly with small yellowish spots, like those made by the attacks of fungi on live leaves, combine to simulate with wonderful effect a green leaf.

Other examples of such protective resemblance and a discussion of the origin and significance of the phenomenon may be found in Chapter XVII of this book.

The genera of Phasmidæ occurring in the United States may be distinguished by the following key:

Tibiæ with a groove at tip to receive the base of the tarsi when bent upon them.
  Antennæ with less than twenty segments, and much shorter than the fore femora.
                                                                    BACILLUS.

Antennæ with many segments, and longer than the fore femora.
  Mesothorax twice as long as prothorax.........................ANISOMORPHA.
  Mesothorax no longer than prothorax..............................TINEMA.
Tibiæ without groove at tip, as above described.
  Hind femora with one or more distinct spines on the median line of the under side
    near the tip................................................DIAPHEROMERA.
  Hind femora without such spines.
    Head, especially in female, with a pair of tubercles or ridges on the front between
      the eyes.......................................................SERMYLE.
    Head without such tubercle or ridges.........................BACUNCULUS.

One day in early summer of the Centennial Year (1876) the people all over Kansas might have been seen staring hard with shaded eyes and serious faces up towards the sun. By persistent looking one could see high in the air a thin silvery white shifting cloud or haze of which old residents sadly said, "It's them again, all right." Now this meant, if it were true, that, far from being all right, it was about as wrong as it could be for Kansas. "Them" meant the hateful Rocky Mountain locusts, and the locusts meant devastation and ruin for Kansas crops and farmers. In 1866 and again in 1874 and 1875 the locusts had come; first a thin silvery cloud high overhead—sunlight glancing from millions of thin membranous fluttering wings—and then a swarming, crawling, leaping, and ever and always busily eating horde of locusts over all the green things of the land. And the old residents spoke the truth in that summer of 1876. It was "them," uncounted hosts of them, and only such patriotic farmers as had laid by money for a rainy day or a grasshopper year could visit the Centennial Exposition.

Not all locusts are migratory or appear in such countless swarms as this invader from the high plateau of the northern Rocky Mountains. In South America another locust species, larger than ours, has similar habits; having its permanent breeding-grounds on the great plateau at the eastern foot of the Chilean Andes and descending almost every year in swarms on the great wheat-fields of Argentina. And in Algeria and Asia Minor occurs the migratory locust of the Scriptures, a still other and larger species. But of the 500 (app.) locust species, members of the family Acridiidæ, which are known in the United States but three or four can be fairly called migratory, and of these the Rocky Mountain locust, *Melanoplus spretus*, is the most conspicuous. The lesser migratory locust, *Melanoplus atlanis*, does much injury in New England and other eastern states, while the pellucid locust, *Camnula pellucida*, is a migratory species that often does much harm in California and other western states. Sometimes large bodies of immature wingless individuals of the large species *Dissosteira longipennis*, abundant on the plains of eastern Colorado and western Kansas will move slowly on, walking and hopping for many miles, eating every green weed and grass-blade in their path, but this is only a limited and local sort of migration.

Almost all the Acridiidæ, despite the many species in the family, are readily recognizable as locusts or grasshoppers — short-horned grasshoppers they may be called, to distinguish them from the meadow green grasshoppers with long thread-like antennæ—because of their general similarity in appearance and habit. The body is rather robust, the head is set with its long axis at right angles

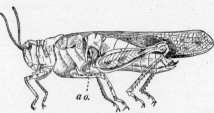

Fig. 165.—Locust from lateral aspect (left wings removed), showing (*ao.*) auditory organ. (Natural size.)

with the axis of the body, so that the mouth with its strong biting and crushing jaws is directed downwards (Fig. 165); the antennæ are never as long as the body and are composed of not more than twenty-five segments; the prothorax is covered laterally as well as dorsally by its large saddle-like horny pronotum, which projects so as also to cover and protect from the sharp grass-blades the soft thin-walled neck and the equally thin-walled suture between prothorax and mesothorax; the abdomen is broadly and closely joined to the metathorax, and in the female ends in a short and strong ovipositor composed of four horny pointed pieces; the hind legs are much larger than the others and fitted for leaping, and the fore wings, called tegmina, are narrow and straight-margined, and serve specially to cover and protect the much larger thin membranous hind wings, which are plaited and folded like a fan when the locust is at rest.

The sounds or stridulation of locusts are made in two ways. When at rest certain species draw the hind legs up and down across the wing-covers so that numerous fine little ridges on the inner surface of the broad femora are rasped across a thickened and ridged longitudinal vein on the outer surface of the wing-covers. When

Fig. 166.—Locust impaled on thorn by shrike (butcher-bird). (Natural size.)

in flight certain locusts rub or strike together the upper surface of the front edge of the hind wings and the under surface of the fore wings or tegmina. This produces a loud, sharp clacking which can be heard for a distance of several rods. The loudest "clacking" of this kind that I have heard is made by a species of Trimerotropis, abundant in the beautiful little glacial "parks" of the Colorado Rockies. Locusts undoubtedly make sounds to be heard by each other, and it is not difficult to find in them—a matter of more difficulty in most other insects—certain organs which are almost certainly auditory organs, or ears. On the outer faces of the upper part of the first abdominal segment is a pair of sub-

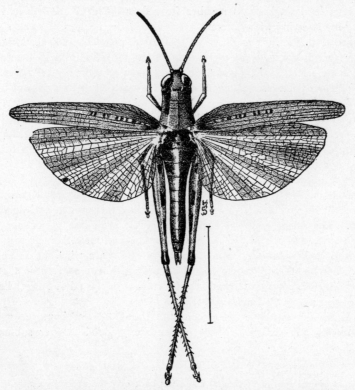

FIG. 167.—The red-legged locust, *Melanoplus femur-rubrum*, female.
(After Lugger; natural size indicated by line.)

circular clear window-like spots (Figs. 165 and 55). These are thin places in the body-wall serving as tympana; on the inner face of each is a small vesicle, and from it a tiny nerve runs to a small auditory ganglion (nerve-center) at one side of the tympanum. From this auditory ganglion a nerve runs to the large ventral ganglion in the third thoracic segment. Similar auditory organs are found in the other singing Orthoptera, the crickets and katydids, but situated in the front legs instead of on the back.

The life-history of all our locusts is, in general characteristics, very similar. The eggs are deposited in oval or bean-shaped packets enclosed in a glutinous substance. They are usually laid just below the surface of the soil, but in some cases are simply pushed to the ground among the stems of grasses, while a few locust-species thrust them into soft wood. The strong, horny ovipositor at the tip of the abdomen is worked into the ground, the four pieces separated, and the eggs and covering mucous material extruded. The eggs in a single mass number from twenty-five to one hundred and twenty-five, varying with different species, and the females of some species lay several masses. The different species also select different times and places for egg-laying, some ovipositing in the fall and some in the spring, while some select hard, gravelly, or sandy spots or well-traveled roads, and others choose pastures and meadows and the uncultivated margins of irrigation-ditches.

If the eggs are laid in the fall, the more usual case, they do not hatch until the following spring. The young hoppers are of course wingless, very small, and pale-colored, but they have the general body make-up of their parents, with the biting mouth and long-leaping hind legs. They push their way above ground and feed, as do the adults, on the green foliage of grasses, herbs, or trees, and in two or three months become full grown and mature, having moulted five or six times during this growth and developed wings. The wings begin to appear as minute scale-like projections from the posterior margins of the back of the meso- and meta-thoracic segments, and with each moulting are notably larger and more wing-like in appearance. During all this development the wing-pads are so rotated that the hinder wings (always underneath the fore wings in the adult locust) lie outside of and above the fore wings (Fig. 156).

The family Acridiidæ includes in the United States about 500 species, representing 107 genera. These genera are grouped in four subfamilies as follows:

### KEY TO SUBFAMILIES OF ACRIDIIDÆ.

Pronotum (dorsal wall of prothorax) extending back over the abdomen nearly or quite to its tip; tegmina (fore wings) short and scale-like..............TETTIGINÆ.

Pronotum not extending back over abdomen or only slightly; tegmina usually well developed (sometimes short or wanting).

    Prosternum (ventral aspect of prothorax) with a prominent thick conical or cylindrical spine....................................................................ACRIDIINÆ.

    Prosternum not spined (sometimes a short, oblique, inconspicuous, obtuse tubercle).

        Face very oblique ................................................TRYXALINÆ.

        Face nearly or quite vertical....................................ŒDIPODINÆ.

In the subfamily Acridiinæ the most conspicuous and economically important member is the Rocky Mountain or hateful migratory locust,

*Melanoplus spretus.* The invasions of the grain-growing Mississippi Valley states by this species have been already mentioned. In 1866, 1874, and 1876 such invasions occurred, and before these still others. "Kansas grass-hoppers" had gained a notoriety which spelled ruin to the state. But, strangely, these grasshoppers, or locusts, not only were not Kansas born, but could not even adopt Kansas as a home. The Rocky Mountain locust

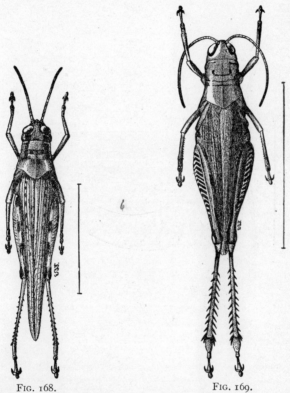

FIG. 168.                    FIG. 169.

FIG. 168.—The lesser migratory locust, *Melanoplus atlanis*, female. (After Lugger; natural size indicated by line.)
FIG. 169.—The differential locust, *Melanoplus differentialis*, female. (After Lugger; natural size indicated by line.)

has its permanent breeding-grounds on the plains and plateaus of Colorado, Idaho, Wyoming, Montana, and British Columbia, at an altitude of from 2000 to 10,000 feet above sea-level, and while able to maintain itself for a generation or two in the low, moist Mississippi Valley, cannot take up any permanent residence there. But in those days there were few ranches and farms on the great plains, and succulent corn and wheat were not at hand to feed the millions of young which hatched each spring. So, after exhausting the scanty wild herbage of their breeding-grounds, and developing to their winged stage, hosts of locusts would rise high into the air until they were caught by the great wind-streams bearing southeast, and, with parachute-like wings expanded and air-sacs in the body stretched to their fullest, would be borne for a thousand miles to the rich grain-fields of the

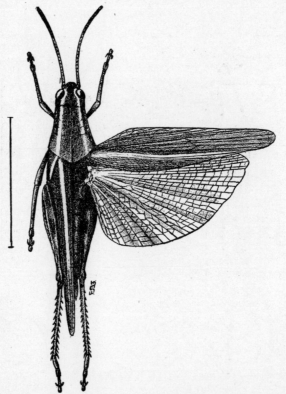

FIG. 170.—The two-striped locust, *Melanoplus bivittatus*, female.
(After Lugger; natural size indicated by line.)

Mississippi Valley. As far east as the middle of Iowa and Missouri and south to Texas these great swarms would spread; and once settled to ground and started at their chief business, that of eating, not a green thing escaped. First the grains and grasses; then the vegetables and bushes; then the leaves and fresh twigs and bark of trees! A steady munching was audible over the doomed land! And this munching was the devouring of dollars. Fifty millions of dollars were eaten in the seasons of 1874–76 alone.

Remedies there were practically none; when the summer hosts laid their eggs in the ground for the one generation that could be reared in the invaded land, these eggs could be plowed up, a remedy that is used with much success in the far western locust-infested states; also when the wingless young "hoppers" appeared in the spring they could be crushed by heavy

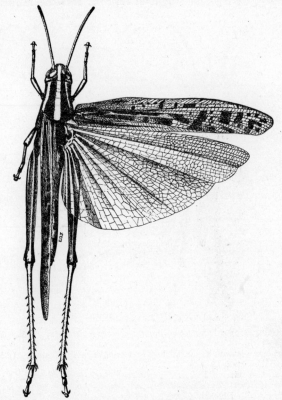

Fig. 171.—The American locust, *Schistocerca americana*, female.
(After Lugger; natural size.)

rollers drawn across the fields by horses, or burned by scattering straw over the helpless host and lighting it. Both of these remedies are also used in western locust-fighting. But against the winged adults there is little that can be done.

In Asia and South America, where there are also migratory locusts (of different, much larger species) the natives sometimes try to frighten away an alighting swarm by smoke and noise, but such a swarm as that which passed over the Red Sea in November, 1889, spread out for over 2000 square miles in area, would be little affected by a bonfire. In Cyprus in 1881, 1300 tons of locust-eggs were destroyed; how many eggs go to make a ton one can only faintly conceive of.

There has been no serious Rocky Mountain locust invasion of the Mississippi Valley since 1876, and there will probably never be another. The locust is being both fed and fought in its own breeding range; many are

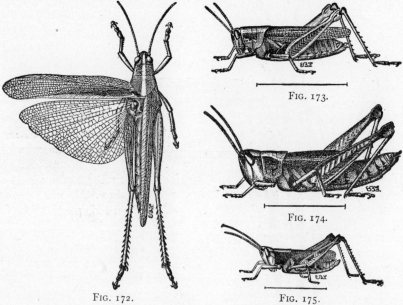

Fig. 172.

Fig. 173.

Fig. 174.

Fig. 175.

FIG. 172.—The emarginate locust, *Schistocerca emarginata*, male.  (After Lugger; natural size.)

FIG. 173.—The pale-green locust, *Hesperotettix pratensis*, female.  (After Lugger; natural size indicated by line.)

FIG. 174.—The short-winged locust, *Stenobothrus curtipennis*, female.  (After Lugger; natural size indicated by line.)

FIG. 175.—The sprinkled locust, *Chlœaltis conspersa*, male.  (After Lugger; natural size indicated by line.)

killed every year, and for those that are left there is food enough and to spare in the great grain-fields of the northwest plains.

The genus Melanoplus, to which the Rocky Mountain locust belongs, is the largest of all our Acridiid genera, one hundred and twenty species found in the United States belonging to it.  Of these species a very common one all over the country is the red-legged locust, *Melanoplus femur-rubrum* (Fig. 167), which is about one inch long, with olivaceous brownish body, clear hind wings and brownish fore wings that have an inconspicuous longitudinal median series of black spots in the basal half (these spots sometimes wanting). The hind tibiæ are normally red (sometimes yellow-ish), hence the name, although these red hind legs are common to many other locust species. The lesser migratory locust, *M. atlanis* (Fig. 168), is a species of about the same size and appearance which sometimes appears in great swarms and does much injury to crops. The largest species of the genus is *M. differentialis* (Fig. 169), over an inch and a half long, with brownish-yellow body, fore wings without spots, and hind wings clear. It is common in the Southwest, where, in company with *M. bivittatus* (Fig. 170), nearly as large but readily distinguished by the pair of longitudinal

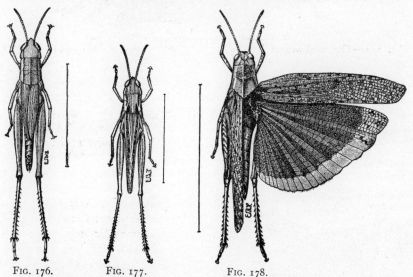

FIG. 176.          FIG. 177.                    FIG. 178.

FIG. 176.—The short-winged green locust, *Dichromorpha viridis*, female. (After Lugger; natural size indicated by line.)

FIG. 177.—The spotted-winged locust, *Orphula pelidina*. (After Lugger; natural size of male 16–19 mm., of female, 20–24 mm.)

FIG. 178.—The Carolina locust, *Dissosteira carolina*, female. (After Lugger; natural size indicated by line.)

pale-yellowish stripes extending from the head across the thorax and along the folded wing-covers nearly to their tips, it often becomes sufficiently abundant to do serious injury. These two species are always to be found commonly in western Kansas, and *bivittatus* ranges far to the north, being one of Minnesota's destructive species.

Among the other genera of the subfamily Acridiinæ Schistocerca is conspicuous because of the large size and wide distribution of its species. The American locust, *S. americana* (Fig. 171), measures three inches from head to tips of tegmina, with reddish-brown body and a longitudinal yellowish strip extending along the head, thorax, and closed tegmina nearly to their tips. The tegmina are opaque and reddish at base, subtransparent distally; the great hind wings arc clear and transparent. This locust is common in the South, where it sometimes assumes a migratory habit and becomes very injurious to crops. The leather-colored locust, *S. alutaceum*, with dirty brownish-yellow body and paler stripe on top of head and thorax,

Fig. 179.—The coral-winged locust, *Hippiscus tuberculatus,* female. (After Lugger; natural size indicated by line.)

semi-transparent tegmina, and clear transparent hind wings, and the rusty locust, *S. rubiginosum*, with light dust-red body and opaque tegmina, are the common eastern representatives of this genus. Both are large and striking forms.

The subfamily Tryxalinæ includes a number of locusts distinguished by the sharp oblique sloping of the face, and in some cases by the much prolonged and pointed vertex (region of the head between the eyes). In

Fig. 180.— Young coral-winged locust, *Hippiscus tuberculatus.* (After Lugger; natural size indicated by line.)

the East the short-winged locust, *Stenobothrus curtipennis* (Fig. 174), recognizable by its short narrow wings, yellow under-body, and prominent yellowish hind legs with black knees, is a common example of this group. It likes to hide among tall grasses, where its sprightly tumbling and dodging usually save it from capture despite its poor flying and leaping powers. The sprinkled locust, *Chlœaltis conspersa* (Fig. 175), is an abundant species throughout the East. It is light reddish brown sprinkled with black spots, and has pale yellowish-brown tegmina with many small dark-brown spots, the wings being clear; it is about three-fourths of an inch long. The males have the sides of the pronotum shining black. This locust lays its eggs in rotten stumps or other slightly decayed wood. Blatchley discovered a female in the act of boring a hole for her eggs in the upper edge of the topmost board of a six-rail fence. One of the most grotesque of all the locusts is a member of this subfamily named *Achurum brevipenne*. The body is very long and thin, measuring an inch and a half in length by one-tenth of an inch wide in the broadest part; the head is pointed and projects far forward and upward, the face being very oblique. The wings are short and the body color brown. Comstock found this locust quite common in Florida on the "wire-grass" which grows in the sand among the saw-palmettoes, and "so closely did their brown linear bodies resemble dry grass that it was very difficult to perceive them." So the grotesqueness has its use.

The subfamily Œdipodinæ is well represented in the United States,

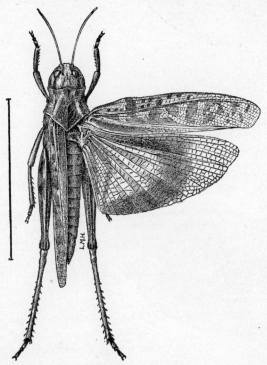

FIG. 181.—*Hippiscus tigrinus*, female. (After Lugger; nat. size indicated by line.)

containing twenty-four genera and about 140 species. Almost all the familiar locusts with showy colored hind wings belong to this subfamily. One of the commonest species all over the United States and Canada is the Carolina locust, *Dissosteira carolina* (Fig. 178), easily recognized by its black hind wings with broad yellow or yellowish-white margin covered with dusky spots at the tip. Its body color is pale yellowish or reddish brown, and it measures 1½–2 inches in length. It flies well; the males have the habit of hovering in the air a few feet above the ground and making a loud "clacking."  The species of Hippiscus are heavy, broad-bodied forms

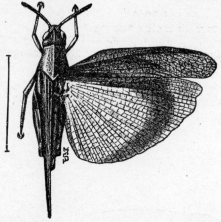

with wings reddish or yellowish at base, then a broad blackish band, and the apex and margin clear.  The fore wings and body are yellowish to brown, with darker blotches and speckles.  *H. discoideus*, with wings red on basal half, is common in the East.  *H. tuberculatus* (Figs. 179 and 180), the coral-winged locust, or king grasshopper, also with red wing-disks, is common in the Mississippi Valley; it makes a very loud rattling while in the air.  The genus Arphia, also characterized by wings with bright red or yellowish disks but having the fore wings without large spots or blotches, usually not even speckled, and with the body slenderer than in Hippiscus, comprises about twenty species scattered over the whole country.  *A. xanthoptera*, with plain smoky brown fore wings and upper body, and hind wings with bright yellow disk, broad smoky outer band and clearer apex, is common in the East; *A. tenebrosa* (Fig. 183), with brown and clayey-speckled fore wings and upper body and hind wings with coral-red disk and smoky broad outer band fading out in apex, is common in the West.  The green-striped locust, *Chortophaga*

FIG. 182.—The yellow-winged locust, *Arphia sulphurea*.  (After Lugger; natural size of male 23–26 mm., of female 28–30 mm.)

FIG. 183.—*Arphia tenebrosa*.  (After Lugger; natural size indicated by line.)

*viridifasciata* (Figs. 184 and 185), abundant and familiar in the East and Mississippi Valley, appears in two forms; in one, the head, thorax, and

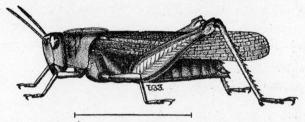

Fig. 184.—The green-striped locust, *Chortophaga viridifasciata*, form *virginiana*, female.
(After Lugger; natural size indicated by line.)

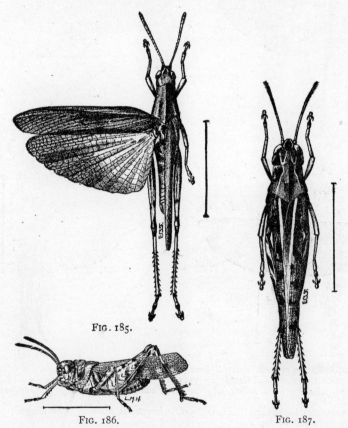

Fig. 185.

Fig. 186.

Fig. 187.

Fig. 185.—The green-striped locust, *Chortophaga viridifasciata*, form *virginiana*, male.
(After Lugger; natural size indicated by line.)

Fig. 186.—The clouded locust, *Encoptolophus sordidus*, male. (After Lugger; natural size indicated by line.)

Fig. 187.—The pellucid locust, *Camnula pellucida*, female. (After Lugger; natural size indicated by line.)

femora are green and there is a broad green stripe on each wing-cover; the other form is dusky brown all over; both are about 1 inch (male) to 1¼ inches (female) long, and have a distinct sharp little median crest on the

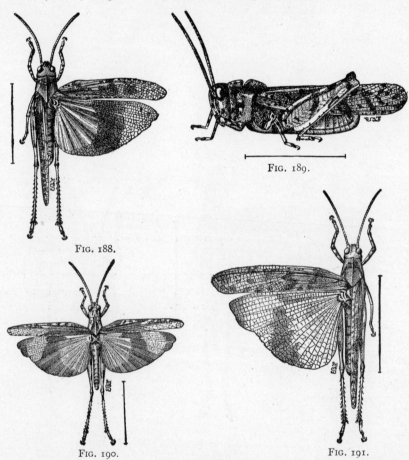

FIG. 189.

FIG. 188.

FIG. 190.

FIG. 191.

FIG. 188.—Barren-ground locust, *Spharagemon bolli*, male. (After Lugger; natural size of male 20–22 mm., of female 27–33 mm.)

FIG. 189.—*Spharagemon collare*, race *scudderi*, male. (After Lugger; natural size indicated by line.)

FIG. 190.—The long-horned locust, *Psinidia fenestralis*, male. (After Lugger; natural size indicated by line.)

FIG. 191.—*Circotettix verruculatus*, male. (After Lugger; natural size indicated by line.)

pronotum. The clouded locust, *Encoptolophus sordidus* (Fig. 186), is another species very common in the fall; it is about an inch long, dusky brown mottled with darker spots; the wing-covers are blotched and the wings clear and transparent; the prothorax looked at from above appears to be "pinched" at its middle. The males make a loud crackling when in the air.

It is familiar knowledge that locusts which are readily seen in the air are extremely difficult to distinguish when alighted. This concealment, resulting from a harmonizing of the body color with that of the grass or soil, is of course an advantage to the locust in its "struggle for existence" and is technically known as protective resemblance (see Chapter XVII). No locusts show this protective resemblance better than the species of Trimerotropis (Fig. 193) especially familiar in the western states. The colors of various individuals of a single species vary with the soil colors of the locality, ranging from whitish to brownish to slaty and bluish. I have taken series of specimens of *Trimerotropis* sp. in Colorado showing this whole range of ground coloration.

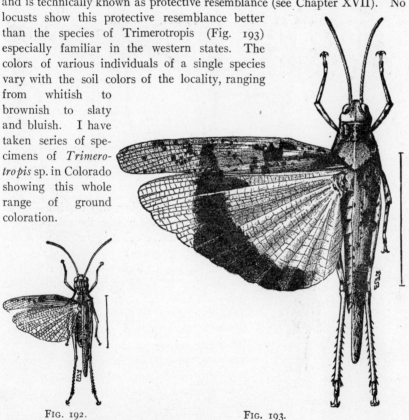

FIG. 192.                    FIG. 193.

FIG. 192.—*Mestobregma cincta*, male. (After Lugger; natural size indicated by line.)
FIG. 193.—The maritime locust, *Trimerotropis maritima*, female. (After Lugger; natural size indicated by line.)

The subfamily Tettiginæ includes the strange little Acridiids known as "grouse-locusts." They are all under $\frac{2}{3}$ inch in length, and most of them are less than $\frac{1}{2}$ inch. They have the wing-covers reduced to mere scales, but the pronotum is so long that it extends back over the rest of the thorax to the abdomen and more or less covers it. In some species the pronotum actually extends beyond the tip of the abdomen. The head is deeply set in the prothorax, the prosternum being expanded into a broad border which nearly covers the mouth. As all the grouse-locusts are dark-colored and without any conspicuous markings, and choose for habitat the dark ground along streams and ponds, or swampy meadows, they are

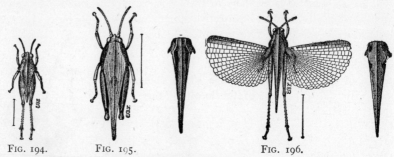

FIG. 194.　　　FIG. 195.　　　　　　　　　FIG. 196.

FIG. 194.—*Nomotettix parvus.* (After Lugger; natural size indicated by line.)
FIG. 195.—*Tettigidea lateralis.* (After Lugger; natural size indicated by line.)
FIG. 196.—*Tettix granulatus,* and pronota of two varieties. (After Lugger; natural size indicated by line.)

infrequently seen except by persistent students. They vary much in coloration and slight markings, and harmonize thoroughly with the soil on which they habitually live. They feed on lichens, moulds, germinating seeds, and sprouting grasses, and are said to eat surface mud and muck containing or largely consisting of decaying vegetable matter. The eggs are laid in a pear-shaped mass in a shallow burrow; in May and June the young hatch in from sixteen to twenty-five days, becoming mature in late fall, or sometimes not until the following spring. The nymphs and adults hibernate, becoming active again early in spring. A common species is *Tettix granulatus* (Fig. 196), slender, length about $\frac{1}{2}$ inch, and with the narrow pointed pronotum extending beyond the abdomen. This species hibernates among rubbish and loose bark, but is more or less active on warm winter days. It is plentiful all through the rest of the year

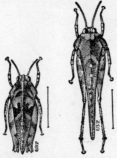

FIG. 197.　　　FIG. 198.

FIG. 197.—*Tettix ornatus.* (After Lugger; natural size indicated by line.)
FIG. 198.—*Paratettix cucullatus.* (After Lugger; natural size indicated by line.)

on its feeding-grounds. *T. ornatus* (Fig. 197) is a shorter, more robust species, and is marked with black spots and indefinite yellow blotches as indicated in the figure. In the genus Tettigidea the antennæ have from 15 to 22 segments, while in Tettix they have only 12 to 14 segments. *Tettigidea lateralis* (Fig. 195) is a common species yellowish brown in color, more yellowish underneath. It is rather robust and the pronotum extends beyond the tip of the abdomen.

Included in the family Locustidæ are katydids, meadow grasshoppers, cave-crickets, wingless crickets, western crickets, Jerusalem crickets, and what not, but no locusts. The general reader of natural history should

always keep clearly in mind the sharp distinction made by naturalists between "scientific" and "vernacular" names. The vernacular name locust is applied to insects of the family Acridiidæ, but not to any of the members of the family whose scientific name is Locustidæ. Of the Locustids the best known representatives are undoubtedly the katydids. Anna Botsford Comstock, the naturestudy teacher of Cornell University, introduces them to her readers as follows: "The chances are that he who lies awake of a midsummer night must listen, whether he wishes to do so or not, to an oftrepeated, rasping song that says, 'Katy did, Katy did; she did, she didn't,' over and over again. There is no use of wondering what Katy did or didn't do, for no mortal will ever know. If, when the dawn comes, the listener has eyes sharp enough to discern one of

FIG. 199.—Broad-winged katydid, and leaf with katydid eggs along edge. (Natural size.)

these singers among the leaves of some neighboring tree, never a note of explanation will he get. The beautiful, finely veined wings folded close over the body keep the secret hidden, and the long antennæ, looking like threads of living silk, will wave airily above the droll green eyes as much as to say, 'Wouldn't you like to know?'"

The katydids are rather large, almost always green insects that live in trees and shrubs, where they feed upon the leaves and tender twigs, sometimes doing considerable injury. With almost all the other Locustids, they will also take animal food if accessible, and some of the ground-inhabiting forms undoubtedly depend largely on animal substances for food. The color and form of the wing-covers and body serve to make them nearly indistinguishable in the foliage, and as they do not flock together in numbers, they are not frequently seen. Their love-calls or songs, however, make the welkin ring at night from midsummer until the coming of frost. Few katydids sing by day: it would bring their enemies, the birds, down on them; but as twilight approaches, the males begin their shrilling, which is kept up almost constantly till daylight. Like the sound-making Acridiids the musical Locustids have a pair of special auditory organs, or ears, for hearing these love-songs. These ears are tympanal organs situated one in the base of each fore tibia (the Acridiid ears are on the upper part of the first abdominal segment), and consist of a thin place in the chitinized body-wall (the tympanum), a resonance-chamber inside, and a special arrangement of nerves and ganglia. There are several genera of these Locustids, corresponding to the distinctions popularly made under the vernacular names narrow-winged, round-winged, angular-winged, oblong leaf-winged, and broad-winged katydids. The true katydid is one of the last-named forms, the commonest and most wide-spread species being *Crytophyllus concavus* (Fig. 200).

Fig. 200.—Broad-winged katydid, *Cyrtophyllus concavus*, male. (After Harris; natural size.)

It is bright dark-green, and is rarely distinguished when at rest in the foliage, although familiar to all from its shrill singing. When specimens of katydids are collected and examined, *concavus* may be readily distinguished by the fact that its wings are shorter than the wing-covers, and these latter are very convex and so curved around the body that their edges meet above and below. The ovipositor of the female is short, compressed, slightly curved and pointed. This katydid is most in evidence in late summer. People disagree about the melody and alleged charm of the song. Many cannot distinguish the "katydid" syllables, and Scudder, an experienced student of the Orthoptera, says that the note, which sounds like *xr*, has a shocking lack of melody, adding that the poets who have sung its praises must have heard it at the distance that lends enchantment. The sounds are made by the males exclusively, and result from the rubbing together of the bases of the wing-covers, which have the veins and membrane specially modified for this purpose (see Fig. 201). *Concavus* lays, in the autumn, flattened dark slate-colored eggs, about ⅛ inch long and one-third as wide, in two rows along a twig, the eggs overlapping a little. These eggs hatch in the following spring, and the young, like the adults, feed on the foliage of the tree.

Fig. 201.—*Cyrtophyllus concavus* sp.

The oblong leaf-winged and round-winged katydids belong to the genus Amblycorypha, and they can be readily recognized by the broad, oblong, and rounded wing-covers, and the strongly curved ovipositor of the female, with serrated tip. They are grass-green and have the wings longer than the wing-covers. The oblong leaf-winged species, *A. oblongifolia* (Fig. 202),

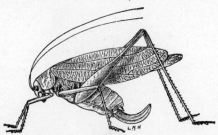

Fig. 202.—The oblong leaf-winged katydid, *Amblycorypha oblongifolia*, female. (After Lugger; natural size.)

is 2 inches long to tips of folded wings, while the round-winged species, *A. rotundifolia*, is 1½ inches or less in length. These katydids prefer bushes and tall weeds or even grass-clumps to tree-tops. *Oblongifolia* is said by McNeill to make a "quick shuffling sound which resembles 'katy' or 'katydid' very slightly," while the song of *rotundifolia* is said by Scudder to be made both day and night without variation and to consist of two to four notes, sounding like *chic-a-chee*, run together and repeated generally, once in about five seconds for an indefinite length of time.

Fig. 203.—Angular-winged katydid, *Microcentrum laurifolium*, male. (After Riley; natural size.)

The angular-winged katydids, genus Microcentrum, are large, numerous, and the most familiarly known of all.  The best-known species, *M. retinervis*, is over 2 inches long (from head to tip of folded wings); the overlapping dorsal parts of the wing-covers form a conspicuous angle with the lateral parts, hence the name "angular-winged."  The ovipositor of the female is very short, strongly curved, and with a bluntly pointed, finely serrate tip.  The song of *M. laurifolium* (Fig. 203) is said to sound like *tic* repeated from eight to twenty times, at the rate of four a second.  The eggs, of which each female lays from 100 to 150 in the fall, are grayish brown, flat, and long-oval, about ¼ inch long by ⅛ inch wide, and are glued in double rows along twigs or on the edges of leaves (Fig. 199).  I have found them on thorns of the honey-locust, and Howard once received "a batch from a western correspondent which was found on the edge of a freshly laundried collar which had lain for some time in a bureau drawer."  The rows are side by side, and the flat eggs overlap each other in their own row.  The young hatch in spring and, slowly growing, moulting, and developing wings, reach full size and maturity by the middle of the summer.

FIG. 204a.                                        FIG. 204b.

FIG. 204a.—The fork-tailed katydid, *Scudderia furcata*, female.  (After Lugger;  nat. size.)
FIG. 204b.—The fork-tailed katydid, *Scudderia furcata*, male.  (After Lugger;  nat. size.)

The narrow-winged katydids, belonging to the genus Scudderia (Figs. 204–206), are smaller than the broader-winged kinds, being not more than 1½ inches in length to tip of folded wing-covers, and the wing-covers are narrow and of nearly equal width for their whole length.  The ovipositor is broad,

FIG. 205.                                        FIG. 206.

FIG. 205.—*Scudderia pistillata*, female.  (After Lugger;  natural size.)
FIG. 206.—*Scudderia pistillata*, male.  (After Lugger;  natural size.)

compressed, and curves sharply upward.  These insects frequent shrubbery and bushes, or coarse grasses and weeds along ravines or ponds;  also marshes, cranberry-bogs, and similar wet places.  Their flight is noiseless and zigzag, and when pursued they will take to the lower branches of trees, especially oaks if near by. The males sing somewhat in daytime as well as at night, and have different calls for the two times. The females lay their eggs in the edges of leaves, thrusting them in between the upper and lower cuticle by means of their flattened and pointed ovipositor.

While almost all katydids are green, a few exceptions are known. Scudder has found certain pink individuals belonging to a species normally green. In mountain regions a few species of gray- or granite-colored katy-

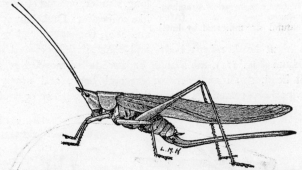

Fig. 207.—The sword-bearer, *Conocephalus ensiger*, female. (After Lugger; nat. size.)

dids are known, the color here being quite as protective as the green of the lowland forms, for these mountain species alight to rest on the granite rocks of the mountainside. I have found these granite katydids in the Sierra Nevada of California.

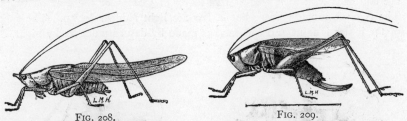

Fig. 208.                          Fig. 209.

Fig. 208.—The sword-bearer, *Conocephalus ensiger*, male. (After Lugger; nat. size.)
Fig. 209.—A common meadow grasshopper, *Orchelimum vulgare*, female. (After Lugger; natural size indicated by line.)

The meadow grasshoppers are small, katydid-like Locustids, green and long-winged, with long, slender hind legs and with the characteristic slender thread-like antennæ longer than the body. These antennæ readily distinguish them from any of the locusts (Acridiidæ) which may be found in their company. The meadow green grasshoppers abound in pastures and meadows, and they dislike to take to wing, trusting, when alarmed, to spry leaping or clever wriggling away and hiding among the lush grasses. Their green color of course aids very much in protecting them from enemies. They

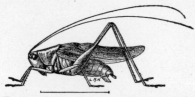

include three common genera, viz.: Conocephalus (Figs. 207 and 208), or cone-headed grasshoppers or sword-bearers with head produced into a long, pointed, forward-projecting, cone-like process, slender body, and very long, slender, straight or angled, sword-like ovipositor; Orchelimum (Figs. 209 and 210), the stout meadow grasshop-

FIG. 210.—A common meadow grasshopper, *Orchelimum vulgare*, male. (After Lugger; natural size indicated by line.)

pers, with blunt head, robust body, and short, slightly curved ovipositor; and Xiphidium (Fig. 211), the slender or lance-tailed meadow grasshoppers, with blunt head, small and slender, graceful body, and nearly straight, slender ovipositor, sometimes larger than the body.   The eggs of all these

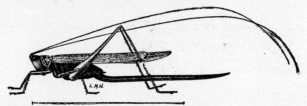

FIG. 211.—The lance-tailed grasshopper, *Xiphidium attenuatum*, female. (After Lugger; natural size indicated by line.)

are laid usually in the stems or root-leaves of grasses, or the pith of twigs. The color is usually green, but a few are light reddish brown.   The song of the males is faint and soft, and is made by day as much as by night.

FIG. 212.
FIG. 213.

FIG. 212.—*Udeopsylla robusta*, female. (After Lugger; nat. size indicated by line.)
FIG. 213.—The spotted wingless grasshopper, *Ceutophilus maculatus*, female. (After Lugger; natural size indicated by line.)

The family Locustidæ includes numerous wingless forms, some with no remaining trace of wing-covers or wings, some with rudimentary or scale-like remnants of wing-covers. These latter kinds can sing because the parts retained are the sound-producing bases of the wing-covers. The genus

Fig. 214.—*Diestrammena marmorata*, male; a Japanese locust species found in Minnesota. (After Lugger; natural size.)

Ceuthophilus (Figs. 213 and 215) includes the various species of stone, or camel, crickets found all over the country, recognizable by their thick,

Fig. 215.—*Ceuthophilus lapidicolus*, female. (After Lugger; natural size indicated by line.)

smooth, wholly wingless, brownish body with arched back and head bent downwards and backwards between the front legs. They are nocturnal,

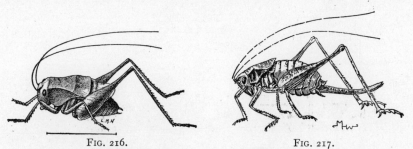

Fig. 216.                              Fig. 217.

Fig. 216.—The shield-backed grasshopper, *Atlanticus pachymerus*, male. (After Lugger; natural size indicated by line.)

Fig. 217.—The California shield-backed grasshopper, *Tropizaspis* sp., female. (Nat. size )

and during the day hide under stones or logs along streams or in damp woods. The individuals of a species which live in the burrows of certain turtles in Florida are called "gophers." Perhaps the commonest species, extending from New England to the Rocky Mountains, is the "spotted wingless grasshopper," *C. maculatus* (Fig. 213), with sooty brown body dotted with pale spots. Some of the wingless Locustids are found in caves, and these are either blind or have the eyes much reduced. One of these cave-crickets, *Hadœnucus subterraneus*, is common in the larger caves of Kentucky, where it may be found creeping about on the walls. Garman states that it speedily dies when removed from the cave. The genus Atlanticus comprises dull-

Fig. 218.—The western cricket, *Anabrus purpurascens*, male. (After Lugger; nat. size.)

colored species with the pronotum extending like a shield back over the base of the abdomen, and although the hind wings are wanting, rudimentary wing-covers are present, and in the males carry a circular stridulating organ. These are called "shield-backed grasshoppers" and are to be found in dry upland woods and on sloping hillsides with sunny exposure. The two common species in the East and the Mississippi Valley are *A. dorsalis*, with pronotum well rounded behind, and *A. pachymerus* (Fig. 216), with pronotum nearly square.

A genus similar to Atlanticus found commonly in California is Tropizaspis (Fig. 217), the males

Fig. 219.                              Fig. 220.

Fig. 219.—The western cricket, *Anabrus purpurascens*, female. (After Lugger; natural size.)
Fig. 220.—The Jerusalem cricket, *Stenopelmatus* sp. (Natural size.)

of which sing very pleasantly. In Idaho and other northwestern states a large corpulent wingless Locustid, called the western cricket, *Anabrus purpurascens* (Figs. 218 and 219), often occurs in such numbers as to be very destructive to crops. The body of this cricket is 1½ inches long and ½ inch thick. The ovipositor is three-fourths as long as the body, slightly curved, and sword-shaped with a sharp point. This species forms marching armies in Nevada, with two miles of front and a thousand feet of depth. On the Pacific Coast occurs a large, awkward, thick-legged, transversely striped form, Stenopelmatus, called sand-cricket or Jerusalem cricket (Fig. 220). It is found under stones or in the soil, has a large smooth head with "baby-face," and is believed to feed on dead plant or animal matter.

The crickets that we know best are the black and brown ones of the house and the fields; but there are members of the cricket family, the Gryllidæ, that live in trees and are pale greenish white, and others that burrow into the ground and have broad shovel-like fore feet, and still other curious little wingless pygmies that live as guests in ants' nests. But the house- and field-crickets represent

FIG. 221. — A common cricket, *Gryllus pennsylvanicus*, female. (After Lugger; natural size indicated by line.)

the more usual or we might say normal and typical kind of Gryllid; the others are modifications or offshoots of this type, both in habit and structure. In all the antennæ are long and slender (except in the burrowing forms, longer than the body), the hind legs long and thickened for leaping, and the ovipositor, when exserted and visible, long, slender, subcylindrical and lance- or spear-like. Well-developed wings and wing-covers are present in most species, and the males are provided with a very effective stridulating organ on the bases of the wing-covers.

FIG. 222.—Cricket and file (part of the sound-making apparatus). (Cricket natural size; the file greatly magnified.)

In the familiar black, bright-eyed, loud-voiced house- and field-crickets the wing-covers when folded on the body are flat above and bent down sharply at the edge of the body like a box-cover, and the veins in the males are curiously changed in course and specially thickened and roughened to make a sound-producing organ. This organ is illustrated in Fig. 222.

To sing, the males lift their wing-covers at an angle of about 45° over the back, and strongly rub together the bases. Their chirping is made either in the daytime or night, and is a love call or song for their mates. We have several common crickets in dwellings, one, *Gryllus domesticus* (Fig. 223),

being the European house-cricket, the "cricket on the hearth," which is becoming at home here, being especially met with in Canada. It is pale brown and less than an inch long. *Gryllus luctuosus* and *G. assimilis* are two native crickets which are common in houses; they are black with brownish-black wing-covers, larger and more robust than *domesticus*, and with the folded wings projecting backward beyond the wing-covers like pointed tails. These house-crickets are most active at night, and seem to have a taste for almost any food-product in the house. They will eat each other when other food is scarce. If they become so numerous in the house that they need to be got rid of, advantage may be taken of their liking for sweet liquids by exposing smooth-walled vessels half filled with such liquids, into which the crickets will fall and drown in their attempts to get at the food. The most abundant and wide-spread outdoors cricket is *Gryllus abbreviatus* (Fig. 224), the short-winged field-cricket. The wings are sometimes wanting, but more often present and shorter than the wing-covers, which in the females are themselves

Fig. 223.—The European house-cricket, *Gryllus domesticus*, female. (After Lugger; natural size indicated by line.)

unusually short, reaching but half-way to the end of the abdomen. The slender ovipositor is as long as the body, and the hind femora are very thick and have a red spot at the base on either side. The life-history of this common insect is not yet fully known, some writers stating that the eggs laid in autumn do not hatch until the following spring, the insect thus passing the winter in the egg stage, while others have taken half-grown

Fig. 224.—The short-winged cricket, *Gryllus abbreviatus*. (Natural size.)

young from beneath logs in late autumn and in midwinter. The field-cricket is "nocturnal, omnivorous, and a cannibal. Avoiding the light of day," says Blatchley, "he ventures forth as soon as darkness has fallen, in search of food, and all appears to be fish which comes to his net. Of fruit, vegetables, grass, and carrion he seems equally fond, and does not hesitate to prey upon a weaker brother when opportunity offers. I have often surprised them feasting on the bodies of their companions; and of about forty imprisoned together in a box, at the end of a week but six were living. The heads, wings, and legs of their dead companions were all that remained to show that the weaker had succumbed to the stronger—that the fittest, and in this case the fattest, had survived in the deadly struggle for existence."

These crickets live in cracks in the soil, or under stones or logs, or sometimes make burrows.

The genus Nemobius contains a number of little crickets known as "striped ground-crickets," which are less than half an inch long, are dusky brownish with hairy head and thorax, and have faint blackish longitudinal stripes on the head. "Unlike their larger cousins, the field-crickets, they do not wait for darkness before seeking their food, but wherever the grass has been cropped short, whether on shaded hillside in the full glare of the noonday sun along the beaten roadway, mature specimens may be seen by hundreds during the days of early autumn." They are powerful jumpers and readily evade attempts to capture them. They feed on living vegetation

Fig. 225.—The small striped ground-cricket, *Nemobius fasciatus;* form *vittatus,* female. (After Lugger; about twice natural size.)

Fig. 226.—The snowy tree-cricket, *Œcanthus niveus.* (Natural size.)

and on all kinds of decaying animal matter, and because of their abundance and voracious appetite must do much damage at times. Scudder gives the following account of the singing of the wingless striped cricket, *Nemobius vittatus* (Fig. 225), our commonest species: "The chirping of the striped cricket is very similar to that of the black field-cricket, and may be expressed by *r-r-r-u,* pronounced as though it were a French word. The note is trilled forcibly, and lasts a variable length of time. One of these insects was once observed while singing to its mate. At first the song was mild and frequently broken; afterwards it grew impetuous, forcible, and more prolonged; then it decreased in volume and extent until it became quite soft and feeble. At this point the male began to approach the female, uttering a series of twittering chirps; the female ran away, and the male, after a short chase, returned to his old haunt, singing with the same vigor, but

Fig. 227.—*Œcanthus fasciatus,* female. (After Lugger; natural size indicated by line.)

with more frequent pauses. At length finding all persuasions unavailing, he brought his serenade to a close."

From midsummer till frost comes there is a shrill insistent night-song that makes familiar an insect rarely seen except by persistent students. *T-r-r—r-e-e; t-r-r—r-e-e*, repeated without pause or variation about seventy times a minute: this is the song of the snowy tree-cricket, or white climbing cricket, *Œcantheus niveus* (Fig. 226), common all through the East and Middle West. These crickets differ much from the better known robust, black-brown house- and field-crickets in shape and color; the body is about one-half inch long, slender, and the long wing-covers are so held, when the insect is at rest, that the back (including the wing-covers) is widest behind and tapers forward to the small narrow head. The body is ivory-white tinged with delicate green, and the wing-covers and wings are clear. The antennæ are extremely long and thread-like and have two slightly elevated black dots on the under side, one on the first segment and one on the second. The females do much harm by their habit of cutting slits in the tender canes or shoots of raspberry, grape, plum, peach, for their eggs. The cane or shoot often breaks off at the place where the eggs are deposited, and by collecting these in the late autumn or winter and burning them many eggs will be destroyed. Several other species of Œcanthus are found in this country; one, *O. fasciatus* (Figs. 227 and 228), with three black stripes on head and prothorax and usually dark body, is common in the Mississippi Valley, and a third species, *O. angustipennis*, with wing-covers just one-third as wide in broadest part as their length, is less common.

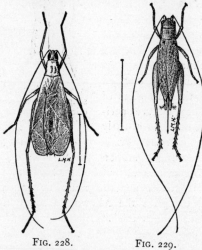

FIG. 228.          FIG. 229.

FIG. 228.—*Œcanthus fasciatus*, male. (After Lugger; natural size indicated by line.)
FIG. 229.—*Orocharis saltator*, female. (After Lugger; natural size indicated by line.)

Occasionally one finds on the ground, or more likely in digging, a curious flattened, light velvety brown insect about an inch and a half long, with the fore feet much widened and strangely resembling those of the common mole, and altogether having an appearance strange and unlike that of any other insect. This is a burrowing, or mole, cricket, which burrows beneath the soil in search of such food as the tender roots of plants, earthworms, and the larvæ of various insects. Its eyes are also like those of the mole, much reduced, being nearly lost, and as this cricket crawls rather than leaps, the hind or leaping legs are not so disproportionately larger than the others as in the above-ground crickets. The males make a sharp chirping loud enough to be heard several rods away. The common species, called the northern mole-cricket, *Gryllotalpa borealis*, has the wing-covers less than half the length of the abdomen, while the wings extend only about one-sixth of an inch beyond them. A less common species, *G. columbia*, the long-winged mole-cricket, has the hind wings extending beyond the tip of the abdomen. The mole-crickets like rather damp places near ponds or streams, where they make channels with raised ridges which resemble miniature mole-hills. These "runs" usually end beneath a stone or small stick. The insects are infrequently seen, as they remain mostly underground, only occasionally coming out at night. The female deposits from two hundred to three hundred eggs in masses of from forty to sixty in underground chambers, and the young are about three years in reaching maturity. When present in any region in large numbers mole-crickets become seriously destructive because of their attacks on plant-roots. In Porto Rico a mole-cricket, *Scapteriscus didactylus* (Fig. 230), called "changa," damages tobacco, sugar-cane, and small crops to the value of more than $100,000 annually and is by far the most serious insect pest in the island.

Fig. 230. — The Porto Rican mole-cricket, *Scapteriscus didactylus.* (After Barrett; natural size.)

Fig. 231.—*Tridactylus apicalis.* (After Lugger; natural size indicated by line.)

Much smaller than the true mole-crickets are the pygmy, burrowing crickets of the genus Tridactylus, of which several species occur in the United States. The largest species, *T. apicalis* (Fig. 231), is about ⅓ inch long. They resemble the mole-crickets in general body characters, but are more brightly colored, and the fore feet, although broad and flat for digging, differ in being curiously armed at the end with three spurs; hence the generic name. They can leap amazingly, so that they seem, on jumping, to disappear most mysteriously, the eye not being able to follow them in the air.

The most aberrant of all the crickets are the tiny flat and broad-bodied species of the genus Myrmecophila, which live as commensals or mess-mates in the nests of ants. They are found only in ants' nests, have no compound eyes, and the hind femora are much swollen and enlarged.

The semi-parasitic life which they lead has resulted in such a change of habits that their body is modified very far from the normal cricket type. The commonest species is *Myrmecophila nebrascensis*, about $\frac{1}{10}$ inch long, shown in Fig. 232.

Formerly included in the order Orthoptera, the earwigs are now recognized as entitled to distinct ordinal rank, and the thirty or more genera in the world, of which but six occur in the United States, are held to constitute the order Euplexoptera. This order is closely related to the Orthoptera, although the insects themselves look more like beetles.

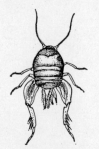

FIG. 232.— *Myrme-cophila nebrascensis*, a degenerate cricket that inhabits ants' nests. (Five times natural size.)

The earwigs are small, brownish or blackish insects, readily recognized by the curious forceps-like appendages on the tip of the abdomen (Fig. 233). They are either winged or wingless, but when winged have small leathery wing-covers only extending about half-way to the tip of the abdomen, with the well-developed nearly hemispherical wings compactly folded, both longitudinally and transversely, underneath them. Earwigs are not often seen because they are nocturnal in habit, but in some places they are rather abundant. They are vegetable feeders, being especially fond of ripe fruit, flower corollas, etc., which they bite off and chew with the well-developed jaws and maxillæ. The female lays her small, yellowish oval eggs in small masses under fallen leaves or in other concealed places, and is said to nestle on them as a hen on her eggs. She is also said to protect the young for some time after they are hatched. The young undergo an incomplete metamorphosis, developing wings externally, and resembling the parents, except in size, from the time of their hatching.

FIG. 233. — An earwig, *Labia minor*. (Six times natural size.)

The commonest representative of the order in the northern and eastern states is the little earwig, *Labia minor* (Fig. 233), measuring to tip of forceps only about $\frac{1}{4}$ inch. Other American species, as *Labidura riparia*, a Florida species, brownish yellow with a pair of longitudinal black stripes on prothorax and wing-covers, with long slender forceps, and *Anisolabis annulipes*, a black wingless California species with short heavy forceps, are larger, these two species being a little more and a little less than $\frac{3}{4}$ inch respectively.

# CHAPTER X

## THE TRUE BUGS, CICADAS, APHIDS, SCALE-INSECTS, ETC. (Order Hemiptera), AND THE THRIPS (Order Thysanoptera)

WHEN an Englishman says "bug"—and he doesn't say it in polite society—he means that particular sort of bug which we more specifically speak of as bedbug; when we say "bug" we are likely to mean any insect of any order; but when a professed student of insects, an entomologist, says or writes bug, he means some member of the insect order Hemiptera. It is to this order of "bugs" that we have now come in our systematic consideration of insects, and it is in this order that we first meet conspicuously the difficulties of treating systematically the populous insect class. From now on the making of this book useful depends on the discriminating selection of the few kinds of insects whose special consideration the limits of text and illustration permit, leaving the great majority of species to be referred to comprehensively and vaguely as the "others."

The Hemiptera, or true bugs, make up a large order compared with any of those so far considered, although a smaller one than certain others yet to be taken up. As regards popular acquaintanceship and interest also this order is still more inferior to the other large ones, namely, the beetles, the moths and butterflies, the two-winged flies, and the ants, bees, and wasps. Most of the true bugs are small, and obscurely, or at least inconspicuously, colored, and few of them attract that attention necessary to gain popular interest.

The order Hemiptera includes over 5000 known species of North American insects, representing a large variety and a great economic importance; some of the most destructive crop pests and most discomforting insect-scourges of man and the domestic animals belong to this order. The chinch-bug's ravages in the corn- and wheat-fields of the Mississippi Valley offer effective evidence to the dismayed farmers of the workings of a displeased Providence; the tiny sap-sucking aphids and phylloxera and insig-

163

nificant-looking scale-insects make the orchardist and vine-grower similar believers in supernatural moral correction by means of insect-scourges, and the piercing and sucking lice and bugs—in the English meaning—make personal and domestic cleanliness a virtue that brings its own immediate reward.

Other not unfamiliar representatives of this order are the loud-singing cicadas with their extraordinarily protracted adolescence, the thin-legged water-striders and skaters of the surface of pond and quiet trout-pool, the oar-legged water-boatmen and back-swimmers of the depths of the same pools, the ill-smelling squash-bugs, calico-backs, and stink-bugs of the kitchen-gardens, the big, flat-bodied, electric-light or giant water-bugs that whirl like bats around the outdoor arc-lights, and the assassin- and "kissing"-bugs of one-time newspaper interest. In structure all the Hemiptera agree in having the mouth-parts formed into a piercing and sucking beak (Fig. 234) capable of taking only liquid food. As that food is nearly always the blood of living animals or the sap of living plants, the nearly uniformly injurious or distressing character of the food-habits of all the members of the order is apparent. This beak is composed of the elongate, tubular under-lip (labium) acting as sheath for the four slender, needle-like piercing stylets (modified mandibles and maxillæ). The labium is not a perfect tube, for it is narrowly open all along its dorso-medial line, but the edges of this slit can be brought closely together and the slit also covered internally by the stylets, so that an effective tubular sucking proboscis is formed (Fig. 14). The name Hemiptera is derived from the character of the fore wings shown by most, though by no means all, of the members of the

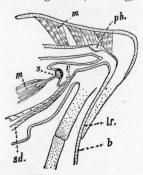

Fig. 234.—Diagram of section through head and basal part of beak of a sucking-bug. *ph.*, pharynx; *m.*, muscles from pharynx to dorsal wall of head; *v.*, valve; *s.*, stopper; *m.*, muscle of stopper; *s.d.*, salivary duct; *lr.*, labrum; *b.*, one of the stylets of beak. To pump fluid up through the beak, the muscle attached to the stopper contracts, thus expanding the cavity closed by the valve. (After Leon.)

order; this is the thickening of the basal half of the otherwise thin, membranous wing, so that each fore wing is made up of two about equal parts of obviously different texture and appearance; hence "half-winged" (Fig. 268). All Hemiptera (excepting the male scale-insects) have an incomplete metamorphosis, the young at birth resembling the parents in most essential characteristics except size and the presence of wings. By steady growth, with repeated moultings and the gradual development of external wing-pads, the adult form is reached, without any of the marked changes apparent in the insects of complete metamorphosis. With similar mouth-parts the young have, in most cases, similar feeding habits, preying on the same kinds of plants or animals that give nourishment to the parents.

The extent of the injuries done by various members of this order to farm and orchard crops, to meadows and forests, and to our domestic animals is enormous. Of the other insects the order of beetles includes numerous crop pests, and the caterpillars of many moths and a few butter-flies do much damage; locusts have a healthy appetite for green things, and many kinds of flies could be lost to the world to our advantage, but perhaps no other order of insects has so large a proportion of its members in the category of insect pests. The single Hemipterous species, *Blissus leucopterus*, better known by its vernacular name of chinch-bug, causes an annual loss to grain of twenty millions of dollars; the grape phylloxera destroyed the vines on 3,000,000 acres of France's choice vineyards; the San José scale has in the last ten years spread from California to every other state and territory of the United States and become a menace to the whole fruit-growing industry. So, despite their small size and their general unfamiliarity to laymen, the Hemiptera are found by economic entomologists, in their warfare against the insect-scourges of the country, to be one of the most formidable of all the insect orders.

The classification of the Hemiptera into subgroups is a matter likely to prove difficult for the amateur and general collector. The order as represented in our country includes thirty-nine families, and the structural characters separating some of these families are slight and not easily made out by untrained students. For the use, however, of readers of this book capable of using them, keys or tables of all the families of the Hemiptera are presented. For more general use, however, I shall try to arrange the families in groups depending on the habits and more obvious appearance and make-up of the insects, characteristics which may be readily noted. And this arrangement will not be less "scientific" than the arrangement in the key commonly used by entomologists, as the latter is confessedly largely artificial and convenient rather than natural in its groupings.

The order is separable into three primary natural groups or sub-orders as follows:

Wingless forms, with a fleshy, unsegmented sucking-beak, living as parasites on man and other mammals . . . . . . . . . . . . . . . . . . . . . . . . . . . . . . . . . . . . . . . . . . .PARASITA.
Winged, or sometimes wingless, but always with the beak segmented.
  Wings of the same texture throughout and usually held sloping or roof-like over the back and sides of the body; sucking-beak arising from the hinder part of the lower side of the head; tne head so closely joined to the prothorax that the bases of the fore legs touch the sides of the head . . . . . . . . . . . . . . . . . . . . . . . . . . . . . . . . . . . . . . . . . . . HOMOPTERA.

> Fore wings with basal half thickened and parchment-like, apical half thin and membranous; the four wings lying flat on the back when folded, the membranous tips overlapping; sucking-beak arising from the front part of head, and the head usually separated from the pro-thorax by a more or less distinct neck................Heteroptera.

Of these three suborders the Parasita, or sucking-lice, are degenerate wingless species and will be considered last. The Heteroptera include the so-called "true bugs" with fore wings thickened at base, and when folded lying flat on the back, as the squash-bug, chinch-bugs, and the great majority of the species in the order, while the Homoptera include the cicadas, the tree- and leaf-hoppers, the aphids or plant-lice, the mealy-winged flies, and the degenerate scale-insects.

## SUBORDER HOMOPTERA.

Key to Families of the Homoptera (includes both Nymphs and Adults). (Adapted from Woodworth.)

Proboscis seeming to rise from the middle of the sternum, or proboscis wanting; insects less than ⅓ inch long.
   Hind femora much larger than other femora........(Jumping plant-lice.)   Psyllidæ.
   Hind femora not much larger than the others.
     Legs long and slender...............................(Plant-lice.)   Aphidiidæ.
     Legs short, or wanting.
       Feet of one joint, or wanting.........................(Scale-insects.)   Coccidæ.
       Feet of two joints...............................(Mealy wings.)   Aleyrodidæ.
Proboscis plainly arising from the head.
   With three ocelli, sometimes (nymphs) with large front tibiæ and no wings.
                       (Cicadas.)   Cicadidæ.
   With two ocelli or none, and the front tibiæ not enlarged.
     Antennæ inserted on head below the eyes..........(Lantern-flies.)   Fulgoridæ.
     Antennæ inserted in front of and between the eyes.
       Prothorax extending back over the abdomen....(Tree-hoppers.)   Membracidæ.
       Prothorax not extending back over the abdomen.
         Hind tibiæ with few spines.................. (Spittle-insects.)   Cercopidæ.
         Hind tibæ with two rows of spines...............(Leaf-hoppers.)   Jassidæ.

Perhaps no other insect-species has any single characteristic of its life-history of the same interest as the extraordinarily long duration of the adolescence of the seventeen-year cicada. That a single one of the 300,000 and more known species of insects should have a period of development from egg to adult of more than sixteen years, while this period in all other insects varies from a few days to not more than three years—comparatively few insects live, all told, more than a year—is perhaps the most striking exceptional fact in all insect biology. The other members of the family Cicadidæ, to which this insect belongs, have, as far as known, an immature life of but one or two years.  But few species of cicadas, dog-day locusts, harvest-flies, or lyremen, as they are variously called, occur in this country —they are more abundant in subtropic and tropic countries—but their large, robust, blunt-headed body, their shrill singing and their wide distribution make them familiar insects.

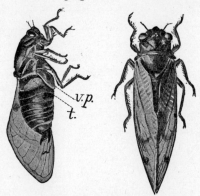

In summer and fall the piercing, rhythmic buzzing of the cicadas comes from the trees from early morning till twilight.  The song, unlike that of the katydids and tree-crickets, is hushed at night.  The sound is made, not by a rasping together of wings or legs, but by stretching and relaxing a pair of corrugated tympana, or parchment-like membranes, by means of a muscle attached to the center of each; much, indeed, as a small boy makes music from the bottom of a tin pan with a string fastened to its center.  These sound-making organs of the cicadas, confined to the males—

FIG. 235. — The seventeen-year cicada, *Cicada septendecim;* specimen at left showing sound-making organ.  *v.p.,* ventral plate; *t.,* tympanum. (Natural size.)

"Happy is the cicada, since its wife has no voice," says Xenarchos—are situated in resonance-cavities or open boxes, furnished with other sympathetically vibrating membranes, at the base of the abdomen (Figs. 235 and 236).  The sound-chambers are incompletely closed (wholly open in the seventeen-year cicada) by a pair of semicircular disks, which are opened or shut by movements of the body so as to give the song a peculiar rhythmic increase and decrease of loudness.

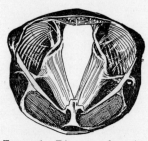

FIG. 236.—Diagram of section of body of cicada, showing attachment of muscles to inner surface of sound-making organ. (Enlarged.)

The cicada that is most familiar, and on hand every summer over most of the country, is the large (2 inches in length to tip of closed wings) black and green dog-day harvest-fly, *Cicada tibicen.*  The life-history of this species is not fully known, but the insect requires, according to Comstock, two years to become mature.  The really famous cicada is *Cicada septendecim,* the seventeen-year locust, or periodical cicada (Fig. 235).  It is about 1¼ inches long, black, banded with red on the abdomen, and with bright red eyes and the veins of both wings red at the base and along the front margin.  The females lay their eggs in early summer in slits which they cut with the sharp ovipositor in the twigs of various trees, in this way often doing much damage to orchards and nurseries. The young hatch in about six weeks and drop to the ground, where they burrow down through cracks and begin their long underground life. They feed on the humus in the soil and, to some extent, on juices sucked from the tree-roots. They grow slowly, moulting probably four or six times at intervals of from two years to four years. In spring or early summer of the seventeenth year (thirteenth in a race in the southern states) they come above ground, and, after hiding for a while under stones and sticks, crawl up on the trunks of trees and there moult for the last time, the winged adult emerging and soon flying into the tree-tops. The various broods or swarms in this country, about twenty in number, are known, and the territory occupied by each has been mapped, so that it is possible for entomologists to predict the appearance of a swarm of seventeen-year cicadas in a particular locality at a particular time. As all the members of one of these swarms issue in the same season, and indeed in the same month or fortnight, they usually attract much attention. The broods to issue in the next few years are the following: a large one in 1905 in the northern half of Illinois, eastern part of Iowa, southern part of Wisconsin, southern edge of Michigan, and northern and western edge of Indiana; a scattered one in 1906 ranging, not continuously, from Massachusetts south and west through Long Island, New Jersey, Pennsylvania, Maryland, West Virginia, Ohio, Indiana, Kentucky, Tennessee, North and South Carolina, and northern Georgia; and a large one in 1907, ranging from central Illinois south and east to the Gulf and Atlantic.

A considerable number of small insects, often seed-like in shape, or with the thorax prolonged into odd horns, spines, or crests, are included in the families of tree-hoppers (Membracidæ) and lantern-flies (Fulgoridæ)

(Fig. 237). Striking members, large and bright-colored, of this latter family are found in the South American tropics, but the North American species are small, and are rarely seen or collected by amateurs. Among the commonest of our forms are the candle-heads, species of Scolops, small insects living on grass and herbage, with the head

FIG. 237.—A fulgorid, *Stobera tricarinata*. (After Forbes; natural length ¼ inch.)

bearing a long slender upcurving projection. The tree-hoppers (Membracidæ) almost all suggest small angular brownish seeds or thorns in shape and color. The prothorax is sometimes widely expanded, sometimes lengthened so as to cover nearly the whole body, sometimes humped or crested, sometimes spined or pitted. The unusual form is probably protective, making the insects simulate seeds or other plant structures. The species of Enchenopa (Fig. 239) are curiously horned. *E. binotata* is common in the east.   It is gregarious and is attended by ants which feed on a sweetish substance excreted by it.   It lays its eggs in little white waxen frothy masses. A curiously humpbacked form is *Senilia camelas* (Fig. 240).   The best known and most injurious tree-hoppers are those of the genus Cerasa, of which the species *C. bubalus*, or buffalo tree-hopper (see initial letter of this chapter), injures fruit-trees both by piercing and sucking sap from

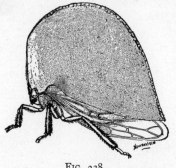

| FIG. 238. | FIG. 239. | FIG. 240. |

FIG. 238.—The black-backed tree-hopper, *Arthasia galleata*.   (After Lugger; natural length ⅕ inch.)
FIG. 239.—A tree-hopper, *Enchenopa gracilis*.   (Three times natural size.)
FIG. 240.—A tree-hopper, *Senilia camelas*.   (Three times natural size.)

them, and by making slits in the twigs to lay eggs in.   It is about ⅓ inch long, light grass-green with whitish dots and a pale yellowish streak on each side.   On the front there are two small sharp processes jutting out one on each side from the prothorax, and suggesting a pair of horns, hence the name.   It is common on apple and many other trees from the middle of summer until late in the autumn.   The eggs are laid in pairs of nearly parallel and slightly curved slits.   The young hatch in the spring following egg-laying.

Walking over our lawns or through pastures and meadows we often startle from the grass hundreds of small, usually greenish, little insects that leap or fly for a short distance, but soon settle again in the herbage.   Nearly all these small and active insects are sap-sucking leaf-hoppers, of the family Jassidæ, one of the largest and most injurious of the Hemipterous families. It is stated by careful students of these grass-pests that from nearly one-fourth to one-half of all the grass springing up annually is destroyed by leaf-hoppers.   Professor Osborn estimates that over one million leaf-hoppers can and often do live on an acre of grass-covered ground.   These insects are rarely more than ⅓ inch long, and most of them are nearer half of that. The body is more slender than in the tree-hoppers, and is usually widest across the prothorax or a little behind it, tapering back to the tip of the folded wings.   The head is more or less triangular, as seen from above, and the face is oblique, sloping back to the base of the fore legs.   The family is a large one, containing many species, of which several are well known to economic entomologists as special pests of grasses, growing grain, grapes, roses, etc.   The injury is caused by the draining away of the sap of the plant by the host of little sucking-beaks thrust into its leaves or stem.   Among the notorious destructive species are the destructive leaf-hopper, *Cicadula exitiosa*, ⅕ inch long, brownish, which often injures seriously the winter wheat of the southern states.   Also the various grape-leaf hoppers, which cause the leaves of grape-vines to wilt and turn brown and prevent the formation of full grapes; one of these, *Erythroneura vitis*, is about ⅛ inch long, crossed by two blood-red bands and a third dusky one at the apex.   I have seen millions of individuals of *Erythroneura comes* (Fig. 242) in the great 3300-acre vineyard of the Vina Ranch in the Sacramento Valley of California.   These leaf-hoppers hibernate in the vineyard or about its edges under fallen leaves and rubbish.   Probably the best remedy for them is to keep the vineyards as clean as possible, or at least to burn up in the winter any accumulated rubbish.   The rose leaf-hopper, *Typhlocyba rosæ*, is often abundant on rose-bushes, and also on apple-trees.   The eggs are laid in the summer, and the young develop through the summer and fall, hibernating as adults under leaves or rubbish.   A common leaf-hopper of grass-fields is *Diedrocephala mollipes*, ⅓ inch long, spindle-shaped, grass-green above, pale yellowish below, with black lines across the face and top of head, and the fore wings with bluish veins and yellowish edges.

Fig. 241.    Fig. 242.

Fig. 241.—The celery leaf-hopper, *Cicadula 4-lineata.* (After Lugger; natural size indicated by line.)
Fig. 242.—Two vine-hoppers, at left *Erythroneura vulnerata*, on right *E. comes*. (After Forbes; much enlarged.)

Occasionally one finds frothy, spittle-like masses adhering to the stems of weeds or shrubs in which may be found imbedded one or more odd-shaped, squat, slant-faced insects from $\frac{1}{10}$ inch to ¼ inch long (Fig. 243). These are the young—they have no wings, only wing-pads or, if very young, not even these—of the spittle-insects or frog-hoppers, family Cercopidæ. The spittle is a viscid fluid expelled from the alimentary canal of the insects, and beaten up into a froth by the whisking about of the body.   What advantage it is to the young insects is hard even to conjecture; it certainly is not known.   The adult frog-hoppers—this name is derived from a popular belief that the spittle is that of tree-frogs—are small flattish, brownish or grayish insects about ⅓ inch long which occasionally occur in sufficient numbers to do some injury to grapes, cranberries, or pasture grasses. A grape frog - hopper, *Aphrophora 4-notata*, has brown wing-covers with three blackish spots on each; another found on grapes in the east, *A. signoreti*, is tawny brown clouded with dull white and thickly dotted with black spots; the cranberry spittle-insect, *Clastoptera proteus*, which occurs on cranberries and blueberries in marshes, is black, with two yellow bands on top of the head, one in the thorax, two oblique stripes on the base of the fore wings, and a cross-bar near the tip; *C. pini* is a small shining black species with pale yellow head with black band at front margin, that occurs on the needles of pine-trees.

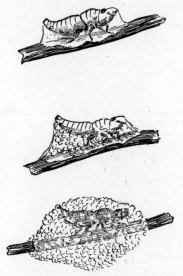

FIG. 243.—The spittle-insect, *Aphrophora*, showing stages of froth production. (After Morse; enlarged.)

Looking like miniature cicadas, but belonging to a different family, and really more nearly related to the aphids or true plant-lice, are the Psyllidæ, or jumping plant-lice. They are not more than ⅕ inch long, their hind legs are enlarged for leaping, some of them exude honey-dew, as the true plant-lice and the scale-insects do, and some make galls on the wings of hackberry and other trees. The best-known and most destructive member of the family is the pear-tree flea-louse, *Psylla pyricola*. This is a minute insect measuring only $\frac{1}{18}$ inch long to tip of folded wings, but it often occurs in such large numbers in pear-orchards in the northeastern and northern states as to destroy extensive orchards. The eggs are orange-yellow and laid on the leaves, each egg having a lash-like process projecting from it. The young is broad and flat and yellow in color, growing brownish as it grows older. The adults hibernate in crevices in the bark and come out in spring to lay their eggs. The pests can be killed by spraying the trees with kerosene emulsion (see p. 189), immediately after the leaves have expanded in the spring.

A very important and very interesting family is that of the Aphidiidæ, the plant-lice or aphis-flies (Figs. 244 and 245). The species, of which there are many, are all small, ¼ inch being a rarely attained maximum length. The most familiar representatives of the family are the tiny, plump-bodied, pale-green insects, some with two pairs of long, delicate, transparent wings, some without wings, common on flowers in conservatories and gardens and known as "green fly." Other often-noticed kinds are the cockscomb gall-louse of the elm and the "blights" of various foliage

trees, as alder-blight, beech-blight, elm-blight, etc., these "blight" aphids all secreting conspicuous white woolly masses of wax and most of them also excreting honey-dew, which is conspicuous on the leaves and on the sidewalks under the trees.

Fig. 244.—The southern grain plant-louse, *Toxoptera gramineum*, winged migrant. (After Pergande; much enlarged.)

Of more economic importance are some of those plant-lice which infest crop-plants, the extraordinarily ruinous grape-phylloxera, for example, the apple-tree root-louse, and the woolly apple-aphis, the cherry-, plum-, and peach-aphids, the corn-root louse, the hop-louse, and the cabbage-aphis, turnip-louse, and other aphid pests of garden vegetables. All of these insects are minute soft-bodied defenceless creatures, which effect their great injuries to their host-plants by virtue of great numbers. Fitch, New York's first state entomologist, estimated the number of cherry-aphids that were living at one time on a small young cherry-tree to be 12,000,000. Although uncounted millions of the toothsome juicy little aphid bodies are being constantly eaten in spring and summer by eager predaceous insects, such as lady-bird beetles, certain syrphid-fly larvæ

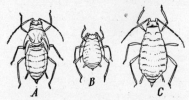

Fig. 245.—The southern grain-louse, *Toxoptera gramineum*, wingless. *A*, female; *B*, young nymph; *C*, older nymph. (After Pergande; much enlarged.)

and aphis-lions (larvæ of lace-wing and hemerobius flies), just as constantly are new millions being produced by the fecund aphis mothers, most of the young being born alive and requiring but a few days to complete their growth and development, and to be ready to take up the production of young themselves.

Professor Forbes has made an estimate of the rate of increase of the corn-root louse that shows this great fecundity. A single stem-mother of the corn-root aphis produces twelve to fifteen young that mature in a fortnight. "Supposing that all the plant-lice descending from a single female hatched from the egg in spring were to live and reproduce throughout the year, we should have coming from the egg the following spring nine and a half trillion young. As each plant-louse measures about 1.4 mm. in length and .93

mm. in width, an easy calculation shows that these conceivably possible descendants of a single female would, if closely placed end to end, form a procession seven million eight hundred and fifty thousand miles in length; or they would make a belt or strip ten feet wide and two hundred and thirty miles long."

The remarkable plasticity of the aphids as regards their possession or lack of wings and, on the physiological side, their reproduction agamically or sexually, introduces certain unusual conditions into their life-history. Although each species is likely to present idiosyncrasies of its own, a fair example of the course of aphid life through a season may be outlined as follows: In spring there hatch, from eggs which have been laid the fall before, wingless females, called stem-mothers, which produce young agamically (i.e., from unfertilized eggs) either by giving birth to them in active free condition or by laying eggs. From these eggs hatch wingless females which produce in turn other agamic broods of wingless females. But at any time in the course of these successive agamic generations either all or a part of the individuals of a brood may be winged, and these winged females fly away to other plants and there found new colonies which continue the series of agamic generations. But toward the end of the season, when the first cold weather announces the approaching winter, broods, still parthenogenetically produced, of sexed individuals, both males and females appear. "The males may be either winged or wingless, but these true females are always wingless." These individuals mate, and each female produces a single large egg which passes over the winter to give birth in the following spring to a wingless stem-mother—that one which begins the

FIG. 246. — Bodies of aphids which have been killed by Hymenopterous parasites, the adult parasitic flies having emerged from the small circular holes. (Enlarged.)

spring series of parthenogenetic generations. The unfertilized eggs, called pseud-ova, produced in numbers by the spring and summer agamic mothers (from which eggs the young frequently emerge while the eggs are still in the body of the mother) should not be confused with the single fertilized egg laid in the late fall by the mated females of the sexed generation. Although these two sorts of eggs are alike in their earliest stages in the ovaries of the females, differences very soon occur, the embryo in the pseud-ovum beginning to develop before the formation of its own egg is properly completed.

Characteristic variations in the general course are described later in connection with the accounts of the few particular aphid species for which we have place, but it should be kept in mind that considerable variations may occur in the case of a single species. Extrinsic influences, such as crowding a host-plant and hence the lessening of food, or an unusual humidity or lack of humidity, an early lowering of temperature in autumn, etc., seem to be very potent in producing or acting as effective stimuli for adaptive variations of the usual course of life. Slingerland reared ninety-four successive generations (in four years) of an aphid species in the insectary at Cornell University under such constant conditions of food-supply and summer temperature that not a single winged aphid nor single sexual generation was produced. Even longer series of identical wingless agamic generations have been obtained by certain European experimenters. Clarke, in California, has been able to produce a winged generation at will by simply changing the chemical constitution of the sap of the host-plant on which the aphids were reared in his laboratory.

FIG. 247.—Rose-aphids visited by ants. (Natural size; from life.)

In addition to the interesting variation as regards wings and reproductive processes among the various individuals of a single aphid species, it has been found that of the wingless males some have no mouth, while others are furnished with functional mouth-parts and opening. An interesting physiological variation also occurs in the matter of the food-plant selected. The winged individuals frequently migrate to a plant of different species from that on which they were born. For instance, the apple-aphids, *A phis mali*, "spend the summer upon grasses, where they continue breeding until autumn, when they return to the apple and the winged females establish colonies of the wingless egg-laying form upon the leaves. The males fly in from the summer host-plant; the eggs are then laid on the twigs and buds, and the cycle for the year is completed." The common cherry-aphis, *Myzus cerasi*, has a similar history, described by

Weed as follows: "It winters over on the twigs in the egg state. Early in spring the young aphids hatch and crawl upon the bursting buds, inserting their tiny sap-sucking beaks into the tissues of the unfolding leaves. In a week or ten days they become full-grown and begin giving birth to young lice, that also soon develop and repeat the process, increasing very rapidly. Most of the early spring forms are wingless, but during June great numbers of the winged lice appear, and late in June or early in July they generally leave the cherry, migrating to some other plant, although we do not yet know what that plant is. Here they continue developing throughout the summer, and in autumn a winged brood again appears and migrates back to cherry. These migrants give birth to young that develop into egg-laying females which deposit small, oval, shining black eggs upon the twigs."

The point of all this is plainly that in the aphids there must be recognized an unusual and, to them, very advantageous adaptive plasticity of both structure and function. Defenceless as are the aphid *individuals* as far as capacity either to fight or to run away is concerned, the various aphid *species* are, on the contrary, very well defended by their structural and physiological plasticity and their extraordinary fecundity.

The two secretions, wax and honey-dew, play an important part in the aphid life. The wax secreted or excreted through various small openings scattered over the body is, of course, liquid when first produced, but quickly hardens; the total waxy secretion appears usually as a mass of felted threads or "wool," and doubtless is an important protection for the delicate body. The honey-dew, long supposed to be secreted through two conspicuous tubular processes on the dorsal surface of the posterior end of the abdomen, is now known to be an excretion from the intestine, issuing in fine droplets or even spray from the anal opening. From the so-called "honey-tubes" issues another secretion, not sweetish, about which little is known. It is common knowledge, however, that the aphid honey-dew is a favorite food of ants—the Germans call it the ants' "national dish"—and many accounts have been written of the care of plant-lice, the ants' cattle, by the ants themselves. Without question there is some basis of fact for these stories. No more evidence of this is needed than the careful observations of Professor Forbes of the extraordinary care of the corn-root louse by the little brown ant, *Lasius brunneus*, of the Mississippi Valley corn-fields (see p. 545 for an account of this). The feeding by ants on the fresh honey-dew can be readily observed in almost any garden (Fig. 247), and undoubtedly the mere presence in the aphid neighborhood of such redoubtable warriors as the ants is a strong deterrent of various predaceous insect enemies of the plant-lice. But most of the stories of ants and aphids printed in popular natural-history books need to be tested by careful observation.

Of all aphid species the grape-phylloxera, *Phylloxera vastatrix* (Fig. 248), has deservedly the widest notoriety.  First made known in 1853 by Fitch from specimens found in New York, it was soon discovered to be well scattered on wild vines over the eastern United States.  "It was introduced into the south of France before 1863, upon rooted vines sent from America; though the insect itself was not found and described there until 1868. The infection commenced at two points: one in the southeast in Gard, the other in the southwest near Bordeaux.  In 1868, when the nature of the pest was understood, it had already invaded considerable areas.  The

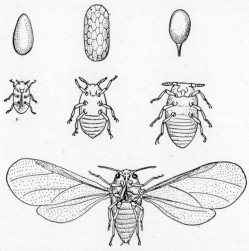

Fig. 248.—The grape-phylloxera.  In upper left-hand corner an egg from which a male has issued, next an egg from which a female has issued; in upper right-hand corner winter egg;  at left hand of middle row a just-hatched young, next a male (note absence of mouth-parts);  at right end of middle row, female;  lower figure, winged form.  (After Ritter and Rübsaamen;  much enlarged.)

two areas first attacked gradually enlarged until they touched about the year 1880, and the insect began to spread northward.  By 1884 about 2,500,000 acres, more than one-third of all the vineyards of France, had been destroyed and nearly all the rest were more or less affected.  The progress of the disease in parts of southern France was so rapid that in some towns vine-stumps became the principal fuel.  Since 1884 the pest has continued to spread with somewhat less rapidity in France, partly because the most densely planted vineyard districts had already been devastated, but also because elsewhere its progress was retarded by quarantine and other restrictive measures.  No remedies yet discovered, however, are capable of exterminating the pest; and to-day there is no vine-growing region of any importance in France, or elsewhere, exempt from phylloxera."

Curiously enough this native American pest came to California, in which state it has done much more damage than elsewhere in our country, from France, introduced on imported cuttings or roots. It was first noticed about 1874; by 1880 vines had been killed by phylloxera in three counties and hundreds of acres had been pulled up in the famous Sonoma Valley. Since then the pest has spread, according to Bioletti, to all the important grape-growing regions of central and northern California, and probably not less than 30,000 acres of vineyards have been destroyed.

The phylloxera appears normally in four forms: (1) the gall form, living in little galls on the leaves, and capable of very rapid multiplication (this form rarely appears in California); (2) the root form, which is derived from individuals which migrate from the leaves to the roots, and which, by its piercing of the roots, sucking the sap, and producing little quickly decaying tubercles on the rootlets, does the serious injury; (3) the winged form, which flies to new vines and vineyards and starts new colonies; and finally (4) the sexual forms, male and female, which are the regenerating individuals, appearing after several agamic generations have been produced.

The life-history of the pest has been described as follows by Bioletti: "Some time during the summer, usually in July or August, some of the eggs laid by the root-insects develop into insects of slightly different form, called nymphs. They are somewhat larger than the normal root form and show slight protuberances on the sides, which finally develop into wings. These are the winged or colonizing insects, which emerge from the soil and, though possessing very weak powers of flight, are capable of sailing a short distance, and if a wind is blowing may be taken many rods or even miles. Those which reach a vine crawl to the under side of a leaf and deposit from three to six eggs. These eggs are of two sizes, the smaller of which produce males and the larger females. The female, after fertilization, migrates to the rough bark of the two-year-old wood, where she deposits a single egg, called the winter egg, which remains upon the vine until the following spring. The insect which hatches from this egg in the spring goes either to the young leaves and becomes a gall-maker, or descends to the roots and gives rise to a new generation of egg-laying root-feeders. The normal and complete life-cycle of the phylloxera appears then to be as follows: Male and female insects (one generation in autumn); gall-insects (one to five generations while the vines are in leaf); root-insects (an unknown number of generations throughout the year); nymphs, which become winged insects (one generation in midsummer). The gall stage may be omitted, as it generally is in California, and the insects which hatch from the fertilized eggs laid by

the female go directly to the root and produce offspring which are indistinguishable from the root form produced in the normal cycle. For
how many generations the root form can exist and reproduce without the
invigoration supposed to come from the production of the sexual form is
not known, but certainly for four years and probably for more.    The

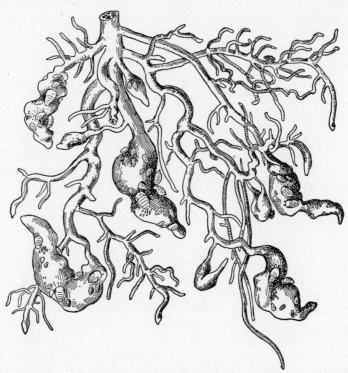

FIG. 249.—Roots and rootlets of grape-vine infested by the phylloxera.  (After Ritter
and Rübsaamen;  enlarged.)

gall form on American vines can be prevented by spraying the vines in
winter with liquids to kill the winter eggs; but this treatment has no
effect on the root forms, which in California hibernate abundantly in the
soil."

All forms of the phylloxera species are very small, about $\frac{1}{25}$ of an inch
being an average for fully developed individuals. The root form is light
greenish yellow in summer, when it can be found by examining the rootlets
of infested vines, and bronzy purplish in winter, when it can be found in
little patches under the bark just at the crown of the vine. The newly

hatched young of the root form moves about freely, but when it reaches the egg-laying stage it becomes fixed.

The chief injury to the vine is not sap-drinking, but the decaying or "cancer" of the roots caused by the punctures and tubercle forming (Fig. 249). It usually takes two or three years for phylloxera to kill a vine, but the results of the infestation are shown each season in the increasingly reduced growth of the new wood and in the lessened bearing. Suspected vines should be dug up and the rootlets carefully examined for tubercles and the insects themselves. The remedies, unfortunately, are either expensive, difficult, or severe. If a vineyard can be submerged for six weeks under at least six inches of water, the insects will be killed (by suffocation). Carbon disulphide can be put into the soil among the roots by an injector at a cost of from ten to twenty dollars an acre. "This method succeeds only in rich, deep, loose soils and cannot be successfully used in soil containing much clay or on dry rocky hillsides." Finally, most severe but most effective is the digging up of the whole of an infested vineyard and replanting resistant vines. "A resistant vine is one which is capable of keeping alive and growing even when phylloxera are living upon its roots. Its resistance depends on two facts: first, that the insects do not increase so rapidly on its roots; and second, that the swellings of diseased tissue caused by the punctures of the insects do not extend deeper than the bark of the rootlets and are sloughed off every year, leaving the roots as healthy as before. The wild vines of the Mississippi States have evolved in company with the phylloxera, and it is naturally among these that we find the most resistant forms. No vine is thoroughly resistant in the sense that phylloxera will not attack it at all; but on the most resistant the damage is so slight as to be imperceptible. The European vine, *Vitis vinifera* L., is the most susceptible of all, and all the grapes cultivated in California, with a few unimportant exceptions, belong to this species." But the preferred French stocks can be grafted on to resistant American roots and the vineyard made practically immune. This is the method which has rehabilitated the French vineyards and is now rehabilitating the California ones.

Another very important aphid pest of this country is the woolly apple-aphis, called in England and in Europe the American blight. This species, like the phylloxera, appears in different forms and lives both above ground on the twigs and larger branches and underground on the roots. It makes itself conspicuous and readily recognizable by the abundant fluffy waxen "wool" which it secretes. Badly attacked trees have the bark of their branches badly "cankered" and the roots covered with excrescences, and may die. The injuries are almost always severe, and the pest is one difficult to eradicate. If but few trees in an orchard are attacked, it is best to dig them up and burn them. The bark can be thoroughly sprayed or scrubbed with a carbolized solution of soft soap (soap 10 parts, carbolic acid 2 parts, water 88 parts) and carbon disulphide injected into the soil about the base of the tree.

Of the various aphids which attack foliage trees, the most familiar are those which resemble the woolly apple-aphis in their habit of secreting flocculent masses of wax, and thus obtain the name of " blight," as elm-blight, beech-blight, alder-blight, etc. The alder-blight, or woolly alder-aphis, *Pemphigus tessellata*, gives birth in autumn to vast numbers which crawl down the trunks to the ground, where they congregate in the crevices between the base of the trunk and larger roots and the soil, or beneath the fallen leaves or other rubbish at the surface. They remain in their hiding-place until spring, when at the coming of the first warm days they crawl up the tree and out to the budding tips of the twigs. Here they begin sucking sap and at the same time secreting waxen "wool." In a week or so they become mature and begin giving birth to living young, and hereafter during the autumn and summer agamic generation after generation is produced. With the oncoming of cold weather the last generation crawls down to the ground to seek winter quarters. No sexual forms of this species have yet been found.

Among the gall-forming aphids, one of special interest, because of the strange character and abundance of its galls, is the cockscomb gall-louse, *Colopha ulmicola*. Elm-trees infested by this aphis develop on the upper side of the leaves narrow, erect, blackish galls irregularly toothed along the top, and suggesting a cock's comb sufficiently to warrant the common name. These aphids secrete much honey-dew, noticeable on sidewalks under the trees and on the leaves, and in this honey-dew where it covers the galls and leaves grows a blackish fungus.

Of all the families of the Hemiptera, probably the most important from the economic entomologist's point of view is that of the Coccidæ, or scale-insects, and from the point of view of the biological student, also, no other is more interesting and suggestive. More nearly on a footing with the Coccids than any other Hemiptera are the Aphididæ, just studied, but the scale-insects are even more specialized in curious and unusual ways, both as regards structure and physiology. In the more specialized scale-insects the females are quiescent in adult life, as well as in part of the immature life, and their fixed bodies are very degenerate, lacking both organs of locomotion and of orientation, viz., eyes, antennæ, wings, and legs. The family is a large and widely distributed one, numbering about 1450 known species in the world, of which 385 occur in the United States, but almost all are small and obscure and so foreign in appearance to the usual insect type that but few others than professional entomologists and the harassed fruit-growers ever recognize them as insects. Most of us have often had opportunity to make easy acquaintance with one or two species at our breakfast-tables; the flattish, nearly circular little red-brown spots, or the more ovate blackish spots, which are occasionally to be seen on carelessly packed oranges are scale-insects and excellent examples of the extreme of degenerate, quiescent type. The adult male scale-insects, unlike the females, are winged (although possessing but a single pair) and have eyes, antennæ, and legs, but, strangely enough, no mouth-parts nor mouth-opening, so that they can take no food and must necessarily have but a few hours or perhaps days, at most, of life. And they are much more rarely seen than the females. Indeed, of many scale-insect species the males are not yet known, it being possible that in some species there is no male sex at all.

The economic importance of the scale-insects has been keenly appreciated on the Pacific Coast ever since fruit-growing came to be a leading industry there, but the rest of the United States had not had to worry itself much because of the existence of these insect-scourges until recent years. A single Coccid species, however, has within ten years called the attention of entomologists and orchardmen and legislators all over the country to itself in a very illuminating manner. This species, the ill-named San José scale, *Aspidiotus perniciosus*,—which should rather be called "the pernicious scale," or, if not that, then the Oriental scale, as it is a native of Japan or China,—was first made known to science, and named, by Prof. J. H. Comstock in 1880.

FIG. 250.—San José scale on bark of fruit-tree. (After Slingerland; natural size.)

Professor Comstock's specimens were collected in the Santa Clara Valley near San José, California. How much earlier the species had been brought to California is not known, but at the time of its naming by Professor Comstock it was already recognized by California fruit-growers as a serious pest, and Comstock wrote: "From what I have seen of it I think it is the most pernicious scale-insect known in this country." In August, 1893, it was found to have got a footing in the east, and since then no other injurious insect—indeed hardly all others together—has received such constant and excited attention as has this obscure little pest. It is found now in every state and territory of the Union, and in Canada as well, and in thirty-five states has been the subject of hurried—and only partly well-advised—legislation. This legislation has been directed toward restricting its spread by (a) quarantining it at the states' borders, and (b) inspecting orchards and nurseries for it within the state and attempting to stamp it out. The structural characteristics and life-history of the insect may be briefly described as follows:

There may be seen on infested branches, leaves, or fruit, small, flat, grayish, irregularly circular scales of varying size (Figs. 250 and 251), the large stones (about $\frac{1}{25}$ inch diameter) being the adult females and the smaller ones being the immature individuals of both sexes. These circles are thin waxen plates, bearing one or more (depending on the age of the individual) faintly yellowish concentric inner circles or plates (the inner one usually blackish and like a tiny nipple) which are the moulted exuviæ of the scale. When the plant is badly infested the scales lie thickly together, even overlapping, and forming a sort of grayish scurf over the smooth bark. By rubbing or crushing this scurf a yellowish oily liquid issues from the injured bodies. If a scale be tipped over with a pinpoint, there will be found underneath it a delicate flattened yellowish sac-like creature, the insect itself (Fig. 252). If adult, this degenerate female will be seen (by examination with magnifier) to have no distinct head, no eyes nor

Fig. 251.—The San José scale, *Aspidiotus perniciosus*, females and young, on bark of fruit-tree. (From living specimens; at left, natural size; at right, considerably enlarged.)

antennæ, no wings nor legs. It does have a long, fine, flexible, thread-like process projecting from near the center of its under side; this is the sucking proboscis, and serves as a means of attachment to the plant as well as the organ of feeding.

Early in the spring, females which have hibernated under their protecting armor begin giving birth to living young, and continue doing this actively for about six weeks, when they die exhausted. The minute orange-yellow young, which have eyes, antennæ, and three pairs of legs, crawl out from under the scale and run about actively for a few hours over the twigs or leaves; then they settle down and each * "slowly works its long bristle-like sucking-beak through the bark, folds its antennæ and legs beneath its body and contracts to a nearly circular form. The development of the scale begins even before the larva becomes fixed. The secretion starts

---

* The following long quotation is made from Howard and Marlatt's "The San José Scale" (Bull. 3, N. S., Div. Ent., U. S. Dept. Agric., 1896).

in the form of very minute white fibrous waxy filaments, which spring from all parts of the body and rapidly become more numerous and dense. At first the orange color of the larva shows through the thickening downy white envelope, but within two days the insect becomes entirely concealed by the white or pale grayish-yellow shell or scale, which now has a prominent central nipple, the younger ones often possessing instead a central tuft. The scale is formed by the slow matting and melting together of the filaments of wax. During the first day the scale appears like a very microscopic downy hemisphere. The matting of the secretion continues until the appearance of down and individual filaments is entirely lost and the surface becomes smooth. In the early history of the scale it maintains its pale whitish or grayish-yellow color, turning gradually darker gray, the central nipple remaining lighter colored, usually throughout development.

"The male and female scales are exactly similar in size, color, and shape until after the first moult, which occurs twelve days after the emergence of the larva. With this moult, however, the insects beneath the scale lose all resemblance to each other. The males (Fig. 252, *a*) are rather larger than the females, and have large purple eyes, while the females have lost their eyes entirely. The legs and antennæ have disappeared in both sexes. The males are elongate and pyriform, while the females are almost circular, amounting practically to a flattened sac with indistinct segmentation, and without organs, except a long sucking-bristle springing from near the center beneath. The color of both sexes is light lemon-yellow. The scales at this time have a decidedly grayish tint, overcast somewhat with yellow.

"Eighteen days from birth the males change to the first pupal condition (propupa), and the male scales assume an elongate oval, sometimes slightly curved shape, characteristic of the sex, the exuvia or cast larval skin showing near the anterior end. The male propupæ are very pale yellow, with the legs and antennæ (which have reappeared) together with the two or three terminal segments colorless. . . . Prominent wing-pads extend along the side of the body.

"The female undergoes a second moult about twenty days from the larva. At each moult the old skin splits around the edge of the body, the upper half adhering to the covering scale and the lower forming a sort of ventral scale next to the bark. This form of moulting is common to scales of this kind.

"The covering scales at this stage are of a more purplish gray, the portion covering the exuviæ inclining to yellowish. The male scales are more yellowish than the female. The effect of the sucking of the insects is now quite apparent on the young growth, causing the bark to assume a purplish hue for some distance around the central portion, contrasting strongly

with the natural reddish green of the uninjured bark. With the second
moult the females do not change materially from their former appearance, retaining the pale-yellow color with a number of transparent spots around the edge of the body. The sucking-bristles are extremely long, two or three times the length of the body of the insect.

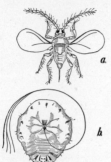

FIG. 252.—The San José scale, *Aspidiotus perniciosus*. *a*, male; *b*, adult female. (Much enlarged.)

"About twenty days after birth the male insect transforms to the true pupa. With the first moult the shed larval skin is retained beneath the scale as in the case of the female; with the later moultings the shed skins are pushed out from beneath the scale. The scale, after the second moult, presents on the inside two longitudinal ridges running from one end to the other, touching the sides of the pupa, and which apparently enable the insect to move backward or forward and assist the imago in pushing itself out.

"The true pupa is pale yellow, sometimes purplish, darkened about the base of the abdomen. The head, antennæ, legs, wing-pads, and style are well formed, but almost colorless. . . .

"From four to six days later, or from twenty-four to twenty-six days from birth, the males mature and back out from the rear end of their scales, having previously, for a day or two, remained practically developed, but resting under the scale. They seem to issue chiefly by night or in the evening.

"The mature male (Fig. 252) appears as a delicate two-winged fly-like insect with long feelers and a single anal style projecting from the end of the body; orange in color, with a faintly dusky shade on the prothorax. The head is darker than the rest of the body, the eyes are dark purple, and the antennæ, legs, and style are smoky. The wings are iridescent with yellow and green, very faintly clouded.

"Thirty days from birth the females are full grown and the embryonic young may be seen within their bodies, each enclosed in a delicate membrane. At from thirty-three to forty days the larvæ again begin to make their appearance.

"The adult female, prior to the development of the young, measures one millimeter in length and a little less in breadth, and is pale yellow with transparent spots near the margin of the body (Fig. 252).

"The length of a generation is determined by the female, and, as shown by the above record, covers a period of from thirty-three to forty days. Successive generations were followed carefully throughout the summer, and it was found that at Washington four full generations are regularly developed, with the possibility of a partial fifth generation. On a number of potted trees a single overwintered female was left to each tree. After the full progeny of this individual had gone out over the tree all were removed again, except one of the oldest and fertilized females. This method was continued for each generation throughout the breeding season. Some interesting records . . . were thus obtained, which indicate the fecundity of the females as well as the number of generations."

From these records it may be fairly estimated that an average of 200 females (in addition to about as many males) are produced by each female, and that there are four generations each year in the latitude of Washington, D. C. Thus the product of a single overwintered female in a single year amounts to 3,216,080,400 male and female descendants. This total is, of course, never reached, because only a part of each generation reaches maturity and produces young, but in a favorable season on a tree newly infested (and thus providing a plentiful food-supply) a large majority of each generation do most probably go through their normal existence. "Neither the rapidity with which trees become infested," add Howard and Marlatt, "nor the fatal effect which so early follows the appearance of this scale-insect is therefore to be wondered at."

But not all scale-insects are so specialized either structurally or physiologically as the pernicious (or San José) scale. The females of some species retain the eyes, antennæ, and legs through their whole life and can crawl about if need be at any time. Others show a sort of transition between these two extremes of activity and quiescence, having the legs present, but in adult life much reduced in size and probably functionless, or at best capable of carrying the insect but feebly and briefly. In the matter of the covering, too, there is much variety; some scales secrete no wax at all, but have the body-wall of the back specially thickened and made firm so as to act as an effective covering-shield underneath which, somewhat as with a turtle, the legs and head can be concealed. Others secrete filaments or tufts of soft white wax which form a sort of felted protecting covering for the body. In a general way the various scale-insects may be instructively gathered into three groups, depending on the characters of the females; in the first group the females retain the antennæ, eyes, and legs, and the segmented condition of the body (typical of normal insects) and are capable of locomotion throughout life; they secrete wax usually in the shape of white cottony filaments or masses with which they cover the body more or less completely, sometimes forming conspicuous waxen egg-sacs at the posterior extremity of the body; the females of the second group retain their legs and antennæ through life, but have them in reduced condition when adult, and although capable of feeble motion, usually lie quiescent; they commonly secrete no wax, but have the body-wall of the dorsum strongly chitinized, and usually very convex, so that it forms a strong rigid protecting shell; finally the females of the third (and largest) group are the so-called armored scales, which in the adult stage are degenerate creatures without distinct body segmentation, without antennæ, eyes, and legs, thus being incapable of locomotion; they form a flattish or convex dorsal scale of secreted wax and of the cast skins or exuviæ of the body.

In all the groups the males (Figs. 252 and 253) are very different in appearance from the females, being minute fly-like creatures with a single pair of wings, a pair of long antennæ, and a plump, soft, little body, usually terminating in a single needle-like process or in a pair of long waxen hairs. Males are not yet known for some of the species.

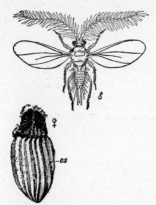

Fig. 253.—The fluted or cottony cushion-scale, *Icerya purchasi*, winged male and wingless female with fluted waxen egg-sac (*es*). (After Jordan and Kellogg, much enlarged.)

Familiar examples of the first group are the mealy-bugs (*Dactylopius* sp.) of greenhouses and gardens, soft-bodied scales, bearing projecting rods and threads of white wax of varying length, and rather prettily arranged. A more famous and interesting member of this group is the fluted or cottony cushion-scale, *Icerya purchasi* (Fig. 253) (so called because of the beautiful fluted wh'te waxen egg-sac secreted by the female), which once threatened to destroy all the orange-groves of California, but was ,brought to bay by a little red and black ladybird-beetle, *Vedalia cardinalis* (Fig. 254), brought from Australia for this very purpose. In 1868 some young orange-trees were brought to Menlo Park (near San Francisco) from Australia. These trees were undoubtedly infested by the fluted scale, which is a native of Australia. These scale immigrants throve in the balmy California climate, and particularly well, probably, because they had left all their native enemies far behind. By 1880 they had spread to the great orange-growing districts of southern California, five hundred miles away, and in the next ten years caused enormous loss to the growers. In 1888 the entomologist Kœbele, recommended by the government division of entomology, was sent at the expense of the California fruit-growers to Australia to try to find and send back some effective predaceous or parasitic enemy of the pest. As a result of this effort, a few Vedalias were sent to California, where they were zealously fed and cared for, and soon, after a few generations, enough of the little beetles were on hand to warrant trying to colonize them in the attacked orange-groves. With astonishing and gratifying success the Vedalia in a

very few years had so naturally increased and spread that the ruthless scale
was definitely checked in its destruction, and from that time to this has
been able to do only occasionally and in limited localities any injury at all.

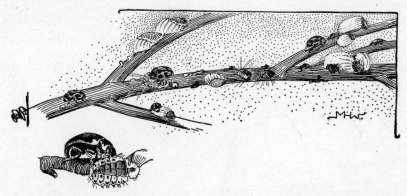

FIG. 254.—The fluted scale, *Icerya purchasi*, attacked by the Australian ladybird-beetle,
*Vedalia cardinalis*. In lower left-hand corner a Vedalia which has just issued from
its pupal case. (From life; upper figure slightly enlarged; lower figure much
enlarged.)

Of the second group, the best-known scales are the various species of the
genus Lecanium (Fig. 256). Of these, the olive or oleander or black scale,
*L. oleæ*, as it is variously called, is the most widely distributed and abundant
and hence economically important. It is a long-known species, having
been described in Europe in 1743, and it was brought to this country in
early days. The adult females are blackish, almost hemispherical, rough-
skinned creatures, with no external indication of head or other body divisions, feet, antennæ, etc., all these parts being visible only from the ventral
aspect, which normally is closely applied to the leaf or twig. On the back
may be distinguished three ridges forming an H. The young are flatter
and light brown, but can be recognized by their even more distinct H-mark.
This scale is found all over the United States and has a wide range of food-
plants, garden-bushes of all kinds, as well as deciduous and citrus fruits
being attacked. In California it is one of the worst insect-pests of the olive-
tree and also one of the worst of the orange enemies. It has certain natural
enemies in the persons of various ladybird-beetle species, and a few special
ladybird-beetles have been imported from Australia and elsewhere in the
hope of repeating the signal Vedalia success. Only a fair measure of success has been achieved. An indirect but serious injury caused to plants
by the black scale is due to the germination in the honey-dew secreted by
it of the spores of a fungus, *Capnodium* sp., which spreads its felted mycelia

over the leaf-surfaces, closing the breathing-pores (stomata) and thus truly suffocating the plant. Although this scale species has been known for a century and a half, the males have been seen but few times and in but few places. Another familiar member of this group, which secretes a distinct white waxen egg-sac, is the maple-scale, *Pulvinaria innumerabilis* (Fig. 255), common on maples in the eastern states.

Of the third group, that of the most specialized (degenerate) scales, the pernicious scale, already fully described, may be taken as a shining example. There is a host of these armored scale-insects, and few trees or

FIG. 255.        FIG. 256.

FIG. 255.—The maple-scale, *Pulvinaria innumerabilis*. Females with egg-sacs on the twig; young scales on under side of leaf, and a single young scale, much enlarged, at left. (After Felt; natural size.)

FIG. 256.—*Lecanium* scales attacked by the fungus *Cordyceps clavulata*. (After Pettit; much enlarged.)

shrubs escape their attacks. The various genera are mostly distinguishable by the shape of the covering scale, but to determine the species exactly requires, for many, careful examination, under high powers of the microscope, of the minute chitinous processes which form a fine fringe along the posterior margin of the last abdominal segment. To make this examination it is necessary to remove the female from under her scale, and mount her cleared body flat in balsam or glycerine on a glass slide. An important species in this group is the red orange-scale, *Aspidiotus aurantii* (Fig. 257), common in orange-groves of southern California. A species very closely resembling it is *A. ficus*, common in the Florida groves. On pine-needles one may often note small, narrow elongate white waxen scales, with the smaller, yellowish-brown exuviæ at one end; these belong to the widely spread species *Chionaspis pinifoliæ*. On apple-trees often occurs a roughened shining blackish narrow elongate curved scale, resembling a little an oyster-shell in miniature; this is the sometimes serious apple-pest, *Mytilaspis pomorum.*

But we have no space to list even the most important of these degenerate but successful insect enemies of our fruit- and foliage-trees.

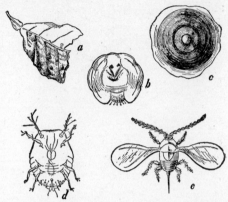

The devising of remedies for scale attack has been given much attention, and a number of effective means have been discovered for fighting the pests. Probably the most effective of all is the fumigation of infested orchard-trees by hydrocyanic gas. A tent capable of enclosing a whole tree is made, and with this in place hydrocyanic gas is generated under it by pouring about 50 oz. of water into 5 oz. of commercial sulphuric acid and

FIG. 257.—The red orange-scale, *Aspidiotus aurantii.* *a*, females, natural size, on leaf; *b*, female, much enlarged, removed from under waxen scale; *c*, the scale, composed of wax and exuviæ, much enlarged; *d*, just hatched young, much enlarged; *e*, male, much enlarged. (After Jordan and Kellogg.)

dropping in 15 oz. of cyanide of potassium, these amounts of acid, water, and cyanide being sufficient to fumigate a tree 12 ft. high by 10 ft. in foliage diameter; that is, to fumigate about 1000 cu. ft. of space. For larger or smaller trees change the amounts of acid, water, and cyanide proportionally. Of washes to be applied in winter, when the leaves are off, the best is one made of lime 50 lbs., sulphur 50 lbs., salt 50 lbs., water 150 gals.; slake the lime with water enough to do it thoroughly, and during the process add the sulphur. Boil one hour with water enough to prevent burning and until the mixture becomes of a deep amber color. Dissolve the salt in water enough to do it quickly and add slowly to the boiling mass. When all is thoroughly mixed together and has actually boiled at least an hour add water enough to make up 150 gals., and apply by spraying or washing while hot. It may be safely applied *when the foliage is off* to any fruit-tree, garden shrub, or small fruit, and is a very effective "scale-killer." Of sprays for the leaves, kerosene emulsion is undoubtedly the safest and best. For use, undiluted crude petroleum should be entirely untreated and of specific gravity of 43° or over on the Beaumé scale. Smith has used this oil safely on all ordinary fruit-trees, but advises not applying it to peach-trees. At time of applying, the trees should be dry, the oil of a temperature not below 60° Fahrenheit, and the nozzles should throw a perpetual fine spray. Kerosene emulsion is made by boiling ½ lb. of hard soap in 1 gal. of water and then adding 2 gals.

of kerosene and churning violently until a thick white cream is formed. Let this cool and jelly; it is the "stock," and will hold for a few weeks; when

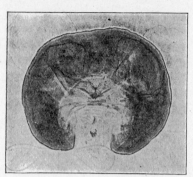

ready to spray, dilute stock with twelve to fifteen times its own bulk of water and spray finely over the foliage. The spraying should be done when the young scales are hatching and crawling about. They are then easily killed by contact with even a single fine drop of kerosene. For peach-trees dilute the stock twenty times.

Some of the scale-insects present such unusual conditions of structural modification and of habits that they are, when first met with, difficult to recognize as insects at all. The waxen covering may be so irregular and

FIG. 258.—Female red orange-scale, *Aspidiotus aurantii*. (Photomicrograph by George O. Mitchell; much enlarged.)

curiously shaped that it gives no clue to the character of the enclosed insect (Fig. 261), but seems to be simply a secretion of the plant in which the insects are found. Or the globular shape and absence of distinct body-parts may make the insects with their hardened blackish cuticle look like small plant-galls; indeed certain scale-insect species were first described by botanists as galls. Some scales live under ground, either in ants' nests or independently; the curious so-called "ground-pearls," small spherical shining bodies found loosely scattered in the soil in certain tropic regions, and really collected to be strung on threads or necklaces, are the strangely modified bodies of *Margarodes formicarum*, a scale-insect. Taken altogether, probably no other family of insects exceeds the Coccidæ in the extremes of strange specializations.

Closely related to the plant-lice and scale-insects are the mealy-winged flies, constituting the family Aleyrodidæ. The adults (Fig. 262), except of two or three of the most abundant species, are rarely seen even by professional entomologists, but careful search will reveal in almost any locality the curious little box-like elliptical bodies of the young (Fig. 263), usually shining black, with pure-white

FIG. 259.—Female rose-scale, *Diaspis rosæ*. (Photomicrograph by George O. Mitchell; much enlarged.)

waxen rods, filaments, or tufts. Examined under a good magnifier, the wax-tufted cases are exquisite objects. These young mealy-wing flies look much like scale-insects and have the same general habits. Provided with a delicate long sucking-beak, each individual remains fixed in one spot on a green leaf, sucking up its food, the plant-sap, as it needs it. The adults which finally issue from the beautiful little cases have four rounded wings, pure white or with small dusky spots and golden yellow, finely beaded margins; each wing has but a single vein, and is dusted with a granular

FIG. 260.—The California live-oak scale, *Cerococcus ehrhorni*. (Photograph by Rose Patterson; natural size.)

white waxen powder or "bloom." The tiny white or pale-yellow eggs are laid on leaves in a circle or the arc of one, in one or more rows, and vary in number from three to thirty; each egg has a minute but noticeable curving stem. The young hatch in from ten to thirteen days, and move freely about, but never seem to get more than about one inch from the deserted shells. This activity lasts for from ten to forty hours; then the young attach themselves to the leaf by inserting the sucking proboscis, and soon moult, losing' at this time the legs and antennæ.  After a second moulting, however, minute new legs and antennæ are again to be seen, and later the wing-pads appear, and wings, legs, and antennæ develop and grow apace; at a last moulting the insect leaves the protection of its beautiful little case and flies away.  Leaving the pupa-case is a slow and toilsome process, the imago often struggling for hours before it is free and ready for flight.

FIG. 261.—The Southern California oak-scale, *Cerococcus quercus.*
(Photograph by Rose Patterson;  natural size.)

All of the pupæ secrete "honey-dew," sometimes in such quantities that the leaf around the case, and the top of the case itself, are covered with it. This honey-dew is emitted from the tip of a little flap-like anal structure called the lingula (Fig. 266).  The sweet liquid honey-dew, when exposed to the air, becomes thick and finally hardens.  The spores of fungi often germinate in the excreted honey-dew, and numerous ant-species collect it for food.

To distinguish any of the various species of mealy-winged flies would be a difficult matter for the beginning entomologist. Two special students of

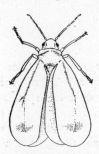

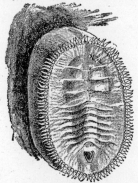

FIG. 262.                              FIG. 263.

FIG. 262.—A mealy-wing, *Aleyrodes pruinosa*, adult.  (After Bemis;  much enlarged.)
FIG. 263.—Pupa of *Aleyrodes tentaculatus*.  (After Bemis;  much enlarged.)

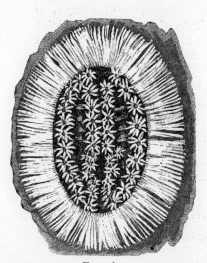

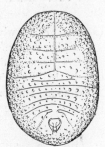

FIG. 265.

FIG. 264.                              FIG. 266.

FIG. 264.—Pupa of *Aleyrodes iridescens*.  (After Bemis;  much enlarged.)
FIG. 265.—Pupa-case of *Aleyrodes merlini*.  (After Bemis;  much enlarged.)
FIG. 266.—Vasiform orifice and lingula of pupa of *Aleyrodes merlini*.  (After Bemis;  much enlarged.)

the American species have published lists and descriptions of all the kinds so far known in this country, namely, Quaintance (Bull. 8, Tech. Ser., Div. of Ent., U. S. Dept. Agr., 1900), who has studied the eastern species, and

Bemis (Proc. U. S. Nat. Mus., vol. 27, 1904), who has studied the Pacific Coast forms.  Mrs. Bemis found twenty hitherto unknown species of mealy-

winged flies in easy collecting range of Stanford University, and these twenty kinds added to those already known make a total of sixty different species so far recorded from the United States.  There are certainly many more species yet unde-scribed.

The mealy-winged flies have some, though not a large, eco-nomic importance.  One or two species, *Aleyrodes vaporariorum*,

FIG. 267.—Pupa of *Aleyrodes merlini*, showing long waxen tufts.  (After Bemis; much en-larged.) .

etc., are recognized as pests in greenhouses; one, *A. citri*, is a pest of oranges, and another, *A. packardi*, injures strawberry-plants.  In all these cases probably as much injury is done by the suffocating fungus growth that is supported by the secreted honey-dew as by the direct sap-sucking of the Aleyrodes themselves.  Fumigation by hydrocyanic gas (see p. 189) is probably the best remedy for the greenhouse and orange mealy-wings, and spraying with kerosene emulsion (see p. 189) the best for the strawberry Aleyrodes.

## SUBORDER HETEROPTERA.

KEY TO FAMILIES OF THE HETEROPTERA (INCLUDES BOTH NYMPHS AND ADULTS).
(ADAPTED FROM WOODWORTH, WITH SOME ADDITIONS.)

Antennæ shorter than the head: aquatic or shore insects.
    With two ocelli........................................(Toad-bugs.)  GALGULIDÆ.
    With no ocelli.
        Hind feet without claws; aquatic insects.
            Prothorax overlapping the head above......(Back-swimmers.)  NOTONECTIDÆ.
            Head overlapping prothorax above.............(Water-boatmen.)  CORISIDÆ.
        Hind feet with claws.
            With two long processes on tip of abdomen which can be held together to form
                a tube......................................(Water-scorpions.)  NEPIDÆ.
            Without abdominal processes, or if any, short flattish retractile ones.
                Hind legs broad and flat............ (Giant water-bugs.)  BELOSTOMATIDÆ.
                Hind legs slender...........................................NAUCORIDÆ.
Antennæ at least as long as the head: a few aquatic forms, but mostly terrestrial.
    Head as long as the whole thorax..............(Marsh-treaders.)  LIMNOBATIDÆ.

Head shorter than thorax.
 Last segment of foot divided and the claws not at the tip.
  Middle and hind legs very long............(Water-striders.) HYDROBATIDÆ.
  Middle and hind legs not very long................................VELIIDÆ.
 Last segment of foot not divided, and the claws at the tip.
  Antennæ 3- or 4-segmented.
   Proboscis (or beak) with three joints.
    Body very long and slender............ (Thread-legged bugs.) EMESIDÆ.
    Body not long and slender.
     Femora of fore legs very wide...........(Ambush-bugs.) PHYMATIDÆ.
     Femora of fore legs not very wide.
      Fore wings usually lacking or rudimentary; when so, ocelli are absent.
                (Bedbugs.) ACANTHIIDÆ.
      Fore wings usually present; when absent, ocelli are always present.
       Hind feet consisting of three joints.
        Beak long and slender..............(Shore-bugs.) SALDIDÆ.
        Beak short and stout...........(Assassin-bugs.) REDUVIIDÆ.
       Hind feet consisting of two joints..........(Flatbugs.) ARADIDÆ.
   Proboscis (or beak) with four joints.
    Without ocelli.
     Heavy-bodied insects, membrane of wings (in adults) with two large cells
      at the base from which arise about eight branching veins (Fig. 268, 2).
              (Redbugs.) PYRROCHORIDÆ.
     Light-bodied insects; membrane of wings (in adults) with one or two closed
      cells at the base and with no longitudinal veins (Fig. 268, 1).
          (Leaf- and flower-bugs.) CAPSIDÆ.
    With ocelli.
     Fore legs very different from the others; wings when present in fully de-
      veloped condition with four long veins in the membrane bounding three
      discal cells, which are often open; from these cells diverge veins which
      form several marginal cells (Fig. 268, 5)... (Damsel-bugs.) NABIDÆ.
     Fore legs not very different from the others.
      Body very narrow...........................(Stilt-bugs.) BERYTIDÆ.
      Body not very slender.
       Feet of two joints; wing-covers (of adults) resembling lace network.
             (Lace-bugs.) TINGITIDÆ.
       Feet of three joints.
        Antennæ inserted below an imaginary line drawn from the eye to the
         beak; membrane of wing (in adults) with four or five simple veins
         arising from its base, the two inner veins sometimes joined to a
         cell near the base (Fig. 268, 3)..(Chinch-bug family.) LYGÆIDÆ.
        Antennæ inserted above an imaginary line drawn from the eye to the
         beak; membrane of wings (in adults) with many usually forked
         veins, springing from a transverse basal vein (Fig. 268, 4).
          (Squash-bug family.) COREIDÆ.
  Antennæ 5-segmented.
   Body flat above.
    With few or no spines on the tibiæ..........(Stink-bugs.) PENTATOMIDÆ.
    With rows of spines on the tibiæ............(Burrower-bugs.) CYDNIDÆ.
   Body strongly convex above.
    Prothorax round in front and nearly straight behind.
          (Negro-bugs.) CORIMELÆNIDÆ.
    Prothorax hexagonal...............(Shield-backed bugs.) SCUTELLERIDÆ.

We come now to the "true bugs," representing twenty-six families and constituting the Heteroptera, the largest of the three suborders of the Hemiptera. The classification of the members of this large group into families, by the use of the keys commonly used by entomologists, demands the recognition of such small and obscure structural characters that I have tried to find some easier means for the use of the amateur and general collector. As collecting and observing in the field imply the discovery of insects in their native haunts, we may acceptably make use of constant habits for a basis of convenient grouping. About one-third of the Heteropterous families are aquatic in habitat, and of these the members of some are to be found on the surface of pools and ponds, of others swimming

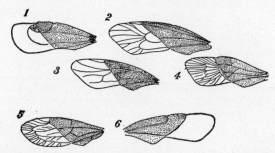

FIG. 268.—Wings of Heteroptera, showing disposition of veins in membrane characteristic of various families: 1, Capsidæ; 2, Pyrrhocoridæ; 3, Lygæidæ; 4, Coreidæ: 5, Nabidæ; 6, Acanthiidæ. (After Comstock.)

or crawling about below the surface, and of two, only partly aquatic, on the shore, but always by the water's edge. Some of these aquatic bugs are to be discovered occasionally in flight far from water, as the giant water-bugs and others, when circling about electric lights or in search of new homes. But the structural signs of the aquatic habitat, legs flattened and fringed so as to be fitted for swimming, will betray these estrays. Occasionally, too, a strictly terrestrial bug will be found on the surface of a pool, but his violent and obviously unaccustomed and awkward attempts to swim to shore will betray him. So we may begin an acquaintance with the Heteroptera by resorting to the nearest pond or quiet stream-pool.

On the surface are the familiar water-striders, or skaters. Their long, spider-like legs, narrow and black or oval and yellow and black body, and swift nervous running distinguish them from all other bugs. They are members of the family Hydrobatidæ, and the commoner species belong to the genus Hygrotrechus (Figs. 269 and 270). Upheld by the tense surface-film of the water, their feet only make little dimpled depressions in the surface, the shadows of which may often be seen on the sandy bottom. The locomotion is really due to a sort of surface rowing or gliding, and not a true running.  The water-striders are predaceous, capturing smaller living insects by running or leaping, and, with the prey held securely in the grasp-

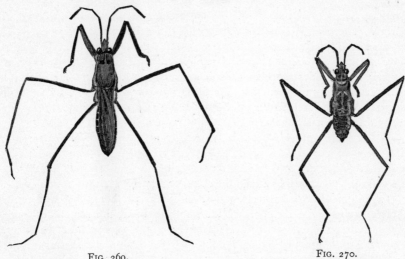

FIG. 269.                                    FIG. 270.

FIG. 269.—Water-strider, *Hygrotrechus* sp., adult.  (Twice natural size.)
FIG. 270.—Water-strider, *Hygrotrechus* sp., young.  (Twice natural size.)

ing fore legs, piercing and sucking the blood of the unfortunate victim, yet alive.  Care should be taken in handling water-striders, as the sharp beak

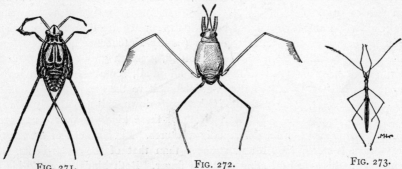

FIG. 271.                    FIG. 272.                    FIG. 273.

FIG. 271.—Broad-bodied water-strider, *Stephania picta*.  (After Uhler; natural size.)
FIG. 272.—An ocean water-skater, *Halobates wüllersdorffi*, from near Galapagos Islands.  (Three times natural size.)
FIG. 273.—A marsh-treader, *Limnobates lineata*.  (One and one-half times natural size.)

can make a painful puncture.  Some of them are winged and some wingless, and both kinds of individuals may belong to the same species.  The young are usually short-bodied, and of course wholly wingless or with small wing-pads only. In late autumn the water-striders conceal themselves in the mud beneath leaves or rubbish or at the bottom of the pool under roots or stones to hibernate, coming out again with the first warm days of spring. The whitish elongate eggs are laid in early spring, being attached by a sort of glue to the leaves and stems of aquatic plants. Some species have several generations each year. Water-striders are easily kept in aquaria if the sides are high enough above water to prevent their leaping out. In bringing them in from the pond covered pails should be used, or they may be enclosed in any small dry receptacle not air-tight. They are easily drowned if shaken about in a covered pail of water.

A few interesting Hydrobatids, belonging to the genus Halobates (Fig. 272), live on the surface of the ocean, especially in subtropic and tropic latitudes. They are said to feed on the juices of dead animals floating on the surface, and probably attach their eggs to floating seaweed (Sargassum).

Certain stout-bodied insects, widest across the prothorax and with much shorter, stouter legs, members of the family Veliidæ, are sometimes to be found, running about on the surface of the water, always near the shore. They can also run readily on land, which the true water-skaters cannot do. Also certain other slender insects, about ½ inch long, with thin long legs and hair-like antennæ and long cylindrical head, are to be found on top of the water. But they creep slowly about on the surface or on the soft mud of the shore, and are found mostly where plants are growing in quiet water. These are marsh-treaders, *Limnobates lineata* (Fig. 273), and this species is the only representative of the family Limnobatidæ known in this country.

Swimming and diving about beneath the surface are the water-boatmen (family Corisidæ) and back-swimmers (family Notonectidæ). The water-boatmen (Fig. 274) are oval, finely mottled, greenish gray and black, and swim with back uppermost. They are all small, some only ⅕ inch long, none over half an inch. The back-swimmers have the back shaped like the bottom of a boat, swim with the back always down, and are usually bluish black and creamy white in color. Both of these kinds of water-bugs are predaceous, feeding on smaller aquatic creatures. But the beak of the back-swimmers is much longer and stronger than that of the water-boatmen, and can make a painful sting on one's finger. Both kinds have the hind legs long and specially flattened and fringed to serve as oars, and both kinds come to the surface for air, although the back-swimmers come up far more often than the water-boatmen. The air taken up clings as a silvery bubble to a large part of the body both under the folded wings and on the under side, being held there by fine hairs which form a pile like that on velvet. A supply of air is thus taken down by the bugs, which enables them to remain for some time under water. Both kinds are attracted to lights, and may often be seen in summer about outdoor electric lamps. The eggs of the water-boatmen are attached to the submerged stems of aquatic plants, while those of the back-swimmers are inserted in the stems, the female having a sharp ovipositor for this purpose. In winter the adults lay dormant in the mud at the bottom of ponds or streams.

All the species of water-boatmen in the country belong to the genus Corisa, while there are three genera of back-swimmers, Notonecta, with hind legs longer than the others and fore wings but little longer than the abdomen, being the most abundant and wide-spread. Plea is a genus with all the legs alike, while Anisops, the third genus, has the wing-covers usually much longer than the abdomen. The complete life-history of no member of either of these families of water-bugs is yet known, but it ought not to be a difficult matter for some persistent observer to add this needed knowledge to entomological science. Both water-boatmen and back-swimmers live

FIG. 274.—A water-boatman, *Corisa* sp. (After Jenkins and Kellogg; twice natural size.)

readily in aquaria, and make thoroughly interesting creatures to observe at leisure. The characteristic habits of obtaining air, swimming, capturing prey, etc., can all be learned from the observation of aquarium specimens. The capacity of the water-boatmen to remain below the surface in pure water for protracted periods, apparently indefinitely long, needs to be better understood than it is at present, and should be an interesting problem for some observer of aquarium life.

Creeping or crawling about among the stems and leaves of submerged plants in reedy and grassy quiet waters, and feeding on smaller insects, may sometimes be found certain small flat-bodied oval insects with front legs thickened and fitted for grasping. These are water-creepers, or Naucoridæ, only five species of which are known in this country. The single species found in the eastern states is known as *Pelocaris femorata*, and is about $\frac{1}{3}$ inch long, broadly oval in shape, and yellowish brown in color. The other species belong to the genus Ambrysus and are restricted to the western states. The life-history of but one member of this family is known.

Occasionally there will be seen resting, or swimming slowly about, at the bottom of the pool a veritable giant bug, $2\frac{3}{4}$ inches long and $1\frac{1}{4}$ inches wide, with heavy strong legs flattened and oar-like and the front ones held out arm-like and bent in an expectant grasping position. Again, in the warm sultry evenings of midsummer and early autumn, among the swarms of insects attracted to the electric lights on the streets, one or two great bugs will go whirling around the bright globe of light, casting large fleeting shadows on the ground below. The giant in the pool's depth and the giant in the giddy swarm at the light are one and the same, viz., the giant water-bug or electric-light bug, a member of the family Belostomatidæ. Most of its life is passed in the water; it hatches from eggs deposited under water, lives its whole immature life in the pool, and only comes out for a short flying season to find mates or a new pool. Two very large species of this family, both common in this country, are *Belostoma americana* (Fig. 275) and *Benacus griseus*, distinguishable by the fact that the former has a groove on each front femur for the tibia to fit in when folded. A smaller kind, more oval in shape, is the commonest form on the Pacific slope. This is *Serphus dilatatus*, the toe-biter,

FIG. 275.

FIG. 276.

FIG. 275.—The giant water-bug or electric-light bug, *Belostoma americana*. (Natural size.)

FIG. 276.—The western water-bug, *Serphus* sp.; male with eggs deposited on its back by female. (Natural size.)

which is 1¼ to 1½ inches long and ¾ to ⅞ inch wide. In the East a still smaller form, *Zaitha fluminea*, is common. This is a little less than 1 inch long. All these Belostomatids are fiercely predaceous, capturing aquatic insects, tadpoles, etc., and are armed with a short, strong, pointed beak with which a serious puncture can be made. They secrete themselves beneath stones or rubbish, whence they dart out on their victims. A considerable amount of poisonous saliva enters the wound made by the beak, and probably aids in overcoming the prey. The larger species attack young fish, seizing them with their strong grasping fore legs and sucking their blood. They can do much injury in carp-ponds or in garden-pools where fishes are kept for pleasure. The females of the species of the smaller genera *Serphus* and *Zaitha* have the curious habit of gluing their eggs upright, in a single layer, on the back of the unwilling male (Fig. 276). For a long time it was believed, and is so stated in most entomological books, that the female deposited the eggs on her own back, but it was discovered by Snodgrass that the female *Serphus* had no ovipositor capable of reaching to her back, and by Miss Slater that the female *Zaitha* is in similar condition. Miss Slater observed the egg-laying by aquarium specimens. The male struggles against the indignity, but is actually overcome by the female.

Another small aquatic family of few species is that of the Nepidæ, or water-scorpions. These dirty brown, stick-like insects can be distinguished from other aquatic Hemiptera by the long slender respiratory tube, made up of separable halves each grooved on its inner face, which projects from the tip of the abdomen. Rather sluggish in habit, they lie at the bottom of a shallow pool and lift this respiratory tube up so that its open tip reaches the surface. They are predaceous and have the fore legs modified for seizing prey, the other legs being fitted for walking or crawling over the bottom. There are two common genera in the family: Nepa, with flattened oval body less than three times as long (not including respiratory tube) as

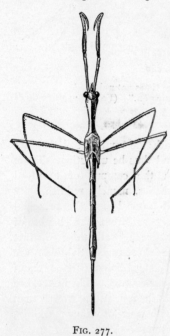

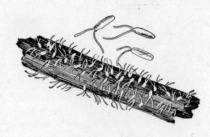

FIG. 277.                    FIG. 278.

FIG. 277.—Young water-scorpion, *Ranatra sp.* (One and one-half times natural size.)
FIG. 278.—Eggs of the water-scorpion, *Ranatra fusca.* (After Pettit; enlarged.)

broad, and Ranatra (Fig. 277), with elongate slender body more than five times as long as broad. Like the giant water-bugs the water-scorpions lie in wait for their prey, trusting to their inconspicuous color and partial concealment in the mud and rubbish of the bottom to hide them from approaching victims.

By the edge of pond or stream may be found representatives of two other small families, most striking in appearance and manner, the dark-colored, squat, broad, rough bodied, big-eyed, leaping toad-bugs (Galgulidæ) and the smaller, soft, long-oval, long-legged, running shore-bugs (Saldidæ). One species of toad-bug, *Gelastocoris oculatus* (Figs. 279 and 280), is common all over the country and may often be found in considerable numbers on

the muddy banks of streams and ponds. It lives upon other insects, which it catches by creeping slowly to within a short distance and then suddenly leaping upon and seizing them with its strong front

FIG. 279.                                        FIG. 280.

FIG. 279.—The toad-bug, *Gelastocoris oculatus.* (Three times natural size.)
FIG. 280.—Three toad-bugs, *Gelastocoris oculatus*, " coming on." (From life; three times natural size.)

legs. Toad-bugs vary in general coloration with the mud or soil they are on, so as to harmonize with the ground color and thus be undistinguishable. The shores of a small pond, Lagunita, on the campus of Stanford University, vary much in ground color, three shades, namely, reddish, slaty

bluish, and mottled sand color, being the principal ones, and toad-bugs collected from the banks of this pond show very noticeably all these distinct schemes of color. The shore-bugs (Saldidæ) are represented by but one genus, Salda (Fig. 281), of thirty or more species, in our country. The insects are about $\frac{3}{16}$ inch long, smooth-bodied, and narrower than the toad-bugs, blackish with white or yellow markings,

FIG. 281. — A shore-bug, *Salda* sp. (Six times natural size.)

and have long slender antennæ. They prefer stream or pond banks which are weedy or grassy and offer good hiding-places. They are common also on seabeaches. They feed on drowned flies and other insects, from which they suck the blood. They thus do some good as scavengers.

The preceding ten families include all of the aquatic and strictly shore-inhabiting Hemiptera. The remaining sixteen families of the suborder Heteroptera, as well as all the families in both other suborders, are terrestrial, being found for the most part (the Parasita wholly excepted) on vegetation, where food, either the juices of the plants, or the blood of other plant-feeding insects, is found. This difference in food-habit is accompanied by more or less obvious structural differences. In the predaceous forms the fore legs are usually spined and fitted for seizing and holding the living victims, the other legs fitted for swift running, the beak is stout, firm, and sharp-pointed, the eyes are often large, protuberant, and flashing bright, and there is a general unmistakable air of ferocity about these miniature bloodthirsty dragons of the garden shrubbery.

Five of the terrestrial families of Heteroptera are predaceous, the remaining eleven being composed of sap-suckers, although in one or two of these families a few species seem to have acquired a taste for blood-sucking.

The largest predaceous family is that of the assassin-bugs, wheel-bugs, and soldier-bugs, the Reduviidæ. More than fifty genera belonging to this family are represented in this country, but so little are the bugs collected or even noticed by amateurs (or professionals either, for that matter) that but few of the species can be said to be at all familiarly known. And to use the word "familiarly" in this connection is to indulge in the figure of speech known as hyperbole.

The Reduviids have an unmistakable look of ferocity, small and insignificant creatures as they are. The eyes are usually large and protuberant, looking like a pair of shining black beads set on the small outstretched head. The beak, 3-segmented, is strong, sharp-pointed, and large for the small head that carries it, and it projects forward in a suggestively eager way. While the ground or body color of the bugs is usually black, they are often conspicuously marked with blood-red and sometimes with yellow. The wingless young are in many species wholly red. A few years ago the newspapers were filled with references to a much dreaded "kissing-bug" (one of the Reduviids), the name being a satire on the stinging and poisoning capabilities of the bug's beak or mouth. The sting, i.e., piercing by the beak, of the kissing-bug, and of all other Reduviids, is poisonous because of the injection of saliva into the wound, and this poisoning, which makes such a wound often very painful and sometimes rather serious to man, must be paralyzing and fatal to the more usual insect victims of the assassin-bugs. The usual "kissing-bug" of the newspapers is the masked bedbug-hunter, *Opsicoetus personatus*, an insect from ½ to ¾ inch long, blackish brown, with prothorax strongly constricted in the middle and longitudinally grooved along the middle of the upper surface. The entomologists' name for this insect comes from the fact that the young exude a sticky substance over the body to which dust, lint, etc., adhere so as to cover or mask the body, and that the bugs enter houses and prey on bedbugs, cockroaches, and flies. The bite or sting is unusually poisonous and severe.

Another assassin-bug which forces its acquaintance on us is the "big bedbug," or cone-nose, *Conorhinus sanguisugus* (Fig. 282), which comes into houses primarily to drink human blood. It is about an inch long, pitchy brown or black, with long narrow head, and with bright red patches on the sides of the body and on the base and apex of the fore wings. These insects, whose normal outdoors food consists of various insects, often noxious ones, as locusts and potato-beetles, are specially common in the South, where Comstock says they not infrequently sting children. The banded soldier-bug, *Milyas cinctus*, is a common wide-spread friend of the farmer, preying on many kinds of noxious insects. It is yellow in all stages of development with conspicuous fine transverse black bands on legs and antennæ. It roams about over plants from early summer to late autumn, benevolently assimilating the blood of its various insect cousins. It glues

FIG. 282.—The blood-sucking cone-nose, *Conorhinus sanguisugus*. (After Howard and Marlatt; natural size.)

its eggs to the bark of trees and covers them with a protecting water-proof gum. Another fairly well-known member of this family is the wheel-bug, *Prionidus cristatus*, especially common in the South. The full-grown bug is about an inch long, black, and has on its thorax a thin convex crest with nine teeth. This is the "wheel." The little jug-shaped eggs are laid in six-sided single-layered masses of about seventy, which are glued to the bark of trees, or on fence-rails, the sides of houses, etc. The young are blood-red, with black on the thorax. The wheel-bugs are specially beneficial because they are among the few predaceous insects that prey on the well-protected hairy caterpillars that infest our shade and orchard trees.

Closely related to the Reduviids are the curious and readily recognized thread-legged bugs, Emesidæ. The few known species have the body very slender and long, and the legs and antennæ simply like jointed threads. The fore legs, however, are spined and fitted for seizing prey. The common species, *Emesa longipes* (Fig. 283), has the body a little less than $1\frac{1}{2}$ inches long, each middle and hind leg a little more than $1\frac{1}{2}$ inches long, and the wings when folded not reaching the tip of the abdomen. It is clayey brown in color with a reddish tinge above. Howard says that one of the thread-legged bugs frequents spiders' webs and robs the spiders of their prey. The damsel-bugs (Nabidæ) are another small family of predaceous insects which usually lurk among flowers and foliage where they capture small insects, but which in autumn may often be seen running about on sidewalks and elsewhere about houses, probably looking for winter hiding-places. One of the commonest and most conspicuous damsel-bugs is the shining jet-black, yellow-legged species *Coriscus subcoleoptratus*. The wings and wing-covers (in most individuals) are reduced to mere scales, the body is wide and plump

behind, tapering forward to the narrow prothorax and head. It is about
½ inch long. The air-bush bug, *Phymata wolfii*, a rough, horny-bodied,
yellowish-green insect with brown or blackish band across the abdomen,
is about ½ inch long or less and the body is
rather like some scaly seed. The abdomen is
curiously widened behind into two thin, angular,
scale-like expansions. It conceals itself in
flower-cups and captures the nectar-sucking
insect visitors. It is very strong and overcomes

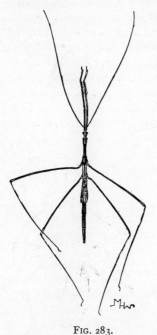

FIG. 283.                     FIG. 284.

FIG. 283.—A thread-legged bug, *Emesa longipes*. (Natural size.)
FIG. 284.—A damsel-bug, *Nabis fusca*. (After Bruner; natural size indicated by line.)

insects, as small butterflies, bees, and wasps, much larger than itself.

Another small family of blood-sucking bugs is the Acanthiidæ, of which
the most familiar is the wingless degenerate pest, the bedbug, *Acanthia
lectularia* (Fig. 285), world-wide in distribution and detestation. To the
fortunate few who have not at one time or other been forced to a personal
acquaintance with this bug species it may be told that it is, when full-grown
and fairly nourished, about ⅕ inch long, reddish brown in color, and broad
and flat bodied. Small wing-scales or pads can be seen on close examination of specimens. The bugs, both immature and adult, can run quickly
and, because of their flatness, can conceal themselves in narrow cracks. In
such crevices in bedsteads, in walls and floors, they hide by day, coming
out at night to feed. In spring the females lay about two hundred oval
white eggs in lots of fifty at a time in their haunts in crevices. The eggs

hatch in about a week and the young become full grown in about three months moulting five times during growth, but active and capable of "finding" for themselves from birth. In the northern states there is but one generation a year. The disagreeable bedbuggy odor is produced by a secretion of small glands opening, in the adult, on the under side of the body. Another species of Acanthia attacks chickens, pigeons, swallows, and bats, and Lugger found this species, *A hirundinis*, or another similar one, attacking in daytime the pupils in a school in western Minnesota. The best remedy is the free application with a quill-feather of a saturated solution of corrosive sublimate (Poison!) in alcohol to all cracks and crevices in infested bedsteads, walls, floors, and ceilings. When bedbugs cannot be found hiding in bedsteads in daytime and yet mysteriously appear every night, it is often because they drop from the ceiling.

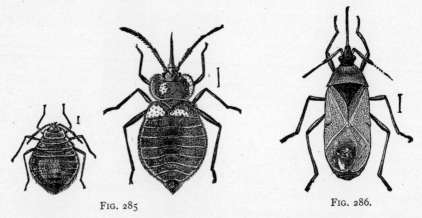

FIG. 285                                              FIG. 286.

FIG. 285.—The bedbug, *Acanthia lectularia;* young at left and adult at right. (After Riley; natural size indicated by line.)

FIG. 286.—A predaceous leaf-bug, *Lyctocoris fitchii*. (After Lugger, natural size indicated by line.)

In this family belong several small inconspicuous insects called flower-bugs, which do much good by their persistent preying on noxious insects. The best-known species is the insidious flower-bug, *Triphleps insidiosus*, which preys on the chinch-bug. Another species is *Lyctocoris fitchii* (Fig. 286), which preys on the larvæ of certain destructive wood-boring beetles.

The remaining families, eleven, of American bugs find their food and drink, for the most part, in the juices of living plants. Like the blood-sucking bugs, they need for their feeding, and have, a well-developed sucking-beak. From the tip of the sheath (labium) can be thrust out the four sharp stylets or lancets (maxillæ and mandibles) to lacerate the plant-tissues, and then the pharyngeal pump sucks up from the wound the flowing sap. When too many pumps are drawing away too much sap, the leaves wilt, yellow, and die.   When too many leaves wilt, the plant starves to death. And if the leaves happen to be the corn-leaves, and the pumpers chinch-bugs, we have the result estimated for us (by the official U. S. statistician) in millions of dollars of loss, as in 1887, when this particular loss in the Missis-sippi Valley states was $60,000,000.

The eleven plant-feeding families of true bugs (Heteroptera) can be distinguished by the following key:

Antennæ 4-segmented.
  Fore wings reticulated and of uniform thin substance throughout . . . . . . .TINGITIDÆ.
  Fore wings of various forms or absent, but not reticulated, and not of uniform thin
    substance throughout.
    Beak 3-segmented;  body greatly flattened. . . . . . . . . . . . . . . . . . . . . . . .ARADIDÆ.
    Beak 4-segmented;  body not greatly flattened.
      Membrane (apical area) of fore wings with one or two closed cells at base, but
        otherwise without veins (Fig. 268). . . . . . . . . . . . . . . . . . . . . . . . .CAPSIDÆ.
      Membrane of fore wings with four or five simple or anastomosing longitudinal
        veins arising from the base;  or with a larger number of veins arising from
        a cross-vein at the base.
        Ocelli wanting;  membrane of fore wings with two large cells at the base, and
          from these arise branching veins (Fig. 268). . . . . . . . . . . . . .PYRRHOCORIDÆ.
        Ocelli present.
          Head with a transverse incision in front of the ocelli. . . . . . . . . .BERYTIDÆ.
          Head without transverse incision.
            Membrane of fore wings with four or five simple veins arising from the
             base of the membrane;  the two inner ones sometimes joined to a
             cell near the base (Fig. 268). . . . . . . . . . . . . . . . . . . . . . . . .LYGÆIDÆ.
            Membrane of fore wings with many usually forked veins springing from
             a transverse basal vein (Fig. 268). . . . . . . . . . . . . . . . . . . . . .COREIDÆ.
Antennæ 5-segmented.
  Scutellum nearly flat, narrowed behind.
    Tibiæ unarmed or furnished with very fine short spines. . . . . . . . . .PENTATOMIDÆ.
    Tibiæ armed with strong spines in rows. . . . . . . . . . . . . . . . . . . . . . . .CYDNIDÆ.
  Scutellum very convex and covering nearly the whole of the abdomen.
    Small, black (sometimes with bluish or greenish tinge). . . . . . . . .CORIMELÆNIDÆ.
    Not black. . . . . . . . . . . . . . . . . . . . . . . . . . . . . . . . . . . . . . . . . . . SCUTELLERIDÆ.

The first of the families in the above table, the Tingitidæ, includes the curious small lace-bugs (Fig. 287), readily recognized by the delicate gauze- or lace-like appearance of the back, due to the uniform thin and reticulated character of the fore wings and of the wing-like expansions of the prothorax. About twenty-five species are found in this country, all being plant-feeders, living mostly on shrubs and trees.  Hawthorn-bushes and oak-, sycamore-, and butternut-trees all have particular species of lace-bugs on them.  In the south cotton and beans are also attacked by lace-bugs. The most familiar eastern species is the hawthorn lace-bug, *Corythuca arcuata*, which is common on the leaves of hawthorn-bushes. The bugs keep almost exclusively on the under side of the leaves. The eggs are laid in small groups on the leaves, each egg being imbedded in a little bluntly conical mass of a brown sticky substance which hardens soon after egg-laying and looks much like

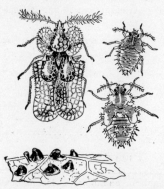

a small fungus. The top of the glistening white egg can be seen, however, by looking down on one of these brown masses. The young is broadly oval and flattened in shape, brown and spiny, and moults five times in its development. The torn, delicate, whitish exuviæ (cast skins) stick to the leaf. The adults hibernate under the fallen leaves on the ground beneath the bushes. In California a similar lace-bug, *Corythuca* sp., (Fig. 287), infests the Christmas berry, *Heteromeles arbutifolia*, a plant whose clusters of bright red berries take the place in Californian Christmas-tide decorations of the holly of the East. The eggs (Fig. 287) are deposited in the same way as the hawthorn lace-bugs', and the life-history is practically the same. But because the California winter is much less severe and the Christmas berry is covered with green leaves all the year, active lace-bugs, young as well as adult, can always be found on the bushes. Lace-bugs, small as they are, injure any plant on which they gather in numbers, by the continual draining away of the sap. Spraying the infested bushes or trees with kerosene emulsion (p. 189) will kill the insects.

Fig. 287. — The lace-bug, *Corythuca* sp., of the California Christmas berry, *Heteromeles arbutifolia;* at bottom, eggs on small tubercles on leaf; above, just-hatched young, intermediate stage, and adult. (Eight times natural size.)

The flattest of all the bugs, flatter than the bedbugs even, are the curious members of the small family Aradidæ. They live in the cracks or beneath the bark of decaying trees, and their dull brown color and flat leaf-like body make them very difficult to distinguish when at rest in their hiding-places. The glistening white eggs are laid under the bark. The flatbugs are often mistaken for bedbugs, as they are nocturnal and are often found in log cabins. But they probably feed exclusively on plant-sap, being especially attracted to mills and recently felled trees, where they suck up the sap exuding from the cut or sawed logs. *Aradus cinnamomeus* (Fig. 288) is about the same size as a full-grown bedbug and is reddish in tinge, so that superficially it does much resemble a bedbug. But most adult flatbugs have wings, while all the bedbugs are wingless.

The flower-bug family, Capsidæ, contains two hundred and fifty known North American species, almost all of which, however, are small and inconspicuous. They mostly live in pastures, meadows, gardens, and along roadsides, on the grasses, weeds, and herbaceous flowering plants of these places, but some infest woody plants and a few species do much damage to garden and orchard shrubs and trees. A few species are predaceous, and Howard has seen one species sucking the eggs of the imported elm-leaf beetle, a great pest of our elm-trees. The structural characteristic by which they can most readily be distinguished from other bugs is the presence of one or two closed cells and no longitudinal veins in the membrane (apical half) of each fore wing (Fig. 268). When examined closely many of these

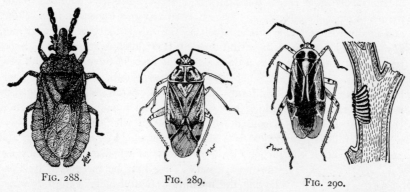

FIG. 288.          FIG. 289.               FIG. 290.

FIG. 288.—A flatbug, *Aradus cinnamomeus.* (After Lugger; enlarged about six times.)
FIG. 289.—The tarnished plant-bug, *Lygus pratensis.* (Five times natural size.)
FIG. 290.—The four-lined leaf-bug, *Pœcilocapsus lineatus;* at right, eggs deposited in plant-stem. (Figure of insect original, enlarged three and a half times; of eggs, after Slingerland, and much enlarged.)

little bugs will be seen to be elaborately patterned and beautifully colored, and their body outline is trim and graceful. They are active and quick to escape from the collecting-net. (The best way to collect them is by sweeping rankly growing herbage with a short-handled stout net.) Among the most abundant and wide-spread Capsids of economic importance is the tarnished plant-bug, *Lygus pratensis* (Fig. 289), which attacks many cultivated plants, as the sugar-beet, strawberry, pear-, plum-, apple-, quince-, and other fruit-trees. It is about $\frac{1}{5}$ inch long, and ranges from dull dark brown to yellowish or greenish brown. A yellowish-white V-shaped mark on the scutellum is its most characteristic marking. It hibernates in the adult stage, under fallen leaves or in any rubbish, and comes out in the spring to pierce and suck sap from tender buds and leaves. The four-lined leaf-bug, *Pœcilocapsus lineatus* (Fig. 290), a small bright-yellow bug with head and under side of body orange-red, and four black stripes on the back, is abundant in the east and north, and is known to attack at least fifty different kinds of cultivated plants. It is especially familiar as a currant-pest. The eggs are deposited in slits cut lengthwise in plant-stems. The best general remedy for these bugs is the jarring of branches of the bushes over a dish partly filled with kerosene. Comstock says that the most abundant flower-bug in the northeastern states is a small greenish-yellow species with two longitudinal black stripes extending from the eyes over the prothorax and scutellum. It is long ($\frac{2}{5}$ inch) and narrow ($\frac{1}{12}$ inch), is found in the grass in meadows, and its name is *Leptoterna dolobrata*. The injury done by all Capsids is by the sucking of sap through small punctures and probably also, in some cases, the pouring of poisonous saliva into the plant-tissues through the punctures. The attacked leaves or buds wilt, turn yellow, and finally wither. One of the beneficial Capsids is the glassy-winged bug, *Hyaliodes vitripennis*, a beautiful small yellowish-white insect with almost transparent fore wings, with a dash across the apex of these wings, and prothorax red. It feeds on other insects, and especially on the grape-phylloxera in its leaf-inhabiting form. *Lopidea media* is an abundant yellowish-red and black Capsid which has learned to like human blood. When it cannot have blood it is content with the sap of wild gooseberries.

The family Pyrrhocoridæ is a small family of comparatively large and stout bugs, often conspicuous by their colors, of which red and black are

the most usual. They may be recognized by their having the membrane (apical half) of the fore wings provided with two large basal cells from which several branching veins arise (Fig. 268). They are commonly known as "redbugs," and the twenty-five species found in our country belong mostly to the south and west. The commonest species in the north is *Largus succinctus* (Fig. 291), a rusty blackish-brown bug about half an inch long, with yellowish or pinkish-orange margins on the front two-thirds of the back, and a transverse stripe of similar color across the base of the prothorax. The young are steel-blue with a small bright-red dash on base of the abdomen between the backward-projecting wing-pads. This species ranges from New Jersey to California and south into Mexico. The commonest species of the southern states, and one of great economic importance, is the red-bug or cotton-stainer, *Dysdercus suturellus*, which does much damage by piercing the stems and bolls of the cotton-plant and sucking the juices, but does even more damage by staining the cotton in the opening bolls

FIG. 291.—Redbug, *Largus succinctus*. (Twice natural size.)

by its reddish-yellow excretions.   Howard says that experiments have
been made with this insect looking towards its use commercially, and that
the whole substance of the insect can be converted into a rich orange-
yellow dye which is readily fixed on woolens or silk by the alum mordant
liquor.   The cotton-stainer is a handsome bug, reddish in color with pale
brown fore wings striped with pale yellow.   The young are bright red with
black legs.   Comstock says that this insect also punctures oranges in
Florida, so that the fruit begins to decay and drops from the tree.   The
insects can be trapped by laying chips of sugar-cane about the cotton-field or
orange-grove: the bugs will gather about these chips and may be scalded
to death.

One of the largest families of true bugs is the Lygæidæ, made notorious
by a small and obscure representative of it, which, according to the estimate
of the United States Entomologist, causes our country an annual loss of
$20,000,000.   This insect is the chinch-bug, the
worst pest of corn, and one of the worst of wheat
and other small grains.   Nearly two hundred species
of Lygæids occur in this country, and most of
them may fairly be called noxious insects.   The
family's structural characteristic most readily noted
is the presence of but four or five simple longitudinal
veins in the membrane (apical half) of the fore wings
(Fig. 268).   The antennæ rise rather from the under
than the upper side of the head, and all of the members
of the family have ocelli (simple eyes).   While most
of the Lygæids are small and inconspicuous, a few
are comparatively large and bright-colored.   The
milkweed-bug, Oncopeltus fasciatus, about $\frac{2}{3}$ inch

FIG. 292.—*Lygæus turci-
cus.*   (After Lugger;
much enlarged.)

long, orange above with most of head and prothorax except the margins
black, and a broad black band across the middle of the fore wings and
large black blotch on their tips, is a common showy bug on various
species of milkweed.   An odd-looking, long-necked, common member of
the family is *Myodocha serripes.*   It is about $\frac{3}{8}$ inch long, with head long
and narrow, expanding in front, and rising from a bell-shaped prothorax,
the rest of the body being elongate and narrow.   It is black, with the
margins, sutures, veins, and some spots on the wing-covers yellow.   It is
common in meadows and thin woods, where it keeps half concealed under
fallen leaves and twigs.   In the south a small species, *Pamera longula,* $\frac{1}{4}$
inch long, dark brown with lighter brown on prothorax and fore wings, is
abundant, feeding mostly on meadow plants.

Among the many smaller species, the chinch-bug, *Blissus leucopterus*
(Fig. 293), is the best known and most important.   It is found nearly all

over the United States and in Canada, but the great losses occasioned by it occur mostly in the corn-growing states of the Mississippi Valley, where it has been known as a pest since 1823. I have seen great corn-fields in this valley ruined in less than a week, the little black and white bugs massing in such numbers on the growing corn that the stalk and bases of the leaves were wholly concealed by the covering of bugs. The chinch-bug when adult is about ⅙ inch long, blackish with the fore wings semi-transparent white and with a conspicuous small triangular black dot near the middle of the outer margin. The very young are red, but become blackish or gray as they grow older. The bug is injurious in all stages, young, half grown, and adult. The life-history, in Kansas, is as follows: The eggs are laid in the spring (from middle of March to middle of May) by bugs which have hibernated in the adult stage. They are laid a few at a time, perhaps five hundred in all by each female. The young "red-bugs" begin work in the wheat-fields, and usually

FIG. 293.—The chinch-bug, *Blissus leucopterus.* (Nine times natural size.)

remain in the wheat until harvest (last of June to middle of July), when the destructive host moves into the fields of young and growing corn. It requires about six weeks for the maturing of the bugs. The adults now pair and the cycle of a new generation begins. The perfect insects of this generation are those which pass through the winter and lay the eggs the following spring for the next year's first brood. It is highly probable if not certain that a third brood often appears in Kansas. The chinch-bug, though winged, uses its powers of flight but little, and its migrations from wheat- to corn-fields in July are usually on foot. The wings are used to some degree at pairing-time.

The remedies for chinch-bug attacks include the gathering together in winter of all rubbish, old corn-leaves, dead leaves, etc., in which the old bugs hibernate, and burning it, which will destroy many parent bugs, thereby largely lessening the spring brood. Disputing the entrance of the bugs into the field, when migrating on foot, by plowing furrows around the field and pouring coal-tar or crude petroleum into these moats, is often effective. There are several natural remedies, namely, the attacks of predaceous insects, as aphis-lions, ladybird-beetles, and others, and the attacks of some birds, as the common quail. Most effective of all, however, is the rapid spread in a crowded field of a parasitic fungus, *Sporotrichum globuliferum*, which kills the bugs by the wholesale. This fungus cannot grow rapidly except in moist warm weather, and the bugs thrive especially in dry weather. So the rapid spreading and effective killing by this disease depends on favorable meteorological conditions.    The "chinch-bug cholera" is well established all through the Mississippi Valley, but it can be artificially spread by distributing dead and infected bugs in fields where it has not begun to develop. This method is followed in several of the corn- and wheat-growing states whose entomolgists keep on hand a supply of this fungus—it can be artificially cultivated on various nutrient media in the laboratory—to send out to farmers on request.    The work was begun by Professor F. H. Snow of the University of Kansas, and though in the beginning its beneficial results were overrated, there is no doubt that much good has come from this widespread attempt to disseminate artificially the "chinch-bug disease."

The family Coreidæ, to which the squash-bug, the box-elder bug, and certain other more or less familiar insects belong, is another of the larger true bug families, being represented in this country by about two hundred species. In this family the membrane (apical half) of the fore wings is furnished with many veins, most of which arise from a cross-vein near the base (Fig. 268), and the antennæ arise from the upper side of the head.    The squash-bug, *Anasa tristis* (Fig. 294), ill-favored and ill-smelling, is a pest of squashes and pumpkins all over the country. It is brownish black above, with some yellow spots along the edges of the body, and dirty yellow below.    It hibernates in the adult stage, comes out in early spring, and lays its eggs on the young sprouts or leaves of squash- and pumpkin-vines.    The young hatch in about two weeks and at first are green, but soon turn brown and grayish. They suck the sap from the growing vine, and soon stunt them or even kill them.    The remedy is to protect the young plants by means of frames cov-

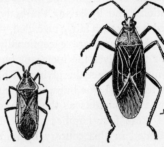

FIG. 294.             FIG. 295.

FIG. 294.—A squash-bug, *Anasa tristis*. (Natural size.)

FIG. 295.—The box-elder bug, *Leptocoris trivittatus*. (Twice natural size.)

ered with netting.    After the plants get well started the bugs cannot injure them so easily.    The box-elder bug, *Leptocoris trivittatus* (Fig. 295), a conspicuous black insect with three bright-red broad lines on the prothorax and the fore wings, with edges and veins of a more dingy red, has become familiar with the increased planting of box-elder trees in gardens and streets. In the Mississippi Valley and in the plains states these box-elders are much used for shade and ornamental trees because of their hardiness, and with this increased supply of trees the box-elder bugs have come to be very abundant. In late autumn they gather under sidewalks or, often, in stables and houses to pass the winter, and have led many housewives to think a new and enlarged kind of bedbug had come to town.    The bug lives on the sap of the trees until winter, and it does not care for much food while hibernating. As its mouth is a sucking-beak, it cannot possibly injure hard and dry household substances, as some housewives claim. Another Coreid, not uncommon, is the cherry-bug, *Metapodius femoratus*, which punctures cherries to suck the juice from them. It is dark brown with a rough upper surface, and its hind femora are curved thick and knobby, while the hind tibiæ have a blade-like expansion. The leaf-footed plant-bug, *Leptoglossus oppositus*, is a Coreid destructive to melon-vines, recognizable by the remarkable leaf-like expansion of its hind tibiæ. A similar leaf-footed species, *Leptoglossus phyllopus*, occurs in the south, where it attacks oranges and other subtropical fruits.

Allied to the Coreidæ is the family Berytidæ, or stilt-bugs, of which but a few species are known in this country. One of these, *Jalysus spinosus*, is common all over the country east of the Sierra Nevadas. It is about $\frac{1}{3}$ inch long, very slender, and light yellowish brown in color, and is found "in the undergrowth of oak woods." Its life-history is not known.

The remaining four families of true bugs are distinguished by their possession of 5-segmented (instead of 4-segmented) antennæ (with a few exceptions) and by having the body broad, short, and flatly convex,—shield-shaped it may then fairly be called,—or very convex or turtle-shaped. Almost all of these bugs are exceptionally ill-smelling and have on this account got for themselves the inelegant but expressive popular name of stink-bugs. As a matter of fact the giving off of offensive odors is characteristic of most of the terrestrial true bugs, the squash-bug, chinch-bug, and others being just about as malodorous as the so-called stink-bugs.

Of these four families of shield-bodied bugs, one, the Pentatomidæ, is represented in this country by numerous species, but the other three contain but one or two genera each. While most of the Pentatomids, or stink-bugs, are plant-feeders, a few are blood-sucking, while some feed indifferently on either animal or plant juices. Several of the more common Pentatomids are green, as the large green tree-bug, *Nezara pennsylvanica*, nearly $\frac{3}{4}$ inch long, flattened, with grass-green body margined with a light yellow line, occurring in the fall on grape-vines and other plants; and the bound tree-bug, *Lioderma ligata*, much like Nezara, but with broader body edging of pale red and with a pale-red spot on the middle of its back, found often abundantly on berries and hazel. Other common stink-bugs are brown, as the various species of Euchistes. Still others are conspicuously colored with red and black, as the abundant small species *Cosmopepla carnifex*, about $\frac{1}{3}$ inch long, shining black with red and orange spots, most conspicuous of which are a transverse and a longitudinal line in the back of the prothorax. The best known and most destructive of these bizarre-colored stink-bugs is the harlequin cabbage-bug, or calico-back, *Murgantia histrionica* (Fig. 296), black with red or orange or yellow strips and spots, which has gradually spread from its native home in Central America to all except the northern states of our country. It feeds on cabbages, radishes, turnips, and other garden vegetables, and often does great damage in market-gardens. In California it has to be fought vigorously in the large market-

FIG. 296.            FIG. 297.            FIG. 298.

FIG. 296.—The harlequin cabbage-bug, *Murgantia histrionica*. (Twice natural size.)
FIG. 297.—The spined tree-bug, *Podisus spinosus*. (After Lugger; natural length, ⅔ inch.)
FIG. 298.—A stink-bug, *Pentatoma juniperina*. (One and one-half times natural size.)

and seed-gardens of the Santa Clara Valley. The adults hibernate, and in the spring each female lays about twelve eggs in two parallel rows on the under surface of the young leaves. The young bugs, which are pale green, hatch in three days, and in two or three weeks are full grown. There can thus be several generations in a season.

Among the predaceous or blood-sucking stink-bugs the species of the genus Podisus are especially common and effective. They destroy many injurious insects. *Podisus spinosus* (Fig. 297), the most familiar species, may be recognized by the prominent spine-like processes projecting from the posterior lateral angles of the prothorax. The large gray tree-bugs of the genus Brachymena with roughened spiny back and grayish body-color may be found resting on the bark of trees, with whose color and roughness they harmonize so thoroughly as to be nearly indistinguishable. They feed indifferently on either plant-sap or the blood of other insects.

Representatives of the three other families of shield-backed or stink-bugs will be rarely found by general collectors. The flea-like negro-bug, *Corimelæna pulicaria* (family Corimelænidæ), is a tiny, very malodorous, polished black species often abundant on blackberries and raspberries, with which it often goes to market and even farther! The burrower-bugs (family Cydnidæ) have an oval rounded or elliptical blackish body with the front legs more or less flattened and fitted for digging. They are found burrowing in sandy places or under sticks or stones. They probably suck the sap from plant-roots.

SUBORDER PARASITA.

The members of the suborder Parasita are the disgusting and discomforting degenerate wingless Hemiptera known as lice. They live parasitically on the bodies of various mammals, the ones most familiar being the three species found on man, all belonging to the genus Pediculus, and the several species of the genus Hæmatopinus found on domestic animals, as dogs, horses, cattle, sheep, etc. Both these genera together with a few others found on various wild animals, belong to the Pediculidæ, the single family of the suborder represented in this country. The only other family, Polycterridæ, contains but two species, both found on bats, one in Jamaica and the other in China.

All the Pediculids are wholly wingless, have the mouth-parts fused to form a flexible sucking-tube, and the feet provided with a single strong curved claw which specially adapts them for clasping and clinging to hairs. The

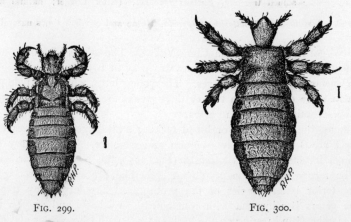

FIG. 299.                    FIG. 300.

FIG. 299.—The head-louse of man, *Pediculus capitus*. (After Lugger; natural size indicated by line.)
FIG. 300.—The body-louse of man, *Pediculus vestimenti*. (After Lugger; natural size indicated by line.)

sucking-beak has been described by Uhler as "a fleshy unjointed rostrum capable of great extension by being rolled inside out, this action serving to bring forward a chaplet of barbs which imbed themselves in the skin to give a firm hold for the penetrating bristles arranged as chitinous strips in a long, slender, flexible tube terminated by four very minute lobes which probe to the capillary vessels of a sweat-pore." Of the three species of Pediculus infesting unclean persons, *P. capitus* (Fig. 299), the head-louse, is longer than wide, whitish with faint dark markings at the sides of the thorax and abdomen; *P. vestimenti* (Fig. 300), the body-louse, is of the same shape and general appearance, but when full grown has the dorsal surface marked with dark transverse bands; while *P. inguinalis* (Fig. 301), the crab-louse, has the body as wide as long, with strong legs spreading out laterally so as to increase the apparent width very

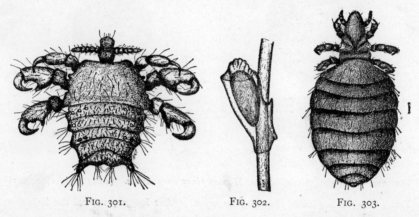

FIG. 301.          FIG. 302.          FIG. 303.

FIG. 301.—The crab-louse of man, *Phthirius inguinalis*. (After Lugger; much enlarged.)
FIG. 302.—Egg of crab-louse, *Phthirius inguinalis*. (After Lugger; much enlarged.)
FIG. 303.—Sucking dog-louse, *Hæmatopinus piliferus* Burm. (After Lugger; natural size indicated by line.)

much. The eggs (Fig. 302), called "nits," of these lice are whitish and are glued to the hairs (in the case of *P. capitus*) or deposited in folds of the clothing (*P. vestimenti*), and the young, when hatched, resemble the parents except in size. The whole life is passed on the body of the host. The prime remedy for these disgusting pests is cleanliness. Various sulphur and mercurial ointments will kill the insects.

The lice of the domestic animals belong to a different genus, Hæmatopinus, but are very similar in appearance and structure to the head-lice of man. *H. piliferus* (Fig. 303), of dogs, is about $\frac{1}{10}$ inch long, reddish yellow, and with the abdomen thickly covered with fine hairs and minute tubercles; *H. eurysternus* (Fig. 304), the short-nosed ox-louse, of cattle, is from $\frac{1}{8}$ inch to $\frac{1}{5}$ inch long, fully half as wide, with the head bluntly rounded in front and nearly as broad as long; *H. vituli*, long-nosed ox-louse, also of cattle, is about ⅛ inch long and not more than ⅓ as wide, with long slender head, narrow in front; *H. urius* (Fig. 305), of hogs, is ¼ inch long, being one of the largest of the sucking-lice, with broad abdomen and long head, and gray in color, with the lateral margins of head, thorax, and abdo-

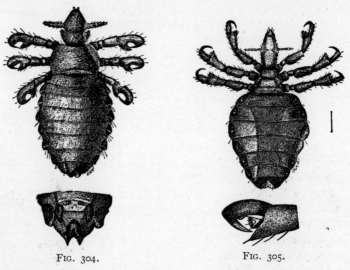

FIG. 304.                                    FIG. 305.

FIG. 304.—Short-nosed cattle-louse, *Hæmatopinus eurysternus*. (After Lugger; natural length 1.5 mm.)
FIG. 305.—The hog-louse, *Hæmatopinus urius*. (After Lugger; natural size indicated by line.)

men black; *H. pedalis*, the sheep-foot louse, found only on the legs and feet of sheep, below the long wool, has a short, wide head and same general shape as the short-nosed ox-louse; *H. asini*, of horses, of about same size as the short-nosed ox-louse, but with long and slender head with nearly parallel sides; *H. spinulosus*, of the rat, small, light yellow, and with the head projecting very little in front of the antennæ and the thorax very short; *H. acanthopus*, of the field-mouse, resembling the rat-louse in color and shape, but larger; *H. ventricosus*, of rabbits and hares, thick-bodied and short-legged and with abdomen nearly circular; *H. antennatus*, of the fox-squirrel, with long slender body and curious curved tooth-like process on basal segment; *H. sciuropteri*, of the flying squirrel, with slender light-yellow body, and head as broad as long, and with front margin nearly straight; *H. suturalis*, of the ground-squirrels and chipmunks, with short broad golden-yellow body. The eggs of all these forms are glued to the hair of the hosts, the young louse escaping by the outer or unattached end and immediately beginning an active blood-sucking life. The most effective and feasible remedy in the case of thin-haired animals, as swine and horses, is the application of a wash of tobacco-water or dilute carbolic acid, or of an ointment made of one part sulphur to four parts lard, or kerosene in lard, or of a liberal dusting with wood ashes or powdered charcoal; in the case of thick-haired animals, as cattle, the best remedy is fumigation by enclosing the animal in a sac or tent with the head left free, and burning sulphur or tobacco inside the sack. One to two ounces of tobacco and exposure of twenty to thirty minutes for each cow have been found effective.

A BRIEF account of the curious little insects known as thrips may be appended here to the chapter on the Hemiptera (Fig. 307). These narrow-

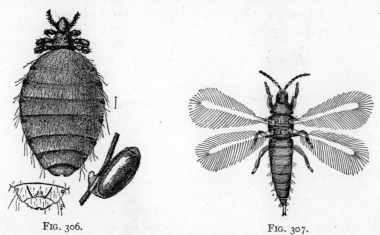

FIG. 306.                              FIG. 307.

FIG. 306.—The sheep-louse, *Hæmatopinus ovis*, female and egg. (After Lugger; natural size of insect indicated by line; egg much enlarged.)
FIG. 307.—Thrips, *Phorithrips* sp. (Much enlarged.)

bodied, fringe-winged, yellowish or reddish brown or blackish little creatures can be most readily found in flower-cups, which they frequent for the sake of sucking the sap from the pistils and stamens or the delicate sepals and petals. Some of them move slowly when disturbed, but others run quickly or leap, and nearly all show an odd characteristic bending up of the tip of the slender abdomen. This movement is usually preparatory to flight (in the case of winged individuals), and is believed to be the means of separating and combing out the fringes which border both fore and hind margins of each wing. There are fine spines on the sides of the abdomen, and the movement of the abdomen seems to draw the fringe-hairs through these comb-like rows of spines. The thrips vary in size from $\frac{1}{50}$ to $\frac{1}{3}$ of an inch, and may be certainly known by their narrow fringed wings (when present), which, when the insect is at rest, are laid back along the abdomen unfolded, and parallel or slightly overlapping at the tips. Only about forty species are yet known in this country, but as practically only one entomologist has attempted to make a systematic study of the group and his specimens were mostly collected in a single locality (Amherst, Massachusetts), it is certain that many species are yet to be found and named. This entomologist, Hinds, has published in a recent paper (Contrib. to a Monograph of the Thysanoptera of N. A., Proc. U. S. Nat. Mus., vol. xxvi, 1902) practically all that is known of our American species, and I have largely drawn on his paper for the present short account.

Although the thrips used to be classified as a family of the order Hemiptera, they are now, and rightly, assigned to an order of their own, called Thysanoptera (fringe-wings). This separation is due to the peculiar characters of their mouth-parts and of the feet, and to the interesting character of their development, which is apparently of a sort of transitional condition between incomplete and complete metamorphosis. The food of the thrips is either the sap of living plants or moist, decaying vegetable matter, especially wood and fungi. The mouth-structure in accordance with this food habit is of a sucking type, with mandibles and maxillæ modified to be needle-like to pierce the plant epidermis. But the mouth-parts are curiously asymmetrical, the right mandible being wholly wanting and the upper lip being more expanded on one side than the other (Fig. 308). The peculiarity in the life-history consists in a quiescent, non-food-taking stage like the pupal stage in insects of complete metamorphosis, but before reaching this stage well-developed external wing-pads have appeared, just as happens in the case of immature insects of incomplete metamorphosis. Finally, the peculiar character of the feet is due to the presence of a small protrusile or expansile membranous sac or bladder at the tip of the tarsus, instead of claws or fixed pads, which seems to play a not well understood function in the holding on by the insect to the leaf or flower parts which it may have occasion to visit. The bladder seems

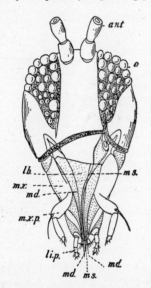

FIG. 308.—Head and mouth-parts, much enlarged, of thrips. *ant.*, antenna; *lb.*, labrum; *md.*, mandible; *mx.*, maxilla; *mx.p.*, maxillary palpus; *li.p.*, labial palpus; *m.s.*, mouth-stylet. (After Uzel; much enlarged.)

to be expanded by becoming suddenly filled with blood, and contracted by a receding of the blood.

The eggs are laid either under bark or on the surface of leaves or, in the case of certain species which have a sharp little ovipositor, underneath the leaf-epidermis. They hatch in from three to fifteen days, varying with the different species observed, and the young grow and feed for from five to forty days. Then follows the brief, quiet, non-feeding stage, and the insect becomes mature. Probably several generations appear in a year. The winter is passed in either larval, pupal, or adult stage, under bark, in dry, hollow plant-stems, in lichens or moss, or on the ground under fallen leaves. A curious variation in the adults of many species has been noted in reference to the wings; adult individuals of a single species may have either fully developed wings, very short functionless wings, or even none at all; both sexes may be winged, or one winged and the other not; one or both sexes may be short-winged or both be wingless. There seems to exist a condition somewhat like that in the plant-lice (Aphididæ), wings being developed in accordance with special needs or influences, as scarcity of food, time of the year, etc.

Another peculiarity of the adults is the rarity, and even, apparently, the total lack of males in some species. Parthenogenetic development (the production of young from unfertilized eggs) is very common throughout the order.

While the food of those thrips most easily found by the beginning student is the sap taken from flower parts, most of the sap-drinking species get their supply from the leaves of various plants, and when these plants happen to be cultivated ones of field or garden, and the thrips are abundant, these tiny insects get the ugly name of "pests." Three species in particular are recognized by economic entomologists as pests, viz., the onion-thrips (*Thrips tabaci*), the wheat-thrips (*Euthrips tritici*), and the grass-thrips (*Anaphothrips striatus*). The first of these is about $\frac{1}{25}$ inch long, about one-fourth as wide as long, and of a uniformly light-yellowish to brownish-yellow color. It feeds on many different cultivated plants, as apple, aster, blue grass, melons, clover, tobacco, tomato, cauliflower, etc., etc., but its chief injuries seem to be to onions and cabbages. It occurs all over Europe, England, and the United States, and is probably the most injurious species in the order. The wheat-thrips, also but $\frac{1}{25}$ inch long, brownish yellow with orange-tinged thorax, attacks many plants besides wheat, and is very fond of puncturing the pistils and stamens of strawberry-flowers, thus often preventing fertilization and consequent development of fruit. The life-cycle of this species is very short, requiring only twelve days. Eggs deposited in the tissues of infested plants hatch in three days, the larvæ are full-grown in five days, and the quiescent pseudo-pupal stage lasts four days. The grass-thrips is the cause of the injury or disease of meadow and pasture grasses known as "silver top" or "white top," a common trouble in the northeastern states. The male sex seems to be wanting in this species, the young all developing parthenogenetically.

# CHAPTER XI

## THE NERVE - WINGED INSECTS (Order Neuroptera) SCORPION-FLIES (Order Mecoptera), AND CADDIS-FLIES (Order Trichoptera).

LINNÆUS, the first great classifier of animals and plants, found in the character of the wings a simple basis for grouping insects into orders. For the wingless insects he established the order Aptera;* the two-winged ones he called Diptera; the moths and butterflies, with scale-covered wings, he called Lepidoptera; the beetles with their horny sheath-like fore wings he termed Coleoptera; the thin- and membranous-winged ants, bees, wasps, and ichneumon-flies he named Hymenoptera; to the roaches, crickets, locusts, and katydids, with their parchment-like straight-margined fore wings, he gave the name Orthoptera; the sucking-bugs with their fore wings having the basal half thickened and veinless, the apical half membranous and veined, he called Hemiptera; and finally he grouped the heterogeneous host of dragon-flies, May-flies, ant-lions, lace-winged flies *et al.*, with their thin netted- or nerve-veined wings, in the order Neuroptera.

In the light of our present greatly increased knowledge of the structure and development (the two bases of classification) of insects, this primary Linnæan arrangement can no longer be accepted as an exposition of the true relationships among the larger groups of insects; that is, it is obviously not a natural classification. Its greatest faults are that it groups together in the Aptera degenerate wingless members of various unrelated groups with the true primitively wingless insects, and places together in the Neuroptera a host of insects of somewhat similar superficial appearance, but of radically dissimilar fundamental structure and development. With increasing knowledge of the characteristics of the various subgroups in the Linnæan order Neuroptera, the too aberrant ones have been gradually one by one removed,

* Aptera, from ἀ, without, *pteron*, a wing; Diptera, from *dis*, double, *pteron*, a wing; Lepidoptera, from *lepis*, a scale, *pteron*, a wing; Coleoptera, from *koleos*, a sheath, *pteron*, a wing; Hymenoptera, from *humen*, a membrane, *pteron*, a wing; Orthoptera, from *orthos*, straight, *pteron*, a wing; Hemiptera, from *hemi*, half, *pteron*, a wing; Neuroptera, from *neuron*, a nerve, *pteron*, a wing.

and in most cases given specific ordinal rank. Thus we now consider the May-flies to from an order, the stone-flies another, the dragon-flies still another, and so on. There are left, grouped together as the order Neuroptera, seven families which possess the common characteristics of netted-veined wings (numerous longitudinal and cross veins), mouths with well-developed biting or piercing jaws (mandibles), and a development with complete metamorphosis. Further than this little can be said to characterize the order as a whole, and we may proceed at once to a consideration of the various distinct families.

### KEY TO THE FAMILIES OF NEUROPTERA.

A. Prothorax as long as or longer than the mesothorax and the metathorax combined.
    B. Fore legs greatly enlarged and fitted for grasping............MANTISPIDÆ.
    BB. Fore legs not enlarged and not fitted for grasping.............RAPHIDIIDÆ.
AA. Prothorax not as long as the mesothorax and the metathorax combined.
    B. Hind wings broad at the base, and with that part nearest the abdomen (the anal area) folded like a fan when not in use....................SIALIDÆ.
    BB. Hind wings narrow at base, and not folded like a fan when closed.
        C. Wings with very few veins, and covered with whitish powder.
                                  CONIOPTERYGIDÆ.
        CC. Wings with numerous veins, and not covered with powder.
            D. Antennæ gradually enlarged towards the end, or filiform with a terminal knob................................MYRMELEONIDÆ.
            DD. Antennæ without terminal enlargement.
                E. Some of the transverse veins between the costa and subcosta forked (in all common forms), wings brownish or smoky.
                                  HEMEROBIIDÆ.
                EE. Transverse veins between the costa and subcosta simple, wings greenish..............................CHRYSOPIDÆ.

While most of the Neuroptera are terrestrial in both immature and adult life, one family, the Sialidæ, includes forms whose larvæ are aquatic. There are only three genera in the family, but all are fairly familiar insects to collectors and field students. The adults of these genera can be distinguished by the following key:

Fourth segment of the tarsus bilobed; no simple eyes (ocelli)..................SIALIS.
Fourth segment of the tarsus simple, cylindrical; three simple eyes (ocelli).
    Antennæ with segments enlarged at the outer ends; hind corners of the head rounded.
                                  CHAULIODES.
    Antennæ with segments cylindrical; hind corners of the head with a sharp angulation or tooth......................................................CORYDALIS.

The larvæ can be distinguished by the following key:

Tip of abdomen bearing a single long, median, laterally fringed tail-like process..SIALIS.
Tip of abdomen forked, the two fleshy projections each bearing a pair of hooks.
    Lateral filaments (soft, slender, tapering processes projecting from the sides of the abdominal segments) with no tuft of short hair-like tracheal gills at base...CHAULIODES.
    Lateral filaments each with a tuft of short, hair-like, tracheal gills at base..CORYDALIS.

Two species of Sialis occur in this country; they are called alder-flies, or orl-flies. The smoky orl-fly, *Sialis infumata*, widely distributed over this country, is a dusky brownish in-sect about ½ inch long, often seen, with wings closely folded, sitting on sedge-leaves near quiet waters. The larvæ (Fig. 309), according to Needham, live in marshy places filled with aquatic plants, on the borders of streams and ponds. When full grown they are about an inch long, and keep up an undulating motion with the abdomen, the long tail being intermittently lashed up and down. When full grown the larva crawls out of the water and at some little distance burrows into the moist soil for a few inches or even a foot or more. Here it forms an oval cell and pupates within it. Two or three weeks after the adult fly issues.

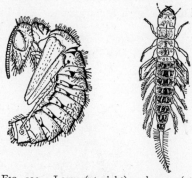

FIG. 309.—Larva (at right) and pupa (at left) of an orl-fly, *Sialis infumata*. (After Needham; twice natural size.)

Of Chauliodes, the fish-flies (Fig. 310), eight North American species are known. The adults are from 1½ to 2½ inches long, and their wings expand from 2½ to 4 inches. The wings are grayish or brownish with whitish spots or bands, and the antennæ are curiously feathered or pectinate. The

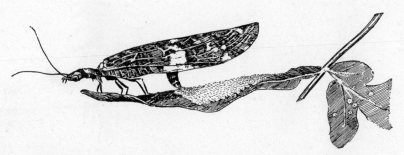

FIG. 310.—The saw-horned fish-fly, *Chauliodes serricornis*, laying eggs. (After a photograph from life by Needham; natural size.)

larvæ live in wet places at the edge of water or in water close to the surface. According to Needham they are perhaps oftenest found clinging to the under side of floating longs or crawling beneath the loosened bark. They are predaceous, feeding upon other aquatic insects. When ready to transform they excavate a cell above the level of the water under a stone or log or layer of moss or in a rotten log, in which they pupate, and from which the adult fly issues in about two weeks.

The genus Corydalis (Fig. 311) is represented by a single species, *C. cornuta*, but it is such a conspicuous and wide-spread insect that it is probably the best-known species in the whole order Neuroptera. The adult fly is most commonly called "hellgrammite," while the larvæ (Fig. 312), much used by fishermen as bait, are known as dobsons or crawlers. But other names are often used. Howard lists the following array of names, collected by Professor W. W. Bailey, which are applied to the larva in Rhode Island alone: dobson, crawler, arnly, conniption-bug, clipper, water-grampus, gogglegoy, bogart, crock, hell-devil, flipflap, alligator, Ho Jack, snake-

FIG. 311.                    FIG. 312.

FIG. 311.—Dobson-fly, *Corydalis cornuta*, male, with head of female above. (Natural size.)
FIG. 312.—Larva of dobson-fly, *Corydalis cornuta*. (Natural size.)

doctor, dragon, and hell-diver. The insect is very common about Ithaca, N. Y., and Professor Comstock of Cornell University gives the following account of its life-history as observed by him there: "The larvæ live under stones in the beds of streams. They are most abundant where the water flows swiftest. They are carnivorous, feeding upon the nymphs of stone-flies, May-flies, and other insects. When about two years and eleven months

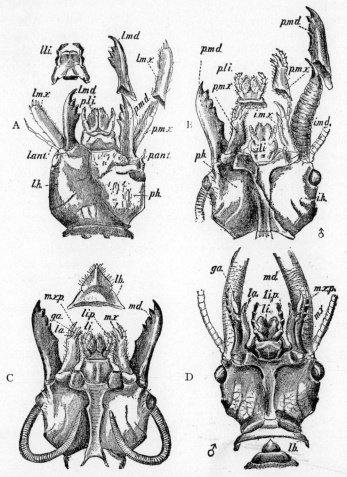

FIG. 313.—Head of larva, pupa, and adult of dobson-fly, *Corydalis cornuta*, showing development of the mouth-parts of the adult within the mouth-parts of the larva. A, head of a larva with its cuticle dissected away on the right-hand side, revealing the pupal parts; B, head of male pupa with cuticle dissected away on right-hand side, revealing developing imaginal parts; C, head of female pupa with cuticle wholly removed, showing imaginal parts; D, head of adult male. *md.*, mandible; *mx.*, maxilla; *li.*, *labium*; *lb.*, labrum; *ant.*, antenna; *l.h.*, larval head-wall; *p.h.*, pupal head-wall; *ga.*, galea; *li.p.*, labial palpus; *mx.p.*, maxillary palpus. Any of these terms may be prefixed by *l*, larva; *p*, pupa; or *i*, imago.

old the larva leaves the water, and makes a cell under a stone or some other object on or near the bank of the stream. This occurs during the early part of the summer; here the larva changes to a pupa. In about a month after the larva leaves the water the adult insect appears. The eggs are then soon laid; these are attached to stones or other objects overhanging the water. They are laid in blotch-like masses which are chalky-white in color and measure from half an inch to nearly an inch in diameter. A single mass contains from two thousand to three thousand eggs. When the larvæ hatch they at once find their way into the water, where they remain until full-grown."

In the Kansas corn-fields I used to find certain wonderfully beautiful, frail, gauzy-winged insects resting or walking slowly about on the great smooth green leaves. The eyes of these insects shone like burnished copper or shining gold, and this with the fresh clear green (tinged sometimes with bluish, sometimes with yellowish) of the lace-like wings and soft body made me think them the most beautiful of all the insects I could find. But a nearer acquaintanceship was always unpleasant; when "collected" they emitted such a disagreeable odor that admiration changed to disgust. These lace-winged or golden-eyed flies are common all over the country and compose a family of Neuroptera called Chrysopidæ. All except two species of the family belong to the single genus Chrysopa, which includes more than thirty species found in the United States. In the Chrysopidæ the larvæ are not aquatic as in the family Sialidæ, but are active and fiercely predaceous little creatures called aphis-lions, that crawl about over herbage and shrubbery in search of living aphids (plant-lice) and other small soft-bodied insects. The aphis-lion (Fig. 314) has a pair of long, sharp-pointed, slender jaws which are grooved on the inner face. Having found a

Fig. 314.—The golden-eyed or lace-winged fly, *Chrysopa* sp.; adult, eggs, larva, "aphis-lion," and pupal cocoons on the under side of leaf. (Natural size.)

plant-louse it pierces its body with the sharp jaw-points, and holds it up, so that the blood of its victim runs along these grooves into its thirsty throat. The Chrysopa larvæ will bravely attack insects larger than themselves, or will quite as readily prey on the defenceless eggs of neighbor insects, or indeed of their own kind. Indeed, probably because of this egg-sucking habit the female lace-winged fly deposits her eggs each on the tip of a tiny slender stem, about half an inch high, fastened at the base to a leaf or twig (Fig. 314). When the first larvæ hatch they crawl down the stems and wander around in this little forest of egg-trees, but fortunately haven't wit enough to crawl up to the still unhatched eggs of their brothers and sisters. When the aphis-lion is full-fed and grown, which, in the studied species, occurs in from ten days to two weeks, it crawls into some sheltered place, as in a curled leaf or crevice in the plant-stem, and spins a small, spherical, glistening, white, silken cocoon, within which it pupates. In another ten days or two weeks the delicate lace-winged golden-eyed green imago bites its way out, cutting out a neat circular piece.

In the family Hemerobiidæ are some insects whose larvæ are also called aphis-lions; these belong to the typical genus Hemerobius. But in two rare genera of the family, Sisyra (Fig. 315) and Climacia, the immature stages are aquatic, the small larvæ (about ¼ inch long) living as parasites

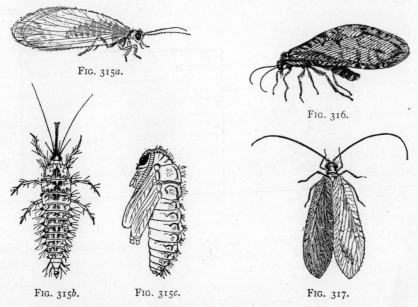

FIG. 315a.

FIG. 316.

FIG. 315b.          FIG. 315c.                    FIG. 317.

FIG. 315.—*Sisyra umbrata.*   a, adult; b, larva; c, pupa. (All about five times natural size.)
FIG. 316.—*Polystœchotes punctatus.*   (Natural size.)
FIG. 317.—*Hemerobius* sp.   (Three times natural size.)

on or in fresh-water sponges (Spongilla). The largest members of the family belong to the genus Polystœchotes, of which two species are known. The commoner one, *P. punctatus* (Fig. 316), is about 1¼ inches long and its wings expand 2 to 3 inches. It is nocturnal and is to be collected about lights. Its body is blackish, and the wings are clear but mottled with irregular brownish-black spots. When at rest the wings are held steeply roof-like over the back. Nothing is known of its life-history. Of the best-known genus, Hemerobius (Fig. 317), twenty species have been noted in this country, but they are small, dull-colored insects, and are rather rare, or at least infrequently seen. Comstock says they occur in forests and especially on coniferous trees. The larvæ are like the Chrysopa larvæ, predaceous and well equipped with big strong head and sharp, curved seizing and blood-sucking mouth-parts. The larvæ (Fig. 318) of some species have the curious habit of piling up on their back the empty, shriveled skins of their victims, until the aphis-lion is itself almost wholly concealed by this unlovely load of relics. This is true of all the Hemerobius larvæ I have seen in California. Stripped of the covering of skins the aphis-lion is seen to have a short, broad, flattened body, with numerous long, spiny hairs arising from tubercles. These hairs help to hold the mass of insect skins together.

Still other Neuroptera with fierce, ever-hungry, carnivorous larvæ are the ant-lions, or Myrmeleonidæ. The horrible pit of Kipling's story, into

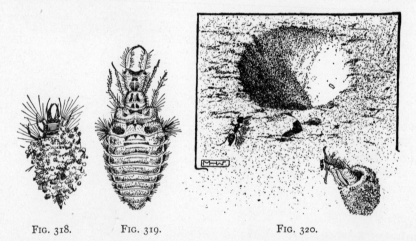

FIG. 318.  FIG. 319.  FIG. 320.

FIG. 318.—Larva of *Hemerobius* sp. covered with detritus. (From life; four times natural size.)

FIG. 319.—Larva of ant-lion, *Myrmeleon* sp. (Three times natural size.)

FIG. 320.—Pit of ant-lion and, in lower right-hand corner, pupal sand-cocoon, from which adult has issued, of ant-lion, *Myrmeleon* sp. (About natural size.)

which Morrowbie Jukes rode one night, is paralleled in fact in that lesser world of insect life under our feet. The foraging ant, too intent on bringing home a rich spoil for the hungry workers in the crowded nest to watch carefully for dangers in its path, finds itself without warning on the crumbling verge of a deep pit (Fig. 320). The loose sand of the pit's edge slips in and down, and the frantic struggles of the unlucky forager only accelerate the tiny avalanche of loose soil and sand that carries it down the treacherous slope. Projecting from the very bottom of the pit is a pair of long, sickle-like, sharp-pointed jaws, adapted most effectively for the swift and sure grasping and piercing and blood-letting of the trapped victims. The body of the ant-lion (Fig. 319) is almost wholly concealed underneath the sand; only the vicious head and jaws protrude above the surface in the pit's depths. Comstock has seen the ant-lion throw sand up from the bottom, using its flat head like a shovel in such a way that the flung sand in falling would strike an ant slipping on the slope and tend to knock it down the side. Ant-lion pits are to be found all over the country, in warm, dry, sandy places. The ant-lions can be brought home alive, and kept in a dish of sand, where their habits may be observed.

The adult ant-lion (Fig. 321) is a rather large, slender-bodied insect with four long oar-shaped gauzy wings, thickly cross-veined and usually more or less spotted with brownish or black. The eggs are laid in the sand

FIG. 321.—Adult ant-lion, *Myrmeleon*. (Natural size.)

and the freshly-hatched larvæ or ant-lions immediately dig little pits. When the larvæ are full-grown—and just how long this takes is not accurately known—each forms a curious protecting hollow ball of sand held together by silken threads, lines it inside smoothly with silk, and pupates in this cozy and safe nest (Fig. 320). The larva is said to lie for some time, even through a whole winter, in this cocoon before pupating. The life-history of no ant-lion species is yet thoroughly known.

The family Myrmeleonidæ includes eight genera, which are usually grouped into two subfamilies as follows:

Antennæ nearly as long as wings.....................................ASCALAPHINÆ.
Antennæ not one-third as long as wings...........................MYRMELEONINÆ.

The subfamily Myrmeleoninæ includes the true ant-lions with habits in general as already described. The five genera in it may be distinguished by the following key:

Claws very stout, swollen.............................................ACANTHACLISIS.
Claws slender at base, not swollen.
   Wings with a black band at tip or eye-like spots....................DENDROLEON.
   Wings not as above.
      Tibia with no spurs (short but conspicuous spines).................MARACANDA.
      Tibia with spurs.
         Wings with a single row of costal areoles (small cells).............MYRMELEON.
         Wings with a double row of costal areoles.. ...................BRACHYNEMURUS.

The subfamily Ascalaphinæ includes but three genera and six species, the larvæ of which do not dig pits (as far as known), but hide under stones sometimes with the body partially covered with sand, or even nearly buried in it, and wait for prey to come within reach of their long, sickle-like jaws. The adults of this subfamily can be readily recognized by their long antennæ, knobbed at the tip, like the antennæ of butterflies. The habits and life-history of *Ulula hyalina*, an Ascalaphid found in the southern states, have recently been studied by McClendon in Texas. The adult fly when at rest clings, motionless, to some small branch or stalk, head down with wings and antennæ closely applied to the branch, and abdomen erected and often bent so as to resemble a short brown twig or dried branch (Fig. 322). The

FIG. 322.                               FIG. 323.

FIG. 322.—An Ascalaphid, *Ulula hyalina*, male. (After McClendon; natural size.)
FIG. 323.—Larva of *Ulula hyalina*. (After McClendon; natural size, ½ inch.)

eggs are arranged in two rows along a stalk and fenced in below by little rod-like bodies called *repagula*, placed in circles around the stalk. The eggs hatch in nine or ten days, and the larvæ (Fig. 323) crawl down, after a day of resting, and hide under stones or in slight depressions. The body is covered with sand and the jaws open widely. When a small insect crawls within reach the jaws snap together, pinioning the victim on the curved points. The jaws are grooved along the inner or lower side and the maxillæ fit into these grooves so as to form a pair of ducts or channels through which the blood is sucked into the mouth. The larva often changes its hiding-place at night. It lives about sixty days, and then seeks a concealed place and forms a spherical cocoon of sand and silk within which it pupates.

Our three genera of the Ascalaphinæ may be determined by the following key:

Eyes entire.................................................................PTYNX.
Eyes grooved.
   Hind margin of wings entire..............................................ULULA.
   Hind margin of wings excised.......................................COLOBOPTERUS.

Under the loose hanging strips of bark on the eucalyptus-trees in California or on the bark of various Pacific Coast conifers, as pine, spruce, and cedar, one may often find certain odd, slender-necked, big-headed, gauzy-winged, blackish insects about half an inch long (Fig. 324). A slangy student once proposed the name "rubber-neck" for them, and it is a fairly fit one. These "rubber-necks," or "snake-flies," belong to the family Raphidiidæ, of which but two genera are known in the world. The species of the genus Raphidia have three simple eyes (ocelli), while those of Inocellia have no ocelli. Twenty-four species are found scattered over Asia Minor, Syria,

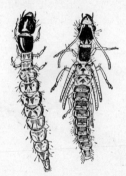

FIG. 324.—*Raphidia* sp., adult, larva, and pupa. (Two and a half times natural size.)

eastern Siberia, Europe, and England, while four species of Raphidia and three of Inocellia occur in the western half of the United States. The snake-flies are predaceous insects, the larvæ being notoriously voracious insectivores. The larvæ live in crevices of bark, or under it, where there are breaks in it, as is always the case on old trees of most eucalyptus species.

Snake-fly larvæ are said to find and eat many larvæ of the codlin-moth, one of the worst pests of apple-trees. Many of the codlin-moth larvæ crawl into crevices in the apple-tree bark to spin their cocoon, and there meet the hungry snake-fly larvæ.

The pupæ (Fig. 324), which are not enclosed in silken cocoons like the other terrestrial Neuroptera (ant-lions, lace-winged flies, Hemerobians), lie concealed in sheltered places. They are active, though, when disturbed, and look much like the larvæ, but are more robust-bodied and bear externally the developing wings. The head, with eyes and antennæ, is more like that of the adult. The complete metamorphosis of these insects seems very simple compared with that of such other holometabolous insects as house-flies and honey-bees. The adult female (Fig. 324) has a long, slender, curved, pointed ovipositor, which probably is used to deposit the eggs in deep, narrow, and safe cracks in the bark. But the oviposition has not yet been seen, and the full life-history of the Raphidians has yet to be worked out.

The extraordinary-looking insect shown in Fig. 325 is one of the few members of the Mantispidæ, the sixth family of the Neuroptera. Its great spiny, grasping fore legs and its long neck make it resemble its namesake, the praying-mantis of the order Orthoptera, but its four membranous, net-veined wings show its affinities with the Neuroptera. The fore legs are like those of the mantis because Mantispa has similar habits of catching live prey with them: it is a case of what is called by biologists "parallelism of structure," by which is meant that certain parts of two animals become developed or specialized along similar lines, not because of a near relation-ship between them, but because of the adoption of similar habits. The wings of bats and those of birds show a general parallelism of structure, although bats and birds belong to two distinct great groups of animals.

FIG. 325.—*Symphasis signata*. (One and one-half times natural size.)

Only two genera, viz., Mantispa and Symphasis, of Mantispidæ are known, and these include but five American species. *Symphasis signata* (Fig. 325) is found in California, while of the four species of Mantispa three are found in the East and South, while one ranges clear across the continent. But they are insects only infrequently seen, and each captured specimen is a prize. The life-history of no one of our species has been studied—an opportunity for some amateur to make interesting and needed observations—but Brauer has traced the life of the European species, *Mantispa styriaca*, and found it of unusual and extremely interesting character. The following account of Brauer's observations is quoted from Sharp (Cambridge Natural History, vol. v): "The eggs are numerous but very small, and are deposited in such a manner that each is borne by a long slender stalk, as in the lace-wing flies. The larvæ are hatched in autumn; they then hibernate and go for about seven months before they take any food. In the spring, when the spiders of the genus Lycosa have formed their bags of eggs, the minute

Mantispa larvæ find them out, tear a hole in the bag, and enter among the eggs; here they wait until the eggs have attained a fitting stage of development before they commence to feed. Brauer found that they ate the spiders when these were quite young, and then changed their skin for the second time, the first moult having taken place when they were hatched from the egg. At this second moult the larva undergoes a considerable change of form; it becomes unfit for locomotion, and the head loses the comparatively large size and high development it previously possessed. The Mantispa larva—only one of which flourishes in one egg-bag of a spider—undergoes this change in the midst of a mass of dead young spiders it has gathered together in a peculiar manner. It undergoes no further change of skin, and is full-fed in a few days; after which it spins a cocoon in the interior of the egg-bag of the spider, and changes to a nymph inside its larva-skin. Finally the nymph breaks through the barriers—larva-skin, cocoon, and egg-bag of the spider—by which it is enclosed, and after creeping about for a little appears in its final form as a perfect Mantispa."

Thus in this insect the larval life consists of two different stages, one of which is specially adapted for obtaining access to the creature it is to prey on.

The Coniopterygidæ include a few tiny, obscure insects, the smallest members of the order. They have wings with very few cross-veins, and both wings and body are covered with a fine whitish powder, hence the name "dusty wings" which entomologists apply to them. Only two species are known in this country, of neither of which is the life-history known. In Europe the larvæ of a "dusty wing" species have been found feeding on scale-insects. When full-fed these larvæ spin a silken cocoon, within which they transform.

THE SMALL and little-known order Mecoptera includes certain strange little wingless, shining black, leaping insects found on snow, some larger net-veined-winged insects with the abdomen of the males ending in a swollen curved tip bearing a projecting clasping-organ resembling slightly a scorpion's sting in miniature, and a number of still larger, slender-bodied, narrow-winged insects. The only popular name possessed by any of these insects is that of scorpion-flies, which has been given the few species with pseudo-stings. For these scorpion-flies are not stinging-insects, although the males can pinch hard with the caudal clasping-organ. But little is known of the life-history of any members of the order, nor is much known of the habits of the imagoes.

There are but five genera in the order, which may be distinguished by the following key:

Simple eyes (ocelli) absent.

Wings well developed; antennæ short and thick; body more than ½ inch long.

MEROPE.

Wings rudimentary; antennæ slender; body less than ¼ inch long...........BOREUS.

Simple eyes (ocelli) present.

Abdomen slender, cylindrical; not ending, in males, in swollen tip with clasping-organ.

BITTACUS.

Abdomen more robust, and in males conspicuously swollen and curved at tip, and bearing pointed clasping-organ.

Beak elongate, tarsal claws toothed....................................PANORPA.

Beak short, triangular; tarsal claws simple........................PANORPODES.

Boreus is the genus of minute leaping black insects which appear occasionally in snow. Four species occur in this country, one, *B. californicus*, on the Pacific coast, two in the northern and northeastern states, and one, *B. unicolor*, found, so far, only in Montana. Of the two eastern species, the snow-born Boreus, *B. nivoriundus*, is shining or brownish black, with the rudimentary wings tawny; the other, called the midwinter Boreus, *B. brumalis*, is deep black-green. Comstock says that both species are found on the snow in New York throughout the entire winter, and that they also occur in moss or tree-trunks. The females have a curved ovipositor nearly as long as the tiny body. Neither their feeding-habit nor life-history is known.

The genus Panorpa includes the scorpion-flies, of which fifteen species are found in the United States. These insects are from ½ to ¾ inch long, with the wings of about the same length. In all, the body is brownish to blackish and the wings are clear but weakly colored with yellowish or brownish, and have a few darker spots or blotches, which in one or two species cover nearly the whole wing-surface. Part of the head projects

 downwards as a short thick beak, the mouth and jaws being at the end. The few observations made on the feeding-habits seem to show that the scorpion-flies subsist mainly on animal matter found dead. They have

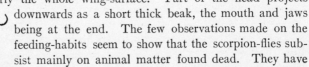

FIG. 326.                                        FIG. 327.

FIG. 326.—A scorpion-fly, *Panorpa rufescens*. (Twice natural size.)

FIG. 327.—Larva of scorpion-fly, *Panorpa* sp. (After Felt; three times natural size.)

been seen to attack living injured and helpless insects. *Panorpa rufescens*

(Fig. 326), the commonest species in the eastern states, lays its eggs, according to Felt, in crevices of the ground; the larvæ (Fig. 327) hatch in from six to seven days and grow rapidly. They burrow in the soil, but not deeply, and spend some time wandering about on the surface hunting for food. They are full-grown in about one month, probably. The further life-history of no American species is yet known, but the larva of a European species, when full-fed, burrows deeper in'o the ground, excavates an oval cell in a small lump of earth and lies in it for several months before pupating. In this condition it shrivels to one-half of its previous length, and the body becomes curved backwards. If taken out, it moves slowly and cannot walk.

The species of the genus Bittacus, of which there are nine known in our country, are long-legged, slender-bodied, narrow-winged insects (a California species is wingless) which do not resemble the scorpion-flies much in general appearance, but have a similar beak (although longer and slenderer) on the head, and have also a similar venation of the wings. All the species as far as known are predaceous, capturing and eating various kinds of insects and probably taking no food except that which they catch alive. *Bittacus strigosus* (Fig. 3 8) is the most familiar form in the East. I inhabits shady swamps or moist coverts along streams, and may be seen restlessly flitting from branch to branch, or resting for short times suspended from a leaf or twig by its long fore legs, sometimes by the middle ones also. Its general appearance, thus suspended, is not very unlike a bit of dried dangling foliage. The position appears restful and one might almost think the insect asleep. "But it is very far from that," says Felt, "as many a small insect could testify were it still alive. The small fly that ventures within reach of the long, dangling legs imperils

FIG. 328. — *Bittacus strigosus.*
(Twice natural size.)

its life. In a second those well-armed tarsi seize the unfortunate, the fourth and fifth segments of the tarsus shutting together like the jaws of a trap with teeth upon their opposing surfaces. The struggle is usually short; two, three, or four of those long legs lay hold of the captive and soon bring it within reach of the sharp beak. It is only a minute's work to pierce a soft part of the body and suck the victim's blood, when the lifeless remains are dropped to the ground and the insatiate insect is ready for the next." The eggs of this species seem to develop and be dropped a few at a time during the adult life. So far as observed, egg-laying consists simply of extruding the eggs and letting them drop at random.

The habits of the curious wingless species, *Bittacus apterus*, common in California, have been observed by Miss Rose Patterson, a student of Stanford University. These long-legged, thin-bodied creatures are not readily distinguished among the drying grass-blades where they live, because the color of the body is almost exactly like the yellowish tan of the plants. Miss Patterson went into the field one windy day when clouds were scudding over the sky. At first not a scorpion-fly was to be seen; then, in a brief period of sunshine, one was seen swinging itself deliberately along from one grass-blade to another. When the wind blew hard it either held firmly to the weeds or dropped down to the ground for protection. Finally it took up its position near a flower-cluster and clung by all its tarsi. When a bee-fly came passing that way it immediately freed two of its legs and held them out in an attitude of expectancy. When the fly had passed it remained in that position for a minute or so and then relaxed into what seemed a more comfortable attitude, holding on by all tarsi. As it became cloudy again, the insect dropped down among the weeds and remained near the ground, its legs resting on the grass-stems and its abdomen pointing almost directly outwards. Miss Patterson disabled a small skipper butterfly and dropped it near the Bittacus, but he seemed to pay no attention. A lady-bug did not arouse him. A fly passed over and still he did not move. She touched him with a pencil-point and he drew back and began to feign sleep. When she continued to disturb him he showed an inclination to fight, but did not leave his shelter until she forced him to do so by repeated pokes with the pencil-point. Then he ran nimbly to the top of a blade of grass and hung there: his tarsi went scarcely around the leaves. He remained in that position, motionless, until a bird twittered overhead; then he promptly found a sheltered place in a drooping grass-leaf.

Near him she discovered another scorpion-fly, with a crane-fly in its clutches. The crane-fly was still alive and struggled feebly while the scorpion-fly sucked its blood. She disturbed them, but though the scorpion-fly stopped its eating, it held its prey as before and moved slowly off with it. The body of the crane-fly was almost cut in two by the grasping tarsi of its enemy.

Finding another of the queer creatures swinging on a weed, its four legs held out hungrily, she gave it a crane-fly, which it grasped firmly, winding the tarsi around its body. The crane-fly struggled, but its captor soon had its head buried almost to the eyes in its body. Finally the mangled crane-fly gave out. She caught another crane-fly and held it out to the scorpion-fly, which thereupon grasped its first victim firmly in one of its hind tarsi and snatched at the second. Then holding both, it began to suck the blood of the fresher prey.

Bringing some scorpion-flies into the laboratory, Miss Patterson placed a crane-fly in the jar with a pair of them. The male scorpion-fly seemed unusually hungry and soon caught its prey and began to eat. The female paid no attention until the male had eaten for some time. Then Miss Patterson observed the male to bend the posterior portion of its abdomen, and between the sixth and seventh and seventh and eighth segments on the norsal side of the body rounded organs were quickly protruded and withdrawn. Shortly after this the female approached and also began to eat the crane-fly. Several times she noted the males attracting the females by protruding the "scent-glands." In every case, when the male began to give off the scent, the female gradually approached.

Eggs were laid by the females in the laboratory jars. These eggs were pink in color and spherical, although slightly flattened at opposite sides. They are simply dropped by the female loosely and singly to the ground.

IN THE Rocky Mountains of northern Colorado are some of the most attractive "camping-out" places in our land; that is, for "campers" who specially like Nature in her larger, more impressive phases. The peaks of the Front Range rise to 14,000 feet altitude, and the ice- and water-worn cañons and great sheer cliffs of the flanks of the Range are only equalled

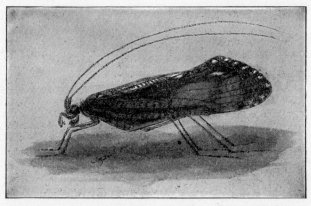

FIG. 329.—*Phryganea cinerea*. (After Needham; enlarged.)

in this country by the similar ones of the Californian Sierra Nevada. The mountain-climber in these wild regions cannot but interest himself in the animal and plant life which he finds struggling bravely for foothold in even the roughest and most exposed places. To the entomologist the few hardy butterfly kinds of the mountain-top, the scarce inhabitants of the heavy spruce forests, and the strange aquatic larvæ desperately clinging to the smooth boulders and rock bed of the swift mountain streams are among the most interesting and prized of all the insect host. So it was that my first summer's camping and climbing in the Rockies acquired a special interest from the slight acquaintanceship I then made with a group of insects which, unfortunately, are so little known and studied in this country that the amateur has practically no written help at all to enable

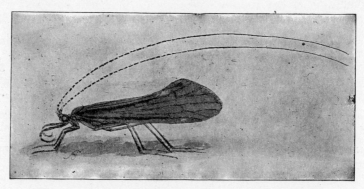

FIG. 330.—*Leptocerus resurgens.* (After Needham; enlarged.)

him to become acquainted with their different kinds. These insects are the caddis-flies; not limited in their distribution by any means to the Rocky Mountains, but found all over the country where there are streams. But it is in mountain streams that the caddis-flies become conspicuous by their own abundance and by the scarcity of other kinds of insects.

In Europe the caddis-flies have been pretty well studied and more than 500 kinds are known. In this country about 150 kinds have been determined, but these are only a fraction of the species which really occur here. Popularly the adults are hardly known at all, the knowledge of the group being almost restricted to the aquatic larvæ, whose cleverly built protecting cases or houses made of sand, pebbles, or bits of wood held together with silken threads give the insects their common name, i.e., case- or caddis-worms. The name of the caddis-fly order is Trichoptera.

These cases are familiar objects in most clear streams and ponds. Figures 331 and 332 show several kinds. There is great variety in the materials used and in the size and shape of the cases, each kind of caddis-worm having a particular and constant style of house-building. Grains of sand may be fastened together to form tiny, smooth-walled, symmetrical cornucopias, or small stones to form larger, rough-walled, irregular cylinders. Small bits of twigs or pine-needles may be used; and these chips may be laid longitudinally or transversely and with projecting ends.  Small snail-shells or bits of leaves and grass may serve for building materials.  One kind of caddis-worm makes a small, coiled case which so much resembles a snail-shell that it has actually been described as a shell by conchologists.  Some cases in California streams gleam and sparkle in the water like gold; bits of mica and iron pyrites were mixed with other bits of mineral picked up from the stream-bed to form these brilliant houses.  An Eng-lish student removed a caddis-worm from its case, and pro-vided it only with small pieces of clear mica, hoping it would build a case of transparent walls. This it really did, and inside its glass house the behavior of the caddis-worm at home was ob-served.  While most of the cases are free and are carried about by the worm in its ramblings, some are fastened to the boulders or rock banks or bed of the stream. These fixed cases are usually com-posed of bits of stone or smooth

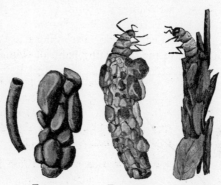

FIG. 331.        FIG. 332a.        FIG. 332b.

FIG. 331.—Two cases of caddis-worms. (Natu-ral size.)
FIG. 332.—Two cases of caddis-worms with the larval insects within showing head and thorax projecting. (Natural size.)

pebbles irregularly tied together with silken threads.  In all the cases silk spun by the caddis-worm is used to tie or cement together the foreign build-ing materials, and often a complete inner silken lining is made.

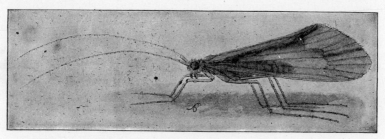

FIG. 333.—*Halesus indistinctus.* (After Needham; enlarged.)

The larvæ within the cases are worm- or caterpillar-like, with head and thorax usually brown and horny-walled, while the rest of the body is soft and whitish.  The head with the mouth-parts, and the thorax with the long strong legs, are the only parts of the body that project from the protecting case, and hence need to be specially hardened.  At the posterior tip of the abdomen is a pair of strong hooks pointing outward. These hooks can be fastened into the sides of the case and thus hold the larva safely in its house. Numerous thread-like tracheal gills are borne on the abdomen and by a constant undulatory or squirming motion of the body a stream of fresh water is kept circulating through the case, thus enabling the gills to effect a satisfactory respiration. The caddis-worm crawls slowly about searching for food, which consists of bits of vegetable matter. Those larvæ which have a fixed case have to leave it in search of food. Some of them make occasional foraging expeditions to considerable distances from home. Others have the interesting habit of spinning near by a tiny net (Fig. 335),

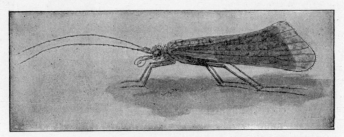

Fig. 334.—*Hydropsyche scalaris.* (After Needham; enlarged.)

fastened and stretched in such a way that its broad shallow mouth is directed up-stream, so that the current may bring into it the small aquatic creatures which serve these caddis-fishermen as food. The caddis-flies live several months, and according to Howard some pass the winter in the larval stage.

When the caddis-worms are ready to transform they withdraw wholly into the case and close the opening with a loose wall of stones or chips and silk. This wall keeps out enemies, but always admits the water which is necessary for respiration. The pupæ in the well-made cases have no other special covering, but in the simple rough pebble houses attached to stones in the stream they are enclosed in thin but tough cocoons of brown silk spun by the larvæ. The free cases are also usually attached just before pupation to submerged sticks or stones. When ready to issue the pupa usually comes out from the submerged case, crawls up on some support above water and there moults, the winged imago soon flying away. Some kinds, however, emerge in the water. Comstock observed the pupa of one of the net-building kinds to swim to the surface of the water (in an aquarium) by using its long middle legs as oars. The insect was unable to crawl up the vertical side of the aquarium, so the observer lifted it from the water on a stick. At this time its wings were in the form of pads, but the instant the creature was free from the water the wings expanded to their full size and flew away several feet. On attempting to catch the specimen Comstock found that it had perfect use of its wings, although they were so recently expanded. The time required for the insect to expand its wings and take its first flight was scarcely more than one second; certainly less than two. As such caddis-flies normally emerge from rapidly flowing streams which dash over rocks, it is evident that if much time were required for the wings to become fit for use, as is the case with most other insects, the wave succeeding that which swept one from the water would sweep it back again and destroy it.

 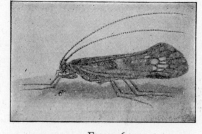

FIG. 335.                                        FIG. 336.

FIG. 335.—Fishing-net of caddis-worm in stream. (After Comstock.)
FIG. 336.—*Goniotaulius dispectus.* (After Needham; enlarged.)

The adult caddis-flies are practically unknown to general students. They are mostly obscurely colored, rather small, moth-like creatures, that limit their flying to short, uncertain excursions along the stream or pond shore, and spend long hours of resting in the close foliage of the bank. So far as observed the flies take no food, although in all the specimens I have examined there are fairly well-developed mouth-parts fitted for lapping up liquids. They probably do not live long, and certainly do not live

FIG. 337.—*Triænodes ignita.* (After Needham; enlarged.)

excitingly. In the Colorado mountains numerous small species occur, some with beautiful snow-white wings and delicate blue-green bodies (Setodes); other black-winged, brown-bodied kinds (Mystacides); and other light-brown winged species (Hydropsyche) in great abundance, but usually the adults are comparatively solitary and inconspicuous. They probably fly chiefly at night, as large numbers have been taken in trap lanterns by Betten. The eggs are laid, according to this observer, in or directly above the water. Many clusters of eggs were found under the bark of submerged trees, which would lead to the conclusion that in some cases the female insect goes under water to deposit the eggs. A spherical cluster found suspended on a submerged twig under a log floating in deep water contained 450 eggs.

Some of the caddis-fly larvæ can be readily kept in an aquarium. Almost any kinds found in ponds will live in aquariums, where their feeding-habits and transformation may be observed. The caddis-worms that build odd cases of small sticks laid crosswise live contentedly in an aquarium and are most interesting to watch. The complete life-history of no single caddis-fly species has yet been worked out completely, and the specific identity of but few of our larvæ is known. For three California species Geo. Coleman, a student of Stanford University, has obtained adults by putting wire-screen cages over the larvæ in the streams. In these cages the larvæ had room enough to hunt food successfully, and they lived, except for the circumscribing of their territory, perfectly naturally. Betten has similarly reared imagoes from four kinds of larvæ in the Adirondack Mountains.

The following keys will enable the collector to classify either his caddis-worms (larvæ) or caddis-flies (adults) to families:

## KEY TO FAMILIES (ADULTS).

Spines on the legs, three simple eyes (ocelli).
    Four spurs on tibiæ (second long segment) of middle legs............PHRYGANIDÆ.
    Two or three spurs on middle tibiæ............................LIMNEPHILIDÆ.
No spines on legs, only hairs or spurs.
    Last two segments of palpi (mouth-feelers) not elongated and flexible.
        Palpi of males 5-segmented; ocelli often present.............RHYACOPHILIDÆ.
        Palpi of males 4-segmented; ocelli absent.
            No spurs on front legs.....................................HYDROPTILIDÆ.
            Spurs on front legs.....................................SERICOSTOMATIDÆ.
    Last segment of palpi elongate and flexible; palpi hairy.
        Basal segment of antennæ long and thick, wings slender, no ocelli....LEPTOCERIDÆ.
        Basal segment of antennæ shorter, wings broader, last segment of palpi composed of numerous subsegments................................HYDROPSYCHIDÆ.

## KEY TO FAMILIES (LARVÆ). (AFTER BETTEN.)

Larva with head bent downward at an angle with the body; tubercles generally present on the first abdominal segment; lateral fringe generally present; gill filaments, when present, usually simple.
    Hind legs more than twice as long as the first pair; cylindrical case of sand and small stones......................................................LEPTOCERIDÆ.
Hind legs not more than twice as long as first pair.

Head elliptical, only pronotum (dorsal wall of prothorax) chitinized (horny and dark), abdominal constrictions deep; cases of vegetable matter laid longitudinally and forming a spiral, widening at front end..............PHRYGANEIDÆ.
Head oval to circular, pronotum chitinized, mesonotum often, and metanotum sometimes chitinized, abdominal constrictions slight.
Lateral fringe well developed; cases various...................LIMNOPHILIDÆ.
Lateral fringe slightly developed; cylindrical case of sand or small stones.
SERICOSTOMATIDÆ.
Larva with head projecting straight forward in line with the rest of body; tubercles and lateral fringe wanting; gill-filaments, when present, branched.
Abdomen much thicker than the thorax; case kidney-shaped, of small stones, or flat and parchment-like.......................................HYDROPTILIDÆ.
Abdomen little if any thicker than the thorax.
Third pair of legs a little longer than the first pair; no larval case..RHYACOPHILIDÆ.
Third pair of legs about the same length as first pair; no portable larval case.
HYDROPSYCHIDÆ.

# CHAPTER XII

## THE BEETLES (Order Coleoptera)

HE moths and butterflies (Lepidoptera) and the beetles (Coleoptera) are the most familiar of the insect orders. They are, too, most affected by collectors: of all the amateur collectors of insects probably nine out of ten collect either Lepidoptera or Coleoptera, or perhaps both. The moths and butterflies obviously owe their special attractiveness to their beautiful colors and patterns, and to the interesting metamorphoses exhibited in their life-history. A gratifyingly increasing number of amateurs and collectors are "rearing" or breeding Lepidoptera, and adding much to our scientific knowledge of them. The beetles owe their place of honor among collectors largely to their abundance of species and individuals, the readiness with which they can be collected, and the little special attention necessary to their perfect preservation. They are mostly large enough, too, to be handled and examined readily, and not so large as to require much cabinet space for their keeping. They also make specially fit specimens for *exchange*. But amateurs give almost no attention to the immature stages of beetles. Although, like the Lepidoptera, they undergo a complete metamorphosis, the larvæ are so obscure and usually so concealed underground or in tree-trunks or decaying matter or in the water, or, if seen, are so often unattractive and even repulsive in appearance—most beetle-larvæ are "grubs"—that rearing beetles is practically an unknown pastime even with the professed "coleopterists."

As a matter of fact, the beetles do not begin to present an interest even to professional entomologists at all in proportion to the dominant number of species in the order. There is a curious uniformity—with of course the startling exceptions which must be mentioned in the same breath with almost any generalization about insects—in the general character of the structure, development, and habits throughout most of the great order of beetles. So that a few life-histories well worked out give us a fair knowledge of the principal characteristics of coleopterous development.

246

# PLATE II.

## BEETLES.

1 = Desmocerus palliatus.
2 = Tragidion armatum.
3 = Chalcophora liberta
4 = Chrysochus auratus.
5 = Silpha americana.
6 = Geotrupes splendidus.
7 = Chrysochus cobaltinus.
8 = Buprestis sp.
9 = Calosoma scrutator.
10 = Tetraopes tetraophthalmus.
11 = Cucujus platipes.
12 = Meloe sp.
13 = Pelidnota punctata.
14 = Parandra brunnea.
15 = Cyllene robiniæ.
16 = Rosalia funebris.
17 = Cicindela genetosa.

PLATE II

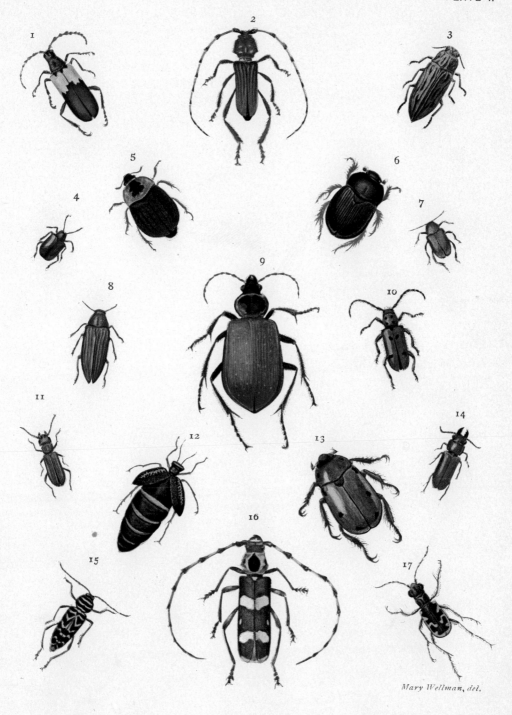

Mary Wellman, del.

It would be reasonable to expect to find the insects of an order so pursued by collectors susceptible of ready classifying and determining. On the contrary, no order presents more difficulty to the elementary and even

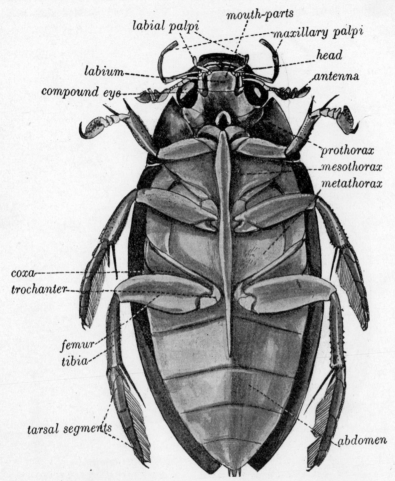

FIG. 338.—Ventral aspect of male great water-scavenger beetle, *Hydrophilus* sp. (Three times natural size.)

advanced students of systematic entomology. The tables and keys prepared by the few specialists really competent to determine accurately the different species of beetles are as nearly impossible to the amateur and elementary student as any "keys" in all the field of classific entomology.

The characters made use of in separating species, genera, and even families are so slight, obscure, and difficult to understand that the tables and keys based on them chiefly result in wholly discouraging any beginner who attempts to use them. And this is not so much the fault of the systematic specialists as of the beetles themselves. When it is recalled that nearly

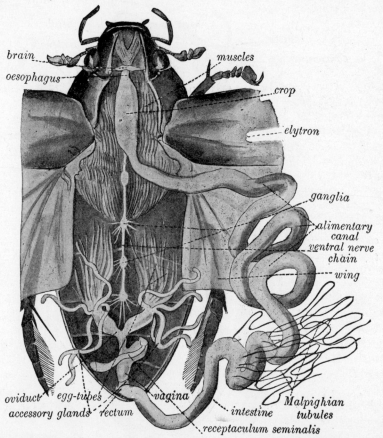

FIG. 339.—Dissection of female great water-scavenger beetle, *Hydrophilus* sp.; the heart and air-tubes (tracheæ) are cut away. (Three times natural size.)

12,000 species of this order are known in North America north of Mexico; that they represent nearly 2000 genera, grouped in 80 families; and that much general similarity of structure as well as of habits prevails throughout the order, it begins to be apparent why difficulties in classification are inevitable. To find structural differences among these thousands of beetles, the specialists have been driven to turn their microscopes on the most obscure and insignificant parts of the body, and to take cognizance of the slightest appreciable constant differences. The real way in which an entomologist gets his beetles classified is to submit specimens to a specialist for determination. Then as his authoritatively determined collection gradually increases, the collector begins to get acquainted with certain well-marked species, and also with the general appearance or *habitus* of the members of any one family. He becomes in time able to classify his new specimens to families, not by tables or keys but by general appearance and a certain few characteristic structural peculiarities, and to determine some species by comparison with the already classified specimens in his collection. The eye thus gradually trained becomes more and more discriminating, and the collector may in time come to be a recognized "coleopterist" both by virtue of his large collection and the rare forms it contains and by his wide personal acquaintanceship with beetle species. In the necessarily limited account of the Coleoptera given in the following pages I purpose to give keys only to tribes and families, and, in order to make even these simple enough to be useful, to leave most of the small, rare, and obscure families wholly out of consideration.

The tables thus freed of over half the families of the order still include five-sixths of all the North American beetle kinds, and will be found to include nine out of every ten beetle species collected. That is, the great proportion, ninety per cent. probably, of species at all common enough to be collected belong to less than half of the recognized families. These more familiar families can also be grouped into a few tribes, each having some simple common structural characteristic, thus still further aiding in the work of the classifier. The collector will thus first classify his specimen to a tribe by means of the table on page 251, and then turning to a discussion of that particular tribe find a key to its families.* In the discussion of each of these will be found accounts of the life of certain of the more abundant, widespread, and interesting species of the family.

The characteristics of the order as a whole are obvious and familiar: most beetles are readily known for beetles, and but few insects of other orders get mistaken for them. The "black beetle" of the house is a cockroach, and several of the hard-bodied, blackish sucking-bugs are sometimes mistakenly called beetles, as are also the earwigs. But the horny fore wings, elytra, serving as a sheath for the large membranous hind wings, the true

* If the collector wishes a further determination of his specimens, he must do as practically all other amateur and most professional entomologists do; that is, send his material to a specialist, who has, by the way, the right recognized by custom of keeping any of these specimens sent him, to add to his own cabinets. It is well, therefore, to send an extra specimen to return in the case of any species likely to interest him.

organs of flight; the firm, thick, usually dark, chitinized cuticle or outer body-wall; the strong-jawed biting mouth, and the compact body, usually short and robust, are structural characteristics obvious and usually dis-

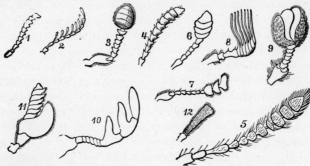

FIG. 340.—The different forms of antennæ of beetles. 1, serrate; 2, pectinate; 3, capitate (and also elbowed); 4–7, clavate; 8–9, lamellate; 10, serrate; 11, irregular (Gyrinus); 12, 2-segmented antennæ of *Adranes cæcus*. (After LeConte.)

tinctive. Especially used in classification are the differences in number of tarsal segments of the feet, and differences in the character of the antennæ. To learn the range of these differences in the antennæ, and the names applied to the various kinds a careful inspection of Fig. 340 will do more than a

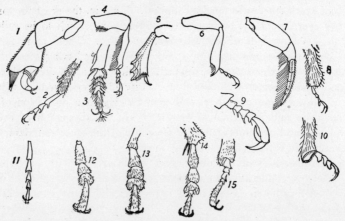

FIG. 341.—Different forms of legs and tarsi of beetles. (After LeConte and Comstock.)

page of description. Similarly Fig. 341 illustrates the range of the characters drawn from the tarsi.

The development of beetles is "with complete metamorphosis"; that is, from the eggs laid underground, or on leaves or twigs, in branches or trunks of live trees, in fallen logs, on or in decaying matter, in fresh water, etc.,

hatch larvæ usually called grubs, with three pairs of legs (sometimes wanting), with biting mouth-parts, simple eyes, and inconspicuous antennæ.
These larvæ are predaceous, as the water-tigers (larvæ of water-beetles),
plant-feeders, as the larvæ of the long-horns, or carrion-feeders, as those of the
burying-beetles, and so on. They grow, moult several times, and finally change
into a pupa either on or in the food, or very often in a rough cell underground. From the pupa issues the fully developed winged beetle, which
usually has the same feeding-habits as the larva. The special food-habits
and characteristics of development are given for numerous common species
in the accounts (*postea*) of the various more important families of the order.

The enonomic status of the order Coleoptera is an important one. So
many of the beetles are plant-feeders, and are such voracious eaters in both
larval and adult stages, that the order must be held to be one of the most
destructive in the insect class. Such notorious pests as the Colorado potato-
beetle, the two apple-tree borers, round-headed and flat-headed, the "buffalo-
moth" or carpet-beetle, the wireworms (larvæ of click-beetles), the white
grubs (larvæ of June beetles), rose-chafers, flea-beetles, bark-borers and
fruit- and grain-weevils, are assuredly enough to give the order a bad name.
But there are good beetles as well as bad ones. The little ladybirds eat
unnumbered hosts of plant-lice and scale-insects; the carrion-beetles are
active scavengers, and the members of the predaceous families, like the
Carabids and tiger-beetles, undoubtedly kill many noxious insects by their
general insect-feeding habits.

The great order Coleoptera is divided into two primary groups, sometimes called suborders, namely, *Coleoptera genuina*, the typical or true
beetles, including those species in which the mouth-parts are all present and
the front of the head is not elongated into a beak or rostrum, and the
*Rhynchophora*, snout-beetles (p. 294), which have the front part of the
head more or less extended and projecting as a beak or rostrum, and the
mouth-parts with the labrum (upper lip) so reduced as to be indistinguishable and the palpi reduced to mere stiff jointless small processes. To
this latter suborder belong those beetles familiarly known as weevils, bill-
bugs, bark-beetles, and snout-beetles.

KEY TO SECTIONS AND TRIBES OF COLEOPTERA GENUINA.

With five tarsal segments in all the feet (with rare exceptions). Section PENTAMERA. (p. 252).
 With the antennæ slender, thread-like, with distinct, cylindrical segments.
    (Carnivorous beetles.) Tribe ADEPHAGA (p. 252).
 With the antennæ thickened gradually or abruptly toward the tip.
    (Club-horned beetles.) Tribe CLAVICORNIA (p. 258).
 With the antennæ serrate or toothed.
    (Saw-horned beetles.) Tribe SERRICORNIA (p. 265).
 With the antennæ composed of a stem-like basal part, and a number of flat blade-like
  segments at the tip. (Blade-horned beetles.) Tribe LAMELLICORNIA (p. 272).

With four tarsal segments in each of the feet.........Section TETRAMERA (p. 277).
   Mostly with slender cylindrical antennæ, sometimes very long and thread-like,
      sometimes shorter and thickened toward the tip; the fourth and fifth seg-
      ments of the tarsus closely fused, the fourth segment being very small and
      sometimes difficult to distinguish.
                 (Plant-eating beetles.)   Tribe PHYTOPHAGA (p. 277).
With three tarsal segments in each of the feet.............Section TRIMERA (p. 286).
With the front and middle legs with 5-segmented tarsi, and the hind legs with 4-seg-
   mented tarsi ................................Section HETEROMERA (p. 288)

## SECTION PENTAMERA.

In the tribe of Adephaga, or carnivorous beetles, are four principal families, which may be distinguished by the following key:

Terrestrial.
   Antennæ inserted on front of the head above the base of the mandibles.
                 (Tiger-beetles.)   CICINDELIDÆ.
   Antennæ inserted on side of the head between the base of the jaws and the eyes.
                 (Predaceous ground-beetles.)   CARABIDÆ.
Aquatic.
   With two eyes.......................(Predaceous diving-beetles.)   DYTISCIDÆ.
   With four eyes, two above and two below.........(Whirligig-beetles.)   GYRINIDÆ.

The attractive tiger-beetles (Cicindelidæ) are great favorites with collectors, and deservedly. Their vivid, sharply marked metallic colors, trim clean body, and constant alertness and activity, together with their fondness for warm, bright hunting-grounds and their clever and "gamy"

FIG. 342.—Larva of a tiger-beetle, *Cicindela hybrida*. (After Schiodte; three times natural size.)

elusiveness of the collecting-net, combine to give these fierce, swift little creatures a high place in the regard of the beetle-catching sportsman. There are but four genera in the family, but the genus Cicindela contains about sixty species, distributed over the whole country. In California we are not provided with quite our share of tiger-beetles, but then there are not so many Cicindelid-hunters as in the East. Look for tiger-beetles on sunny days in hot dusty roads or open sandy spots. In cold and cloudy weather, and at night, they lie hidden under stones or chips or in burrows, although a few species are nocturnal in habit. When out and running or flying about they are hunting; their big eyes and long sharp mandibles and the whole seeming of the body some way betray their predatory habits even before one sees the swift pounce on some dull-witted, slow-footed insect, and the eager blood-drinking immediately thereafter.

The egg-laying habit of the tiger-beetles is not yet known, but the larvæ and their habits are familiar. They are ugly, malformed, strong-jawed

# PLATE III.

**TIGER BEETLES.** (After Leng and Beutenmüller.)

Fig. 1. Tetracha carolina.
" 2. Cicindela unipunctata.
" 3. " celeripes.
" 4. " dorsalis.
" 5. " scutellaris var. rugifrons.
" 6. " longilabris.
" 7. " " var. perviridis.
" 8. " scutellaris var. Lecontei.
" 9. " sexguttata.
" 10. " " var. patruela.
" 11. " purpurea.
" 12. " " var. limbalis.
" 13. " formosa var. generosa.
" 14. " ancocisconensis.
" 15. " vulgaris.
" 16. " repanda.
" 17. " " 12. guttata.
" 18. " hirticollis.
" 19. " punctulata.
" 20 " marginata.
" 21 " puritana.
" 22 " lepida.
" 23 " rufiventris.
" 24 " Hentzii.
" 25 " tortuosa.
" 26 " abdominalis.
" 27 ' marginipennis.

PLATE III

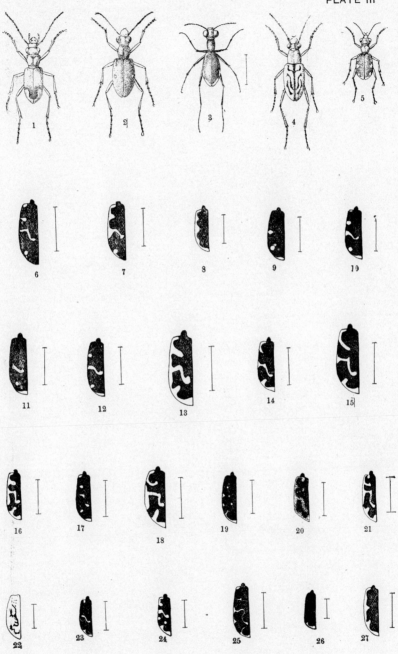

grubs (Fig. 342) which lie in the mouth of a vertical burrow several inches deep, with the dirt-colored head bent at right angles to the rest of the body and making a neat plug for the top of the hole. When an unwary insect comes in reach of this plug the waiting jaws make a quick grasp, and the doomed prey is dragged down into the darkness. On the fifth segment of the abdomen of the larva there is a hump, and on it are two small but strong hooks curved forward. "This is an arrangement by which the little rascal can hold back and keep from being jerked out of its hole when it gets some large insect by the leg, and by which it can drag its struggling prey down into its lair, where it may eat it at leisure. It is interesting to thrust a straw down into one of these burrows, and then dig it out with a trowel. The chances are that you will find the indignant inhabitant at the remote end of the burrow chewing savagely at the end of the intruding straw."

Plate III shows the appearance of the body and the character of the markings of the tiger-beetles, while the vivid color-effects are illustrated in Plate II. In the East occurs, besides Cicindela, the genus Tetracha (Pl. III, Fig. 1) with two species; on the plains of the middle West the largest member of the family, *Amblychila cylindrijormis*, which hunts its prey at twilight, and on the Pacific coast the genus Omus with ten species, all nocturnal.

The family Carabidæ, the predaceous ground-beetles, is a large one, including in North America about 1200 species, representing over a hundred genera. They are mostly dark-colored and are nocturnal in habit, hiding by day under stones, chips, logs, etc., so not many of them are familiar or even often seen. A few, however, are large and brilliantly colored, and get discovered by most collectors. Like the tiger-beetles they are active and predatory, with long strong mandibles and slender running legs. They differ from the tiger-beetles in their dislike of daylight, and in having the head in most species narrower than the thorax. The larvæ (Fig. 343) are "mostly long flattened grubs with a body of almost equal breadth throughout. It is usually protected on top by horny plates and ends in a pair of conical and bristly appendages." Most of the larvæ burrow just beneath the surface of the earth, feeding on various insects which enter the ground to pupate or for other reasons. They destroy large numbers of the destructive leaf-feeding beetles, whose soft-bodied larvæ leave the plants and burrow into the ground when ready to pupate. When full-grown the Carabid larvæ form small rough cells in the soil within which they change to pupæ. When the adult beetles emerge they push their way up to the surface.

Fig. 343.—Larva of *Calosoma* sp. (After Lugger; enlarged.)

Plate IV illustrates several species of this family and shows the characteristic flattened, usually rather broad although trim and compact, shape of the body. In most of the species the elytra are marked with fine longitudinal lines or rows of punctures, and in several species the hind wings are wanting, so that flight is impossible. There is something characteristic and almost unmistakable about the general make-up and appearance of these beetles. Their flatness, and smoothness, their shining black, greenish, or brownish coloration, and their small head with prominent, projecting, slender antennæ, pointed mandibles, conspicuous clubbed palpi, and bright eyes, together with their equally characteristic haunting of hidden places on the ground, their swift alert running, and readiness to bite when caught, distinguish them, almost at a glance, from all other beetles. One of the largest, most conspicuous and well-known Carabids is the searcher, or caterpillar-hunter, *Calosoma scrutator* (Pl. II, Fig. 9), an inch and a half long, with vivid violet-green elytra margined with reddish. It is commonly found at twilight and after dark on trees, and is often seen by collectors when "sugaring" for moths. It is said to make special war on the hairy tent-caterpillars, and thus do much good. Two other species of this genus, *C. frigidum* (Fig. 344) and *C. calidum* (Fig. 345), the latter called the fiery hunter from its characteristic rows of reddish or copper-colored punctures on the black elytra, are keen

Fig. 344.          Fig. 345.          Fig. 346.

Fig. 344.—*Calosoma frigidum*. (After Lugger; natural size.)
Fig. 345.—*Calosoma calidum*. (After Lugger; natural size.)
Fig. 346.—Larva of *Pterostichus striola*. (After Schiodte; two and one-half times natural size.)

hunters of cutworms, canker-worms, etc. At the other extreme of size in the family are the tiny Bembediums and Tachys, some species of which are but $\frac{1}{10}$ inch long. The curious bombardiers, or bombarding beetles (Brachina), when disturbed, spurt out with popgun sound and puff of "smoke" an ill-smelling, reddish, acid fluid from the tip of the body. Comstock says that "these beetles have quite a store of ammunition, for we have often had one pop at us four or five times in succession

PLATE IV.

PREDACEOUS BEETLES. (After Wickham.)

## PLATE IV.

### PREDACEOUS BEETLES.  (After Wickham.)

Fig. 1.  Panagæus fasciatus.
"    2.  Patrobus longicornis.
"    3.  Pterostichus rostratus.
"    4.      "        honestus.
"    5.      "        coracinus.
"    6.      "        sculptus.
"    7.      "        lucublandus.
"    8.      "        tartaricus.
"    9.      "        mutus.
"   10.      "        orinomum.
"   11.      "        erythropus.

PLATE IV

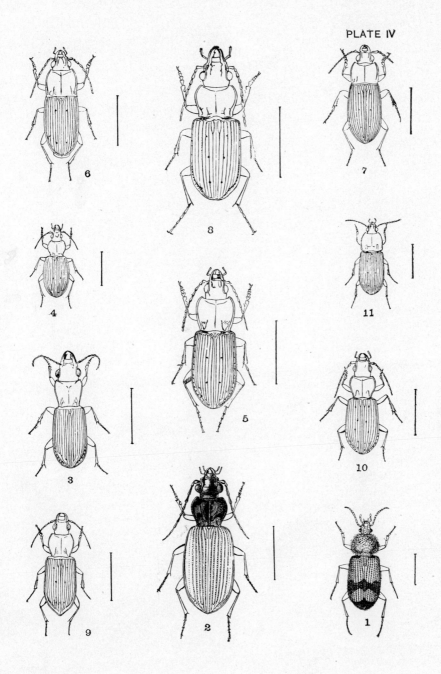

while we were taking it prisoner." These beetles have a narrow reddish-yellow head and prothorax, and blackish-blue elytra. Of similar appearance is *Lebia grandis*, the enemy of the Colorado potato-beetle, feeding on its egg and larvæ. Most abundant of the Carabids are the numerous dull-black medium-sized species of Pterostichus (Pl. IV), in which the prothorax has a narrow, flat, projecting margin. Over one hundred species of this genus have been found in this country. Harpalus is another large genus with some very common species; *H. pennsylvanicus* is often found in orchards eating the larvæ of the codlin-moth and plum-curculio, ravaging fruit-pests. A few Carabids are not such good friends, Lugger record-

Fig. 347.—Predaceous diving-beetles (and back-swimmers, order Hemiptera) in water. (From life; slightly less than natural size.)

ing the fact that *Agonoderus pallipes*, a species abundant in Minnesota, sometimes feeds on sprouting seeds of corn.

Predaceous beetles of very different habitat are the Dyticidæ, the carnivorous water- or diving-beetles. Three hundred species occur in this country, and some members of the family are to be found wherever there are streams and ponds. They vary in size from the large Cybister and Dyticus, an inch and a half long, to small species of Hydroporus and other genera less than a fifth of an inch long, but all are readily distinguishable from their aquatic companions, the whirligigs (family Gyrinidæ) (p. 257), by having but one pair of eyes, and from the water-scavenger beetles (family Hydrophilidæ) (p. 258) by having slender thread-like antennæ instead of clubbed ones. All are oval and flatly convex in shape, with hard smooth body-wall, usually brownish or black, and when at rest hang head downward from the surface of the water, the characteristic breathing attitude. The females sometimes have the elytra furrowed with shallow longitudinal grooves, and the males of most species have a curious clinging-organ on the expanded first three or four tarsal segments of the front feet (Fig. 349). This organ is composed of a hundred or more small capsules on short stems and two or three very much larger pads. It is used for holding the females in mating, and adheres to their smooth body-wall by the secretion of a gummy fluid insoluble in water. The pads and capsules may also act to some extent as "suckers" by atmospheric pressure. The hind legs are long, strong, and flattened to form oars or swimming-organs. This beetle regularly and perfectly "feathers its oars" by a dexterous twist while swimming. To breathe, the beetle comes to the surface—its body being less dense than water, it floats up without effort—and projects the tip of its abdomen through the surface film. It now lifts the tips of the elytra slightly; air pours in and is held there by the fine hairs on the back, where are also the spiracles,

or breathing-openings. Thus when the beetle goes down again it carries with it a supply of air by means of which respiration can go on for some time under water. The diving beetles can be readily kept in aquaria, as can also their larvæ (described in the next paragraph), and the interesting active life with the characteristic swimming, diving, breathing, capturing of prey, and feeding all easily observed.

The life-history of no American species has been completely worked out, but the eggs of some species are dropped irregularly on the water, while those of others are laid in slits cut by the sharp ovipositor of the female in the stems of aquatic plants. The long, slender, semi-transparent,

FIG. 348. FIG. 349.

FIG. 348.—Water-tiger, the larva of the predaceous water-beetle, *Dyticus* sp. (Natural size.)
FIG. 349.—The predaceous water-beetle, *Dyticus* sp., pupa and adult. (Natural size.)

predaceous larvæ (Fig. 348) are known as water-tigers. They have six slender legs and the head is large and flattened. It bears long, slender, curved, sharp-pointed, hollow mandibles, each with a small opening at the tip and another near the base.   When a live insect or other aquatic creature is caught by the active larva its body is pierced by the mandibles and the blood sucked through them into the mouth, the opening at the base just fitting, when the mandibles are closed, into the corners of the small silt-like mouth.   Both larvæ and adults are fierce and voracious, and the larger species attack and kill small fish.   In the middle states these beetles actually do much damage in carp-ponds.   The larva breathes through a pair of spiracles at the slender tip of its body, which is thrust up to the air when it comes to the surface of the water.   When ready to pupate it leaves the water—breathing now also through six pairs of lateral spiracles—and makes a rough cell in the ground of the pond or stream bank.   "The pupa state lasts about three weeks in summer; but the larvæ that transform in autumn remain in the pupa state all winter."

The larger of our common species belong to Cybister, Dyticus, and allied genera.   In Cybister the little cups on the under side of the tarsal disks of the male are similar, and arranged in four rows.   In Dyticus and its allies the cups of the tarsal disks vary in size.   Fig. 349 represents a common species of Dyticus.

"The most common of the diving-beetles that are of medium size belong to the genus Acilius.   In this genus the elytra are densely punctured with very fine punctures, and the females usually have four furrows in each wing-cover."

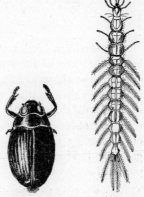

An interesting account of the habits and special structures of the common large European diving-beetle, *Dyticus marginalis*, is given in Miall's Natural History of Aquatic Insects, pp. 39–61.

Smaller than the predaceous diving-beetles, and readily recognized by their curious spinning or circling, in companies, on the surface of ponds or still pools in streams, are the whirligig-beetles (Gyrinidæ), common all over the country.   About forty species of these

FIG. 350.            FIG. 351.

FIG. 350. — Whirligig - beetle, *Dineutes emarginata*. (Twice natural size.)

FIG. 351.—Larva of whirligig-beetle, *Gyrinus marinus*. (After Schiodte; enlarged.)

beetles, varying in size from one-sixth to three-fourths inch in length, have been found in North America, three-fourths of them belonging to the genus Gyrinus.   They are all of similar shape and steely blue-black in color, and have the compound eye, on each side, wholly divided into an upper and a lower part by the sharp lateral margin of the head.   Like the Dyticids, the whirligig-beetles breathe at the surface and carry air down with them when diving or swimming below the surface, by having a bubble attached to the posterior tip of the body. The hindmost legs are broad and paddle-shaped, and fringed with long stiff hairs. The whirligig-beetles can fly, but usually have to climb up on some weed or stick projecting from the water in order to make a start. They can make a curious squeaking noise, probably a call to other whirligigs, by rubbing the under side of the wing-covers against the end of the body. When handled, most of these beetles emit an ill-smelling whitish liquid.

In the winter the whirligigs lie torpid in mud among the roots of water-plants, coming out by twos and threes in the spring. The eggs are laid usually on the leaves of some water-plant, and the curious slender larva (Fig. 351) is provided with long tapering lateral gills fringed with fine hairs. There is a pair of gills on each abdominal segment. It feeds on water-insects and other small aquatic animals, and probably also on the "tender parts of submerged plants." The pupæ of but few species are known. That of a common English species lies in a grayish silken cocoon spun on some water-plant above the water's surface.

TRIBE CLAVICORNIA.

The clavicorn beetles, or those with clubbed antennæ, show much variety in the character of the terminal thickening of the antennæ (Fig. 340, 4-7), which is the characteristic structural feature of the members of the group, and from which the tribal name is derived. The tribe includes, too, beetles of widely different habits, some aquatic, others terrestrial, some predaceous, others plant-feeding, others living on dry stored grains, woolens, and still others feeding on carrion. They have indeed little in common and the grouping is largely a matter of convenience in classifying. The more important families of this tribe can be separated by the following key:

Aquatic; legs fitted for swimming .........(Water-scavenger beetles.) HYDROPHILIDÆ.
Terrestrial; legs not fitted for swimming.
  Antennæ moniliform, i.e., with segments bead-like; elytra usually covering only basal
    half of abdomen...............................(Rove-beetles.) STAPHYLINIDÆ.
  Antennæ moniliform or sub-moniliform; elytra covering most of the abdomen: brown
    or reddish species.............................(Grain-beetles, etc.) CUCUJIDÆ.
  Antennæ capitate, i.e., ending in a little ball, or clavate.
    Large insects, the smaller not much less than half an inch long (except Catops);
      body usually flattened..............(Carrion- or burying-beetles.) SILPHIDÆ.
    Small insects, mostly less than one-half inch long; body thick and convex above.
(Larder-beetles, etc.) DERMESTIDÆ.

In the same ponds and pools with the predaceous diving-beetles and whirligigs may be found other water-beetles, black, shining, and often of large size, which are readily distinguished by their short concealed clavate antennæ (the long slender palpi may be at first glance mistakenly taken for antennæ) as members of the family Hydrophilidæ, the water-scavenger beetles. As the popular name indicates, these beetles feed, for the most part, on decaying material, animal or plant, found in the water, although they feed also on living water-plants, as Nitella; and living insects are certainly taken by some species. They can be distinguished from the Dyticidæ when swimming by their use of the oar-legs alternately, and when at the surface getting air by hanging there head upward. The air spreads in a thin silvery layer over the ventral side of the body, held there by fine pubescence.

The eggs are deposited in a ball-like silken cocoon with a curious handle-like tapering curved stem or spike (Fig. 353). The cocoon floats freely on the water, or is attached to some floating leaf or grass-blade or stem. From fifty to a hundred eggs are enclosed in each sac. The larvæ (Fig. 354) are elongate, but thicker and less graceful than the water-tigers (larvæ of the Dyticidæ), and, unlike the adults, feed chiefly on living insects, snails, tad-

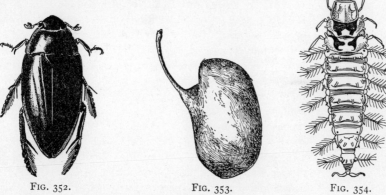

FIG. 352.          FIG. 353.          FIG. 354.

FIG. 352.—Great water-scavenger beetle, *Hydrophilus triangularis*. (Natural size.)
FIG. 353.—Egg-case of great water-scavenger beetle, *Hydrophilus* sp. (Twice natural size.)
FIG. 354.—Larva of great water-scavenger beetle, *Hydrophilus caraboides*. (After Schiodte; natural size.)

poles, etc. They breathe through spiracles at the tip of the body, coming occasionally to the surface to get air. In shallow water they simply lie with the tip of the tail projected up to the surface. When ready to pupate the larvæ leave the water, and, burrowing a few inches into the ground, form a rough cell in which they transform. The adult beetles fly readily, and sometimes, with Dyticids, are to be found at night around electric lights. When winter comes they burrow into the bottom or bank of the pond or stream and lie torpid until spring.

About one hundred and fifty species of Hydrophilidæ are known in this country. The largest species belong to the genus Hydrophilus, are shining bluish or greenish black, and measure nearly two inches in length. "In the genus Hydrocharis the metasternum is prolonged somewhat, but does not form a long, sharp spine as in Hydrophilus and Tropisternus, and the sternum of the prothorax bears a keel-shaped projection. Our most common species is *Hydrocharis obtusatus;* this measures about five-eighths of an inch in length.

"Some of the smaller species of this family are not aquatic, but live in moist earth and in the dung of cattle, where, it is said, they feed on dipterous larvæ."

The rove-beetles, Staphylinidæ, form a large family, numerous in species and individuals over the whole country, and one whose members are readily recognized by the elongate flattened soft body, narrow and parallel sides,

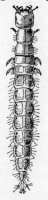

with short truncate leathery elytra under which the hind wings are compactly folded so as to be wholly concealed. They are mostly carrion-feeders and with the Silphidæ (p. 261) are almost sure to be found whenever a mass of decaying flesh or excrementitious matter exposed on the ground is turned over. They run swiftly when disturbed and curve the tip of the flexible abdomen up over the body in a sort of threatening way, as if they would sting. They cannot; they can simply smell bad. Although the more familiar rove-beetles are of fair size, from half an inch to nearly an inch long, the majority of the one thousand or more species found in this country—9000 species are known in the world—are very small. In

FIG. 355.—Larva of a rove-beetle, *Xanthalinus lentus.* (After Schiodte; twice natural size.)

California great swarms of minute rove-beetles dance in the air in April and May, and are a woful nuisance to people driving or bicycling. They get into one's eyes, and when crushed by rubbing, their acrid body-fluids both smell bad and burn. Among these smaller Staphylinids are numerous predaceous species and many which are found in flowers, probably feeding on pollen. Others are found on fungi, on mud, and in other damp places, and some live in ants' nests (see Chapter XV, p. 554).

The larvæ (Fig. 355) are found in the same places as the adults, and are elongate, narrow-bodied, and rather like those of the Carabidæ, but each foot has but a single claw. The pupæ of some species are enclosed in a sort of exudation that dries into a firm protecting coating rather like the horny cuticle of a lepidopterous chrysalid.

Among the more familiar rove-beetles are species of the genus Creophilus.

*C. villosus* (Fig. 356), common all over the country, is about ¾ inch long, blackish, with an incomplete broad transverse patch of yellowish-gray hairs across the elytra and another on the second and third abdominal segments. Leistotrophus is a genus with but one American species, *L. cingulatus*, about same size as the preceding, but of grayish-brown color indistinctly spotted with brown and with a golden tinge on the tip of the abdomen. Staphylinus is a genus of twenty species or more; *S. maculosus*, 1 inch long, is dark cinnamon-brown with a row of squarish black spots along the middle of the abdomen; *S. cinnamopterus*, ½ inch long, is cinnamon-colored, with blackish abdomen; *S. tomentosus*, ½ inch long, is deep dull black; *S. violaceus*, ½ inch long, is black with thorax and elytra violet. Not uncommon along sandy seashore in California is a curious light-brown wingless rove-beetle, *Thinopinus pictus*, with very short

FIG. 356.—Rove-beetle, *Creophilus villosus*. (One and one-half times natural size.)

elytra, each with an open black ring, and with a double row of small black dots on the abdomen. Its abdomen is short and rather broad

Another family of carrion-beetles of comparatively few species, some of which, however, are familiar and widely distributed, is that of the Silphidæ, or burying-beetles. Both adults and larvæ feed almost exclusively on decaying flesh. The antennæ of most species have the last four or five segments expanded and fused so as to form a conspicuous little ball or a compact club. Two genera include most o the familiar species, although the one hundred North American species of the family represent thirty different genera. These two are Silpha (Fig. 357), the roving carrion-beetles, and Necrophorus (Fig. 358), the burying-beetles. The characteristic shape and appearance of these two types are well shown in the figures. The species of Silpha are short, broad-bodied, flat, dull blackish, and with the elytra rather

FIG. 357.          FIG. 358.
FIG. 357.—Carrion-beetle, *Silpha noveboracensis*. (One and one-half times natural size.)
FIG. 358.—Burying-beetle, *Necrophorus marginatus*. (One and one-half times natural size.)

leathery than horny, and lined longitudinally with shallow grooves. The prothorax is subcircular, with thin projecting margins. The larvæ (Fig. 359) and adults are found in and underneath putrid flesh. The larvæ are apparently more active than the adults. *Silpha lapponica*, a common dull black form in both Europe and America, is said to enter houses in Lapland to eat the stores of animal provisions. *S. americana* (Pl. II, Fig. 5) has the large shield-like prothorax yellowish with a black blotch in the center. In *S. noveboracensis* only the margin of the prothorax is yellow.

The burying-beetles, Necrophorus, are large insects from an inch to an inch and a half long, with the body thick and parallel-sided. The commoner species have a pair of dull red transverse blotches on each elytron.

In some species the prothorax and head are also marked with red. The common name comes from the well-known habit of these insects of digging underneath small dead animals, as mice or birds, until the corpse is in a hole; it is then covered over and thus really buried. The female lays her eggs on the corpse, and the larvæ hatching from them feed on the decaying matter. These larvæ have spiny plates on the back of the body and are otherwise unlike the Silpha larvæ. Some Necrophorus larvæ are predaceous and others feed on decaying vegetable matter.

FIG. 359. — Larva of carrion-beetle, *Silpha* sp. (One and one-half times natural size.)

Most of the blind, pale cave-beetles found in caves in this country and Europe are Silphidæ.

The Cucujidæ, with a name derived from the Portuguese Cucuyo, a large luminous Brazilian snapping-beetle or elater, of entirely different family, are a family of small beetles, with flattened reddish or light-brown body, whose outdoors haunts are mostly under the bark of trees. Several species, however, have learned that life in a granary is just as safe from predaceous enemies, and a thousand times safer from starvation. Of these sophisticated Cucujids, *Silvanus surinamensis*, the saw-toothed grain-beetle (Fig. 360), is the most familiar and injurious. The adult is about $\frac{1}{8}$ inch long, flat and chocolate-brown, and may be distinguished from the other small beetles similarly attacking stored grain by the serrated margins of its prothorax. It infests dried fruits, nuts, seeds, and dry pantry stores of all sorts, as well as grain bins and cribs. The larvæ (Fig. 360) are active

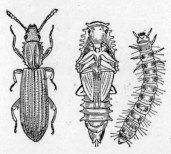

FIG. 360.—Larva, pupa, and adult of the saw-toothed grain-beetle, *Silvanus surinamensis*. (After Howard and Marlatt; much enlarged.)

little six-legged flattened whitish grubs which run about and nibble industriously. When full-grown the larva attaches itself by a gummy excretion to some object, and pupates. When living in light granular substances, as oatmeal, etc., a delicate case is constructed of the material in which to pupate. In summer the life-cycle from egg to adult requires but twenty-four days; in spring from six to ten weeks. Six to seven generations are produced annually in the latitude of Washington. The insect here hibernates in the adult state.

The largest and most familiar of the outdoor Cucujids is a very flat bright-red species, *Cucujus flavipes* (Pl. II, Fig. 11), about half an inch long, with black eyes and antennæ and the legs with dark tibiæ and feet.

The Dermestidæ constitute only a small family of forty or more North American species representing twelve genera, but one which nevertheless is of unusual interest and importance to entomologists, for to this family belong those insects which eat entomological collections. A depraved taste, but one which causes almost constant anxiety and occasional serious discouragement on the part of the industrious collector. Dermestids are not the bane of collectors and museum curators alone, as larder-beetles, "buffalo-moths," and carpet-beetles, various species of this family, help make life a burden to the housewife.

All of the Dermestidæ are small, oval, and plump-bodied, the largest species being about ⅓ inch long, and most of them are covered with small scales, which give them their rather varied colors and markings. The beetles themselves mostly feed on pollen, but come into houses to deposit their eggs. From the eggs hatch soft-bodied little grubs thickly covered with hairs, often very long (Figs. 361 and 362). These larvæ are the real pests of house-

FIG. 361.                                    FIG. 362.

FIG. 361.—Carpet-beetle or "buffalo-moth," *Anthrenus scrophulariæ*, larva and adult. (After Howard and Marlatt; much enlarged.)

FIG. 362.—Black carpet-beetle, *Attagenus piceus*, larva and adult. (After Howard and Marlatt; enlarged.)

hold and museum: they feed industriously on dried insect specimens, stuffed birds and mammals, woolen carpets, furs, feathers, or on meat and cheese (depending on the particular habits of the various species) until full-grown. Then they crawl into a crack or hide in the body of a museum specimen and pupate within the larval cuticle, which serves as a sort of thin hairy protecting shell.

The usual museum pests are two species, *A. varius* and *A. museorum*, of the genus Anthrenus. The adult beetles are tiny, broadly oval, very convex, with the black body covered above with scales some of which are yellowish and some whitish and so arranged as to give the back an irregularly spotted appearance. The hairy larvæ burrow into the specimens and nibble away at the dry bodies. Their presence may be detected by a little pile of dust under the pinned-up specimen and by the falling off of its legs, head, etc. Pour a teaspoonful of carbon bisulphide into a corner of the case and keep it tightly shut for a day. The fumes of the $CS_2$ are fatal to the pests. The carpet-beetle or "buffalo-moth" (Fig. 361) is another species, *A. scrophulariæ*, of this same genus. The beetle is about $\frac{3}{16}$ inch long, marbled black and white above with a central reddish line bearing short lateral offshoots on each side. The larva is thick, soft, active, and covered with stiff brown hairs. It feeds voraciously on carpets, working on the under side, and usually making long slits following the floor-cracks. The beetles are common outdoors on plants of the family Scrophulariaceæ, but come indoors to lay their eggs. The remedy for the carpet-beetle is to use rugs instead of carpets, and to lift and shake these rugs often. Another member of this family attacking carpets is the black carpet-beetle, *Attagenus piceus* (Fig. 362). The beetle is black, and the larva is longer, more slender, and lighter brown than the buffalo-moth, and has a conspicuous pencil or tuft of long hairs at the posterior tip of the body. The larder- or bacon-beetle, *Dermestes lardarius* (Fig. 363), is about $\frac{1}{3}$ inch long, dark brown with a pale-yellowish band, containing six black dots across the upper half of the wing-covers. The larva is elongate, sparsely hairy,

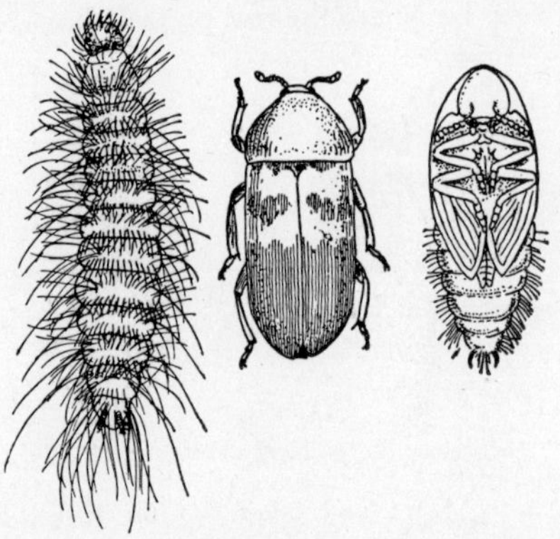

FIG. 363.　　　　　　　　　　FIG. 364.

FIG. 363.—The larder-beetle, *Dermestes lardarius*, larva, pupa, and adult. (After Howard and Marlatt; much enlarged.)

FIG. 364.—Larva of a water-penny beetle of the *Parnidæ*. (Four times natural size.)

brown, and has two short curved spines on top of the last body-segment. It feeds on many kinds of animal substance, as ham, bacon, old cheese, hoofs, horn, skin, beeswax, feathers, hair, and also attacks museum specimens.

Another family of Clavicornia which possesses a special interest is the Parnidæ, or "water-pennies," a family of forty species representing ten genera of small brown robust-bodied insects which live in water and yet do not have their legs fitted for swimming, nor in any other way the body particularly modified for an aquatic life. They crawl around on submerged stones, sticks, and water-plants, carrying a supply of air with them, held by the fine pubescence of the body. The larvæ are curiously flattened, broadly oval to nearly circular small creatures (Fig. 364), which cling to stones and give the family its popular name of "water-pennies." As the legs, mouth-parts, eyes, etc., are all on the under side and concealed, the flat, brownish, leathery little "penny" is usually not recognized as an insect by the observer of brook life.

The family Platypsyllidæ has been established to include a single species of strangely shaped beetle which lives as a parasite on the bodies of beavers. Its name is *Platypsylla castoris;* it is about $\frac{1}{10}$ inch long, blind and wingless, and with the elytra rudimentary. This degenerate condition of the body is due of course to the parasitic habit. Other obscure little beetles of curious habits are the Pselaphidæ and Scydmænidæ, many of which live commensally with ants in their nests. These beetles are rarely over an eighth of an inch long, and some of them have bodies strangely modified to look like ants. (For a further account of these insects see the discussion of myrmecophily in Chapter XV.)

### TRIBE SERRICORNIA.

In this tribe of beetles, characterized by having the antennæ slender, with each segment projecting more or less inward so as to give the whole antennæ a saw-toothed or serrate character (Fig. 340, 10), are included several families certainly not closely related and having widely different habits and appearance. The serrate character of the antennæ, too, is sometimes so slight that it can hardly be distinguished with certainty. The more important families of the tribe can be separated by the following key:

Head inserted in thorax as far as the eyes; body elongate or elliptical, and with unusually hard cuticle.
    Antennæ finely serrate, the first two abdominal segments grown together on the ventral side.............................(Metallic wood-borers.) BUPRESTIDÆ.
    Antennæ often filiform; first two abdominal segments free.
                     (Click-beetles.) ELATERIDÆ.
Head free, but bent under the thorax.
    Small insects usually less than $\frac{1}{4}$ inch long........(Death-watch beetles.) PTINIDÆ.
Head free, but often partly or wholly covered by the thin anterior margin of the thorax.
    Wing-covers flexible; body elongate and flattened; antennæ not enlarged at tip.
                     (Fireflies.) LAMPYRIDÆ.
    Wing-covers firm, thorax convex, body not much flattened; antennæ often enlarged at tip........................................(Checkered beetles.) CLERIDÆ.

The metallic wood-borers, or flat-headed borers, a name suggested by the flat broad head of the larva, constitute the large and important family

Buprestidæ, of which over two hundred species occur in North America. The adult beetles have an elongate body, trim and compact, with a rigid and armor-plate-like cuticle, and have iridescent metallic coloring. Green, violet, reddish, blue, copper, golden they may be, always shining like burnished metal and the whole body looking as if cast in bronze. The antennæ are short and serrate on the inner margin, the head deeply inserted

in the thorax, and the latter fitting closely against the abdomen and wing-covers; and the second and third abdominal segments are rigidly fused. These beetles are diurnal, running actively on tree-trunks or resting on flowers; seeming to delight in the warm bright sunlight, in which their resplendent colors flash and glance like jewels.

The larvæ are mostly wood-borers, although those of some of the smaller species mine in leaves or live in galls. The wood-boring Buprestid larvæ are characterized by the strangely enlarged and flattened, legless, first thoracic

Fig. 365.—A flat-headed borer, larva of *Rhagium lineatum*. (Natural size.)

segment, on which the small head with its powerful jaws sets in front, and the tapering, flattened, legless, meso- and meta-thoracic segments behind. The abdomen is elongate and rather narrow, the segments showing distinctly. The whole larva (Fig. 365) is thus a footless whitish tadpole-like grub, expressively known as a flat-headed or hammer-headed borer. The larvæ that do not burrow in wood are cylindrical and have three pairs of legs.

The most injurious Buprestid is the notorious flat-headed apple-tree borer, *Chrysobothris femorata* (Fig. 366), an obscure bronze or greenish-black beetle about half an inch long. The legs and under side of the body are of burnished copper, and the antennæ green. The eggs are glued to the bark under scales or in cracks; the young larva on hatching eats inward through the bark to the sapwood and there burrows about, sometimes quite girdling the tree. Later it bores into the solid heart-wood, working upward and then again out into the bark, where it forms a cell in which it pupates, issuing as an adult in just about one year from the time of its hatching. This pest attacks peach- and plum-trees and several forest- and shade-trees as well as the apple-tree. It ranges

Fig. 366. — Apple-tree borer, *Chrysobothris femorata*. (Twice natural size.)

over the whole country. To prevent the egg-laying on the bark, the lower trunk of the tree should be washed with fish-oil soap during June and July. When borers are once in the tree, cutting them out is the only remedy.

The genus Agrilus contains a number of species having the head flatly truncate in front, as if cut sharply off, and the body rather cylindrical than flattened, as with most other Buprestids. *A. ruficollis*, the red-necked black-berry-borer, $\frac{3}{10}$ inch long, with dark bronze head, coppery bronze prothorax, and black wing-covers, has a larva that bores into the canes of blackberries and raspberries, burrowing spirally about in the sapwood until full-grown, when it bores to the pith and there pupates. The eggs are laid in June and July on the young canes. Infested canes often show gall-like swellings, and should be cut off and burned.

Our largest Buprestids belong to the genus Chalcophora. *C. virginiensis* is an inch long, dark coppery or blackish with elevated lines and depressed spots on the elytra. The larvæ bore into pines. *C. liberta* (Pl. II, Fig. 3) is a beautiful pink bronze with darker raised lines. *Dicerca divaricata*, $\frac{3}{4}$ inch long, is copper-colored, with the black-dotted elytra tapering behind and separated at the tips. Buprestis (Pl. II, Fig. 8) is a genus of rather large brassy-green or brassy-black species often spotted with yellow on the elytra and beneath.

Resembling the Buprestids much in general shape and appearance, the click-beetles, Elateridæ, are readily distinguished from them by their lack of metallic colors, the backward-projecting, sharp-pointed hinder angles of the prothorax, and their curious capacity, whence their name, of springing into the air with a sharp click when laid back downward. When a click-beetle—snapping-bugs and skipjacks are other common names for them—is disturbed it falls to the ground, lying there for a little while as if dead. Then if it has alighted, as it usually does, on its back, it suddenly gives a spasmodic jerk which throws it several inches high and brings it down right side up. This springing is accomplished by means of an apparatus consisting of a small cavity on the under side of the mesothorax into which the point of a curved projecting process from the prosternum fits (Fig. 367). When the beetle is laid on its back it bends in such a way as to bring the tip of the curved horn to the edge of the cavity, when,

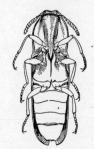

Fig. 367. — Ventral aspect of a large click-beetle, showing snapping apparatus. (Natural size.)

by a sudden release of muscular tension this tip slips and the insect is thrown into the air. The Elateridæ are a large family, about 350 species being known in this country. They are mostly of small or medium size, although some are an inch or more long; a very few reach a length of nearly two inches. As a rule they are uniform brownish; some blackish or grayish and others banded and marked with brighter colors. In the South occur certain luminous click-beetles. In Cuba ladies sometimes use these phosporescent species, which are large and emit a strong greenish light, as ornaments, by keeping them alive in little lace pockets on their gowns or attached to delicate golden chains. Two large eye-like spots on the prothorax, and the under side of the hinder part of the abdomen, are the luminous regions.

The larvæ (Fig. 368) are elongate, slender, horny-skinned, brownish or yellowish white, living in the ground or in decaying wood, and popularly and aptly known as wireworms. They have three pairs of short legs, and a stumpy process on the last segment of the body. They feed on the seeds, roots, and other underground parts of plants and do much damage to various crops. Often whole fields of grain are ruined by the attack of wireworms on the planted seeds; meadows often suffer severely, and strawberries lose their stolons. The beetles fly about in early summer, depositing their eggs in the ground in grassy, weedy, or plowed land. The larvæ soon hatch, dig down into the soil, and feed on roots and seeds for two or three years, when they become full-grown. They pupate in the ground in early fall and the pupæ transform to adults before winter, but the beetles do not issue from the ground until the following spring.

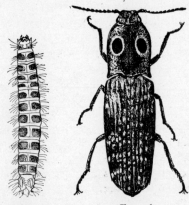

FIG. 368.                FIG. 369.

FIG. 368.—Larva of a click-beetle, *Elater acerrimus*. (After Schiodte; natural size.)

FIG. 369.—An eyed elater, *Alaus oculatus*. (One and one-half times natural size.)

Among our largest click-beetles is the eyed elater, *Alaus oculatus* (Fig. 369), $1\frac{3}{8}$ inch long, blackish with large uneven whitish gray dots, a pepper-and-salt fellow, Comstock well calls him, with a pair of large white-rimmed velvet-black eye-spots on the prothorax. The large larvæ, about 2 inches long, live in decaying wood and are often found in the trunks of old apple-trees. *Elater rubricollis*, $\frac{1}{2}$ inch long, is black with light-red prothorax; *E. sanguinipennis*, $\frac{3}{10}$ inch long, is black with light-red elytra; *E. nigricollis*, $\frac{5}{8}$ inch long, is black with whitish elytra. *Athous scapularis*, $\frac{2}{5}$ inch long, is greensh black with the base of the elytra and the hind points of the prothorax clay-yellow. Several species of Corymbetes have the elytra brownish yellow with transverse zigzag black bands; *C. hieroglyphicus*, $\frac{1}{2}$ inch long, has two bands; *C. hamatus*, rather smaller, has one band near the tip. *Melanactes piceus*, 1 inch long, is glossy black and its large larva is luminous, strong green light being emitted from a narrow transverse region with expanded ends on each segment.

The fireflies are familiar insects which are not flies but beetles, although their soft body and flexible leathery wing-covers are not of the typical coleopterous type. The nocturnal fireflies and their diurnal first cousins, the soldier-beetles, compose a coleopterous family, Lampyridæ, of considerable size and common distribution over the whole world. The "glow-worm" of England and Europe is the wingless female of a common firefly, and the railway-beetle of Paraguay, a worm-like creature 3 inches long, that emits a strong red light from each end of the body and a green light from points along the sides, is also probably the wingless female of a large firefly species. In this country over 200 species of Lampyridæ have been found. Comparatively few of them, however, are luminous. The light-giving organ is usually situated just inside of the ventral wall of the last segments of the abdomen, and consists of a special mass of adipose tissue richly supplied with air-tubes (tracheæ) and nerves. From a stimulus conveyed by these special nerves oxygen brought by the network of tracheæ is released to unite with some substance of the adipose tissue, a slow combustion thus taking place. To this the light is due, and the relation of the intensity or amount of light to the amount of matter used up to produce it is the most nearly perfect known to physicists. Not only are the adult fireflies luminous, but in some species the pupæ and larvæ and even the eggs emit light. The combustion in the egg is of course accomplished wholly without tracheæ or controlling nerves.

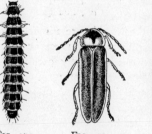

The larvæ (Fig. 370) of Lampyridæ mostly burrow underground, where they feed on soft-bodied insects, slugs, and other similar food. The adults, too, are carnivorous, the diurnal forms, called soldier-beetles, being commonly seen on flowers or tree-trunks hunting prey.

Fig. 370.       Fig. 371.          Fig. 372.

Fig. 370.—Larva of firefly, *Photinus modestus.* (Twice natural size.)
Fig. 371.—Firefly, *Photinus scintillans.* (Three times natural size.)
Fig. 372.—Checker-beetle, *Trichodes ornatus.* (Twice natural size.)

The commoner luminescent fireflies, or "lightning-bugs," belong to the genus Photinus. *P. pyralis*, the common species from Illinois south, is ½ inch long, blackish, with prothorax with red disk, yellow margin, and black spot in center, and the elytra with narrow yellowish border. Farther north and east the commonest species is *P. scintillans* (Fig. 371), similar in marking but smaller. *P. angulatus*, ½ inch long, is pale, with wide yellow margins on elytra and the margin of the prothorax clouded with black. The commoner soldier-beetles belong to the genus Chauliognathus, which is characterized by the possession of a pair of extended fleshy processes belonging to the maxilla, which are used in lapping up flower-nectar and pollen. Two common species in the East are *C. pennsylvanicus*, which is yellow with a black spot in the middle of the prothorax and one near the tip of each wing-cover, and *C. marginatus*, which has the head and lower part of the thighs orange. Telephorus is another common genus without the maxillary processes, the species being black with the prothorax partly or wholly reddish yellow. The larvæ of *T. bilineatus*, the two-lined soldier-beetle, are velvety dark-brown active creatures which are very beneficial in orchards, devouring "immense numbers of such destructive beings as the larvæ of the plum-curculio."

Professor Comstock has given the name checkered beetles to the family Cleridæ; a name apt enough for some of the species which, like the one shown in Fig. 372, have the body conspicuously marked with red and white or other colored "checks." Other species, however, content themselves with a monochrome coat. The family is a fairly large one, over a hundred species being known in this country. "The adults are found on flowers and on the trunks of trees running about rapidly, somewhat resembling brightly colored ants. Indeed some are decidedly ant-like, the prothorax being narrower than the wing-covers and slightly narrower than the head. The legs of the Clerids are rather long, the antennæ with a marked knob at the end, and the body more or less cylindrical, either hairy or not.

"The larvæ are usually carnivorous and are most frequently found in the burrows of wood-boring insects, chiefly of those that live in sap-wood; others are found in the nests of bees, and still others feed on dead animal matter." The slender larvæ possess short legs and a somewhat prominent and pointed head. They are extremely useful in keeping in check such destructive beetles as bark-beetles and other borers.

The species of Clerus are prettily marked and are often found running about on logs and trees. *C. dubius* is $\frac{1}{3}$ inch long, steel-blue with three orange bands across the elytra; *C. nigrifons* is $\frac{1}{4}$ inch long, tawny yellow with smoky markings above and all black below; *C. nigripes* is similar, but all red below; *C. sanguineus* has the thorax brown and elytra scarlet. The species of Trichodes (Fig. 372) are hairy and prettily banded; the larvæ live in nests of bees, and *T. apiarius* is a pest in beehives in Europe. *Necrobia violacea*, $\frac{1}{6}$ inch long or less, dark or greenish blue, is an importation from Europe and is sometimes found in houses, but more commonly on carcasses and especially the bones of dead animals. It has been found under the wrappings of Egyptian mummies. *Necrobia rufipes*, the red-legged ham-beetle, a red-legged steel-blue species $\frac{1}{3}$ inch long, feeds on hams and other stored animal products. The beetles lay their eggs in May and June on exposed hams or other meats. The larvæ hatch in a few days and are slender white active grubs with a brown head and brownish patches above and two small hooks at the end of the body. They feed on the meat until full-grown, when they either burrow deeper into the meat or come out and bore into the wooden receptacle holding it, and make a glistening paper-like cocoon within which they pupate.

The family Ptinidæ is composed of small obscure brownish beetles that would never attract our attention at all were it not for the injurious food-habits of many of the species. The family includes a hundred and fifty species, and among them a few notorious pests of rather unusual tastes. As the Ptinids mostly live on dead and dry vegetable matter, it was not improbable when I began a collecting expedition in a d ug-store that I should find a number of specimens of this family. But to find a majority of the canisters and jars containing vegetable drugs in the condition of roots, stems, leaves, etc., infested by beetles of this family was unexpected. The most abundant species on this collecting-ground was *Sitrodrepa panicea* (Fig. 373), which we may well call the "drug-store beetle." It was found to be attacking blue-flag rhizome, comfrey-root, dogbane-root, ginger-rhizome,

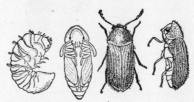

FIG. 373.—The drug-store beetle, *Sitrodrepa panicea*, larva pupa, and adults. (After Howard and Marlatt; much enlarged.)

marshmallow-root, aniseed, aconite-tuber (deadly poison to us!), musk-root, Indian-turnip rhizome, belladonna-root, witch-hazel leaves, powdered coffee-seed, wormwood stems, flowers and leaves, thorn-apple leaves, cantharides (dried bodies of blister-beetles), and thirty other different drugs! Larvæ, pupæ, and adults were side by side in most of the canisters. *Ptinus brunneus*, a larger Ptinid, was in half a dozen jars, and the cigarette-beetle, *Lasiderma serricorne*, suggestively named, though it feeds on tobacco in almost any form, was living contentedly in a jar of powdered ergot.

"Death-watch" is a name popularly applied to several species of Ptinids because of their habit of rapping their heads so sharply against wood in which they are burrowing as to make a regular tapping or ticking sound. This name is claimed by species of Anobium, tiny, robust, hard-bodied, cinnamon-colored beetles, $\frac{3}{20}$ inch long, and also by *Sitrodrepa panicea*, our drug-store beetle. Comstock records finding this species breeding in large numbers in an old book, a copy of Dante's Divine Comedy, printed in 1536. Librarians would call the beetle a "bookworm."

Besides the small members of the family which feed on dried foods, drugs, etc., there are a few larger species of very different habits, although also destructive. The apple-twig borer, *Amphicerus bicaudatus*, $\frac{1}{3}$ inch long, dark chestnut-brown above and black beneath, is the best known of these. It bores into live apple-twigs in early spring, entering close to a bud, and making a burrow several inches long for food and shelter. Twigs of pears and cherries are similarly infested. Both sexes bore these tunnels; the males have two sharp little horns on the prothorax. The eggs are laid in the dead or dying shoots of the greenbrier (Smilax) or in the dead shoots of grape. The larvæ feed on these roots or shoots and pupate in them. The remedy is to cut off and burn infested twigs, and to keep greenbrier from growing near the orchard. The red-shouldered sinoxylon, *Sinoxylon basilare*, ⅛ inch long, black with large reddish blotch at the base of each wing-cover, has a larva which bores into the stems of grape-vines and into twigs of apple and peach. This larva is a much-wrinkled grub, yellowish white with swollen anterior segments, three pairs of short legs, a small head, and an arched body. The pupa is formed inside the burrow and is of a pale-yellowish color. The only remedy is to remove and burn the infested canes and twigs.

### TRIBE LAMELLICORNIA.

In this tribe are only two families, one small but containing strangely shaped and interesting beetles, the other very large. In both the terminal segments of the antennæ have conspicuous lateral prolongations in the shape of teeth or plates (lamellæ) (Fig. 340, 8 and 9). The families may be distinguished as follows:

> Antennæ elbowed, the club (terminal segments) composed of segments with fixed transverse teeth; mandibles of the male often greatly developed.
> (Stag-beetles.) LUCANIDÆ.
> Antennæ not elbowed, the club composed of segments modified to be large flat plates which can be shut together like the leaves of a book; mandibles of males not greatly enlarged.
> (Lamellicorn leaf-chafers and scavenger-beetles.) SCARABÆIDÆ.

The stag-beetles, Lucanidæ, get their name from the extraordinary hyper-development and curious branching stag-horn-like processes of the males of certain of the larger, more conspicuous species. Only fourteen or fifteen North American species of stag-beetles are known, but the abundance and striking appearance of several of them make the family a well-known one. The adult beetles are found on trees, where they presumably live on the sap flowing from bruised places, and on honey-dew secreted by aphids and scale-insects. In captivity they will take moistened sugar. Comstock believes that some species feed on decomposing wood. The large white globular eggs are laid in crevices of the bark near the base of the trunk, and the white, soft, fat-bodied larvæ (grubs) burrow into the tree either in rotten or sound wood, and live there for a long time. It is said that the larvæ of some of the larger species require six years to complete their growth.

The genus Lucanus contains four North American species, three of which are familiar. *L. elaphus* (Fig. 374), the giant stag-beetle, of the southern states, varies from 1½ to 2 inches in length, not including the mandibles, which in the male are 1 inch long and branched; *L. dama*, the common pinching-bug of the East, rich mahogany-brown in color, from 1 inch to 1½ inches long, "flies by night with a loud buzzy sound and is often attracted to lights in houses," and has a white grub larva looking like the white grub of the June-bug, but found in partially decayed trunks and roots of apple-, cherry-, willow-, and oak-trees instead of in the ground; *L. placidus*, not quite an inch long, and black, is a third common species. The antelope-beetle, *Dorcus parallelus*, is less than an inch long, black, and with longitudinal grooves on the elytra. *Platycercus quercus*, ⅖ inch long, brownish black, is widely distributed. *Ceruchus piceus*, ½ inch long and dark brown, is occasionally common in rotten wood. The horned Passalus, *P. cornutus*, large and shining black, has a short horn bent forward on top of its head.

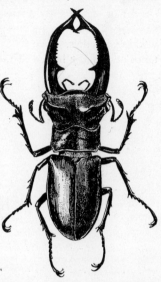

FIG. 374. — Stage-beetle, *Lucanus elaphus* male. (Natural size.)

The great family Scarabæidæ, comprising over five hundred species of North American beetles, includes some of our most familiar kinds. Indeed so many common, conspicuous, and interesting Scarabæid beetles are to be found by any collector, or observed by any amateur naturalist, that the two or three pages of this book which can be devoted to them are confessedly miserably inadequate to help any one. The characteristic club of the antennæ and heavy robust June-bug type of body make most of the members of this family readily recognizable. In practically all, too, the anterior tibiæ are broad and flattened and fitted for digging. Depending on their habits, the Scarabæids are readily divided into two principal groups, the scavengers, of which the tumble-bugs, dung-beetles, etc., are examples, and the leaf-chafers, of which the June-bugs, rose-bugs, rhinoceros-beetles, fig-eaters, and flower-beetles are examples. Some entomologists divide the Scarabæids into several distinct families, but most do not. The scavenger Scarabæids are beneficial to man by their eating or burying of decaying matter, but the leaf-chafers are harmful, some of them being serious pests. The Scarabæid larvæ (Fig. 376) are thick, soft-bodied, whitish, six-footed grubs, which usually lie curved and often on one side. They are found in manure, rotten wood, and in the ground. The familiar white grub, larva of the June-bug, is a typical example.

Of the scavenger Scarabæids the tumble-bugs are wide-spread and well known. The species common in the East belong to three genera: Copris, with middle and posterior tibiæ dilated at the tip; Canthon, with these tibæ slender or only slightly dilated; and Phaneus, with the anterior tarsi wanting, and the others without claws. The species of Canthon, male and female working together, make balls of dung, which are rolled along for some distance and finally buried in the ground. The female lays an egg in the ball,

Fig. 375.    Fig. 376.    Fig. 377.

Fig. 375.—*Polyphylla crinita*. (Natural size.)
Fig. 376.—Larva of a large Scarabeid beetle. (Natural size.)
Fig. 377.—*Phaneus carnifex*. (One and one-half times natural size.)

and the fat white grub hatching from it feeds on the ball until ready to pupate. The adult beetle issues in about two weeks from the time of laying the egg. The common *Copris carolina* does not make a ball, but digs holes close to or under manure, and fills the holes with this substance, on which the larvæ, hatched from eggs placed one in each hole, feed. The species of Phaneus (Fig. 377) are brilliantly colored with metallic green, rose, and bronze, and bear curious projecting horns on the prothorax. The famous Sacred Scarabeus of the Egyptians, *Ateuchus sacer*, was "held in high veneration by this ancient people. It was placed by them in the tombs with their dead; its picture was painted on their sarcophagi, and its image was carved in stones and precious gems. These sculptured beetles can be found in almost any collection of Egyptian antiquities."

Common dung-beetles are the numerous species of Aphodius, $\frac{1}{6}$ to $\frac{1}{3}$ inch long, with oblong, convex, or cylindrical body, and with the front of the head expanded shield-like over the mouth-parts. "These insects are very abundant in pastures in the dung of horses and cattle, and immense numbers of them are often seen flying through the air during warm autumn afternoons." Common species are *A. fimetarius*, $\frac{1}{3}$ inch long, with red elytra;

*A. oblongus*, ⅓ inch long, wholly black; and *A. terminalis*, ⅛ inch long, black with reddish legs and tips of elytra. The earth-boring dung-beetles, Geotrupes, have 11-segmented antennæ, and the upper lip and mandibles can be seen from above. "The females bore holes into the earth either beneath dung or near it: this is to serve as food for the larvæ, an egg being laid in each hole." *G. splendidus* (Pl. II, Fig. 6), ¾ inch long, dark metallic green to purple; *G. excrementi*, ½ inch long, is bronze-black; *G. opacus*, ½ inch, is deep black. Common on dried decaying animal matter, especially skins, and on the hooves and hair of decaying animals are small (⅓ to ½ inch long) rough convex beetles, often with a crest of dirt on their elytra, belonging to the genus Trox. They have the thighs of the front legs greatly dilated.

The Scarabæid leaf-chafers are many and various in color and marking; they feed, when adult, on leaves, pollen, and flower-petals. They have the abdomen usually projecting beyond the wing-covers. The thick, fat, white, horny-headed larvæ live either in rotten wood or underground, feeding on the roots of grasses and other plants, often doing much damage in this way. The June-bugs or May-beetles (Fig. 378), familiar big brown or blackish buzzing creatures, belong to the genus Lachnosterna, of which sixty or more species are found in this country. They are but few, however, on the Pacific coast. The larvæ are familiar white grubs that live underground and feed on the roots of grasses, strawberries, etc. They often do much damage to lawns. They live as larvæ for two or three years, and pupate in an underground cell. The adult beetles fly and feed at night, often injuring the foliage of cherry, plum, and other trees. The familiar rose-chafer, *Macrodactylus subspinosus* (Fig. 379), ⅜ inch long, a slender yellowish beetle with pale red legs,

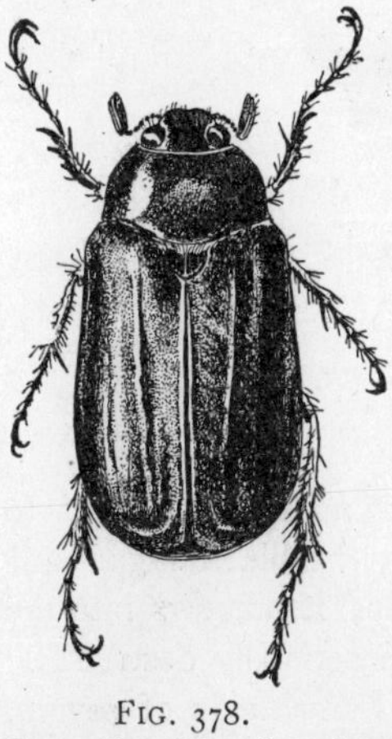

FIG. 378.          FIG. 379.

FIG. 378.—The June-beetle, *Lachnosterna fusca*. (One and one-half times natural size.)

FIG. 379.—The rose-beetle, *Macrodactylus subspinosus*. (Twice natural size.)

does great damage to roses and grapes, appearing in early summer and eating flowers and foliage. The larvæ live underground, feeding on the roots of various plants, but especially grasses. The spotted vine-chafer, *Pelidnota punctata* (Pl. II, Fig. 13), 1 inch long, stout, convex, polished reddish or yellowish brown, with three large black dots on each elytron, with under side of body metallic greenish black, flies during July and August by day, feeding on grape-leaves. The larva lives in rotten wood, especially the decaying roots of apple, pear, hickory, and other trees. It pupates in a cell in the wood. The goldsmith-beetle, *Cotalpa lanigera*, of similar size and shape, is glistening, burnished lemon yellow above with metallic greenish, golden, and rose reflections; below it is copper-colored and thickly covered with whitish wool, hence the name *lanigera*, or wool-bearer. It appears in May and June, flies by night, and feeds on the foliage of various trees. The larva lives in the ground, feeding on plant-roots. It is said to require three years to complete its growth.

The largest beetles in our country are the oddly shaped rhinoceros-beetles, Dynastes, found in the south and west. *D. tityrus* (Fig. 380), 2½ inches long, is greenish gray with scattered black spots on the elytra; the male has a large horn on the head and three horns, one larger than the others, on the prothorax; the female has only a tubercle on the head; it is a southern species. *D. grantii*, of the west, has the large prothoracic horn twice as long as in *tityrus*. In the West Indies occurs *D. hercules*, six inches long! The larvæ

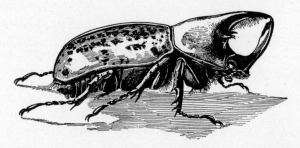

Fig. 380.—The rhinoceros-beetle, *Dynastes tityrus*. (Natural size.)

(Fig. 381) of these beetles live in the roots of decaying trees. Allied to Dynastes is the genus Ligyrus, of which *L. rugiceps*, the black sugar-cane beetle of the southern states, is the best-known species; it burrows into the base of sugar-cane and sometimes corn, and is often seriously destructive. The larva lives in manure. The flower-beetles are Scarabæids of several genera, which are commonly seen flying from flower to flower and feeding on pollen. The bumble flower-beetle, or Indian Cetonia, *Euphoria inda* (Fig. 382), a common species, is ⅝ inch long, yellowish brown, with the elytra irregularly covered with small blackish spots, and with the whole body clothed with short fox-colored hairs; it appears early in spring, and flies near the ground with a loud humming. It feeds on flower-pollen, the tassels and green silk of young corn, and later on ripening fruits of all kinds; it often swarms about wounded trees, lapping up the escaping sap. The larvæ feed on decaying substances underground. The fig-eater, or "southern June-beetle," *Allorhina nitida*, ¾ inch to 1 inch long, is rather pointed in front, velvety green with the sides of thorax and head brownish yellow; the under side is not velvety, but metallic green. It flies with a loud buzzing sound and feeds on ripe fruit. The larvæ are found in richly manured soil, feeding on decaying matter. They cannot use the short legs for crawling, but move along on their backs by means of stiff bristles. "If put on a table

FIG. 381.　　　　　　　　　　　　FIG. 382.

FIG. 381.—Larva and pupa of the rhinoceros-beetle, *Dynastus tityrus*. (After Chittenden; one-half natural size.)

FIG. 382.—*Euphoria inda*. (One and one-half times natural size.)

in normal position, they immediately turn upon their backs and by the alternate contractions and expansions of their body-segments they wriggle away in a straight line."

## SECTION TETRAMERA.

In the four families of beetles constituting this section the feet are apparently composed of four tarsal segments, one of the more usual five being so reduced in size and fused with the last segment as to be practically indistinguishable as a distinct segment (except in the Spondylidæ). The first three tarsal segments are dilated and furnished with brushes of hairs on the sole, the third segment being plainly bilobed (Fig. 341, 12). This section is sometimes named Phytophaga, because of the voracious plant-feeding habits of all its members. The three principal families of the section can be separated by the following key:

Body short and more or less oval; antennæ short.
　Front of head not prolonged as a short broad beak; elytra usually covering the tip of the abdomen; both larvæ and adults live on green plants.
　　　　　　　　　　　　　　　　(Leaf-beetles.) CHRYSOMELIDÆ.
　Front of head prolonged as a short, quadrate beak; elytra rather short, so that the tip of the abdomen is always exposed; larvæ live in seeds.
　　　　　　　　　　　　(Pea- and bean-weevils.) BRUCHIDÆ.
Body elongate; antennæ almost always long, often longer than the body; larvæ are wood-borers . . . . . . . . . . . . . . . . . . . . . . . . . . . . . .(Long-horn beetles.) CERAMBYCIDÆ.

The leaf-beetles, Chrysomelidæ, are one of the largest of the beetle families, over 600 North American species being known. They are mostly small, the familiar Colorado potato-beetle being one of the largest species in the family; the body is short, more or less oval in outline, strongly convex above; the head small, much narrower than the prothorax, and with the antennæ inserted widely apart. The adults walk slowly about on the plants on which they feed, and when disturbed usually fold up the legs and fall, inert, to the ground. However, they sometimes take readily to wing. The eggs are usually laid in little groups on the food-plants, and the larvæ, rather broad, thick, and roughened, crawl about, exposed, on the leaves which they eat. Sometimes they eat only the soft tissue of the leaf, skeletonizing it; some mine inside the leaf, and a few burrow into stems. Most, however, eat ragged holes in the leaves, and, if feeding on cultivated plants, do great injury. Indeed there are perhaps more beetle enemies of our crops, shade-trees, and ornamental plants in this family than in any other in the order.

The Colorado potato-beetle, *Doryphora 10-lineata* (Fig. 383), with robust, oval, cream-colored body, and elytra with five longitudinal black stripes on each, is a notorious Chrysomelid whose gradual extension or

FIG. 383. — The Colorado potato - beetle, *Doryphora 10-lineata.* (Twice natural size.)

migration eastward from its native home in Colorado created much excitement forty years ago. Its native food-plant is the sand-bur, *Solanum rostratum*, a congener of the potato, but after 1850 it began to find its way to the potato-plants of the early settlers; by 1859 it had reached Nebraska, 1861 Iowa, in 1864 and 1865 it crossed the Mississippi and gradually extended eastward until 1874, when it reached the Atlantic Ocean. Finally it obtained a partial foothold in Europe, creating great consternation there, but it has never got to be a serious pest across the ocean. The orange-red eggs are laid on the leaves, and the larvæ are curious humpbacked soft-bodied creatures with black head and Venetian-red body. They crawl down and burrow into the ground to pupate. There are three generations a year in the latitude of St. Louis, the beetles of the last brood crawling underground to hibernate.

The common asparagus-beetle, *Crioceris asparagi*, red, yellow, and black, gnaws holes in young asparagus-heads, and the brown slug-like larvæ which hatch from oval blackish eggs laid on the heads also eat them. The three-lined Lema, *Lema trilineata*, of similar shape, but yellow with three longitudinal black stripes on each elytron, is common on "ground-cherries." Their larvæ have the curious habit of covering their backs with their own excrement. Elm-trees in the East are often badly infested with the imported elm-leaf beetle, *Galerucella luteola* (Fig. 384), a common European pest. It first got to this country in 1834 and is now "in all probability responsible for more ruined elm-trees in the Hudson River valley than all other destructive agencies combined." The beetle, ¼ inch long, is reddish yellow with black spots on head and prothorax, and a thick black stripe on each elytron. From orange-yellow eggs laid on the under side of the leaves hatch larvæ which when full grown are ½ inch long, flattened, marked with blackish and yellow. They skeletonize the leaves. When ready to pupate they crawl down into the ground. The beetles themselves after issuance fly back to the tree-tops and eat holes in the leaves. There are two broods a year, and the adult beetles of the last brood hibernate in concealed places.

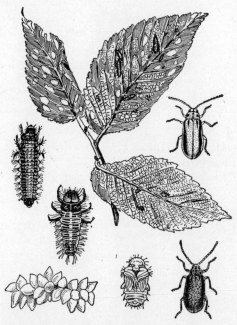

FIG. 384.—The elm-leaf beetle, *Galerucella luteola;* eggs, larvæ, pupa, and adults. (After Felt; eggs greatly magnified; larvæ, pupa, and adults about twice natural size.)

Four species of the genus Diabrotica are common over the country and very injurious: *D. vittata,* the striped cucumber-beetle, is greenish yellow with two black stripes on each elytron, and feeds on cucumber-, pumpkin-, squash-, and melon-vines, the larva also burrowing into the stems and roots of the same plants; *D. 12-punctata* (Fig. 385) is greenish yellow with six black spots on each elytron, and feeds on a great variety of plants, the larva often being injurious to corn in the South; *D. longicornis,* the corn-root-worm beetle, is grass-green with spots or stripes, and its underground larva is very destructive to corn by burrowing into its roots; *D. soror* (Fig. 386), of the Pacific coast, the flower-beetle or "diabrotica," yellowish green with six black spots on the wing-covers (like *12-punctata*), does great damage as an adult by eating into the flower-buds of roses, chrysanthemums, and a host of others, the larva feeding on the roots of alfalfa, chrysanthemums, and many other plants.

FIG. 385. FIG. 386. FIG. 387.

FIG. 385.—The cucumber-beetle, *Diabrotica 12-punctata*. (Three times natural size.)
FIG. 386.—The California flower-beetle, *Diabrotica soror*. (Three times natural size.)
FIG. 387.—*Chrysomela digsbyana*. (Twice natural size.)

*Chrysochus auratus* (Pl. II, Fig. 4), $\frac{2}{5}$ inch long, golden green in color, found in the East, and *C. cobaltinus* (Pl. II, Fig. 7), of same size and shape, but brilliant blue, found in the West, are the two most beautiful Chrysomelids.

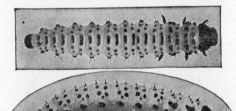

Chrysomela (Fig. 387) is a genus whose species are often curiously marked with short, curved lines and irregular spots. The active little flea-beetles, with swollen hind femora, and able to leap vigor-

FIG. 388. FIG. 389.

FIG. 388.—Larvæ of the grape-vine flea-beetle, *Haltica chalybea*. (After Slingerland; much enlarged.)
FIG. 389.—A tortoise-beetle, *Coptocycla aurichalcea*. (Two and one-half times natural size.)

ously, are common pests of grapes, cucumbers, melons, cabbages, turnips, etc., numerous species being known. They are small, usually about $\frac{1}{10}$ to $\frac{1}{5}$ inch long, and commonly blackish or steel-blue in color. *Haltica chalybea*, the steel-blue flea-beetle (Fig. 388), is common on grape-vines, where it feeds on the fruit and leaves; *Crepidodera cucumeris*, the cucumber flea-beetle, $\frac{1}{12}$ inch long, and black, attacks melons, cucumbers, and other vegetables. The tortoise-beetles (Fig. 389) are curiously shaped, flat below, convex above, and with the prothorax and elytra thinly margined so as to give them a tortoise-like appearance from above; they are usually iridescent greenish and golden in color, and are often called goldbugs. The colors appear and disappear strangely while the insects are alive, but are always lacking in the dead specimen. *Coptocycla clavata* has two projections of the central dark color of each elytron looking like the four short broad legs of a tortoise; *Cassida bicolor* is like "a drop of burnished gold"; *Chelymorpha argus*, $\frac{3}{8}$ inch long, brick-red with many black spots on prothorax and elytra, is found on milkweeds; *Physonota unipunctata*, $\frac{1}{2}$ inch long, the largest of our tortoise-beetles, yellow with whitish margins, is common in midsummer on wild sunflowers.

The small family Bruchidæ contains two common and important beetles, viz., the pea-weevil, *Bruchus pisi* (Fig. 390), and the bean-weevil, *B. obtectus* (Fig. 391). The adult pea-weevil is $\frac{1}{5}$ inch long, general color rusty or grayish black with a small white spot on the thorax. The eggs are small, fusiform, and yellow. The grubs on hatching bore through the pod into the peas. The hole made in the growing pea soon closes up, leaving the voracious larva within. Here it often comes to an untimely end, —which is uncomfortable to think about. If, however, the peas are allowed to ripen and are put away for seed, it eats on until there is

FIG. 390.                                             FIG. 391.

FIG. 390.—The pea-weevil, *Bruchus pisi,* and an infested pea. (Natural size of beetle indicated by line.)

FIG. 391.—The bean-weevil, *Bruchus obtectus,* and an infested bean. (Natural size of beetle indicated by line.)

only a shell left of the pea. Weeviled peas are unfit for food, and, as proved by the experiments of Professor Popenoe, should not be used for seed. During the fall and winter the larvæ pupate and finally mature as weevils (the adult beetles). Some of the beetles emerge from the peas, while others remain in them until they are planted.

"Weevily" peas should be put into a tight box or bin, together with a small dish of bisulphide of carbon, the fumes of which will kill the insects. Or they may be immersed for a minute or two in water heated to 140° F.; this will kill all the beetles and larvæ.

The bean-weevil is a little larger than the pea-weevil and lacks the white spot on the thorax. Its life-history is about the same as that of the pea-weevil, the eggs being laid of course on the young bean-pods. Several eggs are frequently laid in a single bean. The bean-weevil continues to breed also in dry stored beans, and increases its damage materially if the stored beans lie long untouched. It is therefore necessary to treat weeviled beans with bisulphide of carbon or hot water before storing them away.

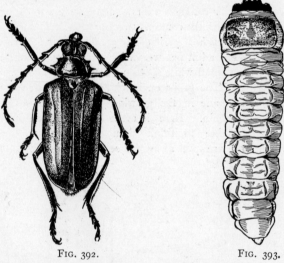

Fig. 392.        Fig. 393.

Fig. 392.—*Prionus californicus.* (Natural size.)
Fig. 393.—Larva of *Ergates spiculatus.* (Natural size.)

The other principal tetramerous family besides the Chrysomelidæ is the Cerambycidæ, or family of long-horn wood-boring beetles: "long horn" because of their long slender antennæ, and "wood-boring" because their larvæ live in burrows in the trunks of trees. The beetles themselves are usually large and strikingly colored and patterned, and whenever seen attract attention. Nearly 600 species are known in North America, and they are common all over the country. As might be concluded from the habits of the larvæ, the family includes numerous serious pests, such species as the round-headed apple-tree borer, the oak-pruners, various hickory-borers, the twig-girdlers, the giant Prionids *et al.*, all causing much damage to orchards and forests.

The eggs are usually laid on the bark, and the whitish, usually footless, soft-bodied but hard-headed and strong-jawed larvæ burrow about in the tree-trunk for a year or two or even three (varying with the different species), feeding on the chewed wood. They pupate in the burrow, in a cell partitioned off with chips, or sometimes specially made just under the bark. The beetle has only to gnaw its way through the bark or the loosely plugged burrow to escape from the tree. These wood-borers usually select a weakened or dying tree for attack.

The largest Cerambycids belong to the subfamily Prionidæ (Fig. 392), whose members have the sides of the prothorax sharply margined and usually toothed. *Prionus laticollis*, the broad-necked Prionus, varies from

FIG. 394.—The sugar-maple borer, *Plagionotus speciosus*, larvæ and adult beetle. (After Felt; natural size.)

1 inch to 2 inches in length, and is pitchy black or brown, the prothorax with three sharp teeth on each lateral margin, and the antennæ 12-segmented; the larvæ, which live three years, are great footless white grubs, 2½ to 3 inches long, which burrow in the roots of oak, poplar, cherry, apple, grape-vine, and blackberries. The tile-horned Prionus, *P. imbricornis*, a similar beetle, has nineteen antennal segments in the male and usually sixteen in the female; *Orthosoma brunnea*, is long (1½ to 2½ inches) and

narrow, with the margins of the body nearly parallel.  In the south occurs
the genus Mallodon, and on the Pacific coast the genus Ergates (with a
single species, *spiculatus*), both 2½ inches long, and with the lateral margins
of the prothorax with many fine sharp teeth.  The larvæ (Fig. 393) of
Ergates live in the giant sugar and yellow pines of the Sierra Nevada forests.

The cloaked knotty-horn, *Desmocerus palliatus* (Pl. II, Fig. 1), is a
beautiful species, dark greenish blue with the bases of the elytra orange-
yellow; the larvæ bore in elder-pith.  *Cyllene robiniæ*, the locust-borer (Pl. II,

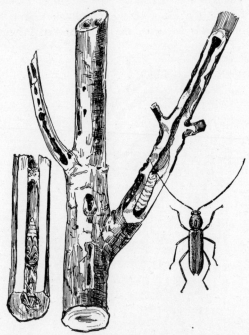

Fig. 395.—Maple-tree borer, *Elaphidion villosum*, larva, pupa, and adult beetle.
(After Felt; natural size.)

Fig. 15), is black, with striking yellow bands often found on goldenrod;
its larvæ live in locust-trees.  A similar species, *Cyllene pictus*, attacks the
hickory.  The red milkweed-beetle, *Tetraopes tetraopthalmus* (Pl. II,
Fig. 10), brick-red with black spots, is a common species on milkweeds;
the larvæ bore into the lower stems and roots.  Two beautiful Cerambycids
of California are shown in Figs. 2 and 16 of Pl. II.

The sugar-maple borer, *Plagionotus speciosus* (Fig. 394), is a serious
pest of sugar-maples in New York and elsewhere in the East.  The beetle,
1 inch long, is black, brilliantly marked with yellow; the eggs are laid in

July or August in the bark, the young borer (a footless, flattened, whitish grub) burrowing first into the sap-wood, where it passes the winter. During the next year it bores vigorously around under the bark, and when about sixteen months old makes a final deep burrow into the heart-wood, in the end of which it pupates. Fig. 394 shows all the stages of this insect. The maple-tree pruner, *Elaphidion villosum* (Fig. 395), ¾ inch long, slender grayish brown, lays its eggs on small twigs in maple-trees in July; the larvæ bore into the center of the twig, eat out a large portion of the woody fiber, plug the end of the burrow with castings, and wait for a strong wind to break off the nearly severed branch. In the fallen twigs thus broken off the larvæ pupates, and the beetles issue, the life-history taking just about a year for completion. This pest also "prunes" oaks, and apple, pear, plum, and other fruit trees. The sawyers, various species of the genus Monohammus, are beautiful brown and grayish beetles with extremely long delicate antennæ; the larvæ bore in sound pines and firs and do great injury to evergreen forests.

One of the worst and most familiar orchard pests is the round-headed apple-tree borer, *Saperda candida* (Fig. 396). The beetle is ¾ inch long, narrow, and subcylindrical, pale brown with two broad creamy-white longitudinal stripes. The eggs are laid on the bark at the base of the tree in June and July. The larva works at first in the sap-wood, making a flat shallow cavity filled with sawdust and castings; later it burrows deeper and works upward. When nearly three years old it bores a tunnel from the heart-wood out nearly to the bark, partly filling the outer part with sawdust and then retires to the inner end and pupates. Two or three weeks after pupation the adult beetle

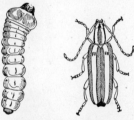

FIG. 396. — The round-headed apple-tree borer, *Saperda candida*, larva and adult beetle. (After Saunders; natural size.)

issues from the pupal skin, works outward along the tunnel and cuts a smooth circular hole in the bark through which it escapes. When several larvæ are working in a tree they may completely girdle it, so that it dies. The most effective remedy is to apply a repellent wash of lime or soft soap from the base of the trunk up to the first branches several times during the egg-laying time, i.e., June and July.

A small family, Spondylidæ, called the aberrant long-horned beetles, is represented in North America by four species, of which the most common is *Parandra brunnea* (Pl. II, Fig. 14), a beautiful polished mahogany-brown beetle found under the bark of pine-trees.

## SECTION TRIMERA.

Only one family is included in this section of beetles with but three tarsal segments in each foot, namely, the familiar little ladybirds or plant-louse beetles, the Coccinellidæ. Their uniformly small size, the semispherical shape, and the "polka-dot" pattern distinguish them readily from all other beetles except perhaps the Chrysomelidæ, a few of which are often mistakenly called ladybirds. This is a particularly unfortunate confusion because of the radically different food-habits and consequent economic relation to man of the two families. The Chrysomelidæ, or leaf-eaters, both as larvæ and adults, attack our crops and trees and flowers; the Coccinellidæ, or ladybirds, both as larvæ and adults, feed on plant-lice and scale-insects, great enemies of our orchards and gardens, and thus are among our best insect friends. A friend of mine found that his roses were suffering from insect attack; he saw little, convex, black-spotted reddish beetles clambering busily up and down the stems, and he set to work to pick these off one by one and drop into a tin cup with petroleum in the bottom. When he had

FIG. 397.—Some Californian ladybird-beetles; beginning at left of upper row the species are *Megilla vitigera, Coccinella californica, C. oculata, Hippodamia convergens;* beginning at left of lower row, *Coccinella trifasciata, C. sanguinea, C. abdominalis, Megilla maculata.* (Twice natural size.)

a full pint he showed them proudly. But the more little round beetles he picked off the more rapidly wilted his roses. And for the wholly sufficient reason that he was collecting and killing the ladybirds that were making a fight—a losing one in the face of my friend's active part in it—against the hosts of tiny inconspicuous green rose-aphids that were sucking the sap out of the rose-stems and buds. So be it remembered that not all bugs are bad bugs, but that some, like the ladybirds, are most effective helpers in waging war against the real pests!

There are about 150 species of ladybirds known in the United States, and almost all are reddish brown with black dots or black with reddish spots. Their colors and markings make them conspicuous, and yet the natural enemies of insects, the birds, obviously let them alone; it is presumed, therefore, that these beetles are ill-tasting to birds, and that their bright colors are of the nature of readily perceived warning signs (see discussion of this subject in Chapter XVII).

The eggs are laid on the bark, stems, or leaves of the tree or plant on which aphids or scale-insects are present. Sometimes they are deposited in little patches right in the middle of a colony of plant-lice. The larvæ (Fig. 398) are elongate, widest across the prothorax and tapering back to the tip, with the skin usually roughened or punctate, bearing hairs and short spines, and marked with blackish, reddish, and yellowish. The larvæ feed steadily on the soft defenceless aphids or young scale-insects, or on the eggs and young of other larger insects. When full-grown they pupate, attached to the leaves or stems without entirely casting off the last larval exuvia (Fig. 398). This cuticle often surrounds the pupa "like a tight-fitting overcoat with the front not closed by buttons." In other cases the larval skin is forced backwards and remains as a little crumpled pad about the posterior end.

The two-spotted ladybug, *Adalia bipunctata*, reddish yellow with a single black spot on each elytron, is common in the East, where it often enters houses to hibernate. The nine-spotted ladybird, *Coccinella novemnotata*, has yellowish elytra with four black spots on each in addition to a common spot just behind the thorax. The "twice-stabbed" ladybird, *Chilocorus bivulnerus*, is shining black with a large red spot on each elytron. *Anatis 15-punctata*, the fifteen-spotted ladybird, is a large species with dark brownish-red elytra bearing seven black spots each, and a median common spot just behind the thorax.

FIG. 398. — A ladybird-beetle, *Coccinella californica*; larva, pupæ, and adult on Lawson's cyprees. (Twice natural size.)

In California the ladybirds are of great importance to the fruit-growers, their steady wholesale destruction of scale-insects being an important factor in successful fruit-raising. Fig. 397 illustrates eight species found on the Pacific coast. A number of ladybird species have been imported from Australia and other countries from which numerous destructive scale-insects had been earlier unwittingly brought on nursery stock. Most conspicuously successful of these attempts to introduce and disseminate original home enemies of imported pests has been the establishment of the small red-and-black ladybird, *Vedalia cardinalis*, which feeds exclusively on the fluted or cottony cushion-scale (*Icerya purchasi*) (Fig. 254). This Australian scale first appeared in California near Menlo Park in 1868 on orange-trees, and in a few years had become so abundant and widely spread over the state that it seriously threatened the extinction of the great orange industry. In 1888 a few live Vedalias (altogether about 500 specimens in five separate lots) were brought from Australia, put on trees infested by the fluted scale, and by helpful scattering of the progeny of these original emigrants this lady-bird species was soon distributed to all scale-infested localities. In a few years it had the pest completely under control, and has ever since remained its master. And California continues to grow Washington oranges.

## SECTION HETEROMERA.

This section includes those beetles which have the front and middle feet with five tarsal segments, the hind feet with four. It is a heterogeneous assemblage, including, besides two large families of widely differing aspect and habits, a number of small ones of obscure, little known, and mostly uncommon species of small size, which present a wide variety of structure and life-history. The two principal families can be distinguished by the following diagnosis:

Head without distinct neck, narrower than thorax and more or less inserted in it; body-wall hard; color usually black.

(Darkling ground-beetles.) TENEBRIONIDÆ.

Head as wide as prothorax, and attached to it by a visible neck; body soft and elytra flexible; colors often diversified, frequently metallic blue or green

(Blister- and oil-beetles.) MELOIDÆ.

The common ground-beetles of the North and East are the swift preda-

ceous Carabidæ; any stone or log turned over will reveal them. In the dry warm western plains and southwestern semi-desert states, however, the slower vegetable-feeding Tenebrionidæ are the common ground-beetles. The most familiar of them on the Pacific coast are large, awkwardly moving, shining black pinacate bugs, Eleodes (Fig. 399) which, when disturbed by the turning over of their covering stone, stand on their fore legs and head and emit an ill-smelling fluid from the tip of the abdomen.

FIG. 399.—Pinacate bug, *Eleodes* sp. (Natural size.)

They have no wings, and the thick horny elytra are grown fast to the back. All the rest of the body is similarly armor-plated, and the collector has to use an awl to make a hole through the body-wall for pinning up his specimens.

The darkling-beetles constitute a large family, more than four hundred species being known in this country, although comparatively few of them are at all familiar. They are mostly dull or shining black, and feed on dry vegetable matter, often in a state of decay. Some live in grain, flour, meal, or sawdust; others in living or dead fungi, and a few are probably predaceous. A common species in mills, stables, grocery-stores, and pantries is the meal-worm beetle, *Tenebrio molitor*, ½ to ¾ inch long, flattened, brownish, with squarish prothorax and longitudinally ridged elytra. The stout, cylindrical, hard-skinned, waxy, yellowish-brown larvæ, or meal-worms, infest flour and meal. They are often bred by bird-fanciers as winter food for insect-eating song-birds. For this purpose they are raised in large numbers in warm boxes partly filled with bran, in which they undergo all their metamorphosis. *T. obscurus* is a darker, almost black, species found also in mills and granaries. Both of these species have been spread all over the world by commerce. A smaller brown species, *Echocerus maxillosus*, ⅓ inch long, is common in the southern states in old and neglected flour.

*Uloma impressa*, ½ inch long, deep mahogany-brown, is common in the east, occurring in decaying logs and stumps. Smaller species of the same genus, lighter in color, are also to be found in similar places. An odd-looking species called by Comstock the forked fungus-beetle, *Boletotherus bifurcus*, is not uncommon in the north and east in and about the large shelf-fungi (Polyporus) that grow on the sides of trees.

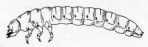

FIG. 400.—Larva of a Tenebrionid, *Boletotherus bifurcus*. (Twice natural size.)

The surface of the body and elytra is very rough, and two conspicuous knobbed horns project forward from the prothorax. The larvæ (Fig. 400) live in the fungi.

The other of the two larger heteromerous families, the Meloidæ, numbering about 200 North American species, includes beetles of unusual structural character and appearance, of peculiar physiological properties, and of a highly specialized and unique kind of metamorphosis. The Meloids are known as oil-beetles from the curious oily fluid emitted by many species when disturbed, and as blister-beetles from the inflammatory and blistering effect of the application of the pulverized dry body substance to the human skin. This powdered blister-beetle is known to pharmacists as cantharides, and is a recognized therapeutic substance. The beetles are rather long and slender-legged and have a soft fleshy body with flexible wing-covers which are sometimes rudimentary, being then short and diverging (Fig. 401). The head is broad and set on a conspicuous neck, and hangs with mouth downward. They are to be found crawling slowly about over field-flowers, as goldenrod, buttercups, etc., often in companies of a score or more individuals. Many of the species are brightly colored, metallic bronze, green, blue, and steel-black being common colors (Pl. II, Fig. 12). Some, however, are grayish, dead black, or yellowish and brown. All are leaf-feeders.

In the development of the blister-beetles an extreme condition known as hypermetamorphosis occurs, which is undoubtedly the result of a purpose-

ful adaptation brought about by long selection, but which seems an almost impossible achievement of such "blind" natural forces. The eggs are deposited in the ground; from them hatch minute active strong-jawed larvæ (Fig. 402) with three pairs of long legs, each terminating in three claw-like spines. These larvæ are called triungulins. They run about seeking food, which, varying with different species, consists of the eggs of locusts, or the eggs and honey of solitary bees. The triungulin of *Epicauta*

FIG. 401.—The striped *vittata*, one of our common Meloid species, studied
potato-beetle, *Epicauta* by Riley, explores cracks and burrows in the ground
*vittata*. (After Pettit; until an egg-pod of a locust (usually of one of the
twice natural size.) destructive Melanoplus species) is found. Into this
the triungulin burrows and begins to devour the eggs. After a few days given to eating a couple of eggs it moults and appears in a very different

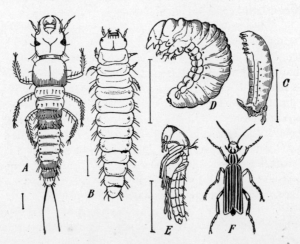

FIG. 402.—Hypermetamorphosis of *Epicauta vittata*. *A*, young larva or triungulin;
*B*, caraboid larva; *C*, coarctate larva; *D*, scarabæoid larva; *E*, pupa; *F*, adult.
(After Riley; natural size indicated by line.)

larval guise with soft skin, short legs, small eyes, and different body form and proportions. One week later a second moult occurs, but without revealing much of a change in the larva, although it is now more curved, less active, and somewhat like a small June-beetle grub; after a third moult it is still more helpless and grub-like. It now grows rapidly. When full-grown it leaves the ruined egg-pod, makes a little cell in the ground near by in which it lies motionless except for a gradual contracting and slow fourth moulting, after which it appears as a completely helpless semi-pupa, or coarctate larva. In this state it passes the winter. In spring the fifth moult takes place, leaving the larva much as before, only smaller and whiter. It becomes now rather active and burrows about, but takes no food, and after a few days again moults for the sixth time, to appear at last as a true pupa. Five or six days later the adult beetle emerges.

Those blister-beetles which live parasitically on bees' eggs instead of on those of the locust probably follow about the course described by Fabre for *Sitaris humeralis*, a European species, an account of which I quote from Sharp (Cambridge Natural History, vol. vi): "The eggs of the Sitaris are deposited in the earth in close proximity to the entrances to the bees' nests, about August. They are very numerous, a single female producing, it is believed, upward of two thousand eggs. In about a month—towards the end of September—they hatch, producing a tiny triungulin of black color; the larvæ do not, however, move away, but, without taking any food, hibernate in a heap, remaining in this state till the following April or May, when they become active. Although they are close to the abodes of the bees, they do not enter them, but seek to attach themselves to any hairy object that may come near them, and thus a certain number of them get on to the bodies of the Anthophora [the bees] and are carried to its nest. They attach themselves with equal readiness to any other hairy insect, and it is probable that very large numbers perish in consequence of attaching themselves to the wrong insects. The bee in question is a species that nests in the ground and forms cells, in each of which it places honey and lays an egg, finally closing the receptacle. It is worthy of remark that in the case of the Anthophora observed by M. Fabre the male appears about a month before the female, and it is probable that the vast majority of the predatory larvæ attach themselves to the male, but afterwards seize a favorable opportunity, transfer themselves to the female, and so get carried to the cells of the bee. When she deposits an egg on the honey, the triungulin glides from the body of the bee on to the egg, and remains perched thereon as on a raft, floating on the honey, and is then shut in by the bee closing the cell. This remarkable act of slipping on to the egg cannot be actually witnessed, but the experiments and observations of the French naturalist leave little room for doubt as to the matter really happening in the way described. The egg of the bee forms the first nutriment of the tiny triungulin, which spends about eight days in consuming its contents; never quitting it, because contact with the surrounding honey is death to the little creature, which is entirely unfitted for living thereon.   After this the triungulin undergoes a moult and appears as a very different creature, being now a sort of vesicle with the spiracles placed near the upper part; so that it is admirably fitted for floating on the honey.   In about forty days, that is, towards the middle of July, the honey is consumed, and the vesicular larva after a few days of repose changes to a pseudo-pupa within the larval skin.   After remaining in this state for about a month some of the specimens go through the subsequent changes, and appear as perfect insects in August or September.   The majority delay this subsequent metamorphosis till the following spring, wintering as pseudo-pupæ and continuing the series of changes in June of the following year; at that time the pseudo-pupa returns to a larval form, differing comparatively little from the second stage.   The skin, though detached, is again not shed, so that this ultimate larva is enclosed in two dead skins; in this curious envelope it turns round, and in a couple of days, having thus reversed its position, becomes lethargic and changes to the true pupa, and in about a month subsequent to this appears as a perfect insect, at about the same time of the year as it would have done had only one year, instead of two, been occupied by its metamorphosis. M. Fabre employs the term third larva for the stage designated by Riley Scolytoid larva, but this is clearly an inconvenient mode of naming the stage. . . . Meloe is also dependent on Anthophora, and its life-history seems on the whole to be similar to that of Sitaris; the eggs are, however, not necessarily deposited in the neighborhood of the bees' nests, and the triungulins distribute themselves on all sorts of unsuitable insects, so that it is possible that not more than one in a thousand succeeds in getting access to the Anthophora nest.   It would be supposed that it would be a much better course for these bee-frequenting triungulins to act like those of Epicauta, and hunt for the prey they are to live on; but it must be remembered that they cannot live on honey; the one tiny egg is their object, and this apparently can only be reached by the method indicated by Fabre.   The history of these insects certainly forms a most remarkably instructive chapter in the department of animal instinct, and it is a matter for surprise that it should not yet have attracted the attention of comparative psychologists. The series of actions to be performed once, and once only, in a lifetime by an uninstructed, inexperienced atom is such that we should, *a priori*, have denounced it as an impossible means of existence, were it not shown that it is constantly successful.   It is no wonder that the female Meloe produces five thousand times more eggs than are necessary to continue the species without diminution in the number of its individuals, for the first and most important act in the complex series of this life-history is accomplished by an extremely indiscriminating instinct; the newly hatched Meloe has to get on to the body of the female of one species of bee; but it has no discrimination whatever of the kind of object it requires, and, as a matter of fact, passes with surprising rapidity on to any hairy object that touches it; hence an enormous majority of the young are wasted by getting on to all sorts of other insects; these larvæ have been found in numbers on hairy Coleoptera, as well as on flies and bees of wrong kinds; the writer has ascertained by experiment that a camel's-hair brush is as eagerly seized, and passed on to, by the young Meloe as a living insect is."

The commonest Eastern species of blister-beetles belong to the genus Epicauta. They feed when adult on the leaves of potato—being therefore often called potato-beetles—and on the pollen of goldenrod. *E. pennsylvanica* is uniformly black; *E. cinerea* is grayish black or even ashy, always with the margins of the elytra gray; *E. vittata* (Fig. 401) is yellowish or reddish above, with head and prothorax marked with black and with two black stripes on each elytron. In Meloe the wings are lacking and the elytra short and diverging; *M. angusticollis*, the buttercup oil-beetle, $\frac{1}{2}$ to $\frac{3}{4}$ inch long, of violaceous color, is the commonest eastern species. In the west the commonest blister-beetles are metallic green and blue and belong to the genus Cantharis.

Another small family of rarely seen heteromerous beetles, which, however, possess an extremely interesting and wonderfully specialized life-history and show a marked degenerate structure due to their parasitic habits, is the Stylopidæ, or wasp parasites. Indeed these curiously modified beetles differ so much from all the other Coleoptera that some entomologists look on them as composing a distinct order which these naturalists call *Strepsiptera*. The males are minute with large fan-shaped wings and reduced, short, club-like elytra. The females are wingless and never develop beyond a larval or grub-like condition. They live in the body of a wasp or bee (Fig. 403)—certain foreign species parasitize ants, cockroaches, and

Fig. 403.—A wasp, *Polistes* sp., parasitized by (*x*) *Xenos* sp. (After Jordan and Kellogg; slightly enlarged.)

other insects—while the free-flying males live from only fifteen or twenty minutes to a day or two: three days is the longest observed lifetime of active adult existence! The youngest larva of the Stylopids—the egg-laying has not been observed—is a minute, active, six-legged creature, not unlike the Meloid triungulin, which attaches itself to the larva of a bee or wasp and burrows into its body. There it lives parasitically, meanwhile undergoing hypermetamorphosis in that after its first moult it becomes a footless maggot or grub. In this state it continues until, if a male, it pupates in the host's body and issues for its brief active adult life. If a female, there is no pupation, but when the host larva itself pupates the Stylops pushes one end of its own body out between two abdominal segments of the host, and there gives birth alive to many little triungulins. How the triungulins find their way to their bee-larva hosts is not very clear, but they probably lie in wait in flowers and when a bee comes along they cling to its leg and are thus carried to the nest where the larvæ are. There are two genera of Stylopidæ in our country, Xenos, which parasitizes the social wasps, Polistes, and Stylops, which parasitizes the mining-bees, Andrena. The triungulins of Xenos, being born in a community nest, can simply roam about over the brood-comb until they they find a wasp-larva to burrow into.

## Rhynchophora.

In this suborder are included all those beetles known as curculios, weevils, bill-bugs, and snout-beetles (excepting the pea- and bean weevils, see p. 281). They are all characterized by the peculiar prolongation of the front of the head into a beak or snout, which may be long, slender and curved, or straight, short, thick, and obtuse. The mouth-parts, of which the small sharp jaws are the conspicuous feature, are situated at the tip of the snout; upper lip (labrum) and palpi are wanting. The antennæ arise from the sides of the snout and are angularly bent or "elbowed" in the middle and end in a knobbed or clavate tip. The body is solid and compact, usually strongly rounded above, and many species are thinly or thickly covered with scales.

Most of the weevils feed, as adults, on fruits, nuts, and various seeds, though some attack stems and leaves, and others hard wood. Many feign death when disturbed, folding up their legs and head and lying inert until danger is past. The larvæ are soft, wrinkled, white, footless grubs which mostly live in fruits, nuts, and seeds. The larvæ and adults of the important family Scolytidæ, variously called timber-beetles, bark-borers, or engraver-beetles, burrow in the bark and wood of trees living or dead.

The principal families of the suborder can be separated by the following key:

The dorsum of the last segment (pygidium) of the male divided transversely, so that this sex appears to have one more body-segment, when viewed dorsally, than the female.
  Mandibles with a scar on the anterior aspect.
                   (Scarred snout-beetles.) OTIORHYNCHIDÆ.
  Mandibles without scar on the anterior aspect........(Curculios.) CURCULIONIDÆ.
Pygidium of both sexes undivided.
  Pygidium vertical; tibiæ not serrate.
               (Bill-bugs and granary-weevils.) CALANDRIDÆ.
  Pygidium horizontal; tibiæ usually serrate............(Bark-beetles.) SCOLYTIDÆ.

The scarred snout-beetles, Otiorhynchidæ, get their vernacular name from the presence of a distinct little scar on the front aspect of each mandible. It is made by the falling off of a mandibular appendage present in the pupa. Most of these beetles are covered with minute scales, much like those of the moths and butterflies, which give them often a bright metallic coloration. Several species of the family are injurious to fruits.

The imbricated snout-beetle, *Epicærus imbricatus*, ½ inch long, dull silvery white with darker markings, and with the elytra with longitudinal lines of deep pits, has the posterior ends of the elytra very steep and cut off almost squarely and ending in a pointed process. It feeds on various cultivated plants, as garden vegetables, strawberries, etc., and gnaws holes in the twigs and fruits of apple and cherry. The pitchy-legged weevil, *Otiorhynchus ovatus*, ½ inch long, dark brown to black with deeply pitted thorax and striated elytra, with deep punctures in the striæ, almost egg-shaped hind body, and thorax with projecting angle on each side, attacks the roots and crowns of strawberry-plants, and also the leaves of apple-trees. Fuller's rose-beetle, *Aramiges julleri*, is perhaps the most familiar species of this family, as it attacks garden and conservatory roses, and in California is an orange pest of some note. It is ¼ inch long, oval, smoky-brown, and thinly covered with scales; its "snout" is short and obtuse. The eggs are laid in masses in concealed places on rose-bushes, the larvæ feeding on the roots of the bushes, while the adults attack the leaves, buds, and flowers. The beetles hide during the day on the under side of the leaves, and can readily be collected and destroyed.

The Curculionidæ, the typical curculios and weevils, compose the largest and most important family of the suborder, comprising over 600 species of North American beetles, and including many seriously destructive pests. Such enemies of the fruit-grower as the plum-curculio, plum-gouger, apple-weevil, and strawberry-weevil, and such a destructive pest of cotton as the boll-weevil (for the study and combating of which Congress has recently appropriated $250,000), are alone

Fig. 404.—The chestnut-weevil, *Balaninus caryatrypes*. (After Lugger; twice natural size.)

sufficient to give this family a high rank in the list of notorious insect pests. The eggs of Curculionids are laid singly in holes bored or cut by the female with her snout in stems or fruits of the food-plant and pushed to the bottom by the snout, which is therefore often very long and slender. The nut- and acorn-weevils of the genus Balaninus are characterized by their possession of an unusually long, slender, curving beak (Fig. 404); in the females this beak may be twice as long as the rest of the body; in the males it is usually about the length of the body. These beetles are from

½ to ¾ inch long, clay-yellow or mottled brownish, and lay their eggs in chestnuts, hazelnuts, acorns, walnuts, hickory-nuts, etc. The white, yellow-headed, maggot-like larva feeds on the kernel, and is full-grown at the time the nuts drop. It either lies in the nut over winter or crawls out and into the ground, where it pupates, and transforms into an adult; *B. rectus* and *B. quercus* are common acorn-weevils, *B. caryatrypes* (Fig. 404) a common chestnut-weevil, and *B. nasicus* a hickory-nut weevil.

The genus Anthonomus includes small pear-shaped, modestly colored weevils with long slender snouts. *A. quadrigibbus*, the apple-weevil, ¼ inch long, dull brown, with four conspicuous brownish-red humps on the hinder part of the body, lays its eggs in little blackish-margined holes drilled into apples; the white, footless, wrinkled, brown-headed larva on hatching burrows into the core, feeds around it, ejecting much rusty-red excrement, and finally pupates, the adult weevil gnawing its way out to the surface. *A. signatus*, the strawberry-weevil, blackish with gray pubescence, punctures the buds, laying an egg in each, and then punctures the flower-pedicel below the bud, so that it drops off; the larva feeds on the fallen unopened bud, changing to a beetle in midsummer. *A. grandis* is the notorious boll-weevil of the South, which has made its way since 1890 from Mexico into this country and is now one of our most serious insect pests; it destroys as much as ninety per cent of the cotton-crop in badly infested localities. The eggs are deposited in the buds and bolls, and the larvæ feed on seed and shell, pupating inside the wall of the boll, through which the issuing beetle gnaws its way. This pest seems to feed only on cotton.

Next to the codlin-moth and San José scale probably the most notorious and destructive fruit-pest is the plum-curculio, *Conotrachelus nenuphar* (Fig. 405), a small beetle, ¼ inch long, brown, and with four small elevated excrescences on the hard wing-covers. The beetles hibernate in rubbish, such as accumulated leaves, about the orchard, and come out in early spring to feed on the tender buds, leaves, flowers, and even green bark. When the plums have set, the

FIG. 405.—The plum-curculio, *Conotrachelus nenuphar.* (After photograph by Slingerland; enlarged.)

females begin to deposit their eggs in them by drilling a tiny hole and pushing an egg into each. Then a concentric slit is cut near the hole so as to leave the egg in a little flap in which the tissue is so injured that the rapid growing of the fruit does not injure the delicate egg buried in it. The whitish larva bores in until it reaches the stone around which it feeds. (The larva of the plum-gouger, *Coccotorus scutellaris*, another destructive Curculionid pest of the plum, bores into the stone.) When the larvæ are full-grown the infested plums fall to the ground, and the larvæ crawl out and into the soil to pupate. The adult beetles soon issue and hunt up hibernating quarters. The plum-curculio attacks cherries, and also peaches, nectarines, and apricots. In many regions of this country it has nearly stopped the growing of plums. Curiously enough, but fortunately, this pest does not seem to be able to maintain itself in California, where plum (prune) growing is one of the chief industries. A remedy of some effectiveness is to jar each plum-tree, under which a sheet has been spread, repeatedly during blossoming and fruit-setting time. The curculios, alarmed by the jarring, fold up their legs and snout and fall to the ground (sheet), where they feign death. This feigning can be turned into reality

FIG. 406.—Larva and pupa of the quince-curculio, *Conotrachelus cratægi*. (After photographs by Slingerland; at left, larva, natural size and enlarged; at right, pupa much enlarged.)

by any one of various means. Excellent "curculio-catchers" consist of wheelbarrows on each of which is mounted a large inverted umbrella split in front to receive the tree-trunk, against which the barrow (with a padded bumper) is driven with force enough to do the jarring. All fallen plums also should be promptly gathered and burned or scalded so as to kill the larvæ within.

The family Calandridæ includes about eighty North American species of weevils, of which several are common and familiar under the names of corn bill-bugs and rice- and grain-weevils. To the large genus Sphenophorus belong the species known as corn bill-bugs, blackish, brown, or rarely gray in color, from $\frac{1}{4}$ to $\frac{1}{2}$ inch long, with thick and hard elytra which are ridged and punctured, as is also the thorax. By day they hide in the soil at the base of young corn-plants, and at night bore little round holes into their stems. The larvæ live in the stems of timothy, sedges, or bulb-rooted grasses, pupating in fall or early spring. To the genus Calandra belongs the destructive rice-weevil, *C. oryzæ*, ⅒ inch long, blackish to pale chestnut, which attacks all kinds of stored grains and is especially injurious in the southern states to rice, and the granary-weevil, *C. granaria*, ⅛ inch long, dark brown, also common in grain-bins. Both these species have been widely distributed by commerce, and by their rapid multiplication and the concealment afforded them by the grain often attain such abundance as to cause great loss in mills, breweries, and elevators. The preventive remedy is cleanliness and the rapid removal of the stored grain. They prefer dark places, therefore a flood of sunlight will prevent their rapid increase. In bins that can be made nearly air-tight these pests may be killed by the fumes of carbon bisulphide.

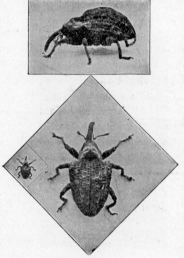

FIG. 407.—The quince-curculio, *Conotrachelus cratægi*. (After photograph by Slingerland; natural size and enlarged.)

One may often see in the woods the curious hieroglyphics of the engraver-beetles (Scolytidæ). Where bark has been torn from a tree-trunk both the exposed trunk-wood and the inner surface of the stripped-off bark reveal the tortuous branching mines or tunnels of the Scolytidæ. A common way of making these tunnels is as follows: The beetles (a male and a female together) burrow from the outside through the thick rough outer bark, usually leaving a little betraying splotch of fine sawdust, to the inner live bark or sapwood; here the pair turn, keep to this live sap-filled region, laying their eggs in masses or scattered along a tunnel. Soon the larvæ hatch, whereupon each digs a tunnel for itself, all of the new larval mines branching out from the original tunnel made by the parent beetles. When full-grown the larva digs a cell at the end of its tunnel and pupates in it. The issuing beetle burrows its way out from the tunnels and is soon ready to begin a new mine. But there is much variation in the mining habits of the various species.

The beetles are small, often microscopic, the larger ones rarely more than ¼ inch long. They are brown to blackish, with stout, nearly cylindrical hard bodies, the hind end of the body usually obliquely or squarely truncate, and the head short, bent downward, and so covered by the thorax as to be almost invisible from above. The larvæ are white and footless little grubs with very strong jaws. The family includes 150 species in North America, and because of the recently awakened interest in forestry is now being given special attention by entomologists. The losses, by the death of trees and the riddling of timber, caused by these obscure little insects are enormous. Pinchot, chief of the United States Bureau of Forestry, has recently estimated the annual forest losses caused by insects to be $100,000,000, and most of the ravages are due to the Scolytidæ.

Among the most destructive genera are Dendroctonus and Tomicus, each with numerous species. They often work in the same tree. For example, the famous Monterey pines of California are attacked by *Dendroc-*

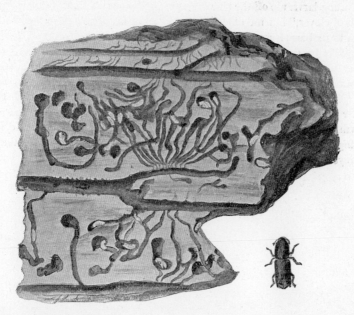

FIG. 408.—Galleries in Monterey pine, with larvæ, pupæ, and adults of the engraver-beetle, *Tomicus plastographus*. (Natural size except the single beetle outside, which is enlarged three times.)

*tonus valens* in the lower three or four feet of the trunk, as many as four hundred individuals (larvæ, pupæ, and adults) occurring in this limited space in badly infested trees, while above this zone on up to the top of the tree are the mines of *Tomicus plastographus* (Fig. 408), from thirty to forty pairs burrowing into each yard of trunk. It is plain that such a combined attack on a single tree means death to it.

The ambrosia-beetles, including half a dozen genera and many species, have special habits which make them comparable in some ways with the social wasps, bees, and ants, and with the termites. They live in mines— the "black holes" often seen in timber—bored into the heart-wood of sick or dead trees, in colonies including numerous adults and many larvæ. Their food is not the wood of the tree, but consists of certain minute and succulent bodies produced by a fungus which grows on the walls of their burrows. This fungus does not grow there by chance, but is "planted" by the beetles. It is started by the female upon a carefully packed bed or layer of chips, sometimes near the entrance of a burrow, in the bark, but generally at the end of a branch gallery in the wood. It spreads, or is spread, from this forcing-bed to the walls of the various galleries and chambers of the mine. The young larvæ nip off the tender tips of the fungus stalks "as calves crop the heads of clover," but the older larvæ and adult beetles eat the whole structure down to its base, from which new hyphæ soon spring up afresh. The fungus is suitable for the insects only when fresh and juicy: if allowed to ripen, the tender protoplasm is shut up in spores, and the galleries are soon filled to suffocation with these spores and the ramifying mycelial threads. Indeed the colony of ambrosia-beetles—ambrosia being the name applied to the tender fungus food—is often overwhelmed and destroyed by the quick growth of their garden-patch. If anything happens to interrupt the constant feeding on and cutting back of the fungus, the colony is almost always destroyed.

# CHAPTER XIII

## THE TWO-WINGED FLIES (Order Diptera)

**N**EXT to the name "bug" there is no other name so popular in point of miscellaneous application to insects as "fly." This looseness of popular nomenclature may be largely due to the fact that entomologists themselves apply the term "fly" in several compound words, as butterfly, alder-fly, caddis-fly, May-fly, saw-fly, and the like, to widely differing kinds of insects. Used as a simple word, however, by fly an entomologist means some species of the order Diptera. The various kinds of true flies have of course special names, as mosquitoes, midges, punkies, gnats, or as in the compounds horse-flies, bee-flies, flower-flies, robber-flies, etc.

The order Diptera is so large and includes insects of such widely differing form and habit that it is difficult to formulate any general account of it. The name itself is derived from the most conspicuous structural condition of flies, namely, their two-winged state. All Diptera have but a single pair of wings, if any; a few are wingless. The

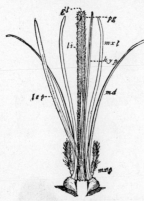

FIG. 409.

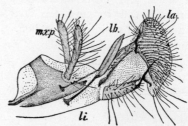

FIG. 410.

FIG. 409.—Mouth-parts of a female mosquito, *Culex* sp. *lep.*, labrum-epipharynx; *md.*, mandible; *mx.l.*, maxillary lobe; *mx.p.*, maxillary palpus; *hyp.*, hypopharynx; *li.*, labium; *gl.*, glossa; *pg.*, paraglossa.

FIG. 410.—Mouth-parts of the house-fly, *Musca domestica*. *lb.*, labrum; *mx.p.*, maxillary palpi; *li.*, labium; *la.*, labellum.

hind wings of other forms are replaced by a pair of strange little structures

301

called balancers, or halteres, whose use seems to be chiefly that of orienting or directing the fly in its flight. The possession of these balancers is a certain diagnostic character in distinguishing Diptera from all other insects. The wings are membranous and usually clear, and supported by a few strong veins. No flies can bite in the sense of the chewing or crushing biting common to beetles, grasshoppers, and other insects with jaw-like mandibles, but some have mandibles elongate, slender, and sharp-pointed, so that they act as needles or stylets to make punctures in the flesh of animals or tissues of plants. The great majority of flies, however, have no mandibles at all and no piercing beak, but lap up

liquid food with a curious folding fleshy proboscis, which is the highly modified labium or under-lip. They feed on flower-nectar, or any exposed sweetish liquid, or the juices of decaying animal or plant substance. To take solid food as the house-fly does from a lump of sugar, the solid has to be rasped off as small particles which are either dissolved or mixed in a salivary fluid that issues from the fleshy tip of the proboscis.

FIG. 411.—Head, antennæ, and beak of mosquito, lateral aspect.

All the Diptera have a complete metamorphosis, the young hatching from the egg as footless and often headless larvæ (maggots, grubs), usually soft and white, and in many cases obtaining food osmotically through the skin. The life-history is usually rapid, so that generation after generation succeed one another quickly. Thus it may be true, as an old proverb says, that a single pair of flesh-flies (and their progeny) will consume the carcass of an ox more rapidly than a lion. The pupæ of the more specialized flies are concealed in the thickened and darkened last larval moult, the whole puparium looking much like a large elliptical brown seed.

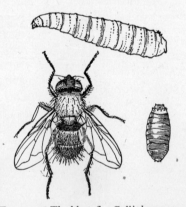

FIG. 412.—The blow-fly, *Calliphora erythrocephala*. Larva, pupa, and adult.

The Diptera include the familiar house-flies, flesh-flies, and bluebottles of the dwelling and stables; the horse-flies and greenheads, that make summer life sometimes a burden for horses and their drivers; the buzzing flower- and bee-flies of the gardens; the beautiful little pomace-flies with their brilliant colors and mottled wings that swarm like midges about the cider-press and fallen and fermenting fruit; the bot-flies, those disgusting and injurious pests of horses, cattle, rabbits, rats, etc.; the fierce robber-flies that prey on other insects, including their own fly cousins; the midges and gnats, that gather in dancing swarms over pastures and streams; the black-flies and punkies, dreaded enemies of the trout-fisher and camper; and, worst of all, the cosmopolitian mosquito, probably the most serious insect enemy of mankind. Only in recent years have we come to recognize the mosquito's real capacity for mischief. Annoying and vexatious they have always everywhere been, by day and night, from tropics to pole, from the salt marshes by the sea to the alpine lakes on the shoulders of the mountain-peaks. But that the mosquito-bite not only annoys but may kill, by infecting the punctured tissues with the germs of malaria or yellow fever or filariasis, three of the most wide-spread and fatal diseases of man—this alarming fact is a matter which has come to be really recognized only recently, and the general recognition of which has given to the practical study of insects an importance which years of warning and protesting by economic entomologists have been wholly unable to do.

The Diptera include about 7,000 known species in North America, thus ranking among the principal orders of insects in degree of numerical representation in this country. About 50,000 species are known in the whole world.

The order may be separated into certain principal subdivisions by the following table:

Living as external parasites on mammals, birds, or honey-bees; body flattened and often wingless; the young born alive as larvæ nearly ready to pupate.
Suborder Pupipara (see p. 351).
Not living on the bodies of other animals; young usually produced as eggs.
Suborder Diptera genuina (see p. 304).
Antennæ with numerous (more than five) segments. .Section Nematocera (see p. 304).
Antennæ with not more than five segments, usually with three, the third sometimes annulated, showing it to be a compound segment, i.e., composed of several coalesced segments............................... Section Brachycera (see p. 327).
Third segment of antennæ annulated, showing it to be composed of several coalesced segments................................................ (see p. 327).
Antennæ consisting of four or five distinct segments.................(see p. 330).
Antennæ with but three segments (rarely less), the third segment with or without a style or bristle........................................ ..........(see p. 332).

Of the two suborders the smaller one, the Pupipara, including certain strangely specialized and degraded parasitic flies, will be considered last. Of he first suborder, the Diptera genuina, the various families of small midge- and mosquito-like flies composing the section Nematocera (flies with slender several-segmented antennæ) will be discussed first, as they are believed by entomologists to be the more generalized or simpler flies.

Of this section the mosquitoes, black flies, and punkies are perhaps best known because of the annoyance and irritation caused by their "bites," that is, the punctures made by the sharp beak of the females in their blood-sucking forays. But the swarms of dancing midges and the sprawling long-legged crane-flies, or leather-jackets, are not unfamiliar members of this group. In addition there belong here a few families of flies little known but possessed of most interesting habits and form.

### KEY TO FAMILIES OF NEMATOCERA.

(The references to the names and character of the veins in the wings which occur in this and other keys used in this chapter may be understood by a comparison of the venation of the specimen being examined with Fig. 18, and with the figures of the venation of various families, as Figs. 425, 436, 444, etc.)

A. Antennæ slender, longer than thorax; usually nearly as long as body or longer; legs long and slender, and abdomen usually so.

    B. Very small moth-like flies, with body and wings hairy; wings with 9–11 longitudinal veins, but no cross-veins except sometimes near the base of the wing.

          (Moth-like flies.) PSYCHODIDÆ.

    BB. Not as above.

        C. Wings with a network of fine vein-like lines near the outer and hinder margins in addition to the regular (heavier) venation.

          (Net-winged midges.) BLEPHAROCERIDÆ.

        CC. The margin of the wings and the veins fringed with scales.

          (Mosquitoes.) CULICIDÆ.

        CCC. With a distinct V-shaped suture on the back of the thorax.

          (Crane-flies.) TIPULIDÆ.

        CCCC. Without distinct V-shaped suture on the back of the thorax.

            D. Anal veins entirely wanting; medial vein wanting or at most represented by a single unbranched fold.

          (Gall-gnats.) CECIDOMYIIDÆ.

            DD. Anal veins present or represented by folds; medial vein present or at least represented by a fold which is usually branched.

                E. Ocelli present; legs slender and with greatly elongate ccxæ (basal segment)...(Fungus-gnats.) MYCETOPHILIDÆ.

                EE. Ocelli absent.

                    F. Wing-veins well developed in all parts of the wing.

          (Dixa-flies.) DIXIDÆ.

                    FF. Wing-veins much stouter near the costal (front) margin of the wing than elsewhere.

          (Midges.) CHIRONOMIDÆ.

AA. Antennæ shorter than the thorax and rather stout.

    B. Ocelli present.............................(March-flies.) BIBIONIDÆ.

    BB. Ocelli absent; wings very broad.............(Buffalo-gnats.) SIMULIIDÆ.

Of the ten families included in the above key the members of five pass the young stages, larval and pupal, in fresh water; of the members of two some have aquatic immature stages and some terrestrial; while the larvæ and pupæ of all the members of the remaining three live in plants or in the ground, none being aquatic.

Best known of the aquatic families, and indeed of the whole suborder, is the mosquito family, the Culicidæ. While the different kinds of mosquitoes are much alike, so much so indeed that most of us are quite content if we can determine an insect to be a mosquito without carrying the identification farther, there are known in the world at least 300 different mosquito species, representing two dozen distinct genera. In North America nearly 60 species are already known, representing 10 genera, and new ones are being found constantly. In the family Culicidæ are included two distinct general types of mosquito, one with mouth-parts forming a long, slender, sucking proboscis, provided with sharp, needle-like stylets for piercing (Fig. 411), the other with the mouth-parts short and better adapted for lapping or sucking up freely exposed liquids. The latter type of mouth is possessed by but two genera, all the others being piercers and blood suckers (in the female sex). Of these piercing genera three are of especial importance and interest to us because of their abundance and

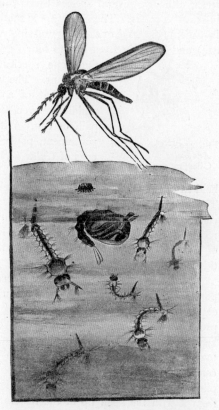

FIG. 413.—The life-history of a mosquito, *Culex* sp A small raft of eggs is shown on the surface of the water, several larvæ ("wrigglers"), long and slender, and one pupa ("tumbler"), large-headed, are shown in the water, and an adult in the air above. (From life; much enlarged.)

their definitely determined relation to the development, incubation, and dissemination of certain serious diseases of man. These three genera are Culex, Stegomyia, and Anopheles. To Culex belong the great majority of familiar mosquitoes which pursue and harass us with their songs and bites; to Stegomyia (and Culex) belong the mosquitoes held responsible for the dissemination of yellow fever and filariasis, and to Anopheles belong the malaria breeding and distributing mosquitoes.

All the mosquitoes agree in having strictly aquatic immature stages. The eggs are laid on the surface of standing or slowly moving water, usually fresh, although several species breed abundantly and probably exclusively in brackish water. These eggs are in small one-layered packets or rafts (usual in Culex) (Fig. 413) or are scattered singly (in Stegomyia and Anopheles) (Fig. 414) and hatch in from one to four days, varying with the species, and in the same species with the temperature and light conditions. The water oviposited on may be, for Culex, that of a pond, a pool, or any temporary puddle, or even that in an exposed trough, barrel, pail, or can. With Anopheles only natural, usually permanent, pools are selected. I have found the eggs of *Culex incidens* on the surface of a bubbling soda-spring in California, and of Stegomyia in water held in slight depressions in a number of ship's metal parts in Samoa. The brackish-water species of Culex usually lay their eggs on the small clear pools scattered through the marshes. A few entomologists have recorded their belief, based on various indirect observations, that the eggs of Anopheles at least may be deposited on the soil, but no direct proof of this is yet on record.

FIG. 414.—The eggs of *Anopheles* sp. (After Giles; much enlarged.)

The larvæ (Figs. 413 and 415) of mosquitoes are the familiar wrigglers of ponds and ditches. The long, slender, squirming body, with its forked posterior extremity and thick head end, is thoroughly characteristic. The head is provided with a pair of vibratile tufts or brushes of fine hairs which are kept, most of the time, in rapid motion, creating currents of water setting toward the mouth, and thus bringing to it a constant supply of food, which consists of organic particles and microscopic animals. Breathing is accomplished by the wrigglers coming to the surface and hanging head downward from it with the open tip of the respiratory tube, one of the prongs of the posterior forking of the body, projecting just through the surface film. If a mosquito wriggler is prevented from coming to the surface, or if, once there, it finds some impediment which restrains it from getting its respiratory tube into connection with the free air above the surface, it will drown. And this fact partly explains the fatal effectiveness of a film of kerosene spread over the surface of a pool in which mosquitoes are breeding. The larval stage lasts from one to four weeks, varying in different species and also varying in the case of each species at different seasons and under different conditions of food-supply, temperature, and light. Larvæ of Culex have lived in breeding-jars in my laboratory for three months. The larvæ moult twice, and on the third casting of the skin appear as active, non-feeding pupæ (Figs. 413 and 415) with thick, broad head end (the thick part includes thorax and head) and slender, curving abdomen, bearing two conspicuous swimming-flaps at the tip. The pupa rests at the surface of the water with its two short horn-like respiratory tubes, which rise from the dorsum of the thorax, extending through the surface film to the air above. When disturbed it swims swiftly down into the water by quick bendings or flappings of the abdomen with its terminal flaps. The pupal stage lasts from two to five days, with comparatively little variation beyond these extremes.

The adults issue through a longitudinal rent in the back of the pupal cuticle, and while drying their wings, legs, and body vesture rest on the surface of the water, often partly supported by the floating discarded skin. The two wings are long and narrow, the legs long and slender, the thorax humped with the small head hanging down in front and the slender sub-cylindrical abdomen depending behind. The body is clothed with scales, as are the veins of the wings, and on the scales, which are of different shapes and sizes on different parts of the body, and vary in different species, depend the colors and pattern, often striking and beautiful, just as all the color patterns of the butterflies and moths are produced by a covering over body and wings of similar scales. The males of all mosquitoes differ from the females in having the slender, many-segmented antennæ provided with many long fine hairs arranged in whorls and combining to give the antennæ a bushy or feathery appearance. These hairs, as has been proved by experiment and histologic study, are a part of an elaborate auditory apparatus, their special function being to be set into vibration when impinged on by sound-waves of certain rates of vibration, and to transmit this vibration to a complex nervous organ in the second antennal segment (Figs. 56 and 57). The males, while having a long, slender, sucking-proboscis, do not possess the piercing stylets characteristic of the female, and hence are not blood-suckers, but probably feed, if at all, on the nectar of plants or on other exposed liquids. The females suck blood when they can get it, but in lieu of this animal fluid feed on the sap of plants. In experimental work in the laboratory cut pieces of banana are provided the imprisoned adult mosquitoes.

At this writing about fifty species of Culex, one species of Stegomyia, and four species of Anopheles have been found in this country. These three genera may be distinguished by the following key:

Palpi (the mouth-feelers projecting by the side of the proboscis) long in both male and
    female, about as long as the proboscis..............................ANOPHELES.
Palpi as long as proboscis in male, but only one-third as long in female.
    Scales on the head narrow and curved ...................................CULEX.
    Scales on the head flat and broad ...................................STEGOMYIA.

Our particular interest in being able to distinguish these genera lies, as already said, in the special relation which their members bear to certain wide-spread and serious human diseases. The rôle played by mosquitoes in the breeding and dissemination of the microscopic germs of malaria has been so well exploited in newspapers and magazines that, although a matter of comparatively recent determination, it is already common knowledge, at least in its more general outline. For a somewhat detailed account of the etiology of the diseases known to be disseminated by mosquitoes, including the exact relation of the mosquito host to the disease-germs, see Chapter XVIII of this book. It is sufficient to say here that the malarial germs seem to live parasitically in and be disseminated by the various species of Anopheles only, the yellow-fever germs only by the species *Stegomyia fasciata*, and the minute worms of filariasis by the same species and two or three tropical forms of Culex, while the score and more of North American species of

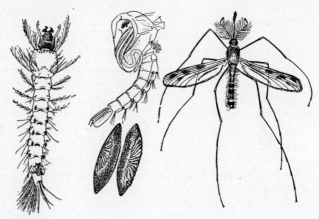

Fig. 415.—A malaria-carrying mosquito, *Anopheles maculipennis;* larva at left, in middle two eggs below and pupa above, male adult at right. (From life; much enlarged.)

Culex compose most of the hordes of piercing and blood-sucking mosquitoes which in so many localities make life distressful. *Stegomyia fasciata* is found in this country only in the Gulf states. In our colonies, the Hawaiian and American Samoan Islands, I have found it to be the most abundant mosquito species, although yellow fever is yet unknown in these islands. But it seems not improbable that, with the cutting of a canal through the Isthmus of Panama so that ships can sail directly from the West Indies to Hawaii continuously within the tropics, Stegomyia individuals infested with yellow-fever germs might be readily carried to our tropical Pacific colonies. Such a possible contingency should at least be had in mind by those charged with the responsibility of public-health affairs in Hawaii and Samoa. Stegomyia is already terrible enough in its disease-spreading capacity in unfortunate Samoa, as explained in Chapter XVIII, the frightful scourge elephantiasis, an incurable and hideously deforming kind of filariasis, from which quite one-third of the natives of Samoa suffer, being disseminated chiefly (so far as our present knowledge permits us to affirm) by mosquitoes of the species *Stegomyia fasciata.*

With a few English investigators and our own government and state entomologists in the lead, a great campaign is being waged against mosquitoes. Despite the hosts of the enemy, its great capacity for providing new individuals to supply the places of the fallen, its effective means of locomotion, and its easily managed department of commissary, local foraging being exclusively relied on for sustaining its armies, we are making headway against it. Our modes of attack are various: by draining swamps, ponds,

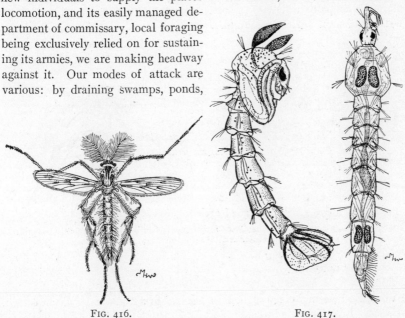

FIG. 416.                    FIG. 417.

FIG. 416.—A short-beaked mosquito, *Corethra* sp. (From life; four times natural size.
FIG. 417.—Pupa (at left) and larva (at right) of short-beaked mosquito, *Corethra* sp. (From life; six times natural size.)

and puddles we restrict the multiplication of these pests, and rid particular localities of them altogether; by introducing into ponds and pools which cannot be drained substances, as kerosene, etc., which are poisonous to mosquitoes, we kill them in their adolescence; by encouraging and disseminating their natural enemies, such as dragon-flies, we pursue them in their own elements, water and air. Mosquitoes do not fly far; when abundant in a locality, breeding-places are to be looked for close at hand. The open rain-water barrel, a little puddle by the lawn hydrant, a cistern with unscreened openings, all of these are welcome invitations to the mosquito to come and rear a large family. Put close screen tops over water in cisterns and barrels;

leave no standing puddles in the back yard or decorative lily-pools in the front; pour kerosene on the surface of ponds and ditches in the neighborhood, and the mosquito problem for localities not adjacent to swamps and marshes is nearly solved. Where the problem includes swamps larger measures must be undertaken, community effort may be necessary, and the municipal or county administration called on to take official action. But when it is remembered that abolishing the mosquito pest means doing away with malaria, and in the subtropic and tropic region with yellow fever and filariasis, no pains will seem too troublesome, no expense too large in this warfare of man against mosquitoes.

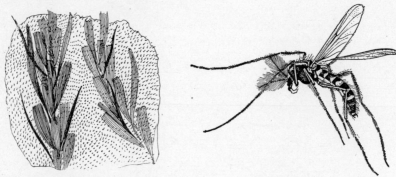

FIG. 418.                                    FIG. 419.

FIG. 418.—Scales on the wings of *Culex fatigans*. (After Theobald; greatly magnified.)
FIG. 419.—A midge, male, *Chironomus* sp. (From life; much enlarged.)

Looking not unlike mosquitoes are the larger species of the family Chironomidæ, whose members are popularly known as midges and punkies, the name blood-worm being applied to the reddish aquatic larvæ of certain species. Like the mosquitoes, the males are distinguished from the females by their very bushy or feathery antennæ, but, unlike the mosquitoes, the females, except in the case of the minute punkies or "no-see-ums" of the New England and Canadian mountains and forests, and their near relatives in the western forests, are not blood-suckers. The midges are particularly noticeable in "dancing-time," that is, when they collect in great swarms and toss up and down in the air over meadows, pastures, and stream sides.

The larvæ (Fig. 420) of most species are aquatic, some of them forming small tubular cases, as caddis-fly larvæ do, and most of them being distinctly reddish in color. They wriggle about in the slime and decaying leaves at the bottom of ponds or lakes, feeding on vegetable matter. The pupæ (Fig. 421) are, like those of the mosquitoes, active, although of course non-feeding, and are provided with two bunches of fine hair-like tracheal gills on the dorsum of the thorax, or with a pair of short club-shaped processes which have a sort of sieve-like skin. In both cases the pupa breathes the oxygen which is mixed with water and is thus not compelled, as are the mosquito pupæ, to come to the surface for air. The larvæ of the genus Ceratopogon and its allies, which include the fiercely biting and blood-sucking little punkies (Fig. 422), so irritating to the fisherman and hunter in the north woods,

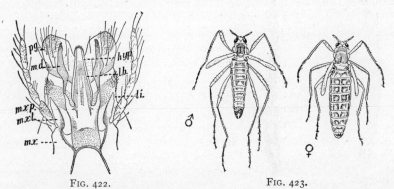

FIG. 420.

FIG. 421.

FIG. 420.—Larva of a midge, *Chironomus* sp. (From life: natural length ⅓ inch.)
FIG. 421.—Pupa of midge, *Chironomus* sp. (From life; natural length ⅓ inch.)

live, according to Comstock, "under the bark of decaying branches, under fallen leaves, and in sap flowing from wounded trees."

Running and half flying about over the spray-wet rocks and on the surface of the smaller tide-pools between tide-lines on the ocean shore near Mon-

FIG. 422.

FIG. 423.

FIG. 422.—Mouth-parts of a female "punkie," *Ceratopogon* sp. *lb.*, labrum; *md.*, mandible; *mx.*, maxilla; *mx.l.*, maxillary lobe; *mx.p.*, maxillary palpus; *li.*, labium; *p.g.*, paraglossa; *hyp.*, hypothorax.
FIG. 423.—The tide-rock fly, *Eretmoptera browni*. (Natural length ⅛ inch.)

terey, California, may be seen in the winter months many small, long-legged, spider-like flies (Fig. 423) whose wings are reduced to mere oar-like veinless rudiments. The larvæ and pupæ live submerged in the salt water of the outer and most exposed tide-pools, where the ocean water is held in shallow depressions in the rocks, and is changed many times daily by the dashing of the waves. Where the flies go when the tide is in and these rocks are either wholly submerged or at least constantly dashed over by the breaking waves, I have not been able to determine; but the larvæ and pupæ cling

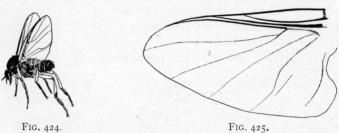

FIG. 424.                    FIG. 425.

FIG. 424.—A black-fly, *Simulium* sp. (Four times natural size.)
FIG. 425.—Diagram of wing of black-fly, *Simulium*, showing venation.

tight and secure in their rock basins to small but strong silken nets spun by the larvæ. They rest on the under side of these nets, indeed are almost enclosed in them as in a cocoon. This little fly is a most interesting insect because of its ocean-water habitat—very few insects live in salt water, and

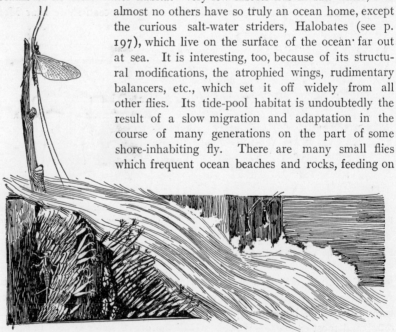

almost no others have so truly an ocean home, except the curious salt-water striders, Halobates (see p. 197), which live on the surface of the ocean far out at sea. It is interesting, too, because of its structural modifications, the atrophied wings, rudimentary balancers, etc., which set it off widely from all other flies. Its tide-pool habitat is undoubtedly the result of a slow migration and adaptation in the course of many generations on the part of some shore-inhabiting fly. There are many small flies which frequent ocean beaches and rocks, feeding on

FIG. 426.—Larvæ and pupæ of *Simulium* sp. on edge of stream, May-fly on projecting twig. (After Felt.)

decaying seaweed, etc., and from among these this species has no doubt gradually worked its way out to the very verge of the shore-line, becoming gradually adapted in habit and structure to the conditions of its new habitat.

Besides the mosquitoes and punkies a third kind of fly assails the rod-and-line fisherman, the hunter, and the camper in forests and along the streams; black, stout-bodied, hump-backed, short-legged, broad-winged flies (Fig. 424) from one-sixth to one-fourth of an inch long, with short but strong piercing proboscis. These are black-flies, buffalo-gnats or turkey-gnats, as they are variously called, composing the small family Simuliidæ, distributed all over this country, but especially abundant in the southern states, where they attack cattle so fiercely and in such great swarms that the animals are driven frantic and sometimes even killed by a violent fever produced by the terrible biting.

The larvæ (Fig. 426) are odd, squirming, slippery, little black "worms," which, clinging by the hind tip of the body, occur in dense colonies or patches on the smooth rock bed in shallow places of swift streams. The lip of a fall is a favorite place for them. The swift-running water constantly affords them an abundant air and food supply. The free or head end of the body is provided

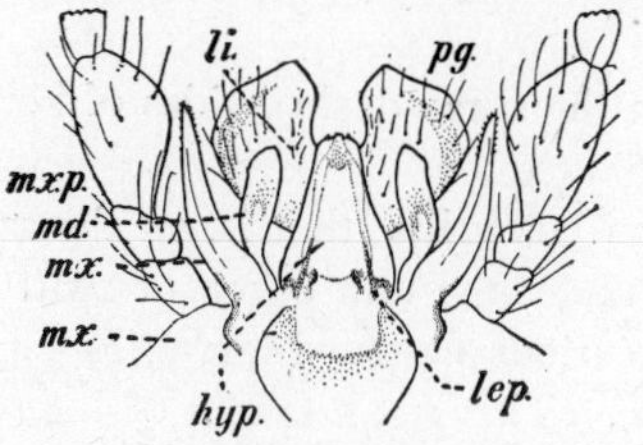

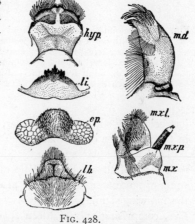

FIG. 427.

FIG. 428.

FIG. 427.—Mouth-parts of female black-fly, *Simulium* sp. *lep.*, labrum; *hyp.*, hypopharynx; *md.*, mandible; *mx.*, maxilla; *mxp.*, maxillary palpus; *li.*, labium; *pg.*, paraglossa. (Much enlarged.)

FIG. 428.—Mouth-parts of larva of black-fly, *Simulium* sp. *lb.*, labrum; *ep.*, epipharynx; *md.*, mandible; *mx.*, maxilla; *mxp.*, maxillary palpus; *mxl.*, maxillary lobe; *li.*, labium; *hyp.*, hypopharynx. (Much enlarged.)

with a conspicuous pair of freely movable brushes which collect food from the water. The clinging to the rock is effected by means of silk spun from the mouth, and by the skilful use of silken threads the larvæ can move about over the submerged rock bed without being washed away by the swift water. When ready to pupate, which is after about a month of larval life (under favorable conditions of temperature and food-supply), the larva spins a little silken cornucopia-like cocoon (Fig. 426) fastened to the rock by the little end, and often fastened by the sides to adjacent cocoons. The large free end is left open. In this cocoon it pupates, and after about three weeks the winged fly issues. The eggs are laid in patches on the rocks

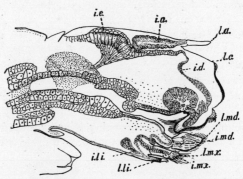

Fig. 429.—Longitudinal section of head of old larva of black-fly, *Simulium* sp., showing adult mouth-parts developing inside of or corresponding with the larval mouth-parts. *l.md.*, larval mandible; *l.mx.*, larval maxilla; *l.li.*, larval labium; *l.c.*, larval cuticle; *l.a.*, larval antenna; *i.md.*, adult mandible; *i.mx.*, adult maxilla; *i.li.*, adult labium; *i.d.*, adult hypoderm (cell-layer of skin); *i.a.*, adult antennæ; *i.e.*, adult eye. (Much enlarged.)

just below the surface of the water, or on the spray-dashed sides of boulders in the stream or on its margin.

In the same places where the Simulium larvæ live, that is, on the smooth rock faces of stream bed and lip of fall under the thin apron of swift silver water of mountain streams, live also the curious flattened larvæ (Fig. 430) of the net-winged midges or Blepharoceridæ. This small family of interesting flies, comprising only eighteen species in the whole world, of which seven belong to this country, is one with which the general collector will hardly become acquainted unless he takes particular pains to do so. But the pains are well worth while, for they are not pains at all, but pleasures. In the first place, the larvæ—and they must be looked for first, the winged flies being very rare, very retiring, and hardly distinguishable, until captured, from a number of other common and less interesting kinds—live only in the most attractive parts of the most attractive mountain brooks. I have found them in a tiny swift stream near Quebec, in two or three hillside brooks near Ithaca, N. Y., in roaring mountain torrents in the Rocky Mountains, and in similar plunging streams in the Sierra Nevada and Coast Range. Clinging by a ventral series of six suckers to the smooth shining rock bed, the short broad larvæ squirm slowly around, feeding on diatoms and other microscopic water

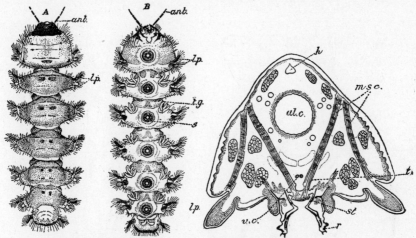

FIG. 430.                                        FIG. 431.

FIG. 430.—Larva of net-winged midge, *Bibiocephala comstocki*. At left, dorsal view; at right, ventral view. *ant.*, antennæ; *l.p.*, lateral processes; *t.g.*, tracheal gills; *s.*, sucker. (Natural length, $\frac{2}{5}$ to $\frac{1}{2}$ inch.)

FIG. 431.—Cross-section of body of larva of net-winged midge, showing anatomical details of sucker and other parts. *h.*, heart; *al.c.*, alimentary canal; *l.p.*, lateral process; *v.c.*, ventral nerve-cord; *r.*, rim of sucker; *s.*, stopper of sucker; *m.s.c.*, muscles for retracting sucker and contracting body; *t.*, tendon at end of muscles. (Much enlarged.)

organisms, and never suffering themselves to get into slow water. Transplanted from the highly aerated swift water of the stream's center to the slow water of eddies or pools along the bank, they die very soon. When ready to pupate they gather in small patches, still keeping in the swift water, and each changes into a curious flattened, turtle-shaped, motionless, non-feeding pupa (Fig. 432) which is safely glued to the rock face by its under surface. The dorsal wall is thick and black, and projecting from it at the broad front head end is a pair of breathing-organs, each composed of three or four thin plate-like gills. When the fly is ready to emerge the pupal skin splits longitudinally along the back, and the delicate body pushes up through this slit, and through the shallow swift water until the wings can be outspread. All this is quickly done, the fly being enchained by its long legs, which cling to the pupal shell until it can fly away. But the

FIG. 432.—Pupa, dorsal aspect, of net-winged midge, *Bibiocephala comstocki*. Note respiratory leaves on dorsum of prothorax. (Natural length, $\frac{1}{3}$ inch.)

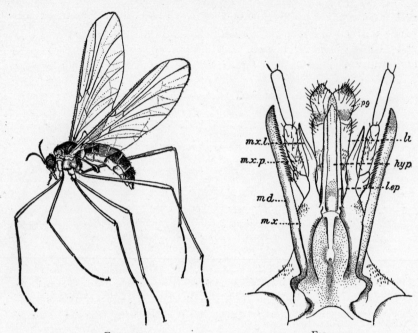

FIG. 433.            FIG. 434.

FIG. 433.—Net-winged midge, *Bibiocephala elegantulus*, female. (Natural length of body, ⅔ inch.)

FIG. 434.—Mouth-parts of female net-winged midge, *Bibiocephala doanei*. *l.ep.*, labrum-epipharynx; *md.*, mandible; *mx.*, maxilla; *mxl.*, maxillary lobe; *mxp.*, maxillary palpus; *li.*, labium; *pg.*, paraglossa; *hyp.*, hypopharynx. (Much enlarged.)

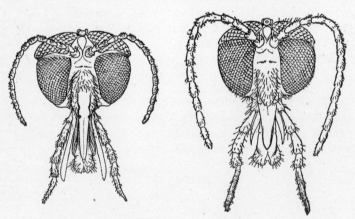

FIG. 435.—Heads of female (at left) and of male (at right) of net-winged midge, *Bibiocephala comstocki*, showing division of eyes into two parts, the upper part with fewer and larger facets than the lower part. (Much enlarged.)

swift water works great havoc among the weak, soft-bodied emerging creatures. I have watched many flies issuing, and a large proportion of them get swept away and presumably drowned before they can get their wings unfolded and themselves clear of the torrent. It is an extraordinary life-history that

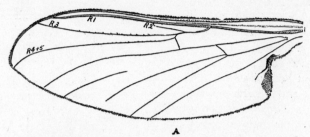

FIG. 436.—Primary venation of wing of net-winged midge, *Bibiocephala comstocki.* $R_1$, $R_2$, etc., branches of the radial vein. (Much enlarged.)

these flies have, and the great danger attending the transformation to the adult stage probably partly explains why the species are so few. It is an unsuccessful type of insect life; the family is probably becoming extinguished. Because the few living species are so widely distributed over the world—

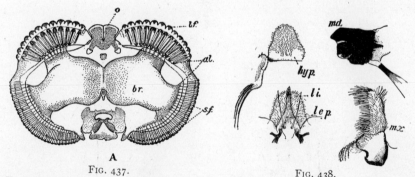

FIG. 437.

FIG. 438.

FIG. 437.—Diagram of cross-section of head through compound eyes of net-winged midge, *Blepharocera capitata*, female. *o*, ocelli; *br.*, brain; *o.l.*, optic lobes; *l.f.*, large facets; *s.f.*, small facets.

FIG. 438.—Mouth-parts of larva of net-winged midge, *Bibiocephala doanei*. *md.*, mandible; *mx.*, maxilla; *l.ep.*, labrum-epipharynx; *li.*, labium; *hyp.*, hypopharynx. (Much enlarged.)

they occur in North America, South America, and Europe—entomologists believe that in past ages the family was much larger than it now is.

The flies (Fig. 433) themselves can be distinguished when in hand by the curious secondary or pseudo net-veining of the wings. These faint cross and diagonal veins are the marks of the creases made by the compact folding of the wings in the pupal shell. The females are provided with long saw-edged mandibles (Fig. 434), and are predatory in habit, catching smaller flying insects, especially Chironomid midges, lacerating their bodies with the mandibular saws and sucking the blood. The males have no mandibles, and probably take flower-nectar for food. Both males and females of several genera have the compound eyes divided into a large-facetted and a small-facetted part (Figs. 435 and 437). The egg-laying has not yet been observed, although the eggs must almost certainly be deposited on rocks in the stream or on its edge.

With the mosquito wrigglers and the blood-worms (larvæ of the Chironomidæ) may perhaps be found a third kind of fly larva (Fig. 440), a slender, pale-colored, cylindrical little "worm," about one-third of an inch long, which can be distinguished from the other aquatic larvæ by its two pairs of short leg-like processes borne on the under side of the

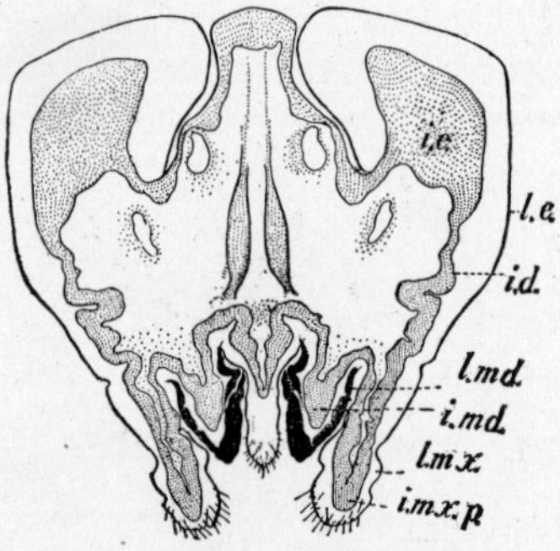

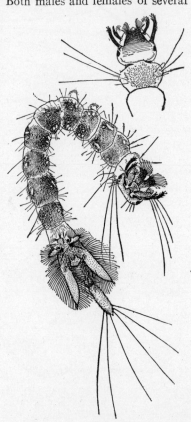

FIG. 439.　　　　　　　　FIG. 440.

FIG. 439.—Diagram of horizontal section through head of old larva of net-winged midge, *Bibiocephala doanei*, showing formation of adult head-parts inside. *l.md.*, larval mandible; *l.mx.*, larval maxilla; *l.c.*, larval cuticle; *i.md.*, adult mandible; *i.mx.p.*, adult maxillary palpus; *id.*, hypoderm (cell-layer of adult skin of head); *i.e.*, adult eye. (Much enlarged.)

FIG. 440.—Larva of *Dixa* sp., with dorsal aspect of head in upper corner. (From life; much enlarged.)

fourth and fifth body segments. It usually keeps the body bent almost double, and when feeding near the surface the head is twisted so that the under or mouth side faces up although the rest of the body has its ventral aspect facing down. This larva belongs to one of the midge-like flies of the genus Dixa (Fig. 440), which is the only genus in the family Dixidæ, represented by about a dozen North American species. The winged flies (Fig. 442) are found in moist places, densely grown over with bushes or rank herbage, in woods.

Although resembling mosquitoes and Chironomid midges in general appearance, they can be readily distinguished from them by the arrangement of the wing-veins (Fig. 444).

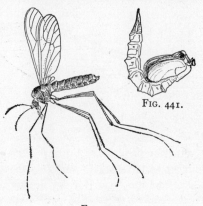

FIG. 441.

An interesting small group of readily recognizable flies is the family Psychodidæ, or "moth-fly" family. The vernacular name comes from the slight resemblance to minute moths shown by these flies because of the hairy broad wings, which are held over the back when the fly is at rest in the roof-like manner of the moths (Fig. 445). The largest of these flies are only about one-sixth of an inch long, and are rarely distinguished

FIG. 442.

FIG. 441.—Pupa of *Dixa* sp. (Much enlarged.)
FIG. 442.—*Dixa* sp. (Much enlarged.)

except by careful observers. I have found them especially common in gardens near the seashore in California, and also in the overhanging foliage

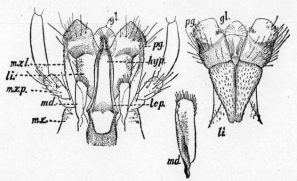

FIG. 443.—Mouth-parts of *Dixa* sp., female. *l.ep.*, labrum-epipharynx; *md.*, mandible; *mx.*, maxilla; *mx.l.*, maxillary lobe; *mx.p.*, maxillary palpus; *li.*, labium; *pg.*, paraglossa; *gl.*, glossa; *hyp.*, hypopharynx.

of trees and shrubs bordering the swift little mountain streams of the Coast Range. In one of these streams I was fortunate enough to find the immature stages of one moth-fly species, *Pericoma californica*, which is, so far, the only North American member of this family whose life-history is known. The larvæ (Fig. 446), which are little slug-like creatures, one-tenth of an inch long, cling by a row of eight suckers on their ventral side to stones in or on the margin of the stream, where they are constantly

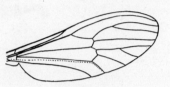

FIG. 444.                     FIG. 445.

FIG. 444.—Diagram of wing of *Dixa* sp., showing venation.
FIG. 445.—A moth-fly, *Pericoma californica*. (Much enlarged.)

wetted by the dashing water. When ready to pupate the larvæ crawl a little higher on the stones, where only the spray will reach them, and, fixing themselves to the rock face by a gummy exudation, change to small flattish, turtle-backed pupæ (Fig. 446), each with a pair of club- or trumpet-shaped respiratory horns on the back of the prothorax. They look indeed much like dwarf net-winged midge pupæ. After about three weeks the adults issue and fly

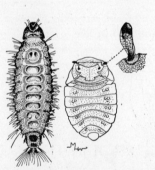

FIG. 446. 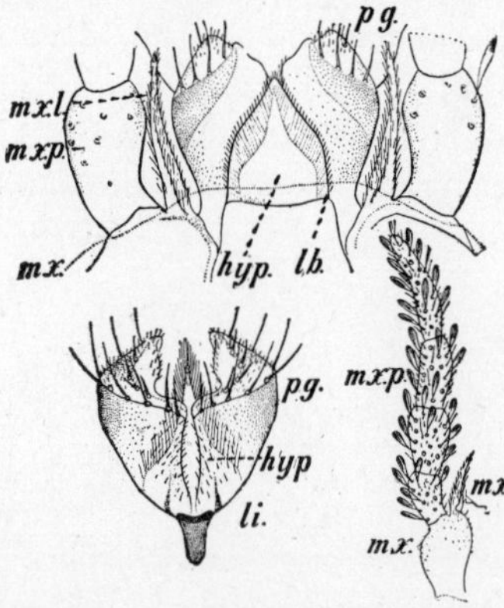                         FIG. 447.

FIG. 446.—Larva, ventral surface (at left), and pupa, dorsal surface (at right), of the moth-fly, *Pericoma californica;* also enlarged prothoracic respiratory tube of pupa. (Much enlarged.)
FIG. 447.—Mouth-parts of moth-fly, *Psychoda* sp. *lb.*, labrum; *mx.*, maxilla; *mx.p.*, maxillary palpus; *mx.l.*, maxillary lobe; *li.*, labium; *pg.*, paraglossa; *hyp.*, hypopharynx.

up into the overhanging foliage, where they spend most of their time resting on the under side of the leaves.

The largest family of nematocerous flies in point of number of species, and that one containing the largest flies in the whole order, is the family Tipulidæ, whose long-legged, narrow-winged members are familiarly known as crane-flies, leather-jackets, and "granddaddy-long-legs." The granddaddy-long-leg flies, which have wings, should not be confused with the often similarly named harvestmen, which are allies of the spiders, have no wings, and have four instead of three pairs of legs. The Tipulid legs are extremely fragile, breaking off at a touch. Most slender-bodied, long- and thin-legged, two-winged insects of more than one-half-inch length of body are Tipulids.

There are some smaller species, however, which might be mistaken for midges or mosquitoes, were it not that all Tipulids bear a distinct V-shaped mark (suture) on the back of the thorax. More than

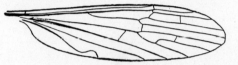

FIG. 448.—Diagram of wing of crane-fly, *Simplecta* sp., showing venation.

three hundred species of this family are known in the United States, and they are common all over the country, in meadows, pastures, along roadsides, stream-banks, and in woods. The flight is uneven, slow, and weak, and the ungainly flies with their long middle and hind legs training out behind, and the front legs held angularly projecting in front, are unmistakable when seen in the air.

The eggs are laid in the ground at the bases of grasses and pasture plants, or, by some species, in mud or slime. The footless, worm-like, dirty-white larvæ feed on decaying vegetable matter, fungi, or on the roots or leaves of green plants. The root-feeders do some damage to meadows and pastures.

The largest Tipulid, and the largest species in the whole order of flies, is the giant crane-fly, *Holorusia rubiginosa* (Fig. 449), common in California. Its body is nearly two inches long, and its legs are from two to two and one-half inches long, so that the spread of legs is four inches. The eggs are laid in the ooze of wet banks of little streams where fallen leaves are decaying and subdrainage water is always slowly trickling out from the soil. The larvæ (Fig. 450) lie in this slimy bed, in crevices or on narrow ledges of rock, with the posterior tip of the body bearing the two breathing-openings (spiracles) held at the surface. The soft ooze, composed of soil and slowly decomposing leaves, is swallowed, and, as it passes through the alimentary canal, the organic material digested out of it. The footless, worm-like larvæ grow to be two and one-half inches long, but can contract to less than an inch. The duration of the larval life is not yet known, but it is at least several months. The pupæ (Fig. 450), which are provided with a pair of long, slender respiratory horns on the prothorax, lie motionless in the slime for twelve days, when the great flies emerge and fly up into the foliage of the stream bank.

Next to the mosquitoes, the worst pests among the nematocerous flies are various species of the gall-midge family, Cecidomyidæ, a family in which all the stages, larval, pupal, and adult, of all the species are terrestrial. The gall-midges are the frailest, smallest, and least conspicuous of all the flies, but their great numbers and vegetable feeding

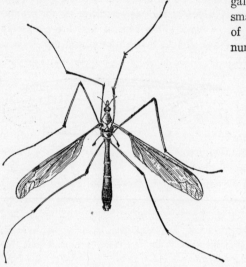

FIG. 449.                                        FIG. 450.

FIG. 449.—The giant crane-fly, *Holorusia rubiginosa*, male.   (Three-fourths natural size.)

FIG. 450.—Larva (at left) and pupa (at right) of giant crane-fly, *Holorusia rubiginosa*; in middle of figure enlarged posterior aspect of larval body, showing spiracles. (Larva and pupa three-fourths natural size.)

and gall-making habits make them formidable enemies of many of our cultivated plants. The tremendous aggregate losses suffered by the wheat-growers of this country from the ravages of the Hessian fly, the damage to clover-fields by the clover-leaf and clover-seed midges, and the injuring or killing of thousands of pine-trees from the attacks of the minute pine Diplosids, are evidences of the great economic importance of the delicate little gall-gnats. About one hundred species are known in this country, and of these most are more or less destructive to cultivated herbs, shrubs, or trees.

The tiny bodies of the flies are usually covered with fine hair, easily rubbed off, and the antennæ bear whorls of larger hairs, which, with some species, are attached by both ends, thus making little hair loops. The minute eggs, reddish or white, are usually deposited in or on growing plant-tissue, and the little footless, headless, maggot-like larvæ probably derive most of their food by imbibing it through the skin. Lying with the body practically immersed in plant-sap, the thin body-wall acts as an osmotic membrane through which an interchange of fluids takes place automatically. The Cecid larva has to eat whether it will or not, and has to eat practically all of the time! These larvæ may be distinguished by their possession of a strange little chitin plate on the under side of the front part of the body, called the breast-bone. What the exact use of this little sclerite is has not yet been determined. Perhaps it helps in locomotion, perhaps in rasping or lacerating the soft plant-tissue to increase the flow of sap. The larvæ pupate where they lie, sometimes spinning a thin silken cocoon, sometimes transforming within the hardened last larval moult, sometimes with no special protecting covering at all.

The most notorious gall-gnat is the wheat-pest, known as the Hessian fly, *Cecidomyia destructor*, and distributed over all the United States east of meridian 100°, as well as in California. By the ravages of its larvæ, feeding as they do on the sap of growing wheat, this minute fly causes an annual loss in this country of approximately ten million dollars. This enormous direct tax is paid by those farmers who prefer to farm in the good old way, with a strong belief in the dispensations of an erratic Providence, rather than to do their farming as modified by modern knowledge and practice. The tax-collecting insect, which is a tiny delicate blackish midge about one-tenth of an inch long, lays its eggs in the creases or furrows of the upper surface of the leaves of young wheat, and the hatching larvæ wriggle down to the sheathing bases of the leaves, where they lie and drain away the sap of the growing plant. When full-grown they pupate within the outer hardened brown last larval cuticle, and resemble very much a small spindle-shaped seed. This is called commonly the "flaxseed" stage. The adult soon issues and after a few days of flight and egg-laying dies. There may be as many as four or five generations in a year, both spring and winter wheat being attacked. The remedies are the late planting of winter wheat, the burning or plowing in of the stubble after harvesting, and the early planting of strips of decoy wheat about the field, which shall attract the egg-laying females and may be afterwards plowed under with the myriad eggs it contains. The Hessian fly is a European insect brought unintentionally to this country about 1778, but probably not, as often said, with the straw brought by the Hessian troopers of the Revolutionary War. It attacks rye and barley as well as wheat, and has, in turn, to withstand the combined attacks of half a dozen hymenopterous parasites, which are said to destroy nine-tenths of all the Hessian-fly larvæ. Without these natural checks to its increase this pest would destroy every wheat-field in this country in a very few years.

In 1896 the Monterey pines, *Pinus radiata*, much grown, together with the famous Monterey cypresses, as ornamental trees on the San Francisco peninsula, showed a peculiar stunting and gall-like swelling of the leaves. Since then this deformation has appeared so abundantly and widely within the range of this tree that the species is actually threatened with extinction, the shortened, swollen needles not being able to perform the essential food-assimilating functions of green leaves. This injury is due to a single species of Cecid fly known as *Diplosis pini-radiata* (Fig. 451),

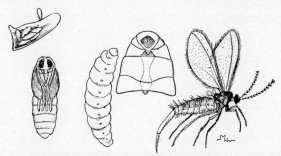

FIG. 451.—The Monterey-pine midge, *Diplosis pini-radiata;* eggs in upper left-hand corner; pupa, larva, breast-bone of larva, and adult female. (Much enlarged.)

which lays its eggs at the base of the growing new needles and whose larvæ hatching and lying here use up the sap necessary for the development of the needles. Hundreds of Monterey pines have been cut down, and unless the natural enemies of this little fly, of which two or three have been discovered, get the upper hand of the pest, this splendid species of pine may be wholly destroyed. A half-dozen other species of Diplosis are known in this country and Europe as pests of conifers, but no other pine species seems to have suffered quite so severely as this interesting Californian one, whose whole geographical range extends over but a thousand square miles, and which is thus specially liable to destruction by concentrated insect attack.

If the collector will break up and examine carefully almost any old or partially decaying toadstools or shelf fungi from trees, he will find in the soft fungous body numerous small translucent white maggot-like larvæ, the larvæ of fungus gnats or members of the family Mycetophilidæ. The gnats themselves are slender delicate flies, mostly with clear wings, though some common species have dark wings, with the basal segment (coxa) of the legs unusually long and the antennæ in most cases free from the whorls of long hairs so characteristic of the Chironomidæ, Culicidæ, and other families of flies otherwise much resembling the fungus-gnats. The flies are to be looked for on decaying vegetable matter, especially fungi, and in damp places.

The eggs are laid variously: on fungi, in decaying wood, among decomposing leaves, in animal excrement, and under the bark of trees. The larvæ feed on the decomposing substance in which the eggs are .aid, sometimes spinning silken webs for protection. They pupate in the food-substance or crawl away to some more sheltered spot, often forming a thick cocoon in

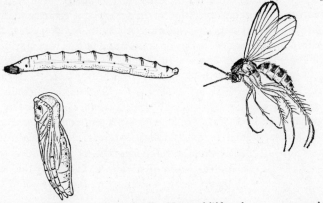

FIG. 452.—A fungus-gnat of the family *Mycetophilidæ;* larva, pupa, and adult. (Much enlarged.)

which to transform. Perhaps the most singular habits noted in the family are those connected with the strong gregarious instinct which leads the larvæ of many species to live closely together. Some of the species of Sciara, known as "army-worms," have "the singular propensity of sticking to-gether in dense patches, and will form processions sometimes twelve or fourteen feet in length and two or three inches broad. This phe-nomenon has been observed fre-quently both in Europe and Amer-ica, but the reason therefor is not yet well understood, though the object of the migration seems to be

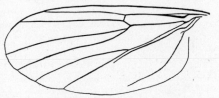

FIG. 453.—Diagram of wing of fungus-gnat, *Mycetophila* sp., showing venation.

the search for better feeding-grounds." Various species of this genus live in potatoes and other vegetables, while the serious injury to potatoes called "scab" is caused by a fungus-gnat known as *Epidapus scabies.*

With larger and more robust bodies and relatively shorter and thicker an-tennæ, the March-flies, Bibionidæ, serve as a sort of transition family between the long-legged, slender-bodied midge type of fly with its thread-like hairy antennæ, and the compact, heavy-bodied, short-legged type of fly with short and club-like three-segmented antennæ, characteristic of the many families grouped in the section Brachycera. The March-flies (Fig. 454) are from one-eighth to one-half inch long, with fairly robust, often hairy, body, black-

ish or black and red, strong legs, large clear or smoky wings, and stout antennæ about as long as head and thorax together and composed of nine to
twelve segments.  They may be seen often in large numbers flying heavily
over gardens and fields or in woods, early in the spring.  The eggs are laid
in the soil or in decaying vegetation or in sewers and excrement, the larvæ
feeding usually on decomposing substances.  With some species, however,
the larvæ feed on the roots of grains or grasses and in this way may do serious
damage.  *Bibio tristis*, discovered in Kansas in 1891, appeared in great
numbers in wheat-fields and frightened many wheat-growers.  As a matter
of fact, little injury seemed to be done.  *B. femorata*, a common species,
is deep red with black wings; *B. albipennis*, another abundant and wide-
spread one, is black-bodied with white wings.  A common Californian species
appears from the ground in damp woods in great numbers in March.  I
have watched these flies issuing in countless numbers
from the soft rich forest floor in the extensive
Monterey pine woods near the Bay of Monterey

FIG. 454.                                    FIG. 455.

FIG. 454.—March-fly, *Bibio albipennis*.  (Three times natural size.)
FIG. 455.—Diagram of wing of *Bibio albipennis*, showing venation.

The air danced with them, and the pine-trees and shrubs bore countless
myriads on their branches.  Professor Needham records a similar sight
in which individuals of *B. fraternus* formed the hosts, and a woodland pasture
near Lake Michigan was the scene of their appearance.  "I have rarely
come upon a scene of greater animation than a sheltered hollow in this wood
presented," writes Professor Needham.  "There was the undulating field
clad in waving grass and set about with the pale-hued foliage of the white
oaks; there were the flowering hawthorns; and there were the myriads
of Bibios floating in the sunshine, streaming here and there like chaff before
sudden gusts and swirls of air.  All the spiders' webs in the bushes were
filled with captives; little groups of ants were dragging single flies away to
their nests, and once I saw overhead a chestnut-sided warbler, perched on
a bare bough directly in a stream of passing flies, rapidly pecking to right
and to left, persistently stuffing his already rotund maw.  I counted a number
of flies I could see resting on the grass in several small areas wide apart, and

found the counts averaged fifteen Bibios per square foot; and there were here in one place forty acres of such Bibio territory."

Two families of nematocerous flies are not included in the key, and have not heretofore been referred to. They are the Orphnephilidæ, of which but a single species is known in this country, viz., *Orphnephila testacea*, a small reddish-yellow fly without hairs or bristles on its body, and with short antennæ apparently composed of two segments, but really of ten, the apparent first segment being made up of three closely opposed segments, and the second of seven. The fly itself is found along stream banks, but nothing is known of its immature stages. The other family, Rhyphidæ, or false crane-flies, is represented in this country by two genera containing several species. The flies

FIG. 456.—Diagram of wing of *Rhyphus* sp.

are small and slender, with broad spotted wings veined in a character-istic way (Fig. 456). The larvæ of Rhyphus are worm-like, legless, naked, more or less transparent, with snake-like movements. They live in water, brooks, pools, or puddles, or in rotting wood, hollow trees, or manure.

## SECTION BRACHYCERA.

The Brachycera, or flies with "short horns," i.e., short thick antennæ composed of few segments, in contrast with the many-segmented antennæ, usually slender and long, of the Nematocera, are separable into three groups of families, as indicated in the key on page 303, based on a further analysis of the structural character of the antennæ. These groups are, first, one includ-ing flies in which the antennæ are composed of more than five segments but with all those beyond the second coalesced to form a single compound segment, bearing more or less distinct annulations indicating the component subsegments; second, one including flies having antennæ made of four or five distinct segments; and third, and by far the largest, one including flies with but three segments in the antennæ.

In the first group are two families and part of a third; this division of a family indicating plainly the artificial character of the subdivision into groups, the subdivision being merely convenient. The three families may be distinguished as follows:

The branches of the radial vein (see Fig. 460) crowded together near the costal (front) margin of the wing.........................(Soldier-flies.) STRATIOMYIDÆ.
Venation normal.
    Alulets, i.e., little whitish wing-like membranous flaps at the base of the true wings, large.............................................(Horse-flies.) TABANIDÆ.
    Alulets small.................................. (Snipe-flies.) LEPTIDÆ (in part).

The most familiar and interesting flies in this group are the well-known horse-flies, gad-flies, or deer-flies, Tabanidæ. They are all fairly large, some indeed being among the largest of our flies.

The great, black, swift horse-flies that in summer dart suddenly at our carriage-horses and with quick shifting flight seem to be fairly carried along in the air close to the horses, are the most familiar representatives of

FIG. 457.—Greenhead, or horse-fly, *Tabanus lineola*. (After Lugger; natural size indicated by line.)

the order. Many of the smaller horse-flies show gleaming metallic colors, especially about the head. Much of this color is in the large compound eyes, and almost any horse-fly caught alive or just killed will astonish the collector by the brilliant bands and flecks of iridescent green, violet, purple,

FIG. 458.—Diagram of wing of *Chrysops* sp., a horse-fly, showing venation.

and copper on the eyes. The biting and blood-sucking are done by the females alone, the males lacking the sharp dagger-like piercing mandibles and contenting themselves with lapping up flower-nectar.

The brown elongate eggs of horse-flies are laid either on stems or leaves of terrestrial plants, or on aquatic plants or submerged stones. The larvæ, whitish, cylindrical, tapering at both ends, and with a series of slightly raised roughened ridges running around the body, either live in water, in slimy places along pond and brook shores, or in soft rich soil, and are predaceous, feeding on small aquatic or underground creatures, especially insect larvæ and snails or slugs.

Nearly 200 species of horse-flies are known in North America. The large bluish-black and brownish-black ones, an inch long and with dusty wings expanding for two inches or more, belong to the genera Tabanus and Therioplectes; the smaller "greenheads" with banded wings and brilliantly

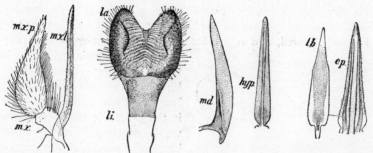

FIG. 459.—Mouth-parts of a horse-fly, *Therioplectes* sp. *md.*, mandible; *mx.*, maxilla; *mx.l.*, maxillary lobe; *mx.p.*, maxillary palpus; *hyp.*, hypopharynx; *lb.*, labrum; *ep.*, epipharynx; *li.*, labium; *la.*, labellum.

colored eyes and black or brown and yellow bodies mostly belong to the genus Chrysops. *Silvius pollinosus* is a beautiful small species with a milk-white bloom over its body, and with clear whitish wings with a few small brown spots.

The soldier-flies, Stratiomyidæ, are unfamiliar insects, although as many species of them as of horse-flies occur in this country. Many of the species have bright yellow or green markings, and most of them have the abdomen curiously broad and flattened. They are found about flowers, and can readily be classified, after capture, by the unusual character of the venation (see Fig. 460). The eggs are laid on the ground or on leaves in or near water, some of the larvæ being terrestrial, while others are

FIG. 460. — Diagram of wing of *Odontomyia* sp., showing venation.

aquatic. The food seems to be mostly vegetable, although the larvæ of some species are believed to be carnivorous. One or two species live in salt or brackish water, and Sharp records that some Stratiomyid larvæ were found in a hot spring in Wyoming with the water temperature only 20° to 30° F. below boiling. They pupate within the last larval skin, which is long and tapering at one end.  Some species inhabit ants' nests, and one is suspected of living parasitically in bee-hives.

Stratiomyia is a genus containing rather large conspicuous yellow-banded flies with broad flattened abdomen, while Sargus, a genus whose species are common, has a subcylindrical abdomen with the whole body metallic green.

The snipe-flies, Leptidæ, are a small family represented by about fifty North American species, including flies having no habits or structural peculiarities appealing specially to popular interest.  They are rather slender and plainly colored, and rather heavy and slow in movement.  They are

FIG. 461.—Diagram of wing of *Chrysophila thoracica* (Leptidæ), showing venation.

apparently all predatory in both larval and adult stages.  The adults may be best found, according to Comstock, in low bushes and grass.  The larvæ live in the ground, in moss, or in decaying wood, sometimes penetrating to the burrows of wood-boring insects.  The species of the genus Atherix deposit their eggs "in dense masses attached to dry branches overhanging water.  Not only do numerous females contribute to the formation of these masses, but they remain there themselves and die.  The larvæ on hatching escape into the water."

In the second group of Brachycera, including flies which have their antennæ composed of four or five distinct segments, there are two families, the Asilidæ, or robber-flies, and the Midaidæ, or Midas-flies.  These latter resemble the robber-flies in size and general appearance, but differ from them by having the antennæ rather long and clubbed at the tip.  They are predaceous, catching and devouring other flying insects, and the larvæ of the few species whose life-history is known are also carnivorous, and seem to have a special fancy for the larvæ of the great wood-boring grubs of the giant Prionus beetles.  Howard believes that the large species, *Mydas luteipennis*, found in the Southwest, mimics in coloration and general appearance for protection or aggression the tarantula-killer wasp found commonly in this country.

The Asilidæ, or robber-flies, compose a considerable family—nearly 1000 species occur in this country—of large, swift, hairy, ferocious-looking flies which live wholly by predatory attacks on other insects.  The body is usually long and slender, tapering behind (Fig. 462), although in a few genera the abdomen is flattened and not unusually elongate.  The proboscis is strong and sharp, the eyes large and keen, and the wings long and narrow and capable of carrying this insect hawk swiftly and strongly in pursuit of its prey.  Some of the robber-flies are very large, an inch and a half or even two inches long, and they do not hesitate to attack other large and strong and well-defined insects, as bumble-bees, dragon-flies, and the fierce and active tiger-beetles. The robber-flies usually rest on the ground or on low

FIG. 462. FIG. 463.

FIG. 462.—A robber-fly, *Stenopogon inquinatus*. (Natural size.)
FIG. 463.—A bumble-bee-like robber-fly, *Dasyllis soceata*. (Natural size.)

foliage, and fly quickly up with a buzzing sound when disturbed or attracted by prey. All the prey is caught on the wing, held in the long spiny feet of the robber-fly, and torn and sucked dry by the sharp piercing-beak.

FIG. 464.—Diagram of wing of robber-fly, *Erax cinerasc͟s* showing venation.

The larvæ live chiefly in decaying wood or in soil containing decomposing vegetable matter, and are also predatory, feeding on grubs and other

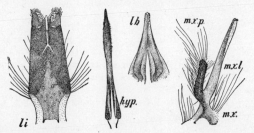

FIG. 465.—Mouth-parts of robber-fly, *Erax cinerascens*. *li.*, labium; *hyp.*, hypopharynx; *lb.*, labrum; *mx.*, maxilla; *mxl.*, maxillary lobe; *mxp.*, maxillary palpus.

underground or wood-boring insects. The pupæ are curiously spiny, the spines being used as a sort of pushing or pulling organ when they get ready to come to the surface of the ground or dead tree to change into imagines.

Some of the species of the genera Laphria and Dasyllis (Fig. 463) look astonishingly like bumble-bees and wasps, probably a case of protective mimicry (see Chap. XVII). Erax is a genus with many common gray and black species about an inch long, with sharp-pointed tip of the abdomen.

The third section or group of Brachycerous families includes many families, in all of which the antennæ have the first two segments small and the third curiously large and club-like, and usually bearing a single conspicuous bristle-like hair. The families of this group can be distinguished by the following table:

A. Antennæ composed of three segments, the third usually large and either with or without a bristle or style.
  B. Empodium pulvilliform, i.e., feet with three little pads instead of two.
                (Snipe-flies.) LEPTIDÆ (in part).
  BB. Empodium not pulvilliform, i.e., feet with two little pads and a median bristle or nothing.
    C. Radial vein four-branched.
      D. Second branch of cubital vein extending free to the margin of the wing or coalesced with the first anal vein for a short distance (see Fig. 466)........................(Bee-flies.) BOMBYLIIDÆ.
      DD. Second branch of cubital vein joining first anal far from the margin of the wing (see Fig. 471).
                (Dance-flies.) EMPIDIDÆ (in part).
    CC. Radial vein with not more than three branches.
      D. Head with a curving suture immediately above the antennæ.
            (House-flies and allies.) MUSCIDÆ.
      DD. Head without such suture.
        E. Radial vein with a knot-shaped swelling at the point where it forks, with a small cross-vein running back just at or near this swelling (Fig. 474)..(Long-legged flies.) DOLICHOPODIDÆ.
        EE. Wings without such characteristics.
          F. Second branch of cubital vein appearing as a cross-vein or curved back towards the base of the wings (Fig. 479).
            G. Proboscis rudimentary; mouth-opening small; palpi wanting; antennæ with dorsal arista.
                (Bot-flies.) ŒSTRIDÆ.
            GG. Proboscis not rudimentary; palpi present; antennæ with terminal style or arista or dorsal arista.
                EMPIDIDÆ (in part).
         FF. Second branch of cubital vein not appearing like a cross-vein.
          G. Front with grooves or a depression beneath the antennæ................(Wasp-flies.) CONOPIDÆ.
          GG. Front convex beneath the antennæ; a spurious vein usually present between radius and media (Fig. 479)............(Flower-flies.) SYRPHIDÆ.

The families of flies named in the above key contain many hundreds of species but few of which are at all popularly known. The bot-flies (Œstridæ), house-flies, flesh-flies, bluebottles and stable-flies (Muscidæ calyptrata), and the cheese-skippers and pomace-flies (Muscidæ acalyptratæ) are about the only names in the list of these hundreds which seem at all familiar. The flower-flies (Syrphidæ) and bee-flies (Bombyliidæ) are numerous, often seen, and, what is more, often definitely noted and admired, but "beautiful flies" is about as specific a name as they ever get. The bristly parasitic Tachinid flies are noticed now and then by the nature student, and the dancing Empidids interest, in a decided but irritating way, drivers and bicyclers in the dance-fly mating-time. But even entomologists, professional as well as amateur, unless they are special collectors and students of Diptera, recognize but few of the hosts of small flies that fill the air during the long summer days.

In the above key only the larger and more commonly represented families are included, so that it will be possible for a collector using this book to find himself possessed of a fly which will prove intractable when an attempt is made to classify it into its proper family. But such unfortunate happenings will be very infrequent, as only small families of obscure or rare species are thus omitted.

Poised almost motionless in the air a few inches above a sunny path or roadway, or darting away, when disturbed, with lightning swiftness and having all the seeming of bees, hairy, plump-bodied, and amber-colored, certain bee-flies (Bombyliidæ) are rather familiar acquaintances of the summer field student. Other bee-flies, as swift and as beautiful, are less bee-like because of the striking "pictures" in the wings, blackish or brown blotches conspicuous in the thin, otherwise clear wing-membrane. Some of these bee-flies have an unusually long slender proboscis held straight out in front of the head like a spear at rest (Fig. 467).

FIG. 466.—Diagram of wing of *Anthrax fulviana*, showing venation.

But this beak has no bloodthirstiness; it is used to suck up sweet nectar from flower-cups. The larvæ of the bee-flies, however, are carnivorous, living parasitically in the egg-cases of grasshoppers or on the bodies of wild bees and various caterpillars. One of these bee-fly larvæ burrowing into a grasshopper's egg-pod can do awful harm to the embryo grasshoppers, but at the same time much good to us, by the satisfaction of its egg-eating propensities. Beautiful, velvet-clothed, swift-winged, and nectar-feeding as a fly, maggot-like and parasitic as larva, the bee-fly is a good example of the great differences in structure and habit which are possible between young and old of the specialized insects.

Bombylius (Fig. 467) is a genus in which the proboscis is very long and slender, the body short and plump and covered with a thick soft coat of longish hair usually light brown or whitish in color. The wings are blotched with brown or blackish. Anthrax contains numerous species with short proboscis, and broad flattened body covered with short hair. The wings are either clear or partly colored with brown or black. In the species of the genus Exoprosopa (Fig. 468) the hair of the body is very short and often in silvery bands across the abdomen, the proboscis is short, and the wings usually beautifully "pictured" with brown and black.

FIG. 467.

FIG. 468.

FIG. 467.—A bee-fly, *Bombylius major.* (Twice natural size.)
FIG. 468.—A bee-fly, *Exoprosopa* sp. (One and one-half times natural size.)

In California the roads and paths, especially along streams and through woods and parks, are made almost intolerable in part of the spring for driving or bicycling because of hosts of small slender blackish flies in swiftly dancing swarms. These are dance-flies, Empididæ, and their aerial dance is their mating flight. I do not know that such hordes of dance-flies occur in the East, but some species of the family have the same dancing habit there, and can be distinguished by it and by the structural characters given in the key. The midges, Chironomidæ, also dance in swarms in the air, but are readily distinguished from the Empidids by their small fragile body, and long many-segmented hairy antennæ. All the dance-flies are predaceous, sometimes catching their prey in the air, sometimes chasing it on the ground.

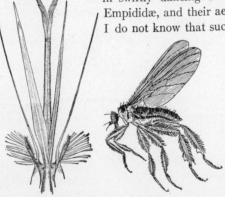
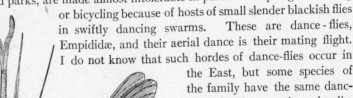

FIG. 469.       FIG. 470.

FIG. 469.—Mouth-parts of a bee-flv *Bombylius* sp. (Much enlarged.)
FIG. 470.—A dance-fly, *Rhamphomyia longicauda.* (Three times natural size.)

The larvæ, slender cylindrical grubs living in the soil or under leaves or other vegetable matter, are also probably predaceous, feeding on smaller insects living in the same places.

The commoner species that dance in large swarms belong to the genera Empis and Rhamphomyia (Fig. 470). The males of certain species of Empis and Hilara have the odd habit of blowing out bubbles of a whitish viscid substance which they carry about with them in the air. It is believed that these toy balloons are attractive to the females. At least, Professor Aldrich, a well-known student of flies, has seen a female choose that male among several which was carrying the largest balloon!

An attractive lot of small slender flies, usually of iridescent green or greenish-black or blue color, with unusually long slender legs, are the Dolichopodidæ, or long-legged flies. They are found especially in marshy or low places where vegetation grows lush and rank. They flit about searching for lesser insects, which they catch and devour. They often get their

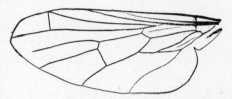

Fig. 471.—Diagram of wing of dance-fly, *Empis* sp., showing venation.

prey by swift chasing over leaves or ground or even on the surface of water. Like the Empidids the larvæ are also predaceous, living underground or in decaying vegetable matter. Some have been found in the exuding sap of

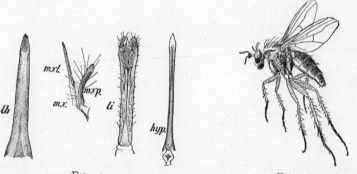

Fig. 472.                    Fig. 473.

Fig. 472.—Mouth-parts of dance-fly *Rhamphomyia* sp. *lb.*, labrum; *mx.*, maxilla; *mx.l.*, maxillary lobe; *mx.p.*, maxillary palpus; *li.*, labium; *hyp.*, hypopharynx.
Fig. 473.—*Dolichopus lobatus.* (Three times natural size.)

trees and elsewhere on or under bark. The larvæ of certain species spin little thin cocoons when ready to pupate, but with most the pupa is naked.

Dolichopus (Fig. 473) is the largest genus of the family, nearly 100 species occurring in this country. The males are curiously ornamented by special outgrowths or expansions on the feet. These make the feet at the end of the long legs very conspicuous and are believed to serve the male to help attract the female in his courtship of her. These ornaments are not confined to the males of this genus, other genera of the family showing similar

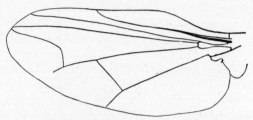

FIG. 474.—Diagram of wing of a Dolichopodid, *Psilopus ciliatus*, showing venation.

characters. Other ornaments, too, are found in various species, some occurring on the face, others on the antennæ and elsewhere. Aldrich says that the males of the flies of this family show more pronounced and various special ornamentation than the males of any other single family of animals. He has seen the males dangle their tufted feet in the faces of the females during courtship.

Occasionally the general collector or nature observer will find an insect that he has taken at first glance for a wasp, but which on examination, after capture, is found to have but a single pair of wings, and short, clubbed antennæ like a fly. The puzzle is readily solved with these clues: the insect is a fly, not a wasp; it simply looks so much like a wasp that it undoubtedly is frequently mistaken for a wasp by certain enemies which are afraid to attack the well-defended hornet, but would make short work of a defenceless fly. The wasp-flies, Conopidæ, thus save their lives by an innocent deception; they are protected by their curiously close mimicry of wasps. All of them are narrow-waisted, and most have the abdomen spindle-shaped and tapering like a wasp's, and often banded and colored so as to increase the similitude. All of them, too, have robust heads and have been sometimes called "thick-head-flies." They are all flower-flies, feeding on nectar and pollen, and hovering on heavy wing about blossoming shrubs. The oval or pear-shaped larvæ are parasitic, living in the bodies of other insects, especially wasps,

FIG. 475. — A wasp-like fly, *Physocephala affinis*. (One and one-half times natural size.)

bumble-bees, and locusts. "The eggs," according to Williston, "are laid directly upon the bodies of the bees or wasps during flight. The young larvæ burrow within the abdominal cavity of their host and there remain, the posterior end directed toward the base of the abdomen, feeding upon the non-vital portions, until ready to transform into the mature fly, when they escape from between the abdominal wings of the insect." The quiescent pupal stage is then passed within the body of the host, a rather unusual phenomenon in insect life.

In the genera Conops and Physocephala (Fig. 475) the abdomen is distinctly peduncled as in the thread-waisted wasps, while in Myopa, Zodion, Oncomyia, and others the abdomen is sessile or constricted only at the very base.

Under the name bot-flies (Œstridæ) some of the most interesting members of the order Diptera are widely, but superficially, known. The flies themselves are much less familiar than their eggs and larvæ, the glistening white eggs of some species being often seen attached to the flanks, legs, or feet of a horse or cow, and the stomach-inhabiting larvæ being well known to stockmen as the cause of much suffering and injury to their animals. In addition to the "bots" which live in the stomach and intestines of horses and cattle, several other species live under the skin of the same animals, as well as of goats, sheep, antelope, rabbits, rats, dogs, cats, and even man. The larvæ of still other species burrow in the nasal passages of the sheep, the antelope, the horse, the camel, the buffalo, and various deer species. The flies are heavy-bodied, often densely hairy, banded in-

FIG. 476. — Larva of bot-fly, *Cuterebra cuniculi*, from wood-rat, *Neotoma* sp. (Natural size.)

sects, looking rather like small bumble-bees whose mouth-parts are so atrophied that they can probably take no food at all. They lay their eggs on the hairs or skin of their special host animal, and the larvæ on hatching bore directly through the skin and into the tissues of the host, or, as in the case of the familiar bot-fly of the horse and the heel-fly or warble of cattle, the eggs are taken into the mouth of the host by licking, swallowed, and thus introduced directly into the stomach, to whose walls the larvæ either attach themselves or through which they burrow into the true body-cavity of the host.

Less than 100 species of bot-flies are known in the whole world, but the parasitic habits and resulting economic importance of these flies have resulted in making the family well known. The most widely distributed and best known species is probably the horse bot-fly, *Gastrophilus equi* (Fig. 477). This fly, which may be seen in open sunny places along the roadways, is about ½ inch long, brownish yellow, with some darker markings, but much resembling a honey-bee in appearance. The female has the abdomen elongate and bent forward underneath the body. The light-yellow eggs are attached by a sticky fluid to the hair of the horse on the shoulders or legs or belly.   They are licked off by the horse and swallowed, and the larvæ hatch in the mouth or stomach and attach themselves to the stomach lining, living at the expense of the host.   When many larvæ thus live in the stomach (and as many as several hundred have been found in one animal) the horse suffers serious injury.   The larvæ live in the stomach

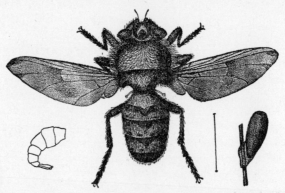

FIG. 477.—Bot-fly of horse, male, *Gastrophilus equi*, abdomen of female and egg.   (After Lugger;   natural size of fly indicated by line.)

and intestines through fall and winter, and late in the spring release their hold, pass through the intestine with the excretions, and burrow into the ground to pupate.   The pupal stage lasts about a month, when the flies issue and the life-cycle begins again.   A smaller species of bot-fly, *Gastrophilus nasalis*, with bright-yellow band across the abdomen, lays its eggs in the lips and nostrils of horses.   For the rest its life-history is about like that of *G. equi*.

The bot-flies, warble-flies, or heel-flies of cattle, whose larvæ are found in small tumors under the skin, also have their eggs swallowed, and the young larvæ may be found in the mouth and œsophagus.   But from here they burrow out into the body-tissues of the host, finally coming to rest underneath the skin along the back.   When the larva or grub is full-grown it gnaws through the skin, drops to the ground, pupates, and in from three to six weeks changes to the adult fly.   The hides of cattle attacked by these flies are rendered nearly valueless by the holes, and are known as "grubby" hides.   Osborn estimates that these warble-flies, of which we have two species, *Hypoderma bovis* and *H. lineata*, cause a loss of $50,000,000 annually in this country.

The genus Cuterebra includes a number of species of which the rabbit bot-fly, *C. cuniculi*, is most familiar.   The larvæ lie in large warbles or tumors under the skin of the infested rabbit, and late in the summer the jack-rabbits and cottontails are so badly infested in some localities that hardly one can be found free from the pest.   The adult is a large fly resembling a bumblebee, with black head, yellow-brown thorax, and the abdomen blue-black with yellow base. The full-grown larva is a large black spiny grub.

One or two species of bot-flies infest man, and also (probably the same species) monkeys and dogs and perhaps other animals. Numerous instances are recorded in which the larvæ of *Dermatobia noxialis* and *D. cyaniventris* have been found under the skin of persons in tropical America, and a few instances of such cases in the United States. The larvæ are thick and broad at one extremity and elongate and tapering at the other.

The family Syrphidæ, Syrphus-flies, flower-flies, or hover-flies, as the English call them, is one of the largest in the order; including fully 2500 species in the whole world, of which over 300 are found in this country. For so large a family few generalizations regarding the appearance or habits of the flies can be made. Many of the Syrphus-flies resemble bees and wasps in appearance, and almost all are rather bright and handsome insects. They feed on nectar and pollen, and hence are to be found in sunshiny hours at flowers, hovering like tiny humming-birds in front of open

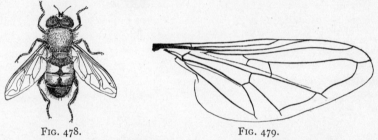

FIG. 478.                              FIG. 479.

FIG. 478.—A flower-fly, *Eristalis tenax*. (One and one-half times natural size.)
FIG. 479.—Diagram of wing of *Syrphus contumax*, showing venation.

blossoms, or crawling bee-like in and out of deep flower-cups. Some make a distinct humming or buzzing as they fly about and thus heighten their suggestion of bees. All can be distinguished, after capture, by the so-called false vein of the wings (see Fig. 479). The larvæ live variously in decaying wood or other vegetation, or decomposing flesh, or in the stems of green plants, or in toadstools, or in water. Some crawl about, slug-like in manner, over leaves, preying on aphids and scale-insects. Some live as guests in ants' nests, and others in the underground nests of bumble-bees.

Those Syrphid larvæ most often written about are the curious "rat-tailed maggots" (Fig. 480), larvæ which live in stagnant water or slime and have the posterior extremity of the body greatly elongate and projecting to serve as a breathing-tube. There is a spiracle (breathing-pore) at the tip of this "tail," and the tail projects upward so that its tip reaches the air, while the rest of the larva's body remains underneath the water. The larvæ of Microdon, which live in ants' nests, look like little mollusks, and when first found were actually described as new molluscous genera. Their body is flat,

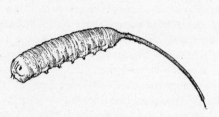 

FIG. 480.            FIG. 481.

FIG. 480.—Rat-tailed larva of a Syrphid. (Twice natural size.)
FIG. 481.—Larva of *Microdon mutabilis*, dorsal view. (Four times natural size.)

broad, unsegmented, and looks like a flat broadly elliptical little shell or plant-seed (Fig. 481).

Among the more common flies of this family which may be taken by the collector are various species of Eristalis, with black, yellow, and amber colors, heavy-bodied, bee-like forms, and especially *E. tenax*, the drone-fly, which resembles very much a honey-bee drone. Its larva is a rat-tailed maggot. The species of Syrphus are black with yellow bands, with the abdomen not so heavy as in Eristalis. The larvæ are predatory, doing great havoc in aphid colonies, but being thus of great benefit to florists and gardeners.

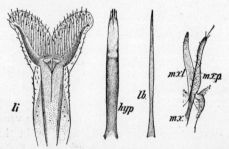

FIG. 482.—Mouth-parts of *Eristalis* sp.  *li.*, labium; *hyp.*, hypopharynx; *lb.*, labrum; *mx.*, maxilla; *mx.l.*, maxillary lobe; *mx.p.*, maxillary palpus.

The species of Volucella are bee-like in appearance and their larvæ live in the nests of bees, but whether as parasites or tolerated guests seems not to be yet known. Sharp thinks that they act as scavengers in the nests, and thus are helpful rather than harmful to their hosts. *Syritta pipiens* is a common Syrphid fly, with slender, elongate, subcylindrical body, blackish with reddish-yellow markings.

The abundant house-flies are the most familiar representatives of the largest of all the Dipterous families: largest if the great heterogeneous group of flies called Muscidæ is to be looked on as a single family, a point of view taken by some entomologists, but not so if this group is called a superfamily, composed of a large number, about twenty in all, of distinct small families. The group includes, besides the house-flies, the buzzing bluebottles, the disgusting flesh-flies and stable-flies, the parasitic Tachina flies, the pomace-flies, fruit-flies, grass-stem flies, brackish-water flies, and numerous other kinds not familiar enough to have a vernacular name. To get acquainted with some of the more abundant and interesting kinds, and to enable us to classify them to subfamilies (if the whole group is called family), we may scrutinize any fly which our key on page 332 leads us to call a Muscid, in the light of the following key:

(The first posterior cell is the space between the little cross-vein in the middle of the wing and the outer margin of the wing. See in Fig. 490.)

Alulets small..........................................ACALYPTRATE MUSCIDÆ.
Alulets large..........................................CALYPTRATE MUSCIDÆ.
  First posterior cell widely open..........................Subfamily ANTHOMYIINÆ.
  First posterior cell narrowly open or closed (Fig. 490).
    Antennal bristle wholly bare..........................Subfamily TACHININÆ.
    Antennal bristle with some distinct hairs.
      Antennal bristle bare near the tip..................Subfamily SARCOPHAGINÆ.
      Antennal bristle plumose or pubescent to the tip.
        Back of abdomen bristly, legs unusually long.............Subfamily DEXIINÆ.
        Back of abdomen not bristly, except sometimes somewhat so near tip.
                         Subfamily MUSCINÆ.

The Acalyptrate Muscidæ include a host of small, mostly unfamiliar, flies, distributed among a score of subfamilies. We shall refer to a few

FIG. 483.                       FIG. 484.

FIG. 483.—House-fly, *Musca domestica*. (After Howard and Marlatt; three times natural size.)

FIG. 484.—Foot of house-fly, showing claws, pulvilli, and clinging hairs. (Greatly magnified.)

of the more interesting kinds in the group after taking up briefly the five subfamilies of larger, more noticeable Calyptrate Muscids.

Most abundant, most wide-spread, and most important to us of all the Muscid flies are the common house-flies. They belong with some other similar forms to the subfamily Muscinæ. A number of species may be found in houses, but the true house-fly, *Musca domestica* (Fig. 483), is by far the most numerous. Dr. Howard, government entomologist, who has paid special attention to the life of house-flies and mosquitoes, because of their dangerous disease-germ carrying habits, says that house-flies undoubtedly contribute materially in the dissemination of infectious diseases by carrying germs in the dirt and filth on their feet, collected during their pilgrimages to the contents of cuspidors, slop-pails, and closets. He advocates a definite crusade against the house-fly like the one now being undertaken in this country against the mosquito.

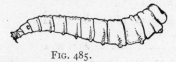

FIG. 485.  FIG. 486.

FIG. 485.—Larva of house-fly, *Musca domestica*. (After Howard and Marlatt; three times natural size.)

FIG. 486.—Pupa, in puparium, of house-fly, *Musca domestica*. (After Howard and Marlatt; three times natural size.)

The eggs of the house-fly are laid in horse-manure, occasionally in other excrementitious or decaying matter. Each female lays about one hundred eggs. These eggs hatch in six or seven hours, and the slender pointed white larvæ called maggots (Fig. 485) lie in their plentiful food-supply for the five or six days necessary for their full growth. They pupate within the last larval skin, which thickens and turns brown at the time of pupation (Fig. 486). The pupal stage lasts five days, and then the fly issues. Its food is liquid and taken up by lapping. The "house-fly" that bites is not the true house-fly, but usually the fiercely piercing stable-fly, *Stomoxys calcitrans*, another member of the subfamily, which looks much like Musca and which is a not infrequent visitor in the house.

FIG. 487.—A stable-fly, *Stomoxys calcitrans*. (Three times natural size.)

This stable-fly and another ally of the house-fly, called the horn-fly, are great pests of stock. The horn-fly, *Hæmatobia serrata* (Fig. 488), which gets its popular name from the habit of clustering, when not feeding, on the bases of the horns of cattle, is a European insect that was accidentally brought to this country in 1886 or 1887.

It quickly established itself, and in two years had spread over the eastern states so widely as o cause much alarm. By 1895 it had spread over all of the United States east of the Rocky Mountains. The flies pierce the skin and suck the blood, thus causing such an irritation and loss of blood that the affected animals cease feeding and soon show great loss in milk or weight. The eggs are laid in fresh cow-manure, and the larvæ become full-grown and pupate in less than a week. The pupal stage lasts from five to ten days. Probably half a dozen generations appear annually. Infested

FIG. 488.—The horn-fly, *Hæmatobia serrata*. (After Lugger; natural size indicated by line.)

cattle may be smeared with a mixture of fresh oil and tar, equal parts, which repels the flies, and lime, which kills the larvæ, may be thrown on the manure. The stable-fly, like the house-fly, lays its eggs in horse-manure, and Dr. Howard foresees a curious benefit to result from the gradual increase in the use of automobiles in cities, and the corresponding decrease in number of horses maintained, in the gradual doing away with the breeding-places of house-flies and stable-flies.

Next to house-flies the commonest ones about houses and outbuildings are the bluebottles and blow-flies or flesh-flies. These all lay their eggs or deposit living larvæ on meat, and, with some other allied species which, however, do not all restrict their egg-laying to animal substances, belong to the subfamily Sarcophaginæ, so named from the flesh-eating habits of the larvæ or maggots of the best-known species   The most abundant flesh-fly in this country is named *Sarcophaga sarraceniæ* (Fig. 489), and looks like an extra-large house-fly. It gives birth to larvæ (hatched from eggs retained in the body of the female) which are deposited on fresh meat, sometimes in open wounds. The larvæ (maggots) feed and grow rapidly, attaining their full size in three or four days. They pupate within the thickened brown last larval skin, and issue as adults in ten or twelve days after birth. The blow-flies and bluebottles, members of this subfamily, have the body steely blue or greenish and are great buzzers. The blow-fly, *Calliphora erythrocephala*, has the thorax black and abdomen steely blue. Its eggs are laid on exposed meat, fresh or decaying, such egg-infested meat being called "blown." The

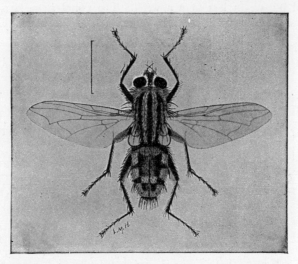

FIG. 489.—A blow-fly or flesh-fly, *Sarcophaga sarraceniæ*. (After Lugger; natural size indicated by line.)

larvæ feed on the juices of the decaying meat and pupate after a few days. The pupæ enclosed in the thickened brown last larval skin look like large smooth shiny brown elliptical seeds, as do indeed the pupæ of all Calyptrate Muscidæ. The commonest bluebottle- or greenbottle-fly is *Lucilia cæsar*, which lays its eggs in cow-dung as well as on flesh, and which often comes into houses, particularly before rain. A flesh-fly of serious importance is the terrible screw-worm fly, *Compsomyia macellaria*, which lays its eggs on flesh, manure, in open wounds, and often in the

FIG. 490.—Diagram of wing of *Lucilia cæsar*, showing venation.

nasal passages of domestic animals and human beings, entering the nose for this purpose while the unfortunate person or animal is asleep. Numerous frightful cases of such attacks on persons are recorded, especially from the southern states. The larvæ fairly eat away the whole inner nose and upper pharynx, causing terrible pain and sometimes death. Indeed, out of twelve cases which came to the knowledge of Dr. Richardson, an Iowa physician, eleven resulted fatally. As many as three hundred screw-worms were taken from the inner nose and region above and behind the soft palate of some of the patients. As a pest of domestic animals the greatest injuries have been caused in Texas. The eggs are laid in any open wound or in the nose or mouth, and the quickly hatching larvæ burrow into the adjacent tissues. Cattle and hogs are particularly attacked, horses and sheep less often.

In the states in which sugar-beets are grown some anxiety for the success of this new industry—new in this country, that is; sugar has long been made from beets in Germany—is felt because of the presence in the beet-fields of an obscure little fly, *Pegomyia vicina*, which may be called the sugar-beet midge. The eggs are laid on the leaves, and in three or four days the tiny white larvæ hatch and burrow into the soft leaf-tissue. When many of the larvæ are at work mining the leaves much injury to the plants results. In the great sugar-beet fields along the California coast four or five generations of this fly appear annually and occasion great loss to the growers. This fly belongs to the subfamily Anthomyiinæ, to which Muscid group two other well-known fly-pests belong, namely, the onion-fly, *Phorbia ceparum*, and the cabbage maggot-fly, *Phorbia brassicæ*. Both these insects in the adult stage are small light-gray flies, looking rather like small house-flies. The onion-fly lays its eggs on the stems of onion-plants, near the soil, and the hatching larvæ burrow into the underground bulb, which they soon nearly destroy. This fly appears to live on no other plant. The cabbage maggot-fly lays its eggs also on the stem just above or even below the ground, and the larvæ burrow into the roots. Cauliflowers as well as cabbages are attacked, and often tens of thousands of acres of these two vegetables are destroyed in a single season by this little fly. The best remedy is the use of cards cut from tarred paper and bound, collar-like, around the stems of the plants. These protecting collars should be put on when the young plants are transplanted from the cold frames into the field. Another familiar member of this subfamily is the little house-fly, *Homalomyia canicularis*, smaller, paler, and more conical in shape than the true house-fly.

Every one who has undertaken to rear butterflies and moths from their caterpillars has been compelled to make the acquaintance of certain heavy-bodied bristly flies which appear now and then from a cocoon or chrysalid in place of the expected moth or butterfly. These are Tachina-flies, and in their appearance and parasitic habits are representative of the large sub-family of house-fly cousins known as Tachiniinæ. The females fasten their eggs to the skin of young caterpillars, the hatching larvæ burrow into the body of their crawling host and feed on its body-tissues. Sometimes the caterpillar is killed before it can pupate, but usually not, spinning its cocoon and pupating with its fatal parasites still feeding inside. But the butterfly never issues: in its place buzz out several of these bristly Tachina-flies. While their habits arouse our indignation at first acquaintance, and particularly if we have set our hearts on rearing a rare moth or butterfly, a moment's reflection assures us of the immense good these flies must really do. Howard tells of an instance observed by him where the buzzing of the swarms of Tachina-flies, hovering over and laying their eggs on the hosts of a great army of army-worms, could be heard for a long distance.

FIG. 491.

FIG. 492.

FIG. 491.—A Tachina-fly, *Dejeania corpulenta*. (One and one-half times natural size.)
FIG. 492.—Tachinid parasite (at left) of the California flower-beetle, and parasitic fungus, *Sporotrichum* sp. (at right) of same beetle. (Slightly enlarged.)

He says that a great outbreak of army-worms in northern Alabama in 1881, when all crops were threatened with total destruction, was completely frustrated by Tachina-flies. These parasites also attack locusts, leaf-eating beetles, and many other injurious insects besides caterpillars, and altogether do much to keep in check some of our worst insect-pests. A single species of Tachina-fly (Fig. 492) is almost the only check on the destructive flower-eating Diabrotica (*D. soror*) of California, which, if allowed to increase unhindered, would soon destroy every blossom in this land of flowers.

Resembling somewhat in appearance the Tachina-flies are the so-called nimble-flies, constituting the small subfamily Dexiinæ. Most of the species in this country belong to the single genus Dexia and have been little studied. The larvæ seem to be all parasitic, although the life-history of no species has been wholly worked through yet. Beetles and snails seem to be the favorite hosts of these flies.

In the large group of flies, some dingy and obscure in coloration, others brightly colored and with beautifully patterned wings, but all small and most unfamiliar, called the Acalyptrate Muscidæ (that is, the house-fly allies with small alulets), we shall not attempt to distinguish the various subfamilies as we have for the Calyptrate Muscids. Dipterologists recognize some twenty distinct subfamilies (or families, if the group Muscidæ be looked on as a super-family) of these small flies, but the distinctions are quite too fine for the general collector to handle. I shall therefore simply refer briefly to a few of the more interesting or abundant or economically important species in this group.

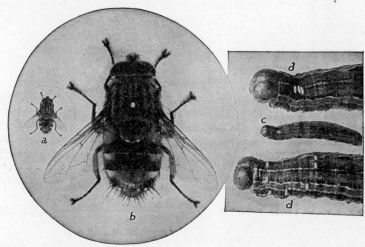

Fig. 493.—Red-tailed Tachina-fly, *Winthemia 4-pustuluta*, a parasite of the army-worm, *Leucania unipuncta*. *a*, fly, natural size; *b*, fly, enlarged; *c*, army-worm, natural size, upon which eggs have been laid; *d*, parasitized army-worms, enlarged. (After Slingerland.)

Of interest because of the extraordinary condition of their eyes are the blackish flies called Diopsidæ, which have the eyes on conspicuous elongate lateral processes of the head. These eye-stalks bear also the antennæ. Only a single species, *Sphyracephala brevicornis*, has been found in this country, and regarding its life-history nothing is known. The flies are to be looked for in woodsy places, and particularly on the leaves of skunk-cabbage.

In the water and cast up in masses along the shores of Mono Lake and certain other similar brackish-water lakes in the desert land just east of the Sierra Nevada Mountains in California may be found, at certain seasons of the year, innumerable larvæ of a small predaceous fly of the genus Ephydra. These dead-sea waters support hardly any other animal life, but this fly finds the water much to its liking and breeds there with extraordinary fecundity. The Pai Ute Indians of this region, who, like the flies, have a questionable palate, gather these larvæ by the bushel, dry them in the sun, and use them for food under the name *koo-chah-bee*. Prof. Brewer of Yale, who made a trial of *koo-chah-bee*, says "it does not taste badly, and if one were ignorant of its origin it would make a nice soup." Other species of Ephydridæ occur abundantly in salt-water marshes, the flies living a preda-

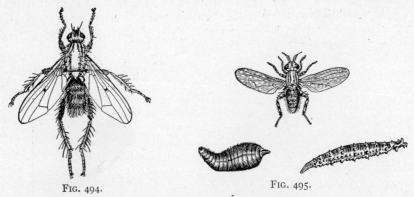

FIG. 494.

FIG. 495.

FIG. 494.—*Scatophaga* sp. (Two and one-half times natural size.)
FIG. 495.—An aquatic muscid, *Tetanocera pictipes*, larva, pupa, and adult. (After Needham; two and one-half times natural size.)

tory life and doing much to reduce the numbers of brackish-water mosquitoes and other small insect-pests.

One of the great packing-houses of Kansas City, Missouri, once called in an entomologist to aid it in fighting a little fly which was causing the packers

FIG. 496.—The cheese-skipper fly, *Piophila casei*. (Five times natural size.)

a loss of many thousand dollars annually. This was the cheese-skipper fly, *Piophila casei* (Fig. 496), which might almost as well be called the ham- and bacon-skipper fly, for the eggs are laid quite as willingly on any smoked meat as on cheese. In the packing-house swarms of the flies were buzzing about at the mouth of the great smoke-shaft from which the hams and pieces of bacon were being constantly taken to be wrapped and made ready for shipping. These flies would dart down and lay their eggs on the smoked meat while actually in the wrapper's hands, and thus thousands of egg-blown hams and bacon sides would be wrapped and sent out. When the cook a thousand miles away tears the wrappings from a "piophilized" ham he quickly sends in an indignant report to his local meat-supplier, who in turn makes a protest to the packer. In time the packer calls for help from an entomologist. The larvæ of this fly have the odd habit of bending nearly double and then with a quick straightening they throw the body some inches into the air. Hence the name skipper, commonly applied to it.

At cider-making and fruit-gathering time, and in vine-growing districts at wine-making time, hosts of tiny yellowish-bodied flies, the pomace-flies or fermenting fruit-flies, Drosophilidæ, may be seen busily lapping up their favorite food, the juices of fermenting fruits. The most abundant and wide-spread species is *Drosophila ampelophila*, the vine-loving pomace-fly. It is a small, clear-winged, red-eyed, brownish-yellow, chubby fly which lays its eggs on gathered fruits, and especially decaying fruit and pomace, and also on grapes still hanging on the vines if they have been broken somewhat by birds  The larvæ or maggots hatch in

FIG. 497.—*Trypeta longipennis.* (Two and one-half times natural size.)

from three to five days, live in the fruit four days, and lie in the pupal stage three to five days, so that a whole life-cycle is gone through in less

FIG. 498 —Larva of cherry-fruit fly, *Rhagoletis cingulata*, dorsal and lateral views. (After Slingerland; natural size and much enlarged.)

than two weeks.  Thus even in the short season of the fruit ripening and gathering much injury can be and often is done by these little tipplers.

A much larger group of fruit-flies is the Trypetidæ, whose larvæ burrow in fruits or plant-stems, often producing galls on these latter.  The familiar spherical swelling or gall on goldenrod stems is the hiding and feeding place

Fig. 499.—Puparia of cherry-fruit fly, *Rhagoletis cingulata*.  (After Slingerland; natural size and much enlarged.)

of the thick white larvæ of *Trypeta solidaginis*, a pretty fly with banded wings.  The longer hollow gall which sometimes occurs on goldenrod is made by the caterpillar of a small moth, *Gelechia gállæ-solidaginis*. Some Trypetid species do much injury by burrowing into fruit, as the apple-maggot, and the larva of a black-and-white fly with banded wings known as *Trypeta ludens*, whose larvæ infests Mexican oranges and may sometime get a foothold in California or Florida.

Another group of small flies whose larvæ are responsible for serious injury to growing grain, meadows, and pasture grasses are the Oscinidæ, or grass-stem flies.  The adults are commonly taken by collectors when beating or sweeping in meadows and pastures.  The flies are minute but plump, and are variously colored, sometimes blackish, sometimes yellowish.  They are so small that they often get into one's eyes in their swarming-time, and are said to cause a prevalent disease of the

Fig. 500. — An aquatic muscid, *Sepedon fuscipennis*, larva, pupa, and adult.  (After Needham; two and one-half times natural size.)

eyes in the South.  The thick cylindrical little larvæ of several species of Oscinis live in the stems of wheat, barley, oats, rye, and grass.  The larva of *Chlorops similis* burrows in the leaves of sugar-beets, and another species of the genus is the notorious "frit-fly," one of the chief grain-pests of Europe.

## SUBORDER PUPIPARA.

Bird-collectors occasionally find on their specimens curious flat-bodied insects with leathery skin and a single pair of wings, which are obviously parasites on the body of the birds. Owls and swallows seem especially infested. Similar parasitic insects, but wingless, are also found on sheep, and a winged form is not uncommon on horses. These degraded insects are flies of the suborder Pupipara which are commonly known as bird-ticks, sheep- and horse-ticks, etc. The animals more rightly entitled to the name "ticks" are really not true insects, but belong with the scorpions, spiders, and mites in the class Arachnida. They have four pairs of legs and are always wingless. Such true ticks are the leathery-skinned cattle-ticks, dog-ticks, and wood-ticks.

The degraded Diptera belonging to the suborder Pupipara, and also called ticks, have of course three pairs of legs and some are winged. Their name Pupipara comes from the curious circumstances of their birth. The female does not deposit eggs outside her body, but gives birth to young which are just ready to assume the pupal stage at the time of their appearance. In the case of one species, the sheep-tick (Melophagus), whose development has been carefully studied, the female has four egg-tubes each of which produces a single germ-cell at a time. Of these four egg-cells three remain small, while one becomes large and develops into an embryo. This embryo lies in the unpaired wide vagina of the female, soon casts off its egg-envelopes, and is nourished as a growing larva by a secretion from two pairs of glands opening into the vagina of the mother. Here the headless, footless larva lies and grows until it is about $\frac{1}{6}$ inch long, when it is born and immediately pupates. The development of the other Pupipara, as far as studied, is similar to that of the sheep-tick.

The suborder includes three families, as follows:

With compound eyes; sometimes with wings.

(Bird-, sheep-, and horse-ticks.) HIPPOBOSCIDÆ.

Without compound eyes, always wingless.

Halteres present; on bats.........................(Bat-ticks.) NYCTERIBIIDÆ.
Halteres absent; on honey-bees............................(Bee-lice.) BRAULIDÆ.

Of the Hipposcidæ the sheep-tick, *Melophagus ovinus*, already referred to, is common and familiarly known. It is wingless, and can crawl readily about through the wool next to the skin. With its strong proboscis, composed of two hard pointed flaps, it punctures the skin and sucks blood from its host's body. The horse-tick, *Hippobosca equina* (Fig. 501), is winged. There are several species of this family found on birds. *Oljersia americana* is a yellowish winged species common on owls, some hawks, and the ruffed grouse. Swallows are often infested, and I have taken bird-ticks from half a dozen other kinds of birds. A careful search for these curious insects will certainly make known numerous new species.

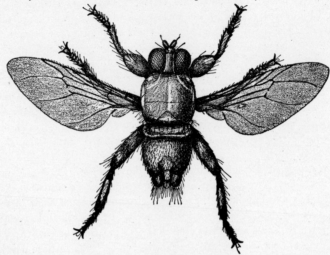

FIG. 501.—A horse-tick or forest-fly, *Hippobosca equina*.    (After Lugger; natural length ¼ to ⅓ inch.)

The genus Lipoptena includes a few known species found on mammals which are winged for awhile, but later cast or bite off the wings. They probably fly about in their search for a host, after finding which they remove their wings and remain for the rest of their life on this host individual. *Lipoptena cervi* is a species found on deer.

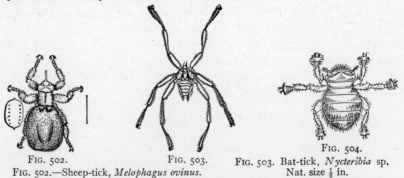

FIG. 502.    FIG. 503.    FIG. 503. Bat-tick, *Nycteribia* sp.
FIG. 504.
Nat. size ⅕ in.
FIG. 502.—Sheep-tick, *Melophagus ovinus*.
FIG. 504.—A bee-louse, *Braula* sp.    (After Sharp; much enlarged.)

The bat-ticks, Nycteribiidæ (Fig. 503), are curious long-legged, wingless, small spider-like creatures about ⅕ inch long or less, which look as if the upper were the under surface. The head is narrow and lies back on the dorsum of the thorax, and the prothorax rises from the upper instead of anterior aspect of the mesothorax. They are found only on bats and are not common.

The strange minute insect, $\frac{1}{14}$ inch long, found clinging to the thorax of queen and drone honey-bees and known as the "bee-louse," *Braula cæca* (Fig. 504), is the only species known of the family Braulidæ. Its legs are rather short and stout, and each ends in a pair of comb-like brushes.

## ORDER SIPHONAPTERA.

The fleas are blood-sucking parasites of mammals and birds which were long classified as a family (Pulicidæ) of the Diptera, being looked on as wingless and otherwise degenerate flies. But they are now given by entomologists the rank of an order, called Siphonaptera, subdivided into three families of its own. Near'y one hundred and fifty species of fleas are known in the world, of which about fifty are recorded from this country. They have been taken from the domestic dog, cat, rat, and fowls, and from various wild animals, such as several rabbit and squirrel species, the lynx, weasel, mole, mountain-rat, shrews and mice, prairie-dog, woodchuck, opossum, etc. Rothschild has recently described a new flea species from the grizzly bear (British Columbia). But from the great majority of our wild mammals fleas have not yet been recorded, although undoubtedly most of them are infested. Baker, who has recently published a monograph * of the known North American species, suggests that particularly interesting forms will probably be found on bats. One flea species, *Pulex avium*, has been taken from several kinds of birds, and two or three other fleas are recorded from bird hosts.

The peculiar structural characteristics of fleas are their winglessness, the extraordinary lateral compression of the body, and the curious modification of their mouth-parts for effective piercing and blood-sucking. The antennæ lie in little half-covered grooves, extending down and back behind the eyes; they can be lifted or stretched up whenever needed. Each antenna is composed of three segments, the terminal one, however, being spirally or transversely lined or grooved and variously shaped, so that it appears to be composed of several segments. The mouth-parts consist of a pair of needle-like mandibles, a pair of slender grooved labial processes, probably the palpi, a pair of short, broad, flattened maxillæ, each with a short antenna-like palpus at its tip, and an unpaired needle-like hypopharynx. The needle-like parts serve for piercing and the grooved labial processes for sucking. Regularly arranged over the body are (in most fleas) many series of stiff, spine-like hairs, often unusually conspicuous and strong on the head and

* Baker, C. F. A Revision of American Siphonaptera. Proc. U. S. Nat. Mus., vol. xxvii, 1904, pp. 365–469.

thorax. The head is ridiculously small and malformed, so that a flea under the microscope always suggests an idiotic (microcephalous) creature. But if its insidious attack and brilliant tactics in retreat be due to wit, this

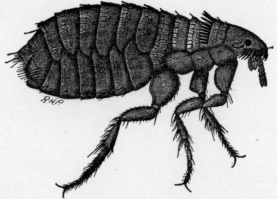

FIG. 505.—Dog- and cat-flea, *Ctenocephalus canis*. (After Lugger; much enlarged.)

small-headedness is truly deceptive. However, our modern mechanical theories of reflex action, negative phototropism (repulsion by light), etc.,

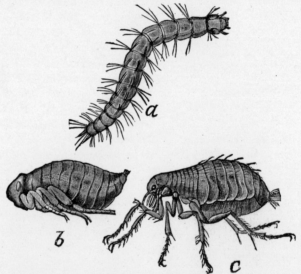

FIG. 506.—The house-flea, *Pulex irritans*. *A*, larva; *B*, pupa; *C*, adult.
(After Beneden; much enlarged.)

allow us to give the elusive flea little credit for its ingenuity; we must look on it as an unusually well-made and smoothly-working organic machine.

While the adult fleas are commonly seen, particularly in lands of soft climate, like Italy and California, in immature form these insects are wholly unfamiliar. The larvæ (Fig. 506) are small, slender, white, footless, worm-like grubs, with the body composed of thirteen segments, the first being the small brown head bearing short antennæ and biting mouth-parts, but no eyes. The larvæ seem to live on dry vegetable dust, the excreta of adult fleas, and other organic detritus. The larval life varies much in duration in different species, and even in the same species under varying conditions. In our commonest species, the cat- and dog-flea, Pergande has found the larval life to last only one or two weeks, the whole development from egg to adult being completed sometimes in a fortnight. When full-grown the larva spins (usually) a thin silken cocoon in the dust or litter in which it lies, within which it pupates.

The parasitic habits of fleas vary from a very temporary character to one approaching permanence. In such forms as the human flea and the dog-flea no stage of the immature life is passed on the body of the host (although the eggs of the dog-flea are usually laid on the hairs of the host, but so loosely attached that they fall off before the larvæ emerge), but in the burrowing kinds like the "chigœ" or "jigger," where the females become completely encysted in the skin of the host, the young hatch in the tumor, and unless carried out by pus probably develop there. But taken altogether the fleas are to be considered as belonging to the category of "temporary external parasites."

The species known in this country represent two families which may be separated by the following key:

> Small fleas with proportionally large head; female a stationary parasite with worm-like or spherical abdomen, burrowing into flesh of the host; labial palpi 1-segmented; no "combs" of spines on head, thorax, or abdomen.
> SARCOPSYLLIDÆ.
> Larger fleas with proportionally small head; adults active temporary parasites, with abdomen always compressed; labial palpi 3- to 5-segmented; head, thorax, or abdomen often with "combs" of spines. ............. PULICIDÆ.

Of the Sarcopsyllidæ but two genera are known, one, Sarcopsylla, including the common jigger-flea, infesting various mammals and man in the tropics and probably occurring in Florida and southern Texas, and Xestopsylla, the common chicken-flea, being distinguished by having the head not angularly produced.

The jigger-flea, or chigœ, *Sarcopsylla penetrans* (not to be confused with a minute red mite, common on lawns, which burrows into the skin and is also called "jigger" or "chigger"), was described by Linnæus in 1767 and has been commonly known as a pest of man in tropical and sub-tropical countries ever since. It also infests many domestic animals, as the dog, cat, horse, cow, sheep, etc., as well as birds. The male jigger-fleas hop on or off the host as other fleas do, but the females, when ready to lay eggs, burrow into the skin, especially that of the feet, and produce a swelling and later a distinct ulcer, sometimes so serious as to result fatally. The remedy is (as also for the chigger-mite) the pricking out entire, with a needle or knife-point, of the pest as soon as its presence is detected. The bursting of the body of the female in the skin, with the release of its eggs, is likely to result seriously. When domestic animals are attacked it is difficult to fight the pest. The liberal use of pyrethrum on the rubbish or dust in which the young stages are developing is recommended. The hen-flea, *Xestopsylla gallinacea*, first described from Ceylon, sometimes becomes a serious pest of fowls in warm regions. The females of the hen-flea burrow into the skin of the fowl and lay their eggs in the small tumor which forms about them. This pest has been known in the Southern United States since about 1890 and is a common pest from Florida to Texas.

The second family, Pulicidæ, includes all the other fleas, none of which burrows into the skin. The various species range in size from $\frac{1}{12}$ inch (*Anomiopsyllus nudatus*, found on a mouse in Arizona) to $\frac{1}{4}$ inch (*Ceratophyllus stylosus*, taken from Haplodon in Oregon), but all fairly similar in shape and appearance to the familiar house-fleas. They are grouped in nine genera, of which Pulex is much the largest and includes the human flea and the cat- and dog-flea, the two species to which the house-infesting pests belong. The human flea, *Pulex irritans*, was described by Linnæus in 1746. It is known all over the world, and often becomes a serious pest. In this country it is probably not so commonly met with in houses as the cat- and dog-flea, *Ctenocephalus canis*, from which it may be readily distinguished by its lack of combs of spines on the back of the head and prothorax. The eggs of *irritans* "are deposited in out-of-the-way places, in the dust or lint under carpets, and the larvæ are said to feed upon the particles of organic matter which may be found in such localities." Raillet states that each female deposits eight to twelve eggs from which larvæ hatch, in summer, in from four to six days, become pupæ eleven days later, and after about twelve days in this stage become adult. In winter, in warmed houses, the whole development takes about six weeks. The cat- and dog-flea lays its eggs on or among the hairs of an infested animal, but the eggs drop to the floor or ground as the animal moves about, and the larvæ live in the dust, feeding on whatever bits of organic substance they can find there. Larvæ placed on dust with birds' feathers mixed with dried blood developed perfectly. Others put on the sweepings of a room developed as well. These fleas are especially abundant and troublesome in houses in the East in damp summers. As flea-larvæ will not develop successfully in places where they are often disturbed, much sweeping and scrubbing will keep them down. Mats and places where dogs and cats lie down should be kept well dusted with pyrethrum. (Buhach is the trade name for this insecticide, which is not injurious to man or domestic animals.) Where fleas get a foothold in a neglected room or cellar, the remedy used by Professor Gage in the basement of one of Cornell University's buildings might be tried; i.e., tying sheets of sticky fly-paper, sticky side out, around the legs from foot to knee of the janitor or a cheap boy and having him tramp for several hours around in the room!

Of the various other flea species, the only ones that come into special relation with man are the rat-fleas. The proof that rats are active agents in the dissemination of the dreadful bubonic plague, and the belief of some pathologists that the disease-germs may be transmitted from rats to man by the bites or punctures of rat-fleas, gives this insect a special interest like that attaching to the malaria- and yellow-fever-disseminating mosquito and the germ-carrying house-fly. Baker pertinently calls attention to the fact that the rat-fleas of this country are only remotely related to *Pulex irritans* and *Ctenocephalus canis*, the two species that bite human beings, while the fleas that infest rats in the tropics are, on the contrary, very nearly related to the man-infesting kinds. The prevalence of the bubonic plague in tropical countries and its rarity with us may be connected with this difference in the rat-flea kinds.

# CHAPTER XIV

## THE MOTHS AND BUTTERFLIES (Order Lepidoptera)

OTHS and butterflies are the insects most favored of collectors and nature lovers; a German amateur would call them the "Lieblings-insekten." The beautiful color patterns, the graceful flight and dainty flower-haunting habits, and the interesting metamorphosis in their life-history make them very attractive, while the comparative ease with which the various species may be determined, and the large number of popular as well as more technical accounts of their life which are accessible for information, render the moths and butterflies most available, among all the insects, for systematic collecting and study by amateurs.

Despite the large number of species in the order (6622 are recorded in the latest catalogue of the North American forms) and the great variety in size and pattern, the order is an unusually homogeneous one, even a beginning student rarely mistaking a moth for an insect of any other order, or classifying a non-lepidopterous insect in this order. A few aberrant species are wingless (females only) and a few (certain "clear-winged" species) have a superficial likeness to wasps and bumblebees, but the general habitus of any Lepidopteron, let alone the readily determinable and absolutely diagnostic character of the scale-covering on the wings, usually indicates unmistakably the affinities of any moth or butterfly.

The diagnostic structural characters are the (already mentioned) presence on upper and lower sides of both wings (as well as over the surface of the body) of a covering of small symmetrically formed scales, which are modified hairs, and to which all of the color and pattern of the insects are due. In Chapter XVII will be found a detailed account of these scales, explaining their structure, their origin, and how they produce the color patterns. The wings themselves are almost always present (in two pairs), the fore wings larger than the hind wings, and with a characteristic venation, in which the modifications, though small, are yet so constant and definite that they are used successfully as the principal basis for the classification of the order into families. Another characteristic is the highly modified and peculiar condition of the mouth-parts. While in some species the mouth-parts are rudimentary (atrophied) and evidently not functional, in most there is a well-developed slender flexible sucking proboscis (Fig. 509) com-

# PLATE V.

## BUTTERFLIES.

1 = Junonia cœnia.
2 = Iphidicles ajax.
3 = Epargyreus tityrus.
4 = Cyaniris pseudargiolus.
5 = Ancyloxypha numitor.
6 = Papilio turnus.
7 = Nathalis iole.
8 = Parnassius smintheus.
9 = Thecla halesus.
10 = Zerene cæsonia.

PLATE V

Mary Wellman, del.

posed of the two greatly elongate maxillæ, so apposed that a groove on the inner face of one fits against a similar groove on the inner face of the other, the two thus forming a perfect tube (Fig. 510). This sucking proboscis, when extended, may protrude five or six inches, as in some of the sphinx-moths, or only a fraction of an inch, as in the small moth "millers," but when not in use it is so compactly coiled up, watchspring-like, under the head, and so concealed by a pair of hairy little tippets (the labial palpi) which project up on each side of it that it is nearly invisible. Of the other mouth-parts, the upper lip (labrum) and under lip (labium) are greatly reduced and are not movable and flap-like as in most insects, while the mandibles are either wholly wanting or, as in the sphinx-moths and some others, represented only by small immovable functionless rudiments. The palpi of the maxillæ are also either wholly wanting or present as mere rudiments. The foregoing description of the mouth-part conditions is true for the great majority of Lepidoptera, but among the lowest (oldest or most generalized) moths some interesting examples of much less specialized conditions occur. Indeed in one family of minute moths, the Eriocephalidæ, all the usual parts of a typical insect mouth are present and in a condition fitted for biting and chewing and in all ways wholly comparable

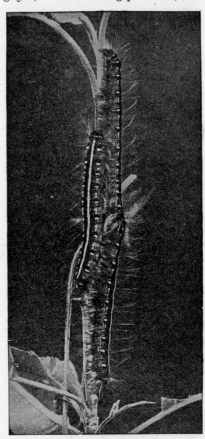

Fig. 507.—A trio of apple tent-caterpillars, larvæ of the moth *Clisiocampa americana*. These caterpillars make the large unsightly webs or tents in apple-trees, a colony of the caterpillars living in each tent. (Photograph from life by Slingerland; natural size.)

with the condition in such biting insects as the locusts and beetles; the mandibles are movable and truly jaw-like, the maxillæ short and also jaw-like and provided with several-segmented palpi, while both labrum and labium are truly lip- or flap-like and fully movable, the labium bearing 3-segmented palpi. Between this most generalized condition and the extreme specialization of the butterfly's mouth an interesting and illuminating gradatory series is discoverable by examining moths of successively more specialized character.

The development of moths and butterflies shows the usual characteristics of development with complete metamorphosis, the larval or caterpillar stage being quite dissimilar from the pupal or chrysalid stage, and that in turn from the

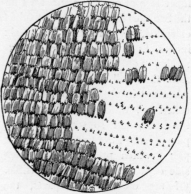

FIG. 508.—Bit of wing of monarch butterfly, *Anosia plexippus*, showing scales; some scales removed to show the insertion-pits and their regular arrangement. (Greatly magnified.)

adult or imaginal stage. The immature stages of Lepidoptera are more familiar than those of any other order; we have all seen, and recognized for what they are, the caterpillars and chrysalids of various moths and butterflies. The great silken cocoons found on orchard-trees in winter-time are known to contain the pupæ of giant moths, as the Cecropia, the Polyphemus, and others, while the soft-bodied green tomato-worms are as well known to be the young (larvæ) of the hawk-moths. As a matter of fact the young stages of no other of the insects with complete metamorphosis are so nearly unmistakably characterized by their common possession of certain well-defined features. The larvæ or caterpillars, for example, with very few exceptions, possess, in addition to three pairs of jointed legs on the first three segments behind the head, from three to five pairs of short fleshy unjointed legs or feet called prop-legs, on certain abdominal seg-

FIG. 509.—Sucking-proboscis of a sphinx-moth; at left the proboscis is shown coiled up on the under side of the head, the normal position when not in use. (Small figure, natural size; large figure, one-half natural size.)

ments; one of these pairs is on the last segment and four, which is the number present in all except the inchworms or loopers (larvæ of the Geometrid moths), are on the sixth, seventh, eighth, and ninth segments behind the head. The inchworms have prop-legs only (with a few exceptions) on the ninth and last segments. These prop-legs, together with the striped or hairy body-surface, make a moth or butterfly larva almost as readily recognizable for what it is as the scale-covered wings make

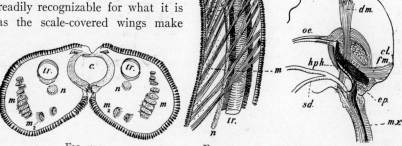

FIG. 510. 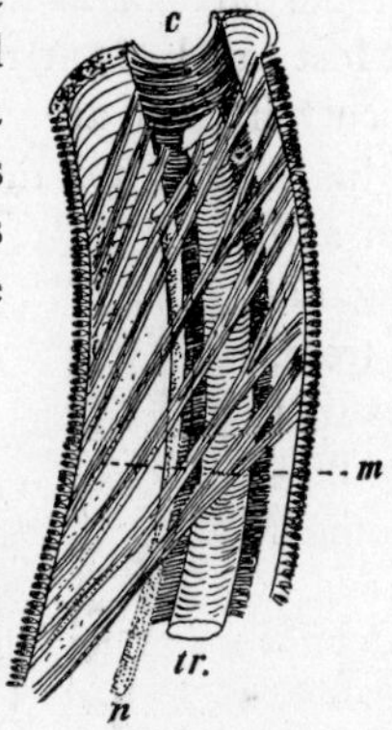     FIG. 511.     FIG. 512.

FIG. 510.—Cross-section of sucking-proboscis of milkweed-butterfly, *Anosia plexippus;* see tubular cavity, *c.,* formed by apposition of the two maxillæ. *tr.,* trachea; *n.,* nerve; *m.,* muscles. (After Burgess; greatly magnified.)

FIG. 511.—Bit of maxillary proboscis of milkweed-butterfly, *Anosia plexippus,* showing arrangement of muscles in the interior; these muscles serve to coil up or to extend the proboscis; see groove on inner face of maxilla. *m.,* muscles; *tr.,* trachea; *n.,* nerve; *c.,* groove.

FIG. 512.—Diagram of arrangement of pharynx, œsophagus, etc., in interior of head of monarch butterfly, *Anosia plexippus,* showing means of producing suction in the proboscis. *oe.,* œsophagus; *dm.,* dorsal muscle; *f.m.,* frontal muscle; *cl.,* clypeus; *hyp.,* hypopharynx; *s.d.,* salivary duct; *ep.,* epipharynx; *mx.,* maxilla.

the adult moth or butterfly distinguishable from any other kind of insect. The chrysalids with their hard shell, but with the folded antennæ, legs, and wings of the enclosed developing adult always indicated, are also hardly to be mistaken for the pupæ of any other orders, while even the eggs, when examined under a magnifier, mostly reveal their lepidopterous parentage by the beautiful fine sculpturing of the shell (Fig. 67). As will be noted from a perusal of the accounts of the life-history of various familiar and representative moths and butterflies given in the following pages, there is much variety in the means shown of protecting the defenceless pupæ; some are subterranean, the leaf-feeding larvæ crawling down from tree-top or weed-stem and burrowing into the ground before pupation; others are enclosed in a tough silken cocoon spun by the larva before making its last moult; while those which are not protected in one or the other of these ways either lie in concealed spots under stones or in cracks of the bark, etc., or are so colored and patterned that they blend indistinguishably with the object against which they are suspended. The larvæ have also their various means of defence; the hairy ones are an uncomfortable mouthful for a bird, the naked and brightly marked ones usually contain an acrid and distasteful body fluid, while still others find protection in a color pattern harmonizing with their habitual environment.

The food-habits of the larvæ make of many of them serious pests of our growing crops.  Most are leaf-eaters and all are voracious feeders, so that an abundance of cutworms or army-worms or maple-worms or tomato-worms always means hard times for their favorite food-plants, which are too often growing grain and vegetables, and leafing orchard and foliage trees. Others attack fruits, as that dire apple pest, the codlin-moth larva; while still others

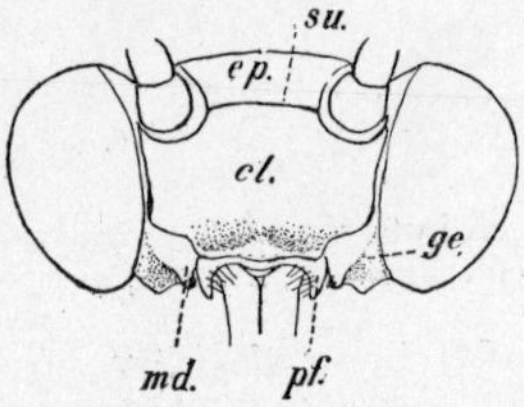

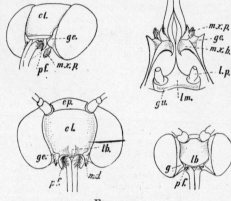

FIG. 513.     FIG. 514.

FIG. 513.—Front of head, with scales removed, of sphinx-moth, showing frontal sclerites and mouth-parts.  *ep.*, epicranium; *su.*, suture; *cl.*, clypeus; *ge.*, gena or cheek; *pf.*, pilifer of labrum; *md.*, mandible.  Between the two pilifers the base of the sucking-proboscis composed of the apposed maxillæ is seen.  (Much enlarged.)

FIG. 514.—Diagram showing mouth-parts of Lepidoptera.  Figure in upper left-hand corner, head, with scales removed, of *Catocala* sp.: *cl.*, clypeus; *ge.*, gena or cheek; *mx.p.*, maxillary palpus; *pf.*, pilifer of labrum.  In upper right-hand corner, ventral aspect of head of *Catocala* sp.: *mx.p.*, maxillary palpus; *ge.*, gena or cheek; *mx.b.*, base of maxilla; *gu.*, gula; *lm.*, labium; *lp.*, basal segment of labial palpus.  In lower left-hand corner, frontal aspect of head, with scales removed, of sphinx-moth, *Protoparce carolina:* *ep.*, epicranium; *cl.*, clypeus; *lb.*, labrum; *pf.*, pilifer of labrum; *md.*, mandible; *ge.*, gena or cheek.  In lower right-hand corner, front of head, with scales removed, of monarch butterfly, *Anosia plexippus* *lb.*, labrum; *g.*, gena or cheek; *pf.*, pilifer of labrum.  (Much enlarged.)

are content with dry organic substances, as the larvæ of clothes-moths, meal-moths, and the like.  For all of this kind of feeding very different mouth-parts are needed from the delicate sucking-proboscis characteristic of the adults, and the lepidopterous larvæ are all provided with well-formed jaw-like mandibles and other parts going to make up a biting mouth structure.  The larval eyes are simple ones, not compound as in the adults; the antennæ are short and inconspicuous, not large and feathered as in the moths, or long and thread-like, with knobbed tip, as in the butterflies.  Altogether the lepidopterous larva is a well-contrived animal for its especial kind of life, which is as different as may be, almost, from that which it will lead after it has completed its metamorphosis. Always when one reads or hears of injurious moths or butterflies it should be kept clearly in mind that the injuries, to crops or fruit or woolen clothing or what not, are caused by the moth or butterfly in its larval stage and never by the fluttering nectar-sipping adult.

The sole compensation, other than the rather immaterial though perhaps not less real one afforded us through our æsthetic appreciation of the beauty and attractive, apparently care-free, flitting about of

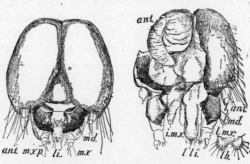

FIG. 515.

FIG. 516.

FIG. 517.

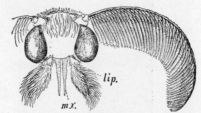

F.G. 518.

FIG. 515.—Front of head of larva of tussock-moth, *Hemerocampa leucostigma. ant.*, antenna; *md.*, mandible; *mx.*, maxilla; *mx.p.*, maxillary palpus; *li.*, labium. (Much enlarged.)

FIG. 516.—Front of head of old larva of tussock-moth, *Notolophus leucostigma*, with head-wall dissected away on right-hand side to show forming adult mouth-parts underneath. *l.ant.*, larval antenna; *ant.*, adult antenna; *l.md*, larval mandible; *l.mx.*, larval maxilla; *i.mx.*, adult maxilla; *lb.*, larval labrum; *l.li.*, larval labium. (Much enlarged.)

FIG. 517.—Developing adult head dissected out from head of larva of tussock-moth, *Notolophus leucostigma. ant.*, antenna; *mx.*, maxilla; *li.p.*, labial palpus. (Much enlarged.) •

FIG. 518.—Head of tussock-moth, *Notolophus leucostigma;* showing adult antennæ and mouth-parts. *mx.*, maxilla; *li.p.*, labial palpus. Note that the two maxillæ are not locked together to form a sucking-proboscis, the mouth-parts of this moth being rudimentary and not capable of taking food. (Much enlarged.)

the butterfly, which the Lepidoptera make for their often disastrous toll on our green things, is the prodigal gift of silk made by the moth species known as the mulberry or Chinese silkworm. Thoroughly domesticated (the wild silkworm species is now not even known), this industrious spinner produces each year over one hundred million of dollars' worth of fine silken thread ready for the loom. In Italy and Japan nearly every country household has its silk-rooms in which thousands of the white "worms" are carefully fed and tended by the women and children, and from which comes enough raw silk to furnish a good share of the annual income of each of these households.

The reader who would undertake the collecting of moths and butterflies, or the rearing of caterpillars in home "crawleries," is referred for some specific directions for this work to the appendix of this book, p. 635 *et seq.*

The order Lepidoptera may be most conveniently divided into two principal subgroups (suborders they are often called), namely, the Heterocera,

FIG. 519.—Larva of obsolete-banded strawberry leaf-roller, *Cacoecia obsoletana.* (Photograph from life by Slingerland; natural size in lower corner and twice natural size above.)

or moths, and the Rhopalocera, or butterflies. All butterflies have antennæ which are slender (filiform) for most of their length, but have the tip expanded or thickened, forming an elongate spindle-shaped dilation or "club"; the moths have their antennæ variously formed, as wholly filiform, pectinate,

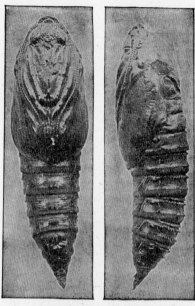

FIG. 520.—Pupa of obsolete-banded strawberry leaf-roller, *Cacoecia obsoletana*. (Photograph from life by Slingerland; natural size a little more than one-half inch.)

FIG. 521.—Moths of the obsolete-banded strawberry leaf-roller, *Cacoecia obsoletana*, male above, female below. (Photograph from life by Slingerland; natural size.)

Fig. 522.—Larva of the royal walnut-moth, *Citheronia regalis*. (Photograph from life by Sachse; natural size.)

etc., but never showing the characteristic swollen-tipped or clubbed condition of the butterflies. The moths, too, are mostly night or twilight flyers, while the butterflies go abroad in sunlight only. Scientific students of Lepidoptera do not give the butterflies a classific value equivalent to that of the moths taken altogether, but rather rank them as a group more nearly equivalent to a single superfamily of moths, as, for example, the superfamily Saturniina, which includes all our great silkworm-moths, Cecropia, Luna, Promethea, Polyphemus, etc., etc. However, the more familiar and readily made subdivision of the order into moths and butterflies is more convenient and

FIG. 523.—Moth and cocoon cut open to show pupa of *Samia cecropia*. (After Lugger; slightly reduced.)

quite as informing for our purpose, so we shall adopt it, taking up the moths first, as including the more generalized members of the order. There are many more moth than butterfly families the numbers represented in this country being 44 to 5. By reference to the following key adapted from Comstock almost any North American moth can be traced to its proper family.

### KEY TO THE SUPERFAMILIES AND FAMILIES OF MOTHS.

This key does not include a few of the smaller families whose members are very few and are rarely taken by collectors. Some of these moths are, however, referred to in the systematic account of the families which follows later.　To use the key requires an acquaintanceship with the plan of venation in the wings and the nomenclature of the veins.　This may be got from an inspection of Fig. 525, and by referring to the various other figures illustrating the typical venation for the various important families. To see clearly the veins, a necessary prerequisite to using the key, a few drops of ether should be put on the outstretched wing of a spread specimen and this held so that bright light, as from a window or lamp, may pass through the wing to the eye.　For a few moments (until the evaporation of the ether) the covering-scales will be transparent and the number and course of the veins plainly visible.　The ether will not injure the specimen at all.　If duplicate specimens are available, the fore and hind wings of one side may be removed and placed in a watch-glass or small saucer containing Eau de Labarraque (to be obtained of a druggist), when the scales will be bleached perfectly transparent.　The wings may be then washed and mounted on glass slides with glycerine jelly and thus be made available for inspection at any time.

A.　Moths which have a thin lobe-like process (jugum) projecting backward from the base of the fore wing, which holds fore and hind wings together when they are outstretched; veins similar in number and arrangement in both wings (Fig. 526).

(The Jugatæ.)

B.　Very small moths, not more than one-fifth inch long.

MICROPTERYGIDÆ and ERIOCEPHALIDÆ.

BB. Moths from one-half to one inch long..........(The Swifts.)　HEPIALIDÆ.

AA. Moths whose wings are not united by a jugum but by a frenulum (Fig. 533), and in which the veins in the hind wing are less in number than in the fore wing.

(The Frenatæ.)

B.　Hind wings with fringe on hinder margin as long as the width of the wing; hind wings often lanceolate in shape........Superfamily TINEINA (part).

BB. Hind wings with narrow or no fringe, and not lanceolate in shape.

C.　Wings fissured, i.e., divided longitudinally into several narrow parts.

(Plume-moths.)　PTEROPHORIDÆ and ORNEODIDÆ.

CC. Wings not fissured.

D.　Fore wings very narrow; part of the hind wings always, and of the fore wings often, clear, i.e., without scales.

(Clear-winged moths.)　SESIIDÆ.

DD. Wings all covered with scales or, if partly clear, the fore wings broad.

E.　Hind wings with three anal veins.

F.　Subcosta and radius of hind wings close together or fused beyond the discal cell (Fig. 533).

Superfamily PYRALIDINA.

FF. Subcosta and radius of hind wings widely apart beyond the discal cell.

G.　Small; palpi usually prominently projecting; fringe on inner angle of hind wings longer than on rest of margin.

H.　Second anal vein of hind wings forked at the base (Fig. 539).....Superfamily TORTRICINA.

HH. Second anal vein of hind wings not forked at base.........Superfamily TINEINA (part).

GG. Medium or large; palpi not conspicuously projecting beyond the head and fringe on inner angle of hind wings only slightly or not at all longer than on rest of margin.

H.   Subcosta and radius of hind wings fused nearly to end of the discal cell (Fig. 553).

    I.   Small black moths.

      (Smoky-moths.)   PYROMORPHIDÆ (part).

    II.   With long, curling, light-colored or brown woolly hairs

      (Flannel-moths.)   MEGALOPYGIDÆ.

HH.   Subcosta and radius of hind wings distinct or only slightly fused.

    I.   Anal veins of fore wings anastomosing so as to appear as a branched vein (Fig. 552).

      (Bag-worm moths.)   PSYCHIDÆ.

    II.   Anal veins not anastomosing.

      J.   Vein $m_2$ of fore wings arising from the discal cell nearly midway between veins $m_1$ and $m_3$ (Fig. 603).

        (Silkworm-moths.)   BOMBYCIDÆ.

      JJ.   Vein $m_2$ of fore wings rising from discal cell nearer to cubitus than to radius, so that cubitus appears four-branched (Fig. 548).

        (Carpenter-moths.)   COSSIDÆ.

EE.   Hind wings with less than three anal veins.

    F.   Fore wings with two distinct anal veins or with these two veins partly fused so as to appear like a single branched vein.

      G.   The two anal veins distinct (Fig. 553).

        PYROMORPHIDÆ (part).

      GG.   The two anal veins partly fused and appearing like a single branched vein (Fig. 552).   PSYCHIDÆ (part).

    FF.   Fore wings with but one complete anal vein (rudiments of one or two others sometimes present).

      G.   Frenulum present.

        H.   Hind wings with subcosta and radius apparently distinct, but connected by a strong oblique cross-vein; moths mostly with narrow, long, strong front wings and small hind wings.

          (Sphinx- or hawk-moths.)   SPHINGIDÆ.

        HH.   Hind wings with subcosta and radius either distinct or fused, but not connected by an oblique cross-vein.

          I.   Vein $m_2$ of fore wings closer to radius than cubitus, cubitus being apparently three-branched.

            J.   Subcosta of hind wings extending from base to apex of wing in a regular curve (Fig. 560); moths with heavy abdomen and rather narrow strong fore wings.

              (The prominents.)   NOTODONTIDÆ.

            JJ.   Subcosta of hind wings with its basal part making a prominent bend into the

humeral angle of the wing (Fig. 567);
moths mostly with slender abdomen
and rather broad delicate fore wings.
Superfamily GEOMETRINA.

II.  Vein $m_2$ of fore wings more closely joined
to cubitus than to radius, so that cubitus
is apparently four-branched.

J.  Subcosta of hind wings distinct from
radius, or the two fused for a very
short distance near the base of the
wing (Fig. 584).

K.  Day-flying moths that are black
with large white or yellow patches
on the wings, or with white front
wings margined with brown, and
having the hind wings pale yellow.

(Wood-nymph moths.)  AGARISTIDÆ and PERICOPIDÆ.

KK. Not such moths.

L.  Ocelli absent; antennæ pectinate.

(Tussock-moths.)  LYMANTRIIDÆ.

LL. Ocelli present or, if absent,
with simple antennæ.

(Owlet-moths.)  NOCTUIDÆ.

JJ. Subcosta of the hind wings fused with
radius for one-fifth or more of the
length of the discal cell.

K.  Subcosta and radius of hind wings
fused entirely or with only the tips
separate (Fig. 591)...ZYGÆNIDÆ

KK. Subcosta and radius of hind wings
united for about one-half their
length, or more, but usually
separating before the apex of the
discal cell (Fig. 597).

L.  Ocelli present.

(Tiger-moths.)  ARCTIIDÆ.

LL. Ocelli absent.

(Footman-moths.)  LITHOSIIDÆ.

GG. Frenulum absent; the humeral angle of the hind
wings largely expanded and serving as a substitute
for the frenulum (Fig. 600).

H. Cubitus of both wings apparently four-branched
(Fig. 600).  (Tent-caterpillar moths *et al.*)

LASICOCAMPIDÆ.

HH. Cubitus of both wings apparently three-
branched; robust moths with broad wings (Fig.
603).  (Giant silkworm-moths.) SATURNIINA.

The jugate moths include but two families, the Micropterygidæ and
Hepialidæ, both represented by but few species and these rarely met with

by collectors and nature students. But these moths are of particular importance and interest to entomologists because they are undoubtedly the oldest
or most generalized of living Lepidoptera; they represent most nearly, among
present-day existing moths, the ancestral moth type. This is shown most
conspicuously by the similarity in size, shape, and venation of the fore and
hind wings, for the primitive winged insects had their two pairs of wings
equal, while nowadays the various orders show a marked tendency to
throw the flight function on one pair, either the fore wings, as among the
flies (Diptera), wasps, bees, etc. (Hymenoptera), and Lepidoptera, or the
hind wings, as with the locusts, crickets, etc. (Orthoptera), and beetles (Coleoptera), the other pair becoming much
reduced in size, or even, as in the
Diptera, wholly lost. Quite as important, if not more, although not so conspicuous, as an evidence of the ancient
character of the jugate moths, is the
condition of the mouth-parts, certain
species in the group having true biting
mouth-parts, with well developed mandibles, short lobe-like maxillæ, and short,
truly lip-like labium. All other moths
and butterflies have the mouth-parts
specialized for sucking, with the mandibles rudimentary or wanting, the maxillæ produced and apposed to form the
long flexible sucking-tube, and the under
lip (labium) reduced to a mere immovable
functionless sclerite. The presence of
the jugum for tying the fore and hind
wings together, as in the caddis-flies,
undoubtedly nearly allied to the moth
ancestors, instead of the specialized
frenulum as in other moths, is also evidence of the ancestral type displayed by
the Jugatæ.

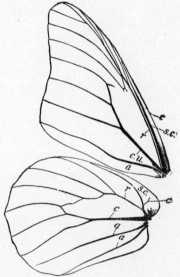

FIG. 524.—Diagram showing venation
of wings in monarch butterfly, *Anosia
plexippus*. *c.*, costal vein; *sc.*, subcostal vein; *r.*, radial vein; *cu.*, cubital vein; *a.*, anal veins. The base of
the medial vein (lying between radius
and cubitus) is obsolete, but its
branches still persist, lying between
branches of radius and cubitus.
(Natural size.)

The Micropterygidæ, represented in
this country by two genera, Eriocephala,
with four species, and Epimartyria (Micropteryx), with two species, are among
the smallest moths we have, the largest not expanding more than one-third
of an inch and the smallest only one-fifth of an inch, the body being about
one-tenth of an inch long. They are indeed almost invisible when flying,
and are only very rarely taken by collectors. They fly in the sunshine,

frequenting flowers, and the different species are so much alike as to be nearly indistinguishable to the amateur. The eggs are laid on leaves, or in tiny pits in them, and the minute larvæ, short and oblong, are either footless and mine the leaf substance, or have eight pairs of abdominal legs and feed exposed on leaves or in moss. The leaf-mining larvæ burrow into the ground to pupate, while the exposed feeders make a slight cocoon of silk and debris above ground. The pupæ are more like caddis-fly pupæ than the usual lepidopterous chrysalids (another indication of the primitive character of the family), and those of certain species have large mandibles which they use to cut their way out of the cocoon. The adults can best be distinguished by the venation of the wings (Fig. 525), and if ever found should be highly prized by the collector as specimens of the most primitive living Lepidoptera.

The Hepialidæ, the ghosts or swifts, although an offshoot from the Micropterygidæ, or at least much more nearly related to them than to any other moths, are very different in appearance, being from an inch to 2½ inches long (some foreign species have a wing expanse of 6 inches) with large broad-ended wings and rather heavy body. They can be recognized by their venation (Fig. 526), which distinguishes them from all other moths of their size. The mouth-parts are rudimentary, but the parts per-

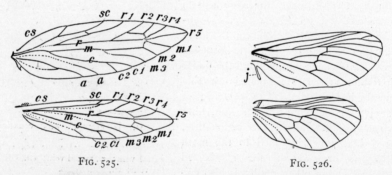

Fig. 525.

Fig. 526.

Fig. 525.—Diagram of wing venation of *Micropteryx* sp. *cs*, costal vein; *sc*, subcostal vein; *r*, radial vein; *m*, medial vein; *c*, cubital vein; *a*, anal veins. (After Comstock; enlarged.)

Fig. 526.—Diagram of wings of *Hepialus gracilis*, showing jugum (*j*), and similarity of venation in fore and hind wings. (After Comstock.)

sisting indicate plainly that they are reduced remnants of a very simple set of structures. The labium is free and truly lip-like and of the type of the under lip of biting insects. Two genera, Sthenopis, four species, and Hepialus, nine species, occur in this country. All of these moths are rather sombre in color, being grayish, yellowish brown, and reddish brown, with a few

silvery-whitish irregular streaks on the upper wing surface. They fly swiftly and are said to prefer twilight. The males of some species give off a strong scent to attract the females. Others seem to show off their silvery spots by hovering for some time in the air at twilight, being conspicuous, despite the semi-darkness and the quiet general coloration of the moth, by a pale silvery appearance. Females have been seen to fly directly to the ghostly hovering males as if strongly attracted. The grub-like larvæ

FIG. 527. — The clothes-moth, *Tinea pellionella;* larva, larva in case, and adult. (After Howard and Marlatt; twice natural size.)

feed in the roots of various plants, as ferns and others, or in the trunk-wood of various shrubs and trees, and live for two or three years. *Sthenopis argenteo-maculatus* feeds first in the roots of alder, later going into the stems. It either pupates in its burrow or in a loose cocoon in the soil. The pupæ are provided with certain short spiny teeth, and can wriggle so strongly that they are able to move about in the burrows or soil, and when ready to transform work their way to the surface of the ground.

The Jugatæ are looked on by Comstock as equivalent in ranking to all the other moths and all the butterflies combined which are given the subordinal name Frenatæ. That is, this scant dozen of persisting representatives of the ancient moth type, or rather of immediate offshoots from the ancestral type, are to be distinguished subordinally from all other living Lepidoptera, however more striking may appear the differences between some of these, as the obscure clothes-moths and the regal Cecropias, or the dull moth-millers and the brilliant day-flying butterflies. The Frenate Lepidoptera include all those forms which have the venation of the hind wings reduced (branches less in number than in the fore wings) and whose wings are tied together by a frenulum (Fig. 533) or by the expanded humeral angle of the hind wing overlapping the base of the fore wing, or by no more elaborate means than the simple overlapping of front margin of hind wing and hind margin of fore wing, but never by a jugum,

FIG. 528.—Larva of the palmer-worm, *Ypsolophus pomatellus,* lying under its web spun on a leaf (After Lowe; natural length ½ inch.)

the caddis-fly-like method common to the Micropterygids and Hepialids.

Among the Frenatæ there is a host of small obscure moths commonly lumped by collectors and amateurs under the name Microlepidoptera, which are little known because little studied, but which professional entomologists recognize as including all together eleven moth families grouped into three distinct superfamilies. Among these microlepidoptera are probably the most generalized of the frenate moths.

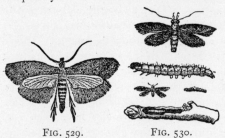

FIG. 529. FIG. 530.

FIG. 529.—The palmer-worm moth, *Ypsolophus pomatellus*. (After Fitch; twice natural size.)

FIG 530.—The strawberry root-borer, *Anarsia lineatella*. (After Saunders; moth and larva both natural size and enlarged.)

The three microlepidopterous superfamilies are the Tineina, including the clothes-moths, leaf-miners, and others, the Tortricina, including most of the leaf-rollers, the notorious codlin-moth and others, and the Pyralidina, including certain leaf-rollers and folders, the close-wings, the curious plume-moths, the injurious meal-moths, and the bee-moth, principal pest of the bee-keeper.

The Tineidæ, only family of the Tineina, are best known by their household representatives, the clothes-moths. Of these there are several species, the moths themselves looking much alike, although distinguished by some differences in marking, but the larvæ, the stage in which the injury to woolens, etc., is done having noticeable differences in habit. The moths lay their eggs on garments and stuffs, preferably woolen, hanging in dark closets or stored in trunks or dressers, and the small white larvæ feed on the dry animal fibers of which the cloth is made. The larva of the most familiar species, the case-bearing clothes-moth, *Tinea pellionella* (Fig. 527), makes a small free tubular case out of bits of cloth fibers held together by silk spun from its mouth; the larva of the tapestry-moth *T. tapetzella*, a rarer species, attacks thick woolen things, as blankets, carpets, and hangings, burrowing into the fabric and forming a long winding tunnel or gallery partially lined with silk; the larva of the webbing clothes-moth, *Tinea biselliella*, a species especially common in the Southern States, although not infrequent in the North, spins no case or gallery, but makes a cobweb covering over the substance it is feeding on. The larvæ of all the species, when ready to pupate, make a cocoon out of bits of woolen tied together by silken threads in which to transform. The moths, on issuing, rest during the day on the garments or stuffs, but fly about at night, often coming to the lights in rooms. They are all small, *pellionella* and *biselliella* expanding about ½ inch and *tapetzella* ¾ inch; *pellionella* has grayish-yellow fore wings without spots, and *tapetzella* has the fore wings black at base and creamy-white with some grayish on the middle and apex. The eggs are laid by the moths directly on the woolen garments or other articles favored by the larval palate, and several generations may appear each year. The remedies for clothes-moths are the admission of light into closets and dressers, the fumigation of infested clothes or rugs in tight chests with bisulphide of carbon (the fumes will kill every larva and moth in the chest), and the keeping of carpets, rugs, hangings, and garments in cold storage during summer absences from home. Send the things to a cold-storage company with instructions to keep at a temperature below 40° F. The insects cannot develop in a temperature below this point. Cloth-covered furniture and cloth-lined carriages, if to be left long unused, may be sprayed once each in April, June, and August with benzine or naphtha.

A sometimes serious pest of stored grains, especially corn in cribs, is the Angoumois grain-moth, *Gelechia cerealella*. The larvæ bore into the kernels, feeding on the inner starchy matter. I have seen ears of corn in Kansas cribs with every kernel attacked. The larvæ feed for about three weeks, then pupate inside the kernel, the moth issuing in a few days. The kernels of infested ears show from one to three little holes from which moths have issued. The adult moth, expanding about half an inch, is light grayish brown, more or less spotted with black, looking much like the case-bearing clothes-moth. The eggs are deposited on grain in the field or bin.

Numerous Tineid species are known as leaf-miners because of the burrows of the larvæ. Leaves of various trees and shrubs often show whitish blotches or lines, which when examined closely are seen to be due to the separation of the epidermis of the leaf from the inner soft tissue or to the complete dis-appearance of the inner tissue. This is the work of the tiny burrowing and feeding "leaf-miners," the larvæ of certain Tineid species. Often the miner,

Fig. 531.—Pupal cocoons of the apple bucculatrix, *Bucculatrix pomifoliella*. (Twice natural size.)

a small white grub with the usual eight pairs of legs characteristic of Lepidopterous larvæ, can be found in his mine, or, perhaps he will have ceased feeding and have transformed to a small light-brown pupa. The species of these leaf-miners are many, and numerous different types of mines may be found; the winding narrow lines called serpentine mines common on wild columbine, the spotted and folded tentiform mines on the wild cherry and the apple, the blotch-mines of the oaks and other forest trees. Even pine-needles are mined by certain species, the pine leaf-miner, *Gelechia pinifoliella*, being abundant in the leaves of pitch-pine.

Interesting little Tineids are the apple and oak bucculatrix-moths, whose larvæ feed on the leaves and when ready to pupate crawl to a stem or branch

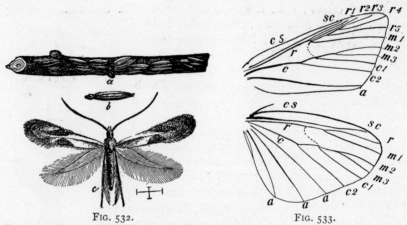

FIG. 532.                 FIG. 533.

FIG. 532.—The apple-leaf bucculatrix, *Bucculatrix pomifoliella*, pupal cocoons on twig, one pupal cocoon removed, and moth. (After Riley; cocoons natural size; size of moth indicated by line.)

FIG. 533. — Venation of a Pyralid moth, *Pyralis farinalis. cs*, costal vein; *sc*, subcostal vein; *r*, radial vein; *m*, medial vein; *c*, cubital vein; *a*, anal veins. Note the hair-like projection, called frenulum, at the base of the anterior margin of the hind wing. This fits into a little "frenulum pocket" on the fore wing. (After Comstock; enlarged.)

and there make long, slender, finely woven little white cocoons, conspicuously ribbed or fluted lengthwise, in which they pupate (Figs. 531 and 532). The pupæ hibernate, the tiny moth issuing the following spring and laying its eggs on the leaves. The larvæ are miners at first, but after the first moulting feed on the outer surface of the leaves under thin flat silken webs.

The Pyralidina include half a dozen families, some of the moths hardly properly called microlepidoptera, for they reach a wing expanse of $1\frac{1}{2}$ inches. But most of the species are small and but few are at all familiar to collectors. The larvæ of numerous species are injurious to fruits, stored grain, etc., and these species have a particular interest for economic entomologists. To collectors and nature students the most attractive Pyralids will be the beautiful plume-moths, or feather-wings, small moths with the wings split or fissured longitudinally for one-half or more the length of the wing. The fore wings are usually thus divided into two parts and the hind wings into three (Fig. 534), but on some there are more divisions. All the feather-wings excepting one species belong to the family Pterophoridæ, the exception being a small moth with both wings deeply cleft into six parts. It is called *Orneodes hexadactyla* and is considered to be the sole representative, so far as known, of a distinct family, the Orneodidæ. Of the Pterophoridæ several species are common in the North and East.

FIG. 534.                     FIG. 535.

FIG. 534. A California plume-moth. (Natural size.)
FIG. 535.—The raspberry plume-moth, *Oxyptilus tenuidactylus*, moth and larva. (After Saunders; moth natural size; larva much enlarged.)

*Oxyptilus tenuidactylus* (Fig. 535), with coppery brownish wings, with the plumes deeply fringed, has a pale yellowish-green larva that feeds on raspberries and blackberries; *O. periscelidactylus* has wings of a metallic yellowish brown, with several dull whitish streaks and spots; its greenish-yellow caterpillars with scattered small tufts of white hairs feed on grape-leaves and often are numerous enough to do much damage. Along the Pacific coast the plume-moths are not at all uncommon.

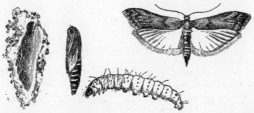

FIG. 536.—The Mediterranean flour-moth, *Ephestia kuehniella;* larva, pupal cocoon, pupa, and moth. (One and one-half times natural size.)

The Crambids, or close-wings, are numerous and perhaps more familiar than any other family of the Pyralidina. The larvæ of most of the species feed on grass, and the adults fly up before one as one walks through meadow or pasture. They may easily be recognized by their characteristic habit of closely folding their wings about the body when at rest. The fore wings often present pretty designs in silver, gold, yellow, brown, black, and white, or they may be uniformly dull-colored; the hind wings are white or grayish. The palpi are long and project conspicuously, so that snout-moth is a name often given to the Crambids.

Pretty little moths with shining black wings, two-spotted with white on the front ones, and one- or two-spotted on the hind wings, are the Desmias, of which the species *maculalis*, the grape-vine leaf-folder, is especially common, and often seriously injurious. The larvæ fold or roll up grape-leaves and feed concealed inside the roll, skeletonizing the leaf by eating away all of its soft tissues. The larva when full-grown is a little less than an inch long, glossy yellowish green, and very active when disturbed. It pupates within the folded leaf. It is abundant in the South.

Among the insects that attack stored grain, flour, meal, etc., are several Pyralids. The meal snout-moth, *Pyralis farinalis*, is a common pest, the larvæ making long tubes of silk in the meal, and taking readily to cereals

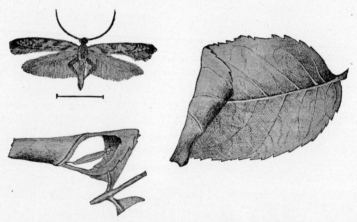

FIG. 537.—A curious hammock and its maker, *Coriscum cuculipennellum*, a leaf-rolling moth, whose larva pupates in the odd little hammock shown in the figure. (After photographs by Slingerland; natural size of moth indicated by line; hammock natural size; a rose-leaf enlarged.)

of all kinds and conditions, in the kernel or in the form of meal, bran, or straw. The moth expands one inch, the wings being light brown with reddish reflections and a few wavy transverse lines. The Indian meal-moth, *Plodia interpunctella*, is another familiar pest in mills and stores, its small whitish larva, with brownish-yellow head, feeding on dry edibles of almost every kind, as meal, flour, bran, grain of all sorts, dried fruits, seeds, and nuts, condiments, roots, and herbs. It spins webs of silk with which it fastens together particles of the attacked food, making it unfit for our use. The moth expands $\frac{5}{8}$ inch and has the fore wings cream-white at base and reddish brown with transverse blackish bands on disk and apex. Another and perhaps the most formidable of all mill pests is the notorious Mediterranean flour-moth, *Ephestia kuehniella* (Fig. 536). This insect first became seriously harmful in Germany in 1877, soon invading Belgium and Holland and by 1886 having got a foothold in England. Three years later it appeared in Canada and since 1892 it has been a pest in the United States. The moth, which expands a little less than an inch, with pale leaden-gray fore wings, bearing zigzag black and transverse bands and semi-transparent dirty-whitish hind wings, lays its eggs where the hatching larvæ can feed on flour, meal, bran, prepared cereal foods or grain. The caterpillars spin silken galleries as they move about, which make the flour lumpy and stringy and ruin it for use. In addition to this direct injury, the mill machinery often becomes clogged by the silk-filled flour and has to be frequently stopped and cleaned, involving in large mills much additional loss. When a mill becomes badly infested the whole building has to be thoroughly fumigated by carbon bisulphide, an expensive and rather dangerous process. Uninfested mills should be tightly closed at night (if not running continuously) and every bushel of grain, every bag or sack brought into the mill, should be subjected to disinfection by heat or the fumes of bisulphide of carbon.

An interesting as well as economically important little Pyralid is the bee-moth, *Galleria mellonella*, whose larvæ live in beehives, feeding on the wax combs. The moths find their way into the hives at night to lay their eggs. This has to be done very quickly, however, as bees are alert even at night to defend themselves against this insidious enemy. I have introduced bee-moths into glass-sided observation-hives both by day and night, and in each case the moths were almost immediately discovered, stung to death and torn to pieces in a wild frenzy of anger. Many must be killed where one succeeds in getting its eggs deposited inside the hive. The squirming grub-like white larvæ protect themselves by spinning silken webs and feed steadily on the wax, ruining brood- and food-cells and interfering sadly with the normal economy of the hive. When ready to pupate they spin very tough bee-proof silken cocoons within which they transform to otherwise defenceless quiescent pupæ. Bee-moths often become so numerous in a hive as to break up the successful life of the community. I have taken thousands of pupæ, lying side by side like mummies in sarcophagi in their impervious stiff silken cocoons, from a single hive from which the bees had all fled.

Third of the superfamilies of microlepidoptera is the Tortricina, comprising three families, two of which number many species. The Tortricid moths get their name from the habit, common to the larvæ of many of them, of rolling up the edges or the whole of leaves in which to lie protected while feeding, and later while in quiescent pupal stage. Not all leaf-rollers are

Tortricids, but the majority of rolled-up leaves so commonly seen on shrubs and trees are the homes of these larvæ. A number of species belonging to the genus Cacoecia are among the commonest and most important of these because they prefer the leaves of apple, plum, and cherry trees, and currants, raspberries, gooseberries, strawberries, cranberries, roses, etc., rather than those of trees and shrubs whose healthfulness is not so important to us. The larvæ of *Cacoecia rosaceana*, the oblique-banded l e a f - roller, pale yellowish-green caterpillars $\frac{3}{4}$ inch long, disfigure and injure many kinds of fruit-trees, small fruits, and garden shrubs. The moth expands about one inch, and has reddish-brown body, light, cinnamon-brown fore wings crossed by wavy dark-brown lines and ochre-yellow hind wings. Choke-berries, and cultivated cherries as well, are often attacked by the cherry-tree leaf-folder,

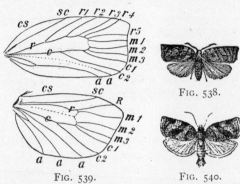

FIG. 538.

FIG. 539.          FIG. 540.

FIG. 538.—The cherry-tree leaf-roller, *Cacoecia cerasivorana*. (After Lugger; natural size.)

FIG. 539.—Venation of a Tortricid, *Cacoecia cerasivorana*. *cs*, costal vein; *sc*, subcostal vein; *r*, radial vein; *m*, medial vein; *c*, cubital vein; *a*, anal vein. (After Comstock; enlarged.)

FIG. 540.—The cranberry leaf-roller, *Cacoecia parallela*. (After Lugger; natural size.)

*C. cerasivorana* (Fig. 538), whose active yellow larvæ "fasten together with silken threads all the leaves and twigs of a branch and feed upon them, an entire brood occupying a single nest. The larvæ change to pupæ within the nest; and the pupæ when about to transform work their way out and hang suspended from the outer portion of the nest." The moths expand from $\frac{4}{5}$ to $1\frac{1}{5}$ inch, have bright ochre-yellow wings with brownish spots, and bands of pale leather-blue on the front ones.

The oak leaf-roller, *C. pervadana*, similarly makes ugly nests in oak-trees in late summer, each nest consisting of a wad of tied-together leaves. Cranberry-plants are sometimes attacked by reddish, yellow-headed, warty-backed caterpillars, which are the larvæ of *C. parallela* (Fig. 540), a leaf-roller moth with reddish-orange fore wings crossed diagonally by numerous fine lines of a darker red-brown, and a pair of broad oblique red-brown bands. The hind wings are pale yellow.

FIG. 541.—The sulphur-colored tortrix, *Dichelia sulfureana*. (After Lugger; natural size.)

Notwithstanding the apparently sufficient protection afforded the leaf-rolling larvæ by their tightly rolled cylindrical cases and webby nests, birds may often be seen cleverly engaged in extracting one by one the toothsome morsels from their homes.  Hovering over a rolled leaf, the bill is carefully thrust into the roll for the unseen caterpillar and rarely withdrawn without it.  Lugger says that the Baltimore oriole is particularly expert at this sort of hunting unseen prey.

A certain Tortricid, accidentally imported many years ago from Europe, has become one of our serious grape pests.  This is the grape-berry moth, *Eudemis botrana*, whose small slender whitish-green, black-headed larvæ bore into green and ripening grapes and feed there on the pulp and seeds.  When full-grown the larva becomes olive-green or dark brown and, forsaking the grape-berry, cuts out of a grape-leaf a little flap which it folds over and fastens with silk, thus forming a small oblong case within which it pupates.  The moth expands $\frac{2}{5}$ inch, and has slaty-blue fore wings, marked with dark

Fig. 542.—The russet-brown tortrix, *Platynota flavedana*. (After Lugger; natural size.)

reddish-brown bands and spots, while the hind wings are uniform dull brown. Another well-known Tortricid pest is the bud-moth, *Tmetocera ocellana* (Fig. 543), whose larvæ burrow into opening fruit- and leaf-buds on apple-trees and eat them.  The moth expands $\frac{3}{5}$ inch and is dark ashen-gray with a large irregular whitish band on the fore wing.

By far the best known and most feared and hated Tortricid is the codlin-moth, *Carpocapsa pomonella* (Figs. 545 and 546), the most important enemy of the apple-grower.  Distributed all over the United States, wherever apples are grown, minute and obscure so as to be easily overlooked until fairly intrenched in the orchard, prolific and subject to no very disastrous parasitic attacks, this frail little species causes losses to fruit-growers of no less than $10,000,000 annually. The moth, which hides by day and is seldom seen, has the fore wings marked with alternate irregular transverse wavy streaks of ash-gray and brown, with a large tawny spot on the inner hind angle, the hind wings and abdomen light yellowish brown with a satiny luster.  It lays its eggs (for the first generation, the species being two-brooded over most of the country) on the top of the newly forming apple, or sometimes, as recently observed in California, on the side of the tiny fruit.  The larvæ, hatching in from three to five days, begin to feed on the green fruit, soon burrowing into its center. They become full-grown before the apples ripen, burrow out and crawl

Fig. 543.—The eye-spotted bud-moth, *Tmetocera ocellana*. (After Lugger; natural size.)

Fig. 544. — The cranberry worm-moth, *Rhopobota vacciniana*. (After Lugger; natural size indicated by line.)

away to some crevice in the bark or sheltered place on the ground, and
there pupate. In two weeks the moths issue and deposit eggs on later
apples for the second brood. The larvæ of this brood are tucked away
in the fall and winter apples when gathered, and are thus carried with
them into cellars, warerooms, etc. They soon issue from the fruit, and
finding concealed spots in the cracks of barrels or boxes or elsewhere
near the stored apples, pupate, the pupæ lasting over the winter and
the moths issuing about apple-blossoming time the following spring. The
pupæ are protected by thin papery cocoons of silk spun by the larvæ. The
remedies are effective, but must be carefully and regularly used. Spraying
the young fruit with an arsenical mixture, as Paris green or London purple,
soon after the blossoms fall and again in about two weeks, will reduce
immensely the possible loss. Banding the tree with strips of old carpet or

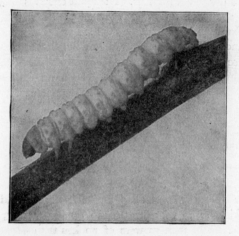

Fig. 545.—The larva or worm of the codlin-moth, *Carpocapsa pomonella*. (After
photograph by Slingerland; three times natural size.)

sacking at the time the larvæ are crawling out of the apples and hunting
for concealed places in which to pupate, will enable the grower to trap and
destroy thousands of them and thus greatly lessen the numbers in the second
brood. All fallen fruit should be promptly gathered and destroyed in such
a way as to kill the larvæ inside.

An interesting insect closely allied to the codlin-moth is the Mexican
jumping bean-moth, *Carpocapsa saltitans* (Fig. 547), which lays its eggs
on the green pods of a euphorbiaceous plant of the genus Croton. The
hatching larvæ bore into the growing beans in the pod, but do not attain
their full growth until after the beans are ripe and hard. The ripe beans
with the squirming larvæ inside act as if bewitched, twitching and jerking,
rolling over and leaping slightly clear of the table or desk on which they

may rest. The larvæ pupate within the beans, first gnawing a circular thin place through which the moth may push its way out. Another Tortricid moth, *Grapholitha sebastianæ*, has similar habits. Most of the jumping beans come from the Mexican province of Chihuahua.

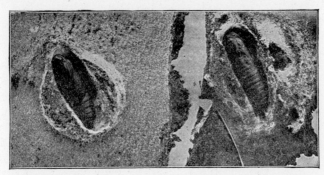

FIG. 546.—Pupæ, in cocoons, of codlin-moth, *Carpocapsa pomonella*. (After photograph by Slingerland; enlarged.)

A few moth families, represented in this country by but few species, may now be referred to briefly, chiefly for the sake of mentioning certain particular forms that are fairly common and wide-spread and hence likely to be taken by the collector.

The flannel-moth family, Megalopygidæ, includes but five North American species, of which the crinkled flannel-moth, *Lagoa crispata*, pale straw-yellow, with long, curling, woolly, brownish and blackish hairs, with wing expanse of about 1 inch, is not uncommon in the north Atlantic states, while *Megalopyge opercularis*, of about the same size, with yellowish-white fore wings overspread except at the tips by woolly purplish-brown hairs, is not uncommon in the southern states. The flannel-moth caterpillars have seven pairs

FIG. 547.—The Mexican jumping bean-moth, *Carpocapsa saltitans;* pupa, croton-bean from which moth has issued, and moth. (Natural size.)

of abdominal prop-legs instead of five, the number common to almost all other caterpillars, and the cocoons in which the pupæ lie have a hinged door for the exit of the moth. The larva of *M. opercularis* looks like an animated bit of cotton-wool or lock of white hair. That of *L. crispata* feeds particularly on blackberry, raspberry, and apple; it is nearly oval in shape, covered with evenly shorn brownish hairs, which form a ridge along the middle of the back. When about $\frac{3}{4}$ inch long it ceases to feed and spins a tough oval cocoon fastened securely to the side of a twig. The moth issues in the summer of the following year. The cocoon of *M. opercularis* so closely resembles a terminal bud of the Southern live-oak on which the caterpillars mostly feed that it is almost impossible to detect it, especially as both twigs and cocoons are covered with small bits of lichen.

Another small family, with thirty-three species, of interest because of the odd character of the larvæ, is that of the slug-caterpillar moths, the Eucleidæ (or Cochlidiidæ). The moths themselves are small and stout, mostly rather strikingly colored, with brown, apple-green, and cinnamon prevailing. The larvæ are slug-like, short, thick, nearly oblong and mostly spiny and gaudily colored. The spiny oak-slug, formidably armed with branching spines and common on oaks and willows in the east, is the larva of *Euclea delphinii*, a small, robust, deep-reddish-brown moth, with bright green spots on the wings. The saddle-back caterpillar, *Sibine* (Empretia) *stimulea*, has a striking squarish green blotch on the back, with an oval purplish spot in the middle. It has branching spiny hairs, which affect some persons like nettles, producing severe inflammation. It feeds on many plants, on oak and other forest trees in the east, and often on corn in the west. The moth is lustrous seal- and chocolate-brown, with a few small white dots on the wings. Another slug-caterpillar is the pale apple-green larva, with dorsal brown blotch, of *Prolimacodes* (Eulimacodes) *scapha*, a stout wood-brown moth, expanding one inch, with a curved silvery line on each fore wing, behind which the wing surface is paler than in front. None of the species of this family has been found west of the Rocky Mountains except in Texas. *Parasa chloris* has the fore wings brown at base and outer margin and elsewhere apple-green; the hind wings are clayey yellow. Its larva is bright scarlet with four blue-black lines along the back and with stinging yellow tubercles. It feeds on cherry, apple, and rose. *Euclea pænulata* has chocolate-brown fore wings with an irregular bright green elongate curving blotch, and the hind wings soft wood-brown.

The most extraordinary species in this family of moths with strange larvæ is the hag-moth, *Phobetron pithecium*, whose larva is one of the oddest known. It is nearly square, dark brown, and bears eight singular fleshy processes projecting from the sides. These processes, which are half as long as the larva itself, are covered with feathery brown hairs, among which are longer black, stinging hairs. Thus covered, and twisting curiously up and back, they resemble heavy locks of hair and give the name hag-moth to the species. The moth is rarely seen; it is dusky purplebrown with ocherous patches on the back and a light yellow tuft on each middle leg; the fore wings are variegated with pale yellowish brown, and crossed by a narrow wavy curved band of the same color; the hind wings are sable, bordered with yellowish in the female.

Much larger moths are the Cossidæ, or carpenter-moths, with slender, smooth, spindle-shaped bodies and long, narrow-pointed, strong wings like those of the hawk-moths (Sphingidæ). The larvæ are wood-borers, burrowing about in the heart-wood of locust- and other shade-trees and also of apple-, pear-, and other fruit-trees. The moths are mostly gray, vaguely patterned with white and blackish, although a few are conspicuously black-and-white spotted. They have no proboscis and hence can take no food. The moths fly at night and lay their eggs on the bark of the trees, the hatching, grub-like, naked larvæ burrowing into the hard wood, where they live for from two to four years, when they make in their tunnel a thin cocoon of silk and chewed wood to pupate within. When ready to transform, the pupa wriggles along the tunnel to its opening, so that the issuing moth finds itself in free air. The locust-tree carpenter-moth, *Prionoxystus robiniæ* (Fig. 549), or goat-moth, so called from its curious offensive odor, expanding $1\frac{1}{2}$ inches (males) to $2\frac{1}{2}$ inches (females), has gray wings with irregular black lines and spots in the female, and darker fore wings and yellowish hind wings in the male. Its larvæ feed on locust-trees and are often abun-

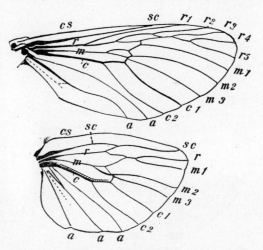

FIG. 548.—Venation of a Cossid, *Prionoxystus robiniæ*. *cs*, costal vein; *sc*, subcostal vein; *r*, radial vein; *m*, medial vein; *c*, cubital vein; *a*, anal veins. (After Comstock; enlarged.)

dant enough to do much injury. The wood leopard-moth, *Zeuzera pyrina*, is strikingly spotted with black on a white ground color, and is common in certain eastern cities, its larvæ infesting maples and other shade-trees. On the Pacific coast the poplar carpenter-moth, *Cossus populi*, with whitish fore wings shaded all over with blackish and irregular black lines, and hind wings yellowish gray, growing darker at the outer margin, is common, its larvæ infesting poplars and cottonwoods. There are only twenty species in North America belonging to this family.

Familiar curiosities of entomology are the moving bags of silk and bits of twigs and needles occasionally found in cedars, firs, and arbor vitæ. The "worms" which make these bags and carry them around, with all the body inside except the projecting head and thoracic legs, are the larvæ of the bag-worm moth, *Thyridopteryx ephemeræformis* (Fig. 550), the females of which are wingless, the males with blackish body and clear brown-veined wings which expand an inch. This moth is the most common and wide-spread of the thirteen moth species which constitute the family Psychidæ, as represented in this country. In the Southern States a common species is Abbott's bag-worm, *Oiketicus abbotti*, whose larvæ make bags with the bits of twigs fastened regularly transversely, the male moth expanding 1½ inches and being sable-brown with a clear bar in the middle of each fore wing. Smaller bag-worm moths are the three species of the genus Psyche, the males expanding from ½ inch to ⅘ inch, *P. confederata*, the best known, being all

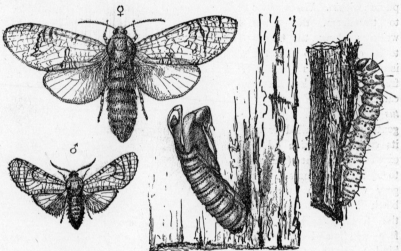

Fig. 549.—The locust-tree carpenter-moth, *Prionoxystus robiniæ*, male and female moths, young larva and empty pupal case. (After Lugger; moths and pupal case natural size; young larva enlarged.)

blackish with opaque wings, *P. gloveri*, a Southern species, dark brown through-out, and *P. carbonaria*, a Texas form, brownish black with subtranslucent wings. The females of all the Psychids are wingless. The larvæ, after moving about over the tree and feeding until full-grown, pupate within their bags, and the issuing wingless grub-like females simply remain in the sac until found by a flying male, after which they lay their eggs in the bag and die. The male Psychids can be readily distinguished from other moths by the growing together of the anal veins of the fore wings until they appear to be a single branching vein (Fig. 552).

The smoky-moths, Pyromorphidæ, of which but fifteen species occur in the United States, are small, expanding from ⅔ inch to 1 inch (a single Western species expands 1½ inches), and with blackish ground-color on body and wings, relieved by brilliant patches of red, yellow, and orange. They are favorites with collectors and, though few in number, are not at all uncommon. The larvæ feed on the leaves of various plants, but grape and Virginia creeper seem to be specially liked. Vineyards indeed often suffer from the presence in considerable numbers of smoky-moth caterpillars. These caterpillars often show a striking gregarious instinct, massing side by side in lines while feeding. The small black and yellow larvæ of *Harrisina americana*, a common Eastern species, may often be found arranged

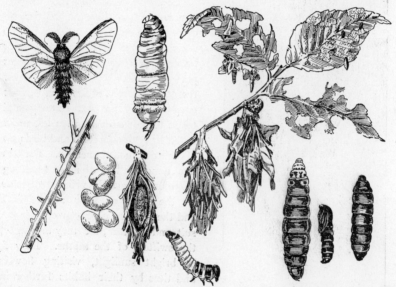

Fig. 550.—The bag-worm moth, *Thyridopteryx ephemeræformis;* eggs, larva, pupa bag containing larva, bag containing pupa, male moth. (After Felt; about natural size except the eggs.)

side by side in single line clear across a grape-leaf. Feeding, when young, only on the soft tissues of the leaves, they skeletonize them; when older, however, they eat everything but the larger veins. When full-grown they disperse, each finding a sheltered spot, where it makes a tough, oblong-oval cocoon of parchment-like silk, in which it pupates. The moth of this species expands one inch, is bluish or greenish black, with orange prothoracic collar broad above and narrow below, and narrow subtranslucent wings. It flies slowly and unevenly during the warmest, brightest hours of the day, frequenting flowers. *H. coracina,* found in Texas and Arizona, expands $\frac{4}{5}$ inch and is all dull black with a bluish tinge on the abdomen; *H. metallica,* the largest Pyromorphid, found in Texas and Arizona, expands $1\frac{3}{5}$ inches and is lustrous bluish green with orange prothorax. *Acoloithus falsarius*, one of the smallest members of the family, expanding $\frac{2}{3}$ inch, common in the East, is black with very narrow reddish collar. *Pyromorpha dimidiata*, expanding 1 inch, common in the Atlantic states, is black with translucent wings. The only other genus in the family so far unmentioned is Triprocris with eight species, all confined to the western states and all but two of them marked on body or wings with orange or yellowish.

Of unusual and often very deceptive appearance are the clear-wing moths, or Sesiidæ. With their often brightly colored black and yellow or red-banded tapering or plump bodies and partly or wholly clear wings, they resemble strongly, at first glance, wasps or bees, and are undoubtedly often taken to be such and thus left unmolested by both collectors and birds, two of their destructive enemies. For birds like almost all moths for food, and collectors especially prize the Sesians for the sake of their attractiveness and the sporting character of their pursuit and capture, for they are among the swiftest of the moths. They fly in bright sunlight, visiting flowers, and thus by their habits further increase their likeness to wasps and bees. There are one hundred species in the family in this country, and almost all have one or both wings partly or mostly clear, i.e., free from scales. A few moths of other families, as the clear-winged sphinges and others, have similarly partly clear wings, but the very narrow fore wings and widely expanded bases of the hind wings will distinguish the Sesians from the few other scattered clear-winged moths. The larvæ are borers, mining in roots of fruit-trees, the canes and roots of small fruits, or in the stems of herbaceous plants. They are grub-like and yellowish white, with darker head and legs. When abundant they become very injurious, the notorious peach-tree borers being probably the most serious insect enemy of the peach-tree.

FIG. 551.—Bag-worm; the larva of a moth that builds a protecting case out of silk and bits of sticks, in which its whole body except horny head, thorax, and legs is concealed. (Natural size.)

For one hundred and fifty years the peach, an imported plant, has suffered in this country from the ravages of this native pest. One Sesian species, *Sanninoidea exitiosa* (Fig. 554) is the peach-tree borer of the eastern states, and another, closely related, *S. pacifica*, works equal injury in the Pacific states. In both species the eggs (Fig. 555) are deposited on the trunk of the tree near its base, in July and August in the East, in April and May in California, and the young larvæ (Fig. 556), hatching after a week or ten days, immediately bore in through the outer bark and begin feeding on the live inner bark. When winter comes they cease feeding—in the East at least—and hibernate quiescent, being now about half-grown. In the spring they become active again, feed and grow rapidly, and by summer are ready to pupate.

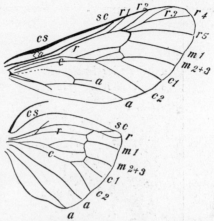

FIG. 552.—Diagram showing venation of wings of bag-worm moth, *Thyridopteryx ephemeræformis*. *cs*, costal vein; *sc*, subcostal vein; *r*, radial vein; *m*, medial vein; *c*, cubital vein; *a*, anal veins.

*Pacifica* begins pupating in California in February. For this they leave their burrows, come out to the surface of the bark, spin about themselves a thin silken cocoon and change (Fig. 557). The pupal stage lasts about three weeks, when the moths issue. The clear-winged male moths, expanding 1 inch, are deep steely-blue, with small golden-yellow markings on head and thorax and abdomen; the larger, heavier-bodied female, expanding $1\frac{1}{2}$ inches, has a broad orange band across the abdomen in the fourth or fifth segments, and has the front wings covered with blackish scales (Fig. 554). The remedy

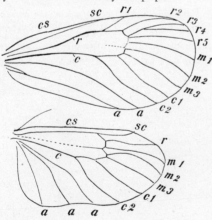

FIG. 553.—Venation of a Pyromorphid, *Pyromorpha dimidiata*. *cs*, costal vein; *sc*, subcostal vein; *r*, radial vein; *m*, medial vein; *c*, cubital vein; *a*, anal veins. (After Comstock; enlarged.)

for this pest is the application, by painting on, of gas tar to the basal part of the tree-trunk just before the flying and egg-laying time of the moths; this prevents the females from ovipositing on the treated trees.  Or the base of the trunk may have a newspaper tied about it.

FIG. 554.—Moths of the peach-tree borer, *Sanninoidea exitiosa*, the upper one and the one at the right being females.  (Photograph from life by Slingerland; natural size.)

The currant-borer, *Sesia tipuliformis*, expanding three-fourths of an inch, has a robust body with a fan-like tuft of scales at the posterior tip,

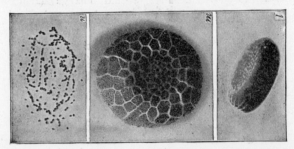

FIG. 555.—Eggs of peach-tree borer, *Sanninoidea exitiosa*.  (After Slingerland; natural size at *n*; one egg enlarged at *l*; micropyle end of egg greatly enlarged at *m*.)

dark abdomen ringed with yellow, and yellow lines on the thorax; the eggs are laid on currant-canes, and the hatching larvæ burrow into the center and then tunnel longitudinally in the pith.  They hibernate in the cane as larvæ, not pupating until the following summer, when the moths escape through holes in the cane thoughtfully made by the strong-jawed larvæ before pupation. The grape-vine-root borer, *Memythrus polistiformis*, looks much like a large Polistes wasp, having a dark body with two bright yellow

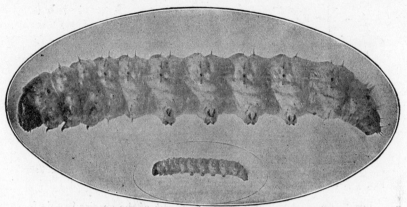

FIG. 556.—Larva of peach-tree borer, *Sanninoidea exitiosa.* (After Slingerland; natural size and much enlarged.)

narrow bands about the abdomen; the fore wings are brownish black, the hind wings clear; the larvæ bore in the roots of wild and cultivated grapes and pupate underground. The raspberry-root borer, *Bembecia marginata*, is also very waspish in appearance, with its black body repeatedly banded

FIG. 557.—Cocoons and empty pupal skins of the peach-tree borer, *Sanninoidea exitiosa*. (After Slingerland; natural size.)

with yellow and transparent fore and hind wings. The eggs are laid on raspberry canes, and the larvæ, first boring into the cane, finally work down into the roots. Squashes are often badly injured by having their stems tunneled by the larvæ of the squash-vine borer, *Melittia ceto*, a Sesian with olive-brown fore wings, clear hind wings, and black or bronze abdomen,

marked with red or orange, and with the hind legs fringed with long hairs,
orange on the outer surface and black on the inner. When full grown the
larvæ leave the stems and go into the soil to cocoon and pupate. The genus

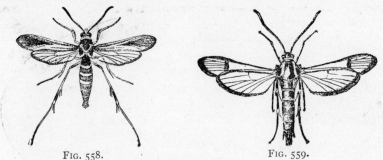

FIG. 558.                                    FIG. 559.

FIG. 558.—The ash-tree borer, *Trochilium fraxini*. (After Lugger; natural size.)
FIG. 559.—*Sesia pictipes*, male. (After Lugger; natural size.)

Sesia (Fig. 563) contains over half (fifty-seven) of the species in this family;
they are found in all parts of the country.

    The family Notodontidæ, comprising the puss-moths, handmaid-moths,
and prominents, is represented in
this country by about ninety-five
species, all of medium size, i.e., with
a wing expanse of from $1\frac{1}{4}$ to 2
inches, and but few of such marked
patterns as to be particularly conspicuous or attractive to collectors.
The name " prominents," sometimes
applied collectively to the moths of
this family, is based on the occurrence in some of them of an angulated or tooth-like projection near
the middle of the hinder margin of
the fore wings. Probably the most
familiar species in this family are
the Datanas, or handmaid-moths;
certainly their larvæ are more often
seen and are better known, under
the names of yellow-necked apple-
tree caterpillars and walnut caterpillars, than the larvæ of any other

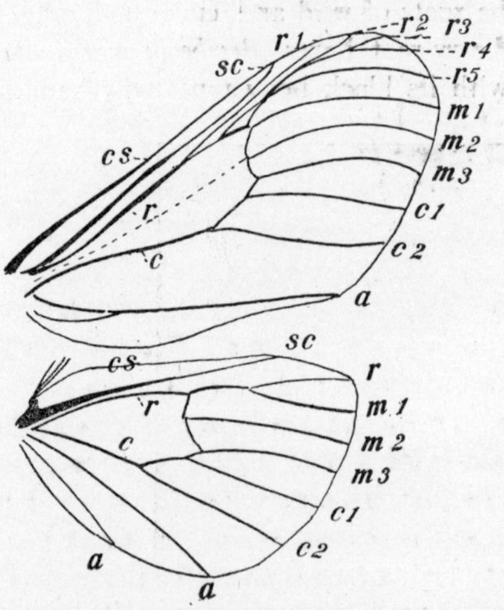

FIG. 560.—Venation of a Notodontid, *Noto-
donta stragula*. *cs*, costal vein; *sc*, subcostal vein; *r*, radial vein; *m*, medial
vein; *c*, cubital vein; *a*, anal veins.
(After Comstock; enlarged.)

Notodontids. Sometimes there may be seen on the trunk of an apple- or
other shade-tree an animated bunch or mass of hundreds of caterpillars,

reddish black with conspicuous yellow longitudinal stripes, each caterpillar curiously jerking its body or resting quietly with both head and body tip held up nearly at right angles to the middle part with its four pairs of clinging prop-legs. These are Datana larvæ, which have come down from their feeding on the leaves of the tree to moult. The jerking frightens away in some measure the numerous parasitic Tachina flies which are always ready to attend on a gathering of this sort and lay a few eggs where they will do the Tachina species the most good, that is, on the body of these plump caterpillars, so

FIG. 561.—The red-humped cater-pillar-moth, *Œdemasia eximia.* (After Packard; natural size.)

that the hatching Tachina grub can burrow into this well-nourished body and feed on its living tissues. When feeding in the tree-tops, too, the Datana

FIG. 562.—Larva of red-humped caterpillar-moth, *Œdemasia eximia.* (After Packard; natural size.)

caterpillars keep closely together, forming rows or files of voracious feeders arranged neatly across each attacked leaf. The common species infesting the apple is *Datana ministra*, and the larvæ have a distinguishing dull orange

FIG. 563. — *Heterocampa guttivitta.* (After Packard; natural size.)

spot on the back of the first body-ring behind the head. The eggs, which are white and spherical, are laid, from 70 to 100 by each female, on the leaves, all cemented well together in neat patches. When the larvæ are full grown they descend from the tree, burrow into the soil for two or three inches, and change to naked brown chrysalids, which last over winter, the moths emerging in the following summer. The moth, expanding. $1\frac{1}{2}$ inches, is reddish or yellowish brown, with the fore wings crossed by from three to five darker brown lines, the outer margin and one or two spots near the middle also being darker; the hind wings are pale yellow and not patterned. The species common on walnuts and hickories is *Datana angusii*, with fore wings varying from chocolate to deep smoky brown, with transverse lines like those of *ministra;* the hind wings are

FIG. 564.—Larva of *Heterocampa guttivitta*. (After Packard; natural size.)

paler brown. The caterpillars are black, with dirty-white hairs and with three equidistant, very narrow, pale-yellow or whitish stripes on each side and three yellow stripes on the under side; when full grown it is a little more than 2 inches long.

Another conspicuous Notodontid larva occurring on apple-trees is a greenish-yellow black-striped caterpillar with a coral-red head and prominent hump on the back of the fourth body-ring. This is the larva (Fig. 562) of the red-humped caterpillar-moth, *Œdemasia concinna* (Fig. 561), a darkish-brown moth expanding about 1½ inches, the fore wings having a darker brown spot near the middle, a spot near each angle, and several longitudinal streaks along the hinder margin.

The puss-moths, Cerura, are readily distinguishable by their characteristic black and white wings, white being the ground color, with two broad, not sharply defined blackish bars across the fore wing, one across the disk, the other, often incomplete posteriorly, across the apex. Along the outer margin of each wing there is a row of distinct small black points. The larvæ (Fig. 793) of Cerura are extraordinary creatures: short, thick, naked body, tapering behind to a kind of forked tail which is held up at an angle with the rest of the body. This tail, which is an organ of defence, consists of two tubes, within each of which is concealed a long orange-colored extensile thread which can be thrust out and drawn in at will. When disturbed, the puss-moth caterpillar thrusts out these vivid tails, waving them threateningly, at the same time giving off a strong odor. It also telescopes its head and front two thoracic segments into the large, humped, third segment, which is so shaped and marked as to suggest some formidable large-eyed creature quite unlike a soft-bodied toothsome caterpillar. With little doubt this elaborate terrifying but actually harmless equipment avails to frighten off many of Cerura's enemies. The larva of a common puss-moth species feeds on wild cherry. When ready to pupate the caterpillars gnaw out a shallow cavity or depression in the wood which they lie in and over which they spin an oval silken net mixed with particles of wood, which makes it almost indistinguishable from the rest of the wood surface. These moths seem to carry very far expedients of Nature for protection by deceit. Other common members of the family are the several species of Schizura, moths strongly resembling owlet-moths (Noctuidæ) with their brown and gray and gray and blackish finely variegated fore wings and unmarked silky white wings. Their brown or greenish larvæ, which feed on fruit-trees, forest trees, small fruits, and other shrubby plants, are distinguished by having a prominent horn or spined tubercle on the fourth body-ring behind the head. They are said to eat out a notch about the size of the body, in the edge of a leaf, fitting themselves along this notch, so that the prominent tubercle and other irregularities of the body seem to simulate the rounded edge of the leaf; they are thus well concealed. The moths, too, are much given to dissimulation. Each moth rests on the trunk or branches of the tree,

FIG. 565.—Canker-worms, larvæ of a geometrid moth.  (After Slingerland;  natural size.)

head downward, with wings closely folded around the body and legs all drawn together, the dull-gray tone of the wings with their bits of lichen-green and whitish color giving the whole a marvelous resemblance to a bit of rough-weathered bark.

Familiar to all observers, although certainly not very often seen and rarely found in large numbers, are the inchworms, spanworms, or loopers as they are variously called, which are the larvæ (caterpillars) (Fig. 565) of the moths of the superfamily Geometrina (earth-measurers). These three common names as well as the scientific one refer to the peculiar mode of locomotion affected by all the Geometrina. Each loop or step is made by the bringing forward of the caudal extremity of the body quite to the thoracic feet, the portion of flexible body between bending up and out of the way each time during the process. The reason for it all will be understood when the inch-worm is examined. It differs from other lepidopterous larvæ in lacking the front three of the four pairs of prop-legs normally belonging to the middle part of the body, which is thus rendered helpless in walking, and the curious looping gait is the outcome of the possession by a long slender flexible body of only anterior and posterior locomotory organs (Fig. 566). Why inchworms are not more often seen, although there

Fig. 566.—Lime-tree inch-worm, larva of the geometrid moth, *Hibernia tiliaria*. (After Pettit; twice natural size.)

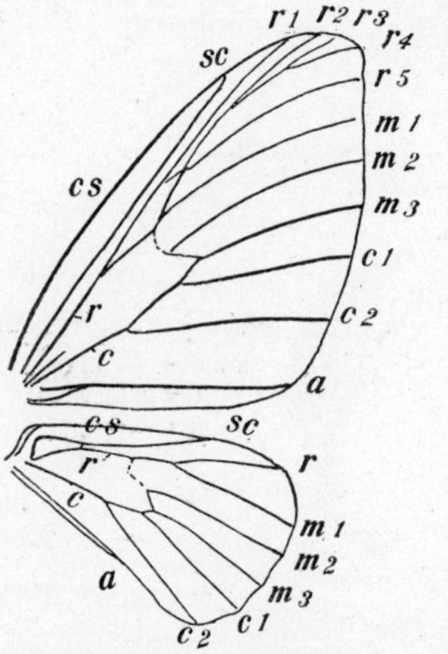

are hosts of different kinds of them and they are well distributed and common all over the country, is due to their habit of "going stiff" when disturbed, clinging by the hinder two pairs of legs to the twig or leaf and holding the rest of the body motionless and rigid at an angle with the support. As the body is always protectively colored and marked, so as to harmonize thoroughly with the habitual surroundings many an inch-worm may be *seen* but not *distinguished* from the leaf or branch on which it rests. Indeed, many of the inchworms are amazingly like a short or broken twig, with buds or leaf scars and lined or scaly bark, a very effective case of protective resemblance.

Fig. 567.—Venation of a geometrid, *Dyspepteris abortivaria*. *cs*, costal vein; *sc*, subcostal vein; *r*, radial vein; *m*, medial vein; *c*, cubital vein; *a*, anal veins. (After Comstock; enlarged.)

The geometer-moths, of which we have 800 species in this country, while of course presenting a great variety of coloration and pattern yet possess a likeness of general appearance due mostly to the slenderness of body compared with the broadness of wings, the impression of fragility or thinness of wings due to the unusually fineness of the covering scales, and the delicate and quiet coloration and patterning, which indicate their identity pretty effectively. Some are small, i.e., less than 1 inch expanse, and a few large, i.e., over 2 inches expanse, but most are of medium size, with white, delicate green, soft yellowish, brownish, grayish, and blackish as predominating color tones, and delicate wavy or zigzagging transverse lines, or point-like spots as characteristic pattern markings. The superfamily is divided into five families based on venational characters rather confusing and apparently not surely indicative of natural relationships. We may content our-

FIG. 568.—Male and female lime-tree canker-moths, *Hibernia tiliaria.* (After Jordan and Kellogg; twice natural size.)

selves with brief reference to some of the more interesting, beautiful, or economically important species.

The best-known Geometrids of economic importance are the canker-worms (Fig. 565), two species in particular, known as the spring canker-worm (*Paleacrita vernata*) and the fall canker-worm (*Anisopteryx pometaria*), being responsible for much damage to orchards, especially apple-orchards. The females of the canker-worm moths are wingless and so have to climb the trees to lay their eggs on the branches and twigs. This fact naturally suggests the most effective remedy for them, namely, banding the trees with tar (mixed with oil to prevent its drying) so as to make effective barriers against them as they crawl upward. Printers' ink, refuse sorghum, or any slow-drying varnish is equally effective. From the eggs laid in the spring by Paleacrita and in the fall by Anisopteryx hatch active

FIG. 569.—*Dyspepteris abortivaria.* (After Lugger; natural size.)

little ·"loopers" which feed voraciously in the foliage. The eggs of the fall canker-worm do not hatch until the following spring, just when the young apple-leaves begin to unfold. The full-grown canker-worms are about 1 inch long, greenish brown and striped longitudinally with pale yellow. Some of these stripes are broad on the fall canker-worm; all are narrow on the other species. When full grown the larvæ crawl down the tree to the ground, burrow into it and pupate in a thin silver cocoon. The males of both species are winged delicate moths; Paleacrita has pale ash-colored or brownish-gray, silky, almost transparent fore wings with four or five broken transverse dark lines; Anisopteryx has glossy brownish fore wings crossed by two irregular whitish bands.

Among the Geometrids are numerous species whose wings are green, the shades varying, but usually with a strong admixture of whitish and also

FIG. 570.                                        FIG. 571.

FIG. 570.—The pepper-and-salt currant-moth, *Eubyia cognataria*. (After Packard; natural size.)

FIG. 571.—*Phigalia strigataria*, the female wingless. (After Lugger; natural size.)

usually barred more or less distinctly with narrow or broader whitish lines. *Geometra iridaria* is such a species common in the East in which the green is very light in tone; *Dyspepteris abortivaria* (Fig. 569) is bluish green and

FIG. 572.                     FIG. 573.                     FIG. 574.

FIG. 572.—The large blue-striped looper, *Biston ypsilon*. (After Forbes; natural size.)

FIG. 573.—The common Cymatophora, *Cymatophora pampinaria*. (After Lugger; natural size.)

FIG. 574.—The plum-geometer, *Eumacaria brunneraria*. (After Lugger; natural size.)

has a grape-feeding larva. The raspberry geometer, *Synchlora glaucaria*, has delicate pale-green wings with two transverse whitish lines; its larvæ feed in the fruit and leaves of raspberries and blackberries and cover over

FIG. 575.—The currant fruit-worm moth, *Eupithecia interruptofasciata*. (After Lugger; natural size.)

the body with bits of vegetable matter like minute pieces of flowers, etc., until it seems to be only a tiny heap of débris. The snow-white Eugonia, *Ennonos subsignarius*, is pure white, expanding an inch and a half; its larvæ feed often destructively on the foliage of elms, lindens, and apple-trees. *Angerona crocataria* (Fig. 576) is a beautiful sulphur-yellow Geometrid, expanding 1½ inches, with a number of irregular pinkish-brown blotches on the wings; its yellowish-green larvæ feed on currants, gooseberries, and strawberries, both wild and cultivated. *Calocalpe undulata* (Fig. 578), the scallop-shell moth, has pale yellowish-brown wings crossed by many fine zigzag darker lines close together; its larvæ feed on wild cherry and live gregariously inside of a nest formed of leaves tied together by silken threads. A very common little moth in meadows and gardens in summer and fall is the chickweed-geometer, *Hæmatopis grataria*, with reddish-

FIG. 576.          FIG. 577.          FIG. 578.

FIG. 576.—The currant-angerona, *Angerona crocataria*. (After Lugger; natural size.)
FIG. 577.—The currant-endropia, *Endropia armataria*. (After Lugger; natural size.)
FIG. 578.—The scallop-shell geometer, *Calocalpe undulata*. (After Lugger; natural size.)

yellow wings and two transverse bands and the outer margins pinkish. The chain-dotted geometer, *Caterva catenaria*, expanding 1½ inches, with white wings dotted with fine black points arranged in two lines and with a few extra ones, appears sometimes, according to Lugger, in such very great numbers as to look like a snow-storm; its larvæ are pale straw-yellow with two fine lines on the back and two on each side interrupted by two

FIG. 579.—The diverse-lined geometer, *Petrophora diversilineata*. (After Lugger; natural size.)

large black dots, a pair on each segment; it feeds on hazel, blackberry, raspberry, and other plants.

A great host of somber-colored moths, blackish, grayish, or brownish, with no conspicuous markings and only rarely any bright colors, compose for the most part the family Noctuidæ, the largest of all the families of moths. Twenty-one hundred North American species—three times as many as there are North American species of birds—belong to the single family Noctuidæ, and for the most part these two thousand mixed species must be as one to the general collector and amateur. Few professional entomologists, indeed, lay claim to a systematic knowledge of the group, or even care to give to it the time necessary to acquire such a knowledge. Some of the

Noctuids have come into prominence because of the destructive vegetable-feeding habits of their larvæ; such are the cutworm-moths, the army-worm moths, the cotton-worm moths, and others, and these species are so often described and pictured that they are fairly well known. Other small groups, of which the interesting Catocalas, the red and yellow under-wings (Fig. 580), are the most conspicuous, have attracted the attention of collectors because of particular habits or patterns, and these are fairly

FIG. 580.—A group of red and yellow underwings; upper moth, *Catocala palæogama;* lower left-hand corner, *Catocala ultronia;* lower right-hand corner, *Catocala grynea.* (After Lugger; natural size.)

well known. Few moth-collectors but have "sugared" for Catocalas, those large night-flyers, somber of fore wing but brilliant of hind wing, that can be so readily attracted and taken by a bait of molasses and stale beer smeared in patches on the trunks of trees in summer-time. The fore wings harmonize in color, shades, and pattern so thoroughly with the bark that when the Catocala rests, as it does during the daytime, on tree-trunks with its brilliant hind wings, strikingly banded with red, yellow, white, or black, covered by the fore wings, it is simply indistinguishable. The Catocala larvæ are curious creatures, with body thick in the middle and tapering towards both ends. The larvæ of *Catocala ultronia* (Fig. 581) feed on plum-tree leaves; they are about 1½ inches long, grayish brown, with two or four small reddish tubercles on each body-segment, a small fleshy horn on the back of the ninth segment and on the back of the twelfth segment a low fleshy ridge tinted behind with reddish brown. It descends to the ground when ready to pupate, making a flimsy cocoon of silk under a dead leaf or chip. The pupa inside the cocoon is covered with a bluish flour-like dust or "bloom." The moth has the forewings rich amber with a broad indefinite ashy band along the middle and several brown and

Fig. 581.—The plum-tree Catocala, *Catocala ultronia*, moth and larva. (After Lugger; natural size.)

white transverse lines; the hind wings are deep red with a wide black band along the outer margin and a narrower one across the middle. The eggs are laid in cracks of the bark in summer. *Catocala grynea* (Fig. 580), with grayish brown forewings marked with zigzag lines of rich brown and gray short dark-brown streaks on the front margin and with hind wings reddish yellow crossed by two wavy black bands, is called the apple-tree Catocala, because the ashen-brown caterpillar feeds on apple-leaves. The two front pairs of abdominal prop-legs of all the Catocala caterpillars are much smaller than the hinder two pairs, hence the caterpillar has a sort of looping gait like that of the Geometrid larvæ, the inchworms. *Catocala relicta* has the fore wings grayish white with several indefinite transverse black bands, and the hind wings black with one curving white band. *Catocala epione* has blackish-brown fore wings with wavy narrow black and lighter brown transverse lines with black hind wings narrowly margined with white.

The largest and most interesting Noctuid, and indeed one of the largest of all the moths, is the curious rare species *Erebus odora*, called the black witch; it expands 6 inches and has both wings blackish brown with many indefinite wavy lines of black and of lighter brown; in the hinder angle of the hind wings are two incomplete eye-spots bounded in front by a curving velvety black line, and on each fore wing is a single irregular eye-spot near the front margin.

"Cutworm" is the name applied to the smooth, "greasy," plump caterpillars of numerous species (representing several genera) of Noctuids. The greasy cutworm, dull blackish brown with pale longitudinal lines attacks all sorts of garden products and other low-growing plants; it is the larva

FIG. 582.—Green-fruit worms, *Xylina grotei*, at left, and *Xylina antennata* at right. (Photograph by Slingerland; natural size.)

of *Agrotis ypsilon*, with brownish-gray fore wings bearing an ypsilon-shaped mark, the hind wings being silky white. The climbing cutworm, *Carneades scandens*, an active climber and great enemy of nurseries and orchards, is light yellowish gray with a dark line along the back and fainter ones along the sides; the moth has light bluish-gray fore wings with darker markings and pearly-white hind wings. Cutworms mostly hide in cracks or burrow in the ground by day, feeding during the night; they will often cut off young plants just at the ground, or will ascend tall trees and feed on the buds and young leaves. When ready to pupate they burrow into the soil and the moths issue in midsummer.

The members of the large genus Plusia (Pl. VIII, Fig. 7), including some of the commonest Noctuids, are recognizable by a small silvery comma-shaped spot on the disk of each fore wing. Another large genus is that of Cucullia, the hooded owlets, in which the thorax bears a prominent tuft of scales and the fore wings are marked with irregular blackish dashes. The

FIG. 583.—Army-worms, larvæ of *Leucania unipuncta*, on corn. (Photograph by Slingerland; natural size.)

dagger-moth Acronycta (Figs. 586 and 587), so called from the rather uncertain small black dagger-like markings of the fore wings, have the larva in some species covered with long colored stiff hairs; the familiar caterpillar

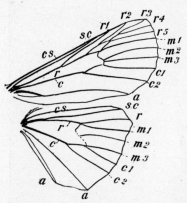

of *A. americana* is densely clothed with yellow hairs, besides bearing a pair of long black pencils on the first abdominal segment, another pair on the third, and a single pencil on the eighth. It feeds on the leaves of elm, maple, and other trees, and when at rest curls sidewise on a leaf.

The army-worm (Fig. 583), a black, yellow, and green striped caterpillar that occurs over nearly all the country and often appears in enormous numbers, causing great losses to grain-fields, is the larva of a dull-brown moth, *Leucania unipuncta*, marked in the center of each fore wing with a distinct white spot. Perhaps as severe a sufferer as any other field product from the attacks of Noctuid larvæ is cotton. The cotton-

FIG. 584. — Venation of a Noctuid, *Agrotis ypsilon*. *cs*, costal vein; *sc*, subcostal vein; *r*, radial vein; *m*, medial vein; *c*, cubital vein; *a*, anal veins. (After Comstock; enlarged.)

worm, *Aletia argillacea*, feeds on the foliage of the cotton-plants and the cotton boll-worm, *Heliothis armigera*, attacks the cotton pods or bolls. These two caterpillars cause losses to the cotton-growing states of millions of dollars

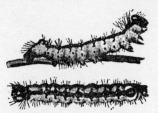

FIG. 585.  FIG. 586.

FIG. 585.—Larvæ of the gray dagger-moth, *Acronycta occidentalis*. (After Lugger; natural size.)

FIG. 586.—Gray dagger-moth, *Acronycta occidentalis*. (After Lugger; natural size.)

every year. The cotton boll-worm is more or less familiar in states farther north, under the name of corn-worm, where it is found feeding on ears of green corn and on tomatoes. It is a naked, greenish-brown, dark-striped caterpillar. The moth has pale clay-yellow fore wings with a greenish tint, the hind wings paler.

Among the most conspicuous of all the caterpillars are the not unfamiliar larvæ of the tussock-moths, Lymantriidæ, one common species infesting our

# PLATE VI.

## MOTHS.

1 = Catocala parta.
2 = Basilona imperialis.
3 = Apanresis virgo.
4 = Pseudohazis eglanterina.
5 = Automeris io.

PLATE VI

*Mary Wellman, del.*

shade-trees in town and country and another, less common, attacking orchards and forest-trees. The caterpillars (Fig. 588) of *Hemerocampa leucostigma*, the white-marked tussock-moth, which is the shade-tree species, are about 1¼ inches long, very hairy, bright yellow with a blackish stripe along the back and one along each side, but chiefly conspicuous by a series of four cream-colored dense tufts of vertical hairs on the back, three long black hair pen-

cils, two on the front part and one on the hind part of the body, and by the coral-red head and similarly colored two small pro-tuberances on the sixth and seventh abdom-inal segment which are scent-organs used to repel enemies. When full-grown these caterpillars pull the hairs from their body and mixing them with some silk make a grayish cocoon on the tree-trunks. The fe-male moth is wingless, light gray in color,

FIG. 587. — The raspberry dagger-moth, *Acronycta impressa*. (After Lugger; natural size.)

and unusually long-legged for a moth; when issued she simply crawls out of the cocoon and lays her 300 to 500 eggs covered by a frothy-looking but firm sub-stance in a grayish mass on the outside of it. The males are ashy gray and have broad short wings, expanding 1¼ inches, the fore wings with darker wavy transverse bands, a small black spot near the tip, an oblique blackish stripe beyond it, and a minute white crescent near the outer hinder angle. The antennæ are feathery, and the

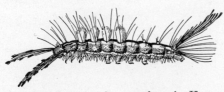

FIG. 588.—Larva of the tussock-moth, *Hemero-campa leucostigma*. (After Felt, natural size.)

fore legs tufted with hairs. The best remedy for these pests is to gather the egg-masses in the winter and put them into a box with its top covered by mosquito-netting. In the spring the larvæ and the egg parasites which are numerous will hatch; the minute parasites will escape through the netting to go on with their good work, while the moths will be retained in the box and may be killed.

The orchard and fruit-tree species, *Parorgyia parallela*, the parallel-lined tussock-moth, is winged in both sexes, the moths being dark gray with darker-colored wavy lines and spots. The caterpillars are gray with lon-gitudinal black stripes; short black tussocks are found on the back of seg-ments 4 to 7, a pair of long black pencils is at each end of the body, and on the back of each of segments 9 and 10 is a small pale-yellow scent-cup. The head is shining black. It feeds especially on plum-, crabapple-, and oak-trees.

The most notorious member of the Noctuidæ is the gypsy-moth, *Porthetria dispar*, a European species brought to Massachusetts in 1868, and from 1890 to 1900 fought at the public expense. A gentleman living in Medford, a town of Massachusetts, imported a number of different kinds of European silk-spinning caterpillars in an attempt to find some species which might be bred in this country in place of the mulberry silkworm (*Bombyx mori*). Some of the moths escaped from his breeding-cages, and among them some gypsy-moths. In a very few years the species had increased to such numbers and spread throughout such an extent of woods that it seriously threatened the destruction of all the forest- and shade-trees in northeastern Massachusetts. By 1891 it was causing great injury to forest-trees over 200 square miles. So far it has been confined because of the wholesale operations against it. The State has employed as many as 570 men at a time in spraying, egg-collecting, trunk-banding, etc., in the great fight

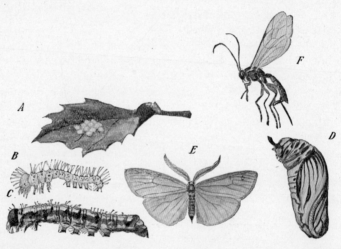

Fig. 589.—The California oak-worm moth, *Phryganidia californica*. *A*, eggs on leaf; *B*, just-hatched larva; *C*, full-grown larva; *D*, pupa, or chrysalid; *E*, moth; *F*, *Pimpla behrendsii*, parasite of the larva. (*B*, much enlarged; *D* and *F*, twice natural size; others natural size.)

against the pest and up to 1900 had expended over a million dollars in the struggle. The caterpillar when full grown is 1½ inches long, creamy white, thickly sprinkled with black, with dorsal and lateral tufts of long black and yellowish hairs. The cocoon is very slight, merely a few silky threads. The male moths, expanding 1½ to 2 inches, are brownish yellow with smoky fore wings bearing darker irregular transverse lines and pale hind wings with darker outer margins. The females are large, expanding 2½ inches, and creamy white in color, with irregular transverse gray or blackish lines.

In California is found a pretty pale-brownish moth that flutters weakly about the live-oak trees in early summer and late autumn, which has the distinction of being the only North American species in the family Dioptidæ. The larvæ of this moth feed chiefly on the leaves of the live-oaks and white oaks in the California valleys and the species may be called the live-oak moth, *Phryganidia californica* (Fig. 589). The moths expand about 1 inch and are uniformly pale brownish, with thinly scaled and hence almost translucent wings. The male has a small yellowish-white ill-defined blotch on the center of each fore wing. The eggs are laid by the early summer brood of moths on the under side of the leaves of the oaks and the naked light-yellowish black-striped larvæ feed until October 1st on the tough leaves. Then they crawl down to the tree-trunks or to near-by fences or logs and change to a naked greenish-white or yellowish chrysalid with many black lines and blotches. The moths issue in from ten to twelve days after pupation and lay their eggs again on the oak-leaves. But here is a curious fact. All the eggs laid on white-oak leaves by these autumn moths are doomed to death because just at the hatching-time the white-oak leaves fall and dry. The live-oak retains its leaves all winter and the larvæ hatched on them feed and grow slowly through the winter, pupating in May and issuing as moths about June 1st. Thus each year about one-fourth of the eggs laid by this species are wasted. The larvæ from the eggs laid on the white oaks in the spring live because they have white-oak leaves all summer to feed on, but those of the fall brood which hatch on the white oaks all die. In some seasons this insect is so abundant as to defoliate the oak-trees in certain localities twice during the year, but whenever the caterpillars get so numerous a certain small slender ichneumon-fly, *Pimpla behrendsii*, which lives parasitically on them becomes also very abundant (there being plenty of food for its young) and soon checks the increase of the moth. Out of 144 chrysalids of the moth which I once gathered but 11 moths issued, 99 of the chrysalids giving forth ichneumon-flies and the rest dying from other causes. I have found the caterpillar most abundant on the live-oaks (*Q. agrifolia*), but it occurs also on *Q. lobata*, *Q. kelloggii*, *Q. dumosa*, and *Q. douglassi*, *Q. chrysolepsis*.

A family represented in this country by only four species is the Pericopidæ. Three of these species are found only in the western states, the fourth in Florida. The single species of the four at all familiar to collectors is the beautiful and abundant *Gnophæla latipennis*, with its two or three varieties. This moth expands about 2 inches and is black, with two large white blotches on the fore wing, each blotch subdivided by the black veins running through it and single large blotch on the hind wing. A variety common in California has the blotches smaller and pale yellowish.

The wood-nymph moths, Agaristidæ, of which about two dozen species are found in North America, include a few strikingly patterned moths not at all uncommon. The moth known as the eight-spotted forester, *Alypia octo-maculata* (Pl. VIII, Fig. 5; also Fig. 590), is common in the Atlantic states;

FIG. 590.—Three eight-spotted forest-moths, *Alypia 8-maculata*, and one beautiful wood-nymph, *Eudryas grata* (the lowest). (After Lugger; natural size.)

it expands about 1¼ inches, has deep blue-black wings, with two large sub-circular whitish-yellow spots on each wing, the spot nearest the base on the hind wing being much larger than the outer one. The patagia (shoulder-lappets) are often yellow and the legs marked with orange. The larvæ, which are light brown with many fine black lines and one broad orange band across each segment and head and cervical shield deep orange with black dots, feed on the Virginia creeper, sometimes on the grape, and often are so abundant as to injure the plants seriously. The caterpillar is nearly 1½ inches long when full-grown, and burrows into soft or rotten wood to pupate, or failing this pupates on or just below the surface of the ground.

The beautiful wood-nymph, *Eudryas grata* (Fig. 590) (classed by some entomologists with the Noctuidæ), is very different in color and pattern, having milk-white fore wings broadly bordered and marked with brownish purple and with two indistinct brownish spots in the center. The under surface of these wings is reddish yellow. The hind wings are yellow with a pale purplish-brown border. The head is black and there is a wide black stripe along the back of the thorax, breaking up into a series of spots along the abdomen. The caterpillar is much like that of the eight-spotted forester and feeds on the same plants. "The moth, which is active at night and sometimes attracted to electric lights in large numbers, is very often discovered during the day upon the surface of the leaves of its food-plants. Its closed wings form a steep roof over its back, and its four legs, which have a curious muff-like tuft of white hairs, are protruded and give the insect a very peculiar appearance."

The grape-vine Epimenis, *Psychomorpha epimenis*, is a small velvety black Agaristid moth with a broad, irregularly lunate, white patch across the outer third of the fore wing and a somewhat larger and more regular patch of orange-red or brick-red on the hind wings. Its bluish caterpillar feeds on grape-leaves.

Delicate and pretty are the little footman-moths, Lithosiidæ, in their liveries of drab or slate, yellow or scarlet, and with their slender bodies and trimly narrow fore wings. The larvæ of but few species are known; they mostly feed on lichens and have the body covered with short stiff hairs. Because these caterpillars are not injurious but little attention has been given to the life-history of the footman-moths, and the amateur has here an opportunity to add to our knowledge of insects in an order popularly supposed to be pretty well "worked out."

The moths themselves although few in number of species are well distributed over the country, although the southwestern and Pacific states have really more than their share. Two common eastern species are the striped footman, *Hypoprepia miniata*, and the painted footman, *H. fuscosa*, each expanding about 1 inch. The first is brick-scarlet, with two longitudinal broad plumbeous bars and the distal half of a third on the fore wing and a broad outer slaty border on the hind wings. The latter has almost the same pattern, but the ground color is distinctly yellowish red in place of scarlet or brown-red. Another common eastern Lithosiid is the pale footman, *Crambidia pallida*, expanding nearly 1 inch and drab all over; *C. cephalica*, found in Colorado and Arizona, expanding not quite an inch, has both wings and the whole body of a delicate shining silvery white. The banded footman, *Cisthene* (Ozonadia) *unifascia*, found all along the Atlantic and Gulf coasts, expands ¾ inch and has the fore wings dark with a narrow curving yellow band and the hind wings with the base and disk pink or yellowish, the apex being dark. *Lithosia* (Lexis) *bicolor*, found in the northern states and Canada, expands nearly 1½ inches and is slate-colored, with yellow on the front margin of the fore wings, the tip of the abdomen, the prothorax, and the palpi. The several Rocky Mountain and desert species mostly have brick-red or drab or slaty ground color, some unmarked and some with dark border on the hind wings if red is the ground color, and smoky-whitish hind wings if body and fore wings are drab or slaty.

Another family of moths expanding about an inch, and with a characteristic habitus due to the long narrow fore wings, the small size of the hind wings, and the contrasting colors of the wing-pattern, are the Zygænidæ, or Syntomidæ, as the newer nomenclature names them. In the hind wing, veins subcosta and radius are fused, usually for the whole length. About twenty species of the family are found in this country, and because, as with the Lithosiidæ, the larvæ are not of much economic importance the life-history of but few of the species is known. The majority of the species, besides, live in the western and southwestern states, and like other mountain, plain, and desert insects are hardly known except in their flying stage. The larvæ of some species feed on grasses, of others on lichens.

One of the most striking species is *Cosmosoma auge*, found in the extreme south, which has both fore and hind wings clear of scales over the base and disk only, a border all around the veins, and a small black patch at the tip of the discal cell of the fore wing covered with black scales. The plump body is scarlet, with the end of the abdomen and a dorsal longitudinal band on it metallic blue-black. The wings expand 1 inch. Lycomorpha is a genus of small Zygænids characterized by having the wings colored in two strongly contrasting shades, black and brick-red or black and reddish yellow. In *L. pholus* the basal two-fifths of each wing is yellow and all the rest black; in *L. miniata* the basal two-thirds is red, the rest black; in *L. grotei* all of the fore wing is red except a narrow black border on the outer margin, while the anterior half of the hind wings is red, the posterior half black. Ctenucha is a genus of larger species which have smoky-brown wings unmarked, as in *C. virginica*, a northeastern species, which has a yellow head and metallic bluish-black body, *C. multifaria* and *C. ruberoscapus*, Pacific coast species which have a coral-red head and shoulder-lappets

and metallic deep-bluish body, or which have the fore wings marked
by a few conspicuous longitudinal
yellowish lines as in *C. venosa*, found
in Colorado, New Mexico, and
Texas. *Scepsis fulvicollis*, found in
the eastern and Mississippi Valley
states, has subtranslucent smoky
wings with a region clear of scales
in the middle of the hind wings; its
prothoracic collar is yellow and its
abdomen metallic blue-black.

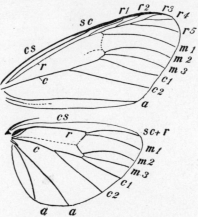

The "woolly-bear" caterpillars
(Fig. 592) and the tiger-moths, which
are the same insects in different
growth stages, are among the most
familiar of caterpillar and moth
acquaintances. They belong to the
family Arctiidæ, represented in this
country by a hundred and twenty
species of which surprisingly many

FIG. 591.—Venation of a Zygænid, *Ctenucha
virginica*. *cs*, costal vein; *sc*, subcostal
vein; *r*, radial vein; *m*, medial vein; *c*,
cubital vein; *a*, anal veins. (After Comstock; enlarged.)

are pretty well known to any ardent collector. The strikingly colored,
spotted, and banded wings of the stout and hairy-bodied moths and the
dense clothing of long strongly colored hairs characteristic of most of the

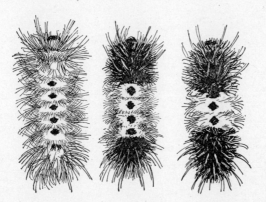

FIG. 592.—Woolly-bear caterpillars, *Halisidota* sp., all three of the same species but
showing variations in extent of the black markings.

larvæ are the recognition-marks of the family. The moths, too, are
mostly fairly large and are readily attracted by lights, while the cater-

pillars, trusting to the uncomfortable mouthful of hairs they offer their bird enemies, travel conspicuously about in the open with a characteristic nervously hurrying gait. Thus the Arctians become familiar to collector and observer.

The woolliest woolly bear is the larva, sometimes called "hedgehog," of the Isabella tiger-moth, *Pyrrharctia* (Isia) *isabella* (Pl. VII, Fig. 3), common all over the United States; it is covered with a stiff furry evenly shorn coat black at either end and red-brown in the middle, and is commonly seen in the autumn traveling rapidly about in open places. It hibernates in larval stage under loose bark or logs or sidewalks, and, after a brief activity in the spring, pupates within a slight cocoon made up of silk and its own brown and black hairs. The moth which issues soon is dull orange with the front wings variegated with dusky and spotted with black; the hind wings are lighter and also black-spotted; it expands 2 inches. The caterpillars feed on various plants, sometimes becoming destructive, when in sufficient numbers, to black-berry and raspberry bushes and to nursery stock. Lugger says that they are especially susceptible to attack by *muscardine*, a parasitic fungus disease much feared by silkworm-growers. "Hedgehogs" killed by muscardine are found stiffly attached to their food-plants with a whitish powder over the body at the base of the dense hair covering.

The yellow bears, common caterpillars on the leaves of vegetables, flowering plants, and fruits, distinguished by their dense but uneven coat of long creamy-yellow, light or even dark brown hairs, are the larvæ of the beautiful snowy-white miller-moth, *Spilosoma virginica*. The wings bear a few (two to four) small black dots, and the abdomen is orange-colored with three rows of black spots. The larvæ pupate in the fall in cocoons composed almost wholly of their own long barbed hairs, and the moths issue in the spring. There is usually a second brood each year. This moth is kept in check by many parasites, few other insects having to contend with so many of these insidious enemies of their own animal class.

The most destructive member of the family is the fall web-worm, *Hyphan-tria cunea*, which makes the large unsightly silken "nests" in various trees, both wild and cultivated, so familiar in late summer and autumn. The eggs are deposited in regular clusters of 400 or more on the plum-leaves, and the hatching pale-yellow larvæ spin small silky web-nests close together which finally get included in one large one. The full-grown larvæ are pale yellow-ish or greenish with a broad dusky stripe along each side; they are covered with whitish hairs which rise from black and orange-yellow warts. They often hang from the nest or branches by a long silken thread. They pupate in crevices of the bark and other sheltered places on the ground, passing the winter in this stage. The milk-white moths, sometimes with small black spots on the wings, sometimes unspotted, issue in late spring or early summer. They expand 1¼ inches. There is much variation in color and pattern in both moths and caterpillars, many varieties being found in a single tree.

Among the most strikingly colored and patterned Arctians are the numerous species of Apanresis (Arctia). *A. virgo* (Pl. VI, Fig. 3), a common species in the Atlantic states, whose larva feeds on pigweed and other uncultivated plants, expands 2½ inches, has black fore wings with the veins broadly marked with pinkish yellow, and red hind wings with large angularly irregular black blotches. The thorax is colored like the fore wings, the abdomen like the hind wings. Sharply angled black spots on a ground of reddish, pinkish, salmon, and yellowish characterize almost all the many species in this genus.

Fig. 593.—Caterpillar of *Halisidota tesselata*. (After Lugger; natural size.)

Striking moths are *Arachnis picta* (Pl. VIII, Fig. 4), with whitish fore wings marked with wavy band-like blotches of pearl-gray, and red hind wings with three uneven gray bands; *Ecpantheria deflorata*, the leopard-moth of the south Atlantic states, and *E. muzina*, of the southwestern states, both creamy white with circular or elliptical black spots or rings thickly scattered over the fore wings, but only in a single submarginal series on the hind wings; and *Utetheisa bella* (Pl. VII, Fig. 7), a familiar little moth of the Atlantic states with its pinkish-red hind wings with black branching border and yellowish-red fore wings crossed by six bending white bands containing small black spots.

Attractive and familiar moths are the various species of Halesidota, whose larvæ feed on the leaves of hickory, oak, and several kinds of orchard trees. These caterpillars (Fig. 593) are covered with short spreading tufts of hairs white and black or yellow, and bear, too, a single pair of long hair pencils usually black or orange. They are often called tussock-caterpillars and are not unlike the true tussock-moth larvæ (see p. 404). The moths

(Fig. 594) have long narrow fore wings, and hind wings only about half as long; in *H. tessellata* the hind wings are almost transparent yellowish (while the fore wings have faint darker short transverse lines or blotches); *H. maculata* (Fig. 595) has yellowish fore wings thickly

FIG. 594.

FIG. 595.

FIG. 594.—*Halisidota caryæ*, above, and *H. tesselata*, below. (After Lugger; natural size.)
FIG. 595.—*Halisidota maculata*. (After Lugger; natural size.)

sprinkled with brown and blotched with creamy-white spots, the pale hind wings being unmarked; *H. lobecula* has the wings nearly transparent, the fore wings dusted with dark scales, and a regular check pattern on the front and hind margins, the hind wings unmarked, and the abdomen of a beautiful rose color; *H. argentata* has the fore wings blackish brown with distinct white spots all over the surface, white hind wings bearing a single irregular brown spot near the apex. The Callimorphas (Fig. 596) are pretty, slender-bodied Arctians with snow-white, creamy, or soft warm yellow-brown wings, banded with dark brown or blackish; they belong to the genus Haploa, whose larvæ are blackish studded with blue spots, and covered with short stiff hairs. All the species of Haploa are found in the Atlantic states. *H. clymene* (Pl. VII, Fig. 5) has the wings brownish yellow, paler on the fore wings, which are incompletely bordered with blackish brown, a curious blunt arm of this color projecting in from the hinder margin; the hind wings have a subcircular dark spot; *H. lecontei* has white hind wings, and brown fore

# PLATE VII.

## MOTHS.

1 = Anisota rubicunda.
2 = Geometra iridaria.
3 = Pyrrharctia isabella
4 = Tropæa luna.
5 = Haploa clymene
6 = Melittia ceto
7 = Utetheisa bella.

PLATE VII

Mary Wellman, del.

wings with six large white blotches; *H. fulvicosta* has all the wings pure white with the front margin of the fore wings weakly fulvous. A familiar Arctian is the salt-marsh-caterpillar moth *Eustigme acræa*, expanse 1½ inches, with creamy-white fore wings and soft yellow-brown hind wings, all the wings sparsely dotted with black.

A small family which includes a few widely distributed and well-known moths is the Lasiocampidæ, of which the tent-caterpillar moths are the most familiar. All the Lasiocampid moths, which are robust, hairy, and fairly large, lack the frenulum, having, however, the humeral angle of the hind wing expanded so as to overlap the inner hind angle of the fore wing. In this humeral angle are one or two short supporting veins or vein-spurs.

FIG. 596.—*Haploa fulvicosta* (above) and *H. contigua* (in the middle and below). (After Lugger; natural size.)

The best-known eastern species is the apple-tree tent-caterpillar, the forest tent-caterpillar being also familiar; on the Pacific coast also occur two common species, one specially affecting orchard trees. These four species belong to the genus Clisiocampa (Figs. 598, 599); the moths expand about 1½ inches and are all brown, varying in shade from yellowish to walnut to chocolate-brown, with a pair of pale or distinct light or darker oblique lines on the fore wings. *C. americana*, the apple-tree tent-caterpillar, lays its three hundred eggs in the summer in a band or ring glued around a small twig of an apple or wild-cherry tree; the eggs do not hatch until the following spring, when the young larvæ feed on the buds and young leaves of the tree. The social larvæ build a little web or nest in the fork of a branch,

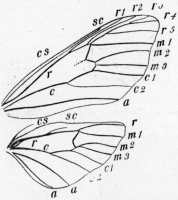

going out of it only to feed. As the caterpillars grow they enlarge the web until it becomes a bulky ugly affair perhaps two feet long, partly filled with excrement and cast skins. The full-grown caterpillars are blackish with yellow and bluish spots, white striped along the back, and covered with fine yellowish hairs. "They feed on the young and tender leaves, and eating on an average two leaves a day the young of one pair of moths consume from ten to twelve hundred leaves, and

Fig. 597.—Venation of *Halesidota tessellata*. *cs*, costal vein; *sc*, subcostal vein; *r*, radial vein; *m*, medial vein; *c*, cubital vein; *a*, anal veins. (After Comstock; enlarged.)

as it is not uncommon to find from six to eight nests on a single tree not less than seventy-five thousand leaves are devoured, a loss which no tree can long endure." In about forty days the larvæ are ready to pupate, when they scatter from the nest, find sheltered places under eaves, fence-rails, etc., and spin spindle-shaped cocoons of white, almost transparent silk, within which they change. After twenty to twenty-five days of pupal life the winged moths issue and soon after lay their eggs for next year's brood. The life-history of the various other species is similar to this although other trees are chosen for feeding-grounds.

The lappet-moths, so-called from the curious lobes or lappets arranged along the sides of their caterpillars, are of several species. *Tolype velleda*, expanding 1½ to 1¾ inches, has a white body with a black spot and dusky-gray wings crossed by white lines; its caterpillar feeds on the foliage of apple-, cherry-, and plum-trees, and is hair-fringed and protectively colored so that it looks much like an excrescence of the bark on which it habitually lies when not feeding. *Gastropacha americana* (Fig. 601), the American lappet-moth, expanding 1½ inches, is so like a dead leaf in appearance that it can hardly be distinguished when at rest; it varies somewhat in color, but most individuals are reddish brown with a broad interrupted whitish band across both wings; the hinder and outer edges of the fore wings and the outer edges of the hind wings are deeply notched. The caterpillar feeds on apple, cherry, and oak, hiding during the day but becoming active at night. It is broad, convex above and flat beneath, ash-gray with fringes of blackish or gray hairs, and when at rest it is almost impossible to recognize.

It grows to be 2 inches long and spins a peculiar gray cocoon which looks very much like a slight swelling of the twig to which it is fastened. The pupa hibernates, the moth issuing in June of the next year.

FIG. 598.                                    FIG. 599.

FIG. 598.—A family of young forest tent-caterpillars, *Clisiocampa disstria*, resting during the day on the bark. (Photograph from life by Slingerland; one-third natural size.)

FIG. 599.—The forest tent-caterpillar moth, *Clisiocampa disstria*, in its various stages. *m*, male moth; *f*, female moth; *p*, pupa; *e*, eggs in a ring about twig; *g*, eggs after hatching; *c*, larva or caterpillar. (After Slingerland; moths and caterpillar natural size, eggs and pupa slightly enlarged.)

Including the largest, the most beautiful—in popular eyes at least—and the favorite moths for rearing in "crawleries," the superfamily Saturniina includes as well one of the only two insects that have been domesticated by man and reared for the sake of their useful products. The honey-bee and the silkworm moth are fairly to be called domesticated animals. To the Saturniina belong the great cecropias, the marvelous lunas, the regal and imperial walnut-moths, and the soft-tinted rosy dryocampas. Although the whole group, divided commonly into four families, includes but forty-two North American species, almost every one of these is more or less familiarly known to the amateur collector and crawlery owner. And popular books like Dickerson's "Moths and Butterflies," Eliot and Soule's "Caterpillars and Their Moths," etc., which tell in detail of the life-history and habits of various Lepidoptera, mean by "moths," first Saturnians, then Sphingids, and finally a scant sprinkling of "others." The giant vividly colored caterpillars, the great silken cocoons safely enclosing their mystery until that day when a marvel of

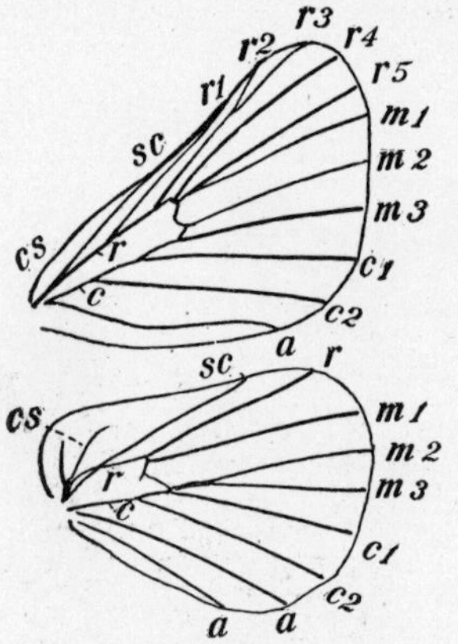

FIG. 600.  FIG. 601.

FIG. 600.—Venation of *Clisiocampa americana*. *cs*, costal vein; *sc*, subcostal vein; *r*, radial vein; *m*, medial vein; *c*, cubital vein; *a*, anal veins. (After Comstock; enlarged.)

FIG. 601.—The American lappet-moth, *Gastropacha americana*. (After Lugger; natural size.)

living color and pattern slowly crawls out and unfolds and takes on the seeming of the perfect cecropia or polyphemus, it is little wonder that the giant silkworm-moths are—always never overlooking the swift and masterful Sphingids—the moths of popular fancy.

Just because these moths are so well known and so well and fully written of elsewhere I may limit my account of them to a brief descriptive catalogue of adults and larvæ with the particular aim of making the more common species determinable by amateurs. The particular species in hand once safely identified, details of life-history and habits can be looked for in the many popular or technical accounts of the various kinds. In all, the males can be distinguished from the females by their large antennæ and smaller bodies. In some species the sexes are very different in color and pattern.

Of the genus Samia, the real giant silkworms, four species occur in this country. *S. cecropia*, the great cecropia-moth of the eastern states, expands 5 to 6 inches, has red thorax with white collar, red abdomen banded with white and black lines, wings with grizzled gray ground, and markings, as shown in Fig. 602, of reddish white and blackish with clay-colored outer margins. The large discal spots on the wings are whitish in the center, surrounded and encroached on by reddish, and margined with a narrow black line. The full-grown larva (Fig. 604) is nearly 4 inches long, pale limpid green, and bears on its back conspicuous tubercles, coral-red on the second and third thoracic segments, blue on the first thoracic and last abdominal, and yellow on the others; smaller blue lateral tubercles are present. It feeds on many kinds of orchard- and forest-trees, most small fruits, and some herbaceous plants. The winter is passed in the pupal stage enclosed in a great pod-shaped rusty-gray or brownish silken cocoon about 3 inches long and 1 inch wide in the middle, composed of two layers, an outer strong "brown-paper" layer and an inner loose fibrous one. The pupæ may be easily found on trees when the leaves are off and brought

FIG. 602.—Cecropia-moth, *Samia cecropia*. (Photograph by author; natural size.)

into the house. The moths will issue in early summer through an opening which is left by the larva in one end of the cocoon. *S. columbia* of the north-eastern states and Canada is smaller than *cecropia*, the angulated discal wing-spots have hardly any reddish border and the transverse outer wing-border of white has no red outer margin as in *cecropia*, the abdomen is dark-red brown rather than red, and the basal half of the front wings is tinged with reddish brown. *S. gloveri*, found in the Rocky Mountains and west to Arizona, is like *columbia*, but as large as *cecropia*. *S. ceanothi* of the Pacific coast has the ground color of the wings strongly reddish, the outer markings weak to wanting, the white transverse wing-band narrow and with no reddish border, the discal spots also without reddish margin.

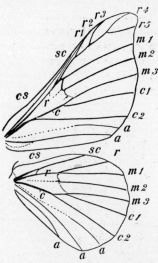

FIG. 603.—Venation of a Saturniid, *Bombyx mori*. *cs*, costal vein; *sc*, subcostal vein; *r*, radial vein; *m*, medial vein; *c*, cubital vein; *a*, anal veins. (After Comstock; enlarged.)

The polyphemus-moth, *Telea polyphemus* (Fig. 605), expanse 4 to 5 inches, common in the whole country, is ocherous brown with a pinkish margined blackish outer transverse band across each wing and a discal spot on each wing with unscaled clear center; this latter character makes the species at once unmistakable; the hind wing-spots are in the center of a large blackish blotch with bluish scales by the inner margin of the clear spot. The larva (Fig. 606), which feeds on various forest-, shade-, and orchard-trees, reaches a length of 3 inches or more, is light green with seven oblique pale-yellowish lines on each side of the body, and bears numerous little black wart-like processes provided with small stiff bristles, and each body segment has a small silvery spot on the middle. The dense oval, completely closed cocoon is made of silk and a few leaves closely wrapped and tied together. It usually falls to the ground in autumn, but sometimes remains on the tree. The moth secretes a fluid from its mouth which softens and partly dissolves one end of the cocoon for its emergence.

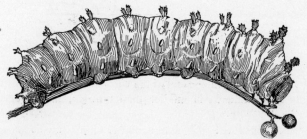

FIG. 604.—Larva of *Samia cecropia*. (After Dickerson; natural size.)

In Plate VII, Fig. 4, is shown in color the luna-moth, or pale empress of the night, *Tropœa luna* (Fig. 607), a marvel of delicate green tinting and exquisite symmetry of curving outlines. It expands $4\frac{1}{2}$ inches, and ranges over the whole country. The larva is rather like that of the polyphemus-moth, being clear, pale bluish green with a pale-yellowish stripe on

FIG. 605.—The polyphemus-moth, *Telea polyphemus*, and cocoon.
(After Lugger; reduced about one-fourth.)

each side of the body; each segment bears about six small purplish or rosy-tinged pearl tubercles; at the tip of the body are three brown spots edged with yellow. It feeds on hickory and walnut, on other forest-trees, and

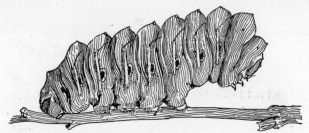

FIG. 606.—Larva of polyphemus-moth, *Telea polyphemus*.
(After Dickerson; natural size.)

makes a rather thin but compact cocoon of silk and leaves.

In the eastern states the Asiatic ailanthus-worm moth, *Philosamia cynthia*, expanse 5 inches, with angulated wings, olive-brown ground-color on body and wings, a whitish lunate discal spot and a white and purplish transverse bar on each wing, and body with longitudinal series of white tufted spots, has become common near several cities.

The promethea-moth, *Callosamia promethea*, expanse 3 to 4 inches, light reddish brown in female, and blackish and clay color in male, with markings as shown in Fig. 609, is perhaps the most abundant of all these giant moths. Its larva when full-grown is 2 inches or more in length; it is bluish green and the body bears longitudinal series of black polished tubercles, two of these tubercles on each of the second and third thoracic segments

Fig. 607.—The luna-moth, or pale empress of the night, *Tropæa luna.* (After Lugger; reduced about one-fourth.)

being larger and red instead of black. It feeds on many kinds of trees, but Comstock has found it more frequently on ash and wild cherry than on others. The cocoon is long and slender and enclosed in a dead leaf whose petiole has been fastened to the branch with silk by the larva. "At the upper end of the cocoon there is a conical valve-like arrangement which allows the adult to emerge without the necessity of making a hole." *C. angulifera* is a moth slightly larger than *promethea*, but otherwise hardly distinguishable from it except that the shape and markings of the wings,

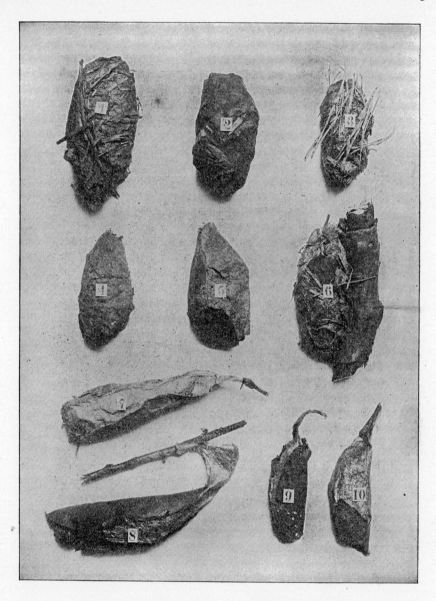

FIG. 608.—Cocoons: 1, 2, 3, of *Tropæa luna;* 4, 5, 6, of *Callosamia angulifera;* 7, 8, 9, 10, of *Callosamia promethea.* (After Laurent; somewhat reduced.)

which vary a little in male and female of *promethea*, are identical in this.    It is found also only in the Atlantic states.

The Io emperor-moth, *Automeris io* (Pl. VI, Fig. 5; also Fig. 610), expanse 2½ to 3 inches, is the most familiar and the only eastern species of the four members of this genus.    It can be recognized by the large blue and black eye-spots in hind wings and by its unmarked fore wings.    The female has rich purplish-brown fore wings, the markedly smaller male yellow fore wings.    The larva (Fig. 611), which feeds on trees, small fruits, corn, clover, etc., when full-grown is 2½ inches long, and is pale green with a

FIG. 609.—The promethea-moth, *Callosamia promethea*, male.
(After Jordan and Kellogg;   natural size.)

broad brown stripe edged with white and reddish lilac on each side, and has the body covered with clusters of black-tipped green branching spiny hairs which are very sharp and strongly stinging.    The thin, irregular parchment-like cocoon made of tough gummy brown silk is spun under dead leaves or other rubbish on the ground.    In Texas is found *A. zelleri*, expanse 5 inches, reddish brown, without any yellow color in hind wings; in Arizona *A. pamina*, expanse 2½ to 3 inches, with yellow around the white-centered black eye-spots of the hind wings;  and in New Mexico *A. zephyria*, expanse 2½ to 3 inches, with brown-black fore wings and pale-brown abdomen broadly banded with red.

With a single species, the maia moth, in the eastern states, and but half a dozen in the Rocky Mountains, desert and Pacific slope states, the genus Hemileuca presents a striking difference from the other Saturnians so far described in the thinly scaled, not hairy, condition of the wings and the prevalence of black and white in the pattern instead of warmer colors. *H. maia*, expanding 2½ inches, is subtransparent black with a broad middle transverse band of white on each wing; in this band is a small blackish blotch

FIG. 610.—The Io emperor-moth, *Automeris io*, and cocoon; female moth above; male below. (After Lugger; natural size.)

isolated in the hind wings, but connected with the black of the base in the fore wings. This species occurs in the eastern states; a similar species, *H. nevadensis*, being found from the Rocky Mountains to the Pacific; *H. electra*, found in southern California, has the hind wings blackish red; other species, found in New Mexico and Arizona, are mostly black and white with a reddish or pinkish tinge here and there.   The larva of *H. maia* feeds on oak; it is brownish black with a lateral yellow stripe, and has large branching spines over the body which sting severely.

In Plate VI, Fig. 4, is shown in proper color and pattern a bizarre moth, *Pseudohazis eglanterina*, not uncommon in the Rocky Mountains, which

Fig. 611.—Larva of Io emperor-moth, *Automeris io*.　(After Dickerson; natural size.)

we may call the clown.   An allied species, *P. shastaensis*, similarly marked and colored, is found on the Pacific slope, and a third species, *P. hera*, with pale yellowish-white ground-color in the wings instead of purplish red, occurs in the region between the Rocky Mountains and the Sierra Nevada.

Two great moths, the imperial (Pl. VI, Fig. 2) and the regal walnut-moth (Fig. 612), are the most impressive of a subgroup of the Saturniina called the Ceratocampidæ.   They are all short-bodied and hairy and show for colors exclusively rich warm browns and soft yellows, light purple and rose.   A curious structural characteristic of the family is the limiting of the pectinations on the antennæ of the male to the basal half of the antenna. The regal walnut-moth, *Citheronia regalis* (Fig. 612), expands fully 5 inches, has a rich brown ground-color on body and hind wings, with the fore wings slaty gray with yellow blotches, and veins broadly marked out in red-brown. The larva (Fig. 613), 4 to 5½ inches long, and yellowish brown, reddish brown, or greenish, is distinguished from all other caterpillars by the great, threatening, but harmless blue-black horns of the body; it feeds on butter-nut, walnut, ash, pines, and other trees.   *Basilona imperialis*, the imperial moth, is as large as the regal walnut, but with ground-color of rich yellow, overspread on base and outer part of fore wings and as a spot and band on hind wings with soft brownish purple.   The larvæ when full-grown are 3 inches long, brown or greenish, thinly clothed with long whitish hairs, and bear conspicuous spiny horns on the second and third thoracic segments. They feed on hickory, oak, elm, maple, and other deciduous forest-trees, as well as on spruce, pine, juniper, and hemlock.   The larvæ of both these great moths burrow into the ground to pupate, the rough brown naked chrysalids wintering over.

FIG. 612.—The regal walnut-moth, *Citheronia regalis*. (Photograph by author; natural size.)

Anisota is a genus of smaller moths containing five species limited to the eastern states, four of which are brown and one, *A. rubicunda*, rosy and

FIG. 613.—Larva of regal walnut-moth, *Citheronia regalis*.
(Photograph by author; natural size.)

yellow. This latter, called the rosy dryocampa, is shown in color in Plate VII, Fig. 1. Its larva, sometimes called the green-striped maple-worm, is pale yellowish green and is striped with many fine longitudinal lines alternating lighter and darker than the ground-color. There are two horns on the second thoracic segment, and dorsal spines on the eighth and ninth abdominal segments.

    *A. virginiensis* is purplish red or brown, and the wings are nearly trans-

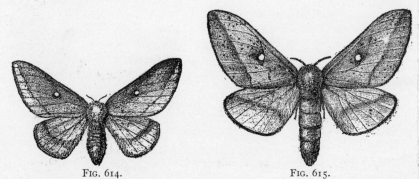

Fig. 614.               Fig. 615.

Fig. 614.—The orange-striped oak-worm moth, *Anisota senatoria*, male. (After Lugger; natural size.)

Fig. 615.—The orange-striped oak-worm moth, *Anisota senatoria*, female. (After Lugger; natural size.)

parent in the center; the larva, found on oak, is grayish or greenish with brownish-yellow or rosy stripes and with small white warty processes all over

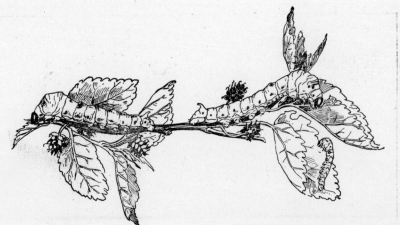

Fig. 616.—Mulberry silkworms, larvæ of *Bombyx mori*. (From life; natural size.)

the skin; *A. stigma*, expanse 2 inches, is light ocherous brown with many blackish dots; its bright tawny or orange caterpillar has long spines on the back; *A. senatoria* (Figs. 614 and 615) is like *A. virginiensis*, but lacks the transparent place in the middle of the wing; the caterpillar is black with four stripes. All these Anisota larvæ feed on oaks, and that of *A. senatoria* also on blackberries and raspberries. *Sphingicampa* (Adelocephala) *bicolor* is a beautiful moth with brown fore wings and dark-pink hind wings with dusky dots, which is not uncommon in the Mississippi Valley and southern states; its larvæ feed on the locusts and the Kentucky coffee-bean. In the southwest are two or three species of the genus Syssphinx resembling *Sphingicampa bicolor*, but one, *S. heiligbrodti*, in Arizona, has iron-gray fore wings.

Now unknown in wild condition, the long-cultivated Chinese or mulberry silkworm, *Bombyx mori*, is spread over most of the world, living exclusively, however, under the personal care of man. Indeed it is often said that the worm is so degenerate, so susceptible to unfavorable circumstances, that it could not live out of doors uncared for. As a matter of fact, however, I have bred moths from silkworms placed exposed on mulberry-trees in California immediately after the first moult. And these individuals experienced considerable hardship in the way of low temperatures and dashing rains. The heavy creamy-white moths, with wing expanse of $1\frac{3}{4}$ inches, take no food at all, and most of them cannot even fly despite their possession of well-developed wings, so degenerate are the flight-muscles from

FIG. 617.—Mulberry silkworm, showing front view of head and thorax. (From life; natural size.)

generations of disuse. The eggs, about 300, are laid by the female on any bit of cloth or paper provided her by the silkworm-growers. They are yellow at first, but soon change to a slaty color due to the beginning development of the embryo. In the annual race of silkworms, i.e., the variety which produces but one generation a year as compared with those others which produce two (bivoltins), three (trivoltins), and even five or six (multivoltins), the development of the eggs soon ceases, and they go over the winter, hatching in the following spring at the time the mulberry-trees begin leafing out. The larvæ (Figs. 616 and 617) must be well fed with fresh mulberry or osage-orange leaves (they may at a pinch be carried through on lettuce) from which all rain- or dew-drops should be wiped off. The worms moult every nine or ten days, ceasing to feed for a day before each moulting, during the forty-five days of larval life, spinning before the last moult (pupation) the dense white or golden silken cocoon which is, to man, the silkworm's *raison d'être*. In this spinning the thread is at first attached irregularly to near-by objects, but after a sort of loose net or web has been made the spinning becomes more regular, and by the end of three days a thick firm symmetrical closed cocoon, composed of a single continuous silken thread averaging over 1000 feet long, is completed. Inside this cocoon the larva pupates, and if undisturbed the chrysalid gives up its damp and crumpled moth after from twelve to fourteen

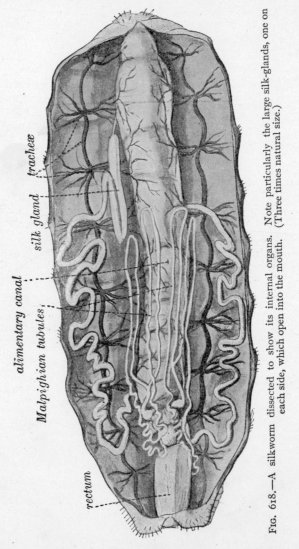

FIG. 618.—A silkworm dissected to show its internal organs. Note particularly the large silk-glands, one on each side, which open into the mouth. (Three times natural size.)

trachex

silk gland

alimentary canal

Malpighian tubules

rectum

days or longer. A fluid secreted by the moth softens one end of the cocoon so that the delicate creature can force its way out. But this is not the usual fate of a silkworm pupa. The professional grower must save the cocoon from injury by the moth, so he kills his thousands of pupæ by dropping the cocoons into boiling water or by putting them into a hot oven. Then, after cleaning away the loose fluffy silk of the outside, he finds the beginning of the long thread which makes the cocoon, and with a clever little reeling-machine he unwinds, unbroken, its hundreds of feet of merchantable silk floss. From here to the silk-dress stage is a story not entomological, but one of elaborate machines and processes of human devising.

Hovering, humming-bird-like, in the early dusk over the deep flower-cup of a petunia or honeysuckle or great jimson-weed, with its long flexible proboscis thrust deep down to the nectaries, and the swift wings making a

FIG. 619.—Larva of the achemon sphinx-moth, *Philampelus achemon.*
(After Lugger; natural size.)

faint haze on either side of the trim body, the sphinx-moth, or hawk-moth, or humming-bird moth, as variously called, is a familiar garden acquaintance. But that he is but one of a hundred different American species; that he has cousins red and cousins green, somber cousins and harlequin cousins; that, strong-winged, clean-bodied, exquisitely painted, and honey-fine in his taste as he is now, his earliest youth was passed as a "disgusting," soft, fat, green tomato-worm or tobacco-worm or grape-vine dresser, and that at a later adolescent period he lay buried in the ground, cased, mummy-like, in a dark-brown sarcophagus—all this may not be as familiar. Still, excepting the giant silkworm-moths, the Saturnians, no other moth group is so much affected by collectors and crawlery proprietors as the Sphingidæ. Thus the various adolescent stages of several hawk-moth species are known to many amateurs, and numerous different sphingid species will be found in any collection of Lepidoptera. The uniformity of structural character in larvæ and adults of the various species, and the general similarity of habits and life-history, make the family a coherent one, and one readily distinguishable from other moths. These moths, with few exceptions, have long, nar-

FIG. 620.—Larva of the sphinx-moth, *Phlegethontius carolina*. (After Jordan and Kellogg; one-half natural size.)

row, pointed fore wings, very small hind wings, a smooth-coated, compact, cleanly tapering body, and a long proboscis, coiled when not in use, like a watch-spring, on the front of the head (Fig. 509). The colors and patterns are extremely varied, but uniformly quietly beautiful and harmonious.

FIG. 621.—Larva of *Phlegethontius celeus*. (After Soule; somewhat reduced.)

The larvæ (Fig. 619) are naked, usually green, often with repeated oblique whitish lines on the sides, and bear a conspicuous sharp-pointed horn, or, in fewer instances, a flattish, button-like shining tubercle, on the back of the eighth abdominal segment. The caterpillars, or "worms," feed on the foliage of various plants, and when full-grown most of them descend and burrow into the ground to pupate. The chrysalid is naked, with firm, dark-brown wall, and is distinguished by the odd jug-handle-like sheath for the developing long imaginal proboscis. A few larvæ pupate on the

Fig. 622.—*Pholus achemon*, above, and *Pholus pandorus*, below.
(After Lugger; natural size.)

ground in a slight cocoon made of silk and a few leaves tied together. The insects hibernate in the pupal stage; a few are said to be double-brooded. The name sphinx, applied to these moths by Linnæus a century and a half ago, is suggested by the curious attitude assumed by the larvæ when disturbed; the front part of the body is lifted (Fig. 620) clear of the object on which the insect is resting, and the head is bent forward on the thoracic feet. This position may be held rigidly for hours.

Of the many species found in this country we can refer to but a few of the more familiar or beautiful or interesting ones, and these references may be made brief because of the colored figures which are grouped in our frontispiece. These figures render descriptions unnecessary.

Best known of all the hawk-moths, both in larval and adult stage, are the five-spotted sphinges, the tomato- and tobacco-worm moths, *Phlegethontius quinquemaculata* (*celeus*) and *P. sexta* (*carolina*) (Pl. VIII, Fig. 3).

FIG. 623.—Larva of *Pholus achemon*. (After Soule; natural size.)

*Quinquemaculata* is the commoner in the north, *sexta* in the south; in both the larva (Figs. 620 and 621) is green with oblique white stripes on the side and a long sharp caudal horn, and feeds on tomato-, tobacco-, and potato-leaves or jimson-weed. The horn of *sexta* is red, that of *quinquemaculata* green or blue-black. The pupæ are long and slender and dark brown (green at first), and are often found when plowing or digging up fields in which these plants have been grown. The moth of *P. quinquemaculata* has ashy-gray wings, with zigzag markings, while the wings of *sexta* are not thus marked. The great pandorus sphinx, *Pholus* (Philampelus) *pandorus* (Pl. I, Fig. 1), found in the eastern and central states, is one of the most beautiful of all moths. The larvæ feed on grape-vines and Virginia creeper, and, measuring four inches long when full-grown, are rich reddish brown with five conspicuous cream-colored spots along

FIG. 624. — Grape - vine sphinx - moth, *Ampelophaga myron*. (Natural size.)

each side; a shining black eye-like tubercle takes the place of a caudal horn. It pupates underground. *P. achemon* (Fig. 622), with markings much like *pandorus*, but with strong rosy coloration instead of greenish, has a larva which also feeds on grape and Virgina creeper and may be recognized by its six (instead of five) lateral cream-colored blotches.

## PLATE VIII.

### MOTHS.

1 = Deilephila lineata.
2 = Chærocampa tersa.
3 = Phlegethontius sexta.
4 = Arachnis picta.
5 = Alypia octomaculata.
6 = Anatolmis grotei.
7 = Plusia simplex.

PLATE VIII

*Mary Wellman, del.*

The beautiful little *Ampelophaga myron*, with soft red-brown hind wings and brownish-gray fore wings, patterned as shown in Fig. 624, has a pea-green, cream-banded, and yellow and lilac spotted larva known as the hog-caterpillar of the vine, so named from its form—the third and fourth segments being greatly swollen, the head and first two segments small—and its destructiveness to grape-vines. When ready to pupate it spins a brown silken open-meshed cocoon on the ground under leaves or other rubbish.

FIG. 625.—The double-eyed sphinx, *Smerinthus geminatus*, above; *Paonias excæcatus*, in middle; and *P. myops*, below. (After Lugger; natural size.)

*A. versicolor* (Pl. I, Fig. 3) is a beautiful cousin of *myron* with greenish overlaid on the brown. An extremely slim, slender-bodied, and slender-winged sphinx is *Chærocampa* (Theretra) *tersa* (Pl. VIII, Fig. 2), found in the northern states. It is very swift. An abundant and familiar hawk-moth found all over the United States is the white-lined sphinx, *Deilephila lineata* (Pl. VIII, Fig. 1). Its caterpillar feeds on various plants, as grape, apple, watermelon, buckwheat, turnip, and purslane; the latter seems to be the preferred plant.

Exceedingly variable in color and pattern, it is usually yellow-green with a conspicuous longitudinal row of elliptical spots on each side of the back,

FIG. 626.—Larva of *Smerinthus geminatus*.  (After Lugger;  natural size.)

each spot consisting of two curved black lines enclosing a bright crimson blotch and a pale-yellow line; all the spots are connected by a pale-yellow

FIG. 627.—*Sphinx gordius*.  (After Lugger;  natural size.)

line edged above with black.  Sometimes the larvæ are black, with a narrow yellow line along the back and a series of paler- and darker-yellow spots. The double-eyed sphinx, *Smerinthus geminatus* (Pl. I, Fig. 2; also Fig. 625), is a common species whose larvæ feed on apple, plum, ash, willow, birch, and other trees; the full-grown caterpillar (Fig. 626) is 2¼ inches long, apple-green, with seven oblique yellow stripes on each side of the body and a violet caudal horn. The genus Sphinx (Fig. 627) contains nearly twenty species, all of them soberly patterned with grayish, brownish, and blackish, and most of them expanding more than three inches.

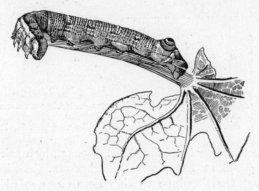

FIG. 628.—Larva of the abbott-sphinx, *Thyreus abbotti*. (After Soule; natural size.)

While most hawk-moths have narrow tapering fore wings and a slender tapering smooth-coated body, structural conditions indicating a well-developed flight power, a familiar species, the modest sphinx, *Marumba modesta* (Pl. I, Fig. 4), found all over the country, is hairy, heavy-bodied, and

FIG. 629.—Larva of abbott-sphinx, *Thyreus abbotti;* note difference in pattern from larva shown in Fig. 628. (After Soule; natural size.)

broad-winged. The full-grown larvæ are 3 inches and more long, whitish, yellowish, and bluish green, with fine white dots all over the skin; the caudal horn is short. They feed on "balm-of-Gilead," poplar, and other trees. Another species of unusual shape is the beautiful dark-brown and canary-yellow small tufted-bodied abbott-sphinx, *Thyreus* (Sphecodina) *abbotti* (Pl. I, Fig. 6), found in the Atlantic and Mississippi Valley states. Its larvæ (Figs. 628 and 629) feed on woodbine and grape. They are "ashes-of-rose" color, finely transversely lined with dark brown and with longitudinal series of brown blotches. They have a large circular, eye-like tubercle in place of a caudal horn. They may appear in two different patterns as

shown in Figs. 628 and 629.   The pupa is found under dead leaves or other
rubbish.   Very similar in appearance and habits is the grape-vine amphion,
*Amphion nessus* (Fig. 630), of the same size and shape and colors and found

FIG. 630.                                    FIG. 631.

FIG. 630.—The grape-vine amphion, *Amphion nessus*.   (After Beutenmüller; natural
    size, 1¾–2 inches expanse of wings.)
FIG. 631.—Larva of clear-winged sphinx, *Hemaris diffinis*.   (After Soule; natural size.)

in the same states; it may be distinguished, however, by a pair of conspicuous narrow, bright-yellow bands across the abdomen.   The larvæ are pale
yellowish green or chocolate-brown with various obscure darkish stripes.

FIG. 632.—The death's-head sphinx-moth; note skull-like markings on thorax between
    wings.   This moth is looked on with superstitious dread by many people.   (Photo-
    graph by author; natural size.)

A few sphinx-moths have the wings partly clear.   These are called the
clear-winged sphinxes and belong to the genus Hemaris.   *H. thysbe* (Pl. I,

Fig. 5) is the most abundant Eastern species, although *H. diffinis,* with bright-yellow hairs in place of brownish yellow on thorax and abdomen, is common. In Colorado and Utah is found a smaller species, *H. brucei,* with yellowish thorax and abdominal band, and in California are one or two varieties of *H. diffinis.* The larva of *H. diffinis* (Fig. 631) feeds on honey-suckle and snowberry-bush and is pale green above, darker green on the sides, with three brown stripes on the under side; the caudal horn is yellow with blue-black tip; some of the caterpillars, as is common among the larvæ of this family, are brown instead of green. It is two-brooded. Moths just issued from the chrysalid have scales over all of the wing surface, but these scales are so loosely attached on the discal area that the first few flights dislodge them, so that the "clear-wing" comes about. The larvæ of *H. thysbe* feed on viburnum, snowberry, and hawthorn.

## BUTTERFLIES.

Taken all in all the butterflies are the most familiar and attractive insects to people in general; their size, beautiful color-patterns, and daytime flight

Fig. 633.—The Parnassian butterfly, *Parnassius smintheus,* which lives in the Rocky Mountains and Sierra Nevada at an altitude of 5000 feet and more. (Natural size.)

chiefly account for this. Six hundred and fifty butterfly species (compare with the six thousand species of moths) are accredited to this country in the latest authoritative catalogue of North American Lepidoptera. These represent, according to this catalogue, thirteen families; a more usual classification, however, groups all these species into six families. As this latter arrangement is in use in most of the insect manuals, it will be adopted in this. Comstock, who has given the classification of the Lepidoptera much attention, gives the following key to families:

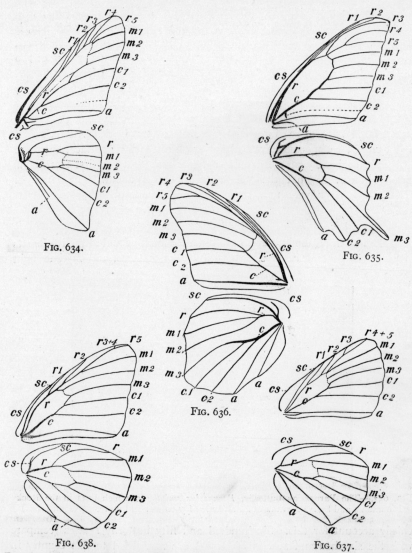

FIG. 634.

FIG. 635.

FIG. 636.

FIG. 638.

FIG. 637.

FIG. 634.—Venation of a Hesperid, *Epargyreus tityrus*. (After Comstock; enlarged.)
FIG. 635.—Venation of a Papilionid, *Papilio polyxenes*. (After Comstock.)
FIG. 636.—Venation of a Nymphalid, *Basilarchia astyanax*. (After Comstock; enlarged.)
FIG. 637.—Venation of a Lycænid, *Chrysophanus thoe*. (After Comstock; enlarged.)
FIG. 638.—Venation of a Pierid, *Pontia protodice*. (After Comstock; enlarged.)
*For all: cs*, costal vein; *sc*, subcostal vein; *r*, radial vein; *m*, medial vein; *c*, cubital
vein; *a*, anal veins.

## KEY TO FAMILIES OF BUTTERFLIES (LEPIDOPTERA WITH THE ANTENNÆ FILIFORM, WITH A CLUB, OR KNOB, AT THE TIP).

A.   With the radius of the fore wings five-branched and with all of these branches arising from the discal cell (Fig. 634); club of antennæ usually terminated by a recurved hook.........................(Skippers.)   Superfamily Hesperiina.

    B.   Head of moderate size; club of antennæ large, neither drawn out at the tip nor recurved.   Large skippers with wing expanse of 2 inches or more.

                                                Megathymidæ (p. 441).

    BB.   Head very large; club of antennæ usually drawn out at the tip and with a distinct recurved apical crook.   If the crook is wanting, the species expand less than 1¼ inches.............................Hesperiidæ (p. 442).

AA.   With some of the branches of radius of the fore wings coalesced beyond the apex of the discal cell (Fig. 635); club of antennæ not terminated by a recurved hook.

                    (The butterflies.)   Superfamily Papilionina.

    B.   Cubital vein of the fore wings apparently four-branched (Fig. 635); most of the species with tails on the hind wings.

             (The swallow-tails and parnassians.)   Papilionidæ (p. 446).

    BB.   Cubital vein of fore wings apparently three-branched (Fig. 636).

        C.   With only four well-developed legs, the fore legs being unused, much shorter than the others, and folded on the breast like a tippet, except in the female of Hypatus; radius of fore wings five-branched (Fig. 636).

              (The brush-footed butterflies.)   Nymphalidæ (p. 450).

        CC.   With six well-developed legs; radius of fore wings, with rare exceptions, only three- or four-branched (Fig. 637).

            D.   Medial vein of the fore wings arising at or near the apex of the discal cell (Fig. 637), except in *Feniseca tarquinius,* in which the wings are dark brown with a large fulvous spot on each.

               (The blues and coppers.)   Lycænidæ (p. 443).

            DD.   Medial vein of the fore wings united with last branch of radius for a considerable distance beyond the apex of the discal cell (Fig. 638); ground color white, yellow, or orange.

             (The whites and sulphurs.)   Pieridæ (p. 444).

The family Megathymidæ, or giant-skippers, contains but one genus, Megathyma, represented by but five species, of which none is found outside of the southern and southwestern states. The best-known and most widely distributed species is the yucca-borer, *M. yuccæ,* whose larvæ live as burrowers in the roots of several species of yucca, and are from 4 to 6 inches long. The eggs are laid on the leaves and the young larvæ spend a short time above ground in a cylinder made of a rolled leaf tied across with silk. Later they tunnel into the stem and downwards into the root, sometimes to a distance of 2 feet or more. When ready to pupate they crawl up to the chimney-like funnel at the top of the burrow and transform there. The moth expands 2½ inches, is deep umber-brown with a notched ferruginous band and other smaller blotches on the fore wings, and the hind wings with a ferruginous border. The other giant-skippers are of similar size and markings, and all of them are more moth-like than butterfly-like in general appearance. They may be looked on, indeed, as a sort of connecting link between the moths and the true butterflies.

The Hesperidæ, or skipper-butterflies (Pl. IX), are a great family of small, big-headed, robust-bodied butterflies of obscure patterning in browns and blackish (a few forms white and dark gray). Nearly two hundred species are known in this country, but few of them are at all familiarly recognized as distinct species; general collectors and amateurs know them better grouped into generic units, as Erynnis, Amblyscirtes, Eudamus, Thorybes, Pholisora, etc. Indeed, but few professional entomologists feel competent to undertake the identification of Hesperid species. A few well-marked or specially numerous and wide-spread forms are, however, fairly well known. The caterpillars of all have large heads, constricted necks, and bodies thick in the middle and tapering both ways, and often make protecting nests of leaves and silk. The silver-spotted skipper, *Epargyreus tityrus* (Pl. V, Fig. 3), is abundant over all the country and is readily recognizable by its large size and distinctive pattern; the broad, irregular, silver spot is on the under side of the hind wing. The caterpillar feeds on various Leguminosæ, especially wistaria and locust, and when full-grown is $1\frac{1}{2}$ inches long, with large, ferruginous head bearing two large orange spots, and lemon-green body transversely banded with darker green; it builds a nest or case of leaves, in which it remains when not feeding; it pupates either in this larval nest or makes a loose cocoon somewhere on the ground, hibernating in this stage. Another of the larger species is the curious long-tailed skipper, *Eudamus proteus*, found in the south Atlantic states (ranging as far north as New York City) and distinguished by the tailed hind wings and iridescent green-brown color. The genus Hesperia includes a dozen or more species which are thickly white-spotted on a blackish-brown ground, giving them a checkered gray appearance; most of these checkered skippers are limited to the western states, but one, *H. tessellata*, is found commonly all over the country. It expands $1\frac{1}{3}$ inches, and has even more white than dark on the wings; it flies rapidly about close to the ground and lays its eggs on various mallows; the larva is green with a dark interrupted dorsal line, dark lateral bands, and a pale band below the spiracles.

A whole host of skippers are the "sooty-wings," members of several genera, but almost impossible to be distinguished by means of written descriptions. They vary in size from an expanse of 1 inch to nearly 2 inches, and have the wings grayish brown to blackish brown to truly sooty, usually with obscure indications of markings on both wings and almost always with a few small distinct white spots near the apex of the fore wings. The small sooty-wing, *Pholisora catullus*, common in the east, expands 1 inch and has uniformly nearly black wings with a few distinct white dots on

## PLATE IX.

SKIPPER BUTTERFLIES.   (After Skinner.)

Fig.  1.   Pamphila hobomok, male, upper side.
"  2.        "            "        " under side.
"  3.        "            " female, under side.
"  4.        "            "        " upper side.
"  5.        " zabulon, male, upper side.
"  6.        "            "        " under side.
"  7.        "            " female, under side.
"  8.        "            "        " upper side.
"  9.        " scudderi, male, upper side (type).
"  10.       "            " female, upper side (type).
"  11.       " bellus, male, upper side.
"  12.       "            "        " under side.
"  13.       " panoquin, male, upper side.
"  14.       "            "        " under side.
"  15.       " stigma, male, upper side (co-type).
"  16.       "            "        " under side.
"  17.       " pittacus, male, upper side.
"  18.       "            "        " under side.
"  19.       " rhesus, male, upper side.
"  20.       "            "        " under side.
"  21.       " nemorum, male, upper side.
"  22.       " massasoit var. suffusa, male, under side
"  23.       " draco, female, under side.
"  24.       " loammi, male, under side.
"  25.       " alcina, male, upper side (type)
"  26.       " panoquinoides, male, upper side (type)
"  27.   Ægiale streckeri, male, upper side.
"  28.   Neophasia terlooti, upper side.

PLATE IX

the fore wings. Several large species, known as dusty-wings, expanding $1\frac{1}{2}$ to $1\frac{3}{4}$ inches, with grayish-brown to blackish-brown wings, belonging to the genus Thanaos, are common. Another large group of nearly indistinguishable species is that of the Pamphilas (Pl. IX). These skippers are mostly tawny and are specially recognizable by a discal black patch in male specimens, which appears like an oblique scorched streak near the center of each fore wing. This patch contains certain peculiar scales which give off scent presumably attractive to the females. *Erynnis sassacus* (Pl. X, Fig. 5), common in the Atlantic states, is a good example of the group. The least skipper, *Ancyloxypha numitor* (Pl. V, Fig. 5), is the smallest commonly seen and differs from other skippers in lacking the recurved hook at the tip of the antennæ and in having a slender body. The pale-yellow pilose larva feeds on grasses, especially those that grow in wet places.

The small butterflies popularly known as blues, coppers, and hair-streaks compose the family of Lycænidæ, or gossamer-winged butterflies, of which a hundred and twenty-five species are recorded from the United States, mostly the western half. The popular names express well the colors and pattern characteristic of the group. They are delicate, light-winged, slender-bodied butterflies rarely expanding more than an inch and a half and either bluish (pale whitish blue to brilliant metallic dark blue) or coppery or reddish or dark brown, often with small blackish spots, or marked with short fine little lines, hair-streaks, on the under side of the wings, and often with delicate little tail-like processes projecting from the hinder margin of the hind wings. The larvæ are flattened, short, broad, small, forked, slug-like caterpillars with small retractile heads; those of a few species distinguish themselves from all other butterfly larvæ by feeding on other insects, especially aphids. The chrysalid is naked, suspended from the posterior tip and supported by a silken line, or "bridle," about its middle.

Often to be seen fluttering or clustered about wet spots in the roadway are numbers of delicate little pale-blue butterflies with under side of wings almost white and conspicuously dotted with small black spots and with white-ringed slender antennæ; these are "blues," some species of the old genus Lycæna now broken up by modern systematists into a half dozen or more different genera. The spring azure, *Cyaniris pseudargiolus* (Pl. V, Fig. 4), is a wide-spread and common example of the group; with its several varieties it ranges over the whole continent, and it is one of the few "blues" whose young stages are known. The larvæ, which curiously secrete honey-dew from little openings on the seventh and eighth abdominal segments, feed on the "buds and flowers of various plants, especially those of dogwood (*Cornus*), *Cimifuga*, and *Actinomeris*." As many as three broods appear in a year. The various species of blues differ slightly in size, in shade of coloring, as grayish blue, lilac-blue, purple-blue, etc., in number and distinctness of the small black spots, but only an expert can determine the species.

Less in number of species and perhaps not quite so familiar are the "coppers" with orange, red-brown or dark-brown wings conspicuously spotted with black. Fig. 4 of Pl. X shows the color, markings, and size of a typical "copper," *Heodes hypophlæas*, "one of the commonest butterflies in the United States." Most of the other coppers have, however, hardly as bright-red a ground color on the fore wings, some being really somber. Most of them, too, are a little larger than *hypophlæas*. A species patterned and colored much like *hypophlæas*, but a half larger, is *Chrysophanus thoe*, found in the Atlantic states and west to the Rocky Mountains. The harvester, *Feniseca tarquinius*, small, with bright orange-yellow above spotted with black and mottled gray and brown underneath, is a common species all through the eastern states west to the Mississippi River; its larva feeds on the woolly plant-lice like the alder blight, apple-tree aphid, etc.

The hair-streaks, mostly belonging to the genus Thecla, have short narrow lines or streaks on the under sides of the wings, and are usually provided with one or more delicate little "tails" on the hind wings. They vary in color from a dull brown to a splendid glancing blue or blue-green. They usually have one or more reddish spots at the base of the "tails" and the under sides of the hind wings are often greenish or parti-colored. *Thecla halesus*, the "great purple hair-streak" (Pl. V, Fig. 9), is our largest species, and is found in the southern half of the country. Like the blues the hair-streaks are very difficult to classify to species; indeed professional entomologists are not at all satisfied with our present systematic knowledge of the Lycænidæ.

In the extreme southwest are found rather rarely the few species of "metal-marks," Lemonias and Calephelis, black and reddish checkered Lycænids, which occur in this country. Sometimes, as in *L. virgulti*, the wings are spotted with white. The vernacular name is derived from a few small lead-colored or pearly-white spots near the outer margin of the wings. The tiny metal-mark, *Calephilis cænius*, expanding only ¾ inch, and with the reddish-brown wings spotted with small steely-blue markings, comes as far north as Virginia.

A smaller family than the Hesperidæ or Lycænidæ, but with numerous better-known members, is the Pieridæ, the whites, yellows, and orange-tips. Because the larvæ of several species feed on cabbage and other cruciferous plants, the unhappy name of cabbage-butterflies is sometimes applied to them. The common whites and yellows are the most familiar of roadside butterflies, but of the sixty species composing the family in this country, only half a dozen occur in the northeastern states, the south and west being the favored regions of distribution. All the species except two or three are of medium size, that is, have an expanse of $1\frac{1}{2}$ to 2 inches, and have white or yellow, from light sulphur to orange, as ground color, with markings of black. The larvæ are mostly green, longitudinally striped, with more or less distinct lines usually paler, and harmonize so thoroughly in coloration and appearance with the green foliage on which they feed that they are not often seen. The chrysalids are naked, supported at the posterior tip and also by a loose silken bridle, and distinguished from other butterfly pupæ by a conspicuous median-pointed process on the head end. The males of many Pierids give off a pleasing aromatic odor which comes from certain scent-scales (androconia) scattered about over the wing-surface. If the fore wings of a freshly caught male cabbage-butterfly be rubbed between thumb and finger, this scent can be readily smelled on the fingers. It is used to attract or excite the females.

The three most abundant whites in the eastern and northern states are *Pontia protodice*, *P. napi*, and *P. rapæ*, the larvæ of all three species being voracious cabbage-eaters. *P. rapæ*, the European cabbage-butterfly, is a European butterfly which got to Quebec about 1860 and since then has spread over the whole country and is the most serious pest among all the butterflies; it expands from $1\frac{2}{5}$ inches (male) to nearly 2 inches (female), has faintly yellowish-white wings with the base and apex of fore wings blackish and with two circular black dots on fore wings of the female and one in the male; there is a single black spot (in male very faint) on front margin of hind wings; under sides of hind wings and tip of fore wings lemon-yellow. *P. protodice*, the southern cabbage-butterfly, or checkered-white, has at least three black spots besides a blackish apical border on the fore-wings of the male, while both the wings of the female are much checkered with blackish brown; the under side of the hind wings is white in the male. *P. napi*, the northern cabbage-butterfly, or mustard-white, appears in eleven or twelve appreciably different patterns, but characterized through all this variety by the pale or distinct grayish bordering of the veins; there is but little blackish on the wings of the male, at most one or two circular spots and a blackish apical border. In the western states the species of Pontia which will be found by most collectors are *beckeri*, distinguished by green markings on the under side of the hind wings; *occidentalis*, much like *protodice*, and *sisymbri*, a small species with the veins of the hind wings widely bordered with blackish brown on the under side. A beautiful Pierid is the pine-white, *Neophasia menapia*, of the Pacific states and Colorado; in both male and female the black color above is limited to the fore wings; there is a border along the costal margin from base to beyond the middle, where it bends in along the outer margin of the discal cell as a swollen club-like blotch; in addition the apex is broadly bordered with black in which three or four white spots appear; in some specimens the hind wings have a narrow broken border of scarlet on the under side.

Of the yellows, or sulphurs, the most familiar in the eastern states is *Eurymus philodice*, the clouded sulphur, expanding $1\frac{1}{2}$ to 2 inches; the wings are pale sulphur-yellow with black outer borders and with a discal black spot on each fore wing and orange spot on each hind wing; in the female the black border of the fore wings is very broad and contains five or six irregular yellow spots. Similar in pattern, but with the ground color of the wings bright orange instead of pale yellow, is the orange-sulphur, *E. eurytheme*, common through all the West. Both of these species are polychromatic and polymorphic, that is, show marked variation in ground color and in size, some individuals called albinos being white, some called negros being suffused with blackish; some are very small, others unusually large. A variety of names has been given to some of these aberrations because of their regular appearance under certain seasonal conditions. The longitudinally striped green larvæ of both species feed on clover. Another common sulphur in the southern and western states is the dog-face, large with pointed-tipped front wings and the yellow color of these wings so outlined by the black base and broad border as to produce a rough likeness to a dog's head seen in profile; a small discal black spot serves as the eye. The southern species is *Zerene cæsonia* (Pl. V, Fig. 10), the Pacific coast species *Z. eurydice*. The caterpillars, which are green with a whitish longitudinal stripe and a transverse dark line on each segment, feed on various Leguminosæ. Another common southern and western species is *Terias nicippe*, the black-bordered orange (Pl. XI, Fig. 2), whose larvæ feed on cassia. A striking species is the cloudless sulphur, *Catopsila eubule*, the largest of the Pierids, expanding $2\frac{1}{2}$ inches; it occurs in the southern and southwestern states, its larva feeding on cassia. At the other extreme in size is the dainty sulphur, *Nathalis iole*, (Pl. V, Fig. 7), the smallest member of the family, expanding but 1 inch; it has the same range and food habits as the cloudless sulphur.

In the western states occur seven or eight species of the pretty little Pierids known as orange-tips; only one species, *Synchloë genutia* (Pl. XI, Fig. 3), is found in the east. All are small and most of them are readily distinguished by the characteristic orange-colored apex of the fore wings as shown in the colored figure of *genutia*. *S. sara*, with two named varieties, *reakirtii* and *stella*, is the commonest western species. The larvæ of the orange-tips, so far as known, feed on Cruciferæ.

Perhaps the most striking and admired of all familiar insects are the great swallowtail butterflies. They have an easy, half-fluttering, half-soaring flight; their unusual size and their black and yellow (or greenish-white) tiger-like markings make them so conspicuous that they are fascinatingly apparent to the most casual observers. Twenty-one different swallowtail butterflies are found in the United States. Combined with them in the family Papilionidæ are two species of curious thinly scaled black- and red-spotted white butterflies called parnassians, which live exclusively in high

Fig. 639.—Swallow-tailed butterflies, *Papilio rutulus*. (From life; one-half natural size.)

altitudes in the Rocky and Sierra Nevada Mountains. Two more species are found in high latitudes on this continent, namely in Alaska. *Parnassius smintheus* (Pl. V, Fig. 8; also Fig. 633) with four varieties is found in both the Colorado Rockies and Sierra Nevada, while *P. clodius*, a larger species with more translucent fore wings, is found only on the Pacific coast and in the Wyoming mountains. I have seen *P. smintheus* in great numbers in the beautiful flower-dotted glacial parks of Colorado from an altitude of 6000 feet upward. The wings are so thinly scaled that they are nearly translucent, and the scales themselves are narrow and club-like, so different indeed from those of other butterflies that they probably have some special function not yet understood. The larvæ are "flattened," having a some-what leech-like appearance; they are black or dark brown in color, marked with numerous light spots. The chrysalis is short and rounded at the head, and pupation takes place on the surface of the ground, among leaves and rubbish, a few loose threads of silk being spun about the spot in which transformation occurs.

The swallowtails (Fig. 639), all except five of which belong to the genus Papilio (a name given them a century and a half ago by Linnæus, the first great classifier of animals and plants), are readily distinguished by the longer or shorter "tails," one to three, which project backward from the hind wings. The ground color is black, sometimes suffused with metallic bluish or greenish, and the markings consist of yellow or greenish-white bands and blotches together with a few red, orange, and blue eye-spots on the upper and under sides of the hind wings. The larvæ are large, cylindrical, fleshy, naked caterpillars usually conspicuously banded or spotted with green, black, yellow, orange, and white. They are provided with a pair

Fig. 640.—Chrysalid of a swallow-tailed butterfly, *Papilio* sp. (Natural size.)

of fleshy and flexible colored "horns" (osmateria) which can be protruded from, or withdrawn into, the front thoracic segment and which give off a strong musky scent sufficiently disagreeable to repel many threatening enemies of the caterpillar. The chrysalids (Fig. 640) are naked, suspended by the tail from a silken button and supported by a silken girdle or "bridle." They often mimic very closely the coloration and surface configuration of the tree-trunk or other object to which they are attached (Fig. 640). Poulton, an English naturalist, has been able to obtain chrysalids of a single swallowtail species of many different colors by enclosing the larvæ just before pupation in separate boxes lined with paper of different colors. The color-tone of the chrysalid tended strongly toward that of the environing paper. Such a color plasticity is certainly of much advantage to the insect in rendering the exposed and defenceless chrysalid indistinguishable. (See Chapter XVII for a discussion of "color and its uses.")

One of the best-known butterflies of the east is the zebra swallowtail,

## PLATE X.

### BUTTERFLIES.

1 = Cercyonis alope.
2 = Vanessa atalanta.
3 = Papilio cresphontes.
4 = Heodes hypophlœas.
5 = Erynnis sassacus.
6 = Basilarchia arthemis.
7 = Euvanessa antiopa

PLATE X

Mary Wellman, del.

*Iphidicles ajax* (Pl. V, Fig. 2), which is distinguished from all other swallowtails by its black and greenish-white wings and its long tails; it appears in three forms, one, *marcellus*, emerging in early spring with tails ¾ inch long and tipped with white; another, *telamonides*, appearing in late spring, a little larger, with tails ⅖ inch long and bordered with white on each side for half the length or more, and the third the typical *ajax*, still larger, appearing in late summer and autumn. Both of the first two forms may come from a single brood, some of the hibernating chrysalids producing butterflies earlier than others. It seems to depend wholly on the time of issuance and not at all on the character of the parent whether an individual shall be of the *marcellus* or of the *telamonides* form. The *ajax* individuals are those that are produced from eggs laid in the spring by either *marcellus* or *telamonides* individuals. Also some few chrysalids in every brood delay disclosing butterflies until the next spring. "*Marcellus* and *telamonides* thus produce *ajax* the same season, or either *marcellus* or *telamonides* in the following spring; *ajax* produces itself the same season or one of the others in the spring; but neither *marcellus* nor *telamonides* is produced the same season by any of the forms" (Scudder). The larvæ of this species are pea-green, naked, thickest in the thorax, with transverse markings consisting of black dots and lines and slender yellow stripes besides a yellow-edged, broad, velvety b'ack stripe on the thorax. They feed on papaw.

*Papilio turnus*, the tiger swallowtail, or Turnus butterfly (Pl. V, Fig. 6), is another common species, with a striking "negro" form called *glaucus*. In *glaucus* the disk of the wing is wholly dusted over with black scales so that the bands can be hardly seen. It is found only in regions where there are two or more broods a year, and is represented by females alone. The tiger swallowtail ranges clear across the continent, and sometimes occurs in great numbers; Scudder says that on a cluster of lilacs 69 specimens were captured at one time by closing the two hands over them. The larvæ, which feed on many plants but particularly like wild-cherry, are naked and leaf-green, with the front part of the body much enlarged and bearing a double stripe of yellow and black across the back, as well as a pair of yellow-black and turquoise eye-spots in front of this band and several rows of turquoise dots behind it. On the Pacific coast occur *P. rutulus* (Fig. 639) and *P. eurymedon* of the same general pattern of *turnus*, the first being black and yellow as *turnus* is, but the second being black and pale greenish or yellowish white. In the Rocky Mountains is found the splendid Daunus swallowtail, *P. daunus*, larger than Turnus and with two tails on the hind wings and a third tail-like lobe at the inner angle. The larva of *rutulus* feeds on alder and willow, of *eurymedon* on Rhamnus and other plants, and of *daunus* mostly on rosaceous plants.

Of different pattern is the fine giant swallowtail, *P. cresphontes* (Pl. X,

Fig. 3), native in the south, but now gradually spreading north. The caterpillar, sometimes called "orange-puppy" in Florida, feeds on orange- and lemon-trees, besides other plants, and is swollen in front of the middle, with the anterior part of the body rusty brown with lateral stripe, the hinder end of which, including two or three segments and a broad saddle in the middle, is cream-yellow flecked with brown.

A smaller widely distributed and well-known Papilio is the common Eastern black swallowtail, *P. polyxenes*, represented by five named varieties besides the type form. The black wings are crossed by two rows of yellow spots, the inner ones the larger, and there is a series of yellow marginal lunules; incomplete bluish spots lie between the two yellow rows of spots on the hind wings, specially distinct and large in the female. The larva feeds on parsnips, caraway, etc., and is green-ringed with black and spotted with yellow. *P. troilus*, the spice-bush swallowtail of the eastern and middle states, has a single row of well-separated yellow spots near the outer margin of each wing, with indications of a bluish or greenish row inside this, specially distinct on the hind wings; there is an orange spot at each end of this row on the hind wings. The larva lives on spicewood and sassafras and makes a protecting nest by tying the edges of a leaf together. The pipe-vine swallowtail, *Laertias philenor*, has no band of yellow spots, but only a few indicated lilac-colored remnants of spots, and has the hind wings suffused with beautiful glossy blue-green, especially beyond the base; its caterpillar feeds on Dutchmen's pipe and a wild species of Aristolochia, common in the Appalachian forests. There are two Papilionids without tails, viz., *Ithobalus acauda*, found in New Mexico, and *I. polydamas*, found in Florida; both are beautiful butterflies, much like *P. philenor* in color and marking.

The largest family of Rhopalocera is that of the Nymphalidæ, or brush-footed butterflies, the vernacular name partly describing their most distinctive structural peculiarity, namely the marked reduction (atrophy) of the fore legs to be functionless little hairy brush-like processes without tarsal claws on the feet; in both sexes these fore feet lie folded on the thorax, "like a tippet," as Comstock has said. This and the possession of an always five-branched radial vein in the fore wing are about the only structural characteristics common to all the butterflies of this large family. The species range from small to large, present a bewildering variety of coloring and pattern and an equal variety of larval habit and appearance. All the chrysalids are naked, usually angular, and are suspended head downward by the tail without other support. Nearly 250 species of Nymphalids are recorded from this country, and the majority of the best-known and most abundant butterflies in any locality belong to the group. Some systematists consider the brush-footed butterflies to form several distinct families—this is the point of view taken by the author of the latest catalogue of North American Lepidoptera—while those who believe in the family unity of the group subdivide it into a number of subfamilies.

In the face of the large number of beautiful, interesting, and familiar species of Nymphalidæ we can only select, for description in our limited space, a few of the most familiar and interesting. The special collector and student of butterflies will find awaiting him a large literature mostly readily available, and to this he must refer for anything like a comprehensive account of the species of this family.

The all-conquering American butterfly is the monarch, *Anosia plexippus* (Pl. XI, Fig. 4; also Fig. 641), sometimes called the milkweed-butter-

FIG. 641.—The monarch butterfly, *Anosia plexippus* (above), distasteful to birds, and the viceroy, *Basilarchia archippus* (below), which mimics it. (Three-fourths natural size.)

fly because of the food-plant of its larva. This great red-brown butterfly king ranges over all of North and South America, and has begun its invasion of other countries by getting a foothold on the west coast of Europe and in almost all of the Pacific islands and in Australia. I have found the monarch the most abundant butterfly through all of the Hawaiian Islands 2000 miles distant from the Californian coast, and still 2000 miles farther into the great Pacific in the Samoan Islands it is also the dominant butterfly species. Its success is due to its hardiness, its strong flight power, the abundance and cosmopolitan distribution of its food-plant, and finally and most important its inedibility—to birds. It secretes in its body an ill-tasting acrid fluid, and birds soon learn to let these disagreeable butterfly morsels alone. For the sake of this immunity another butterfly species, the viceroy, *Basilarchia archippus* (Pl. XI, Fig. 1; also Fig. 641), which is not ill-tasting, mimics in extraordinary degree the color pattern of the monarch, so that it must be constantly mistaken for the disagreeable monarch and is passed unmolested by experienced birds. The monarch in the eastern states has a migratory habit not unlike that of birds, great swarms flying south in the autumn to the Gulf states and West Indies, returning north again in the spring, not in swarms, however, but singly. It ranges as far north as Canada. It has, too, a curious habit of assembling in great numbers in a few trees, like blackbirds or crows in a "roost," and hanging there quietly in masses and festoons, many individuals clinging only to each other and not to the branches at all. On certain great pine trees near the Bay of Monterey on the Californian coast I have seen myriads of monarchs thus "sembled." The eggs are laid singly on the leaves of various milkweed species, *Asclepias cornuti* the favored kind, and hatch in about four days. The larva (Fig. 791) attains its full growth in two or three weeks and is a conspicuous object with its greenish-white body regularly banded with narrow black and yellow stripes; it has two pairs of slender black filaments, one on the second thoracic and the other on the eighth abdominal segment. The beautiful plump chrysalid is pea-green, smooth, and rounded with a few black and gilt spots and bands. The pupal stage lasts from nine to fifteen days. There is but one generation a year in the north, but two appear in the south. The winter is passed by the adult butterfly in the warm region of the subtropics.

Although the viceroy, *Basilarchia archippus*, closely resembles the monarch in its red-brown ground-color, black-bordered veins, and small white spots, only one of the half-dozen other species of the same genus is at all like it. This one is *B. floridensis* found in the southern states. The others have a blackish ground-color with the hind wings suffused with greenish blue and a few conspicuous reddish blotches on the under side of both wings, as in the red-spotted purple, *B. astyanax*, common in the East, or broadly banded with white, as in the banded purple, *B. arthemis* (Pl. X, Fig. 6), of the northeastern states, or have a blackish-brown ground with broad white band and red-brown apex of the fore wings, as in Lorquins Admiral, *B. lorquini*, of the Pacific states. The larvæ of Basilarchia feed on oaks, birches, willows, currants, and various other trees and shrubs, and are odd-appearing caterpillars with numerous prominent tubercles or bosses on the back.

Beautiful and abundant Nymphalids are the angle-wings, tawny above with black markings, dead-leaf-like below and often with a little silvery comma-spot. The comma-butterfly, *Polygonia comma* (Pl. XI, Fig. 6; also Fig. 642), is a familiar eastern representative of the angle-wings. On the under side of each hind wing is a small but distinct silver comma or C spot.

FIG. 642.—The comma-butterfly, *Polygonia comma;* two butterflies, a caterpillar, and empty chrysalid on gooseberry branch. (After Lugger; natural size.)

The spiny greenish-brown larvæ feed on hops, nettles, and elms. The pale wood-brown chrysalids with metallic golden or silver spots are commonly known as hop-merchants.  If the spots are golden, hops are to bring high prices; if silvery, low prices!  The violet-tip, *P. interrogationis*, is another common eastern angle-wing and has on the under side of the hind wings a double silver spot a little like a question-mark but more like a semicolon.

FIG. 643.—The larva of the violet-tipped butterfly, *Polygonia interrogationis*, making its last moult, i.e., pupating.  (Photograph from life by author; slightly enlarged.)

Its chestnut-colored, pale-spotted, spiny larva feeds on hops, elms, and linden.  Fig. 643 shows a caterpillar just pupating, and Fig. 644 shows the formed chrysalid.  There are eight other species of Polygonia in the United States.

The Vanessas are among the best known of our butterflies.  Three species, *V. atalanta* (Pl. X, Fig. 2), the red admiral, *V. huntera*, the painted beauty, and *V. cardui*, the thistle-butterfly, are found all over the United States, and in addition a fourth, *V. caryæ*, the west-coast lady, occurs on the Pacific coast.  The latter three species are but little like *atalanta*, having the wings blackish brown, plentifully and irregularly marked with orange and whitish; underneath there are true eye-spots; *huntera* may be distinguished from *cardui* by having but two complete eye-spots instead of several, and *caryæ* differs from *cardui* by the absence of the rosy tint peculiar to that species, the tawnier ground-color of the upper surfaces, and the complete black band which crosses the discal cell of the fore wings.  *Atalanta*

## PLATE XI.

### BUTTERFLIES.

1 = Basilarchia archippus.
2 = Terias nicippe.
3 = Synchloe reakirtii.
4 = Anosia plexippus.
5 = Anæa andria.
6 = Polygonia comma.

PLATE XI

*Mary Wellman, del.*

and *cardui* occur also in Europe, and *cardui* is held to be the most nearly cosmopolitan of all butterflies, ranging over nearly the whole earth outside the arctic and antarctic regions. Its larvæ feed on thistles by preference, but on almost any composite if necessary: those of *huntera* on everlasting and other Gnaphalieæ; those of *atalanta* on nettles; while those of *caryæ* feed on *Lavatera assurgentiflora*. All these larvæ are spiny.

Two striking, widely distributed, and abundant butterflies are the mourning-cloak, *Euvanessa antiopa* (Pl. X, Fig. 7), and the peacock-butterfly, or buckeye, *Junonia cœnia* (Pl. V, Fig. 1). Both are found over nearly all of our country, and the mourning-cloak is common in Europe. The

FIG. 644.—Chrysalid or pupa of the violet-tipped butterfly, *Polygonia interrogationis*. (Photograph from life by author; slightly enlarged.)

larva of the buckeye is black-gray marked with minute black-edged orange dashes and dots transversely arranged, and has long spines all over its body; it feeds on Scrophulariaceæ, especially Gerardia. The larva of the mourning-cloak is velvety black sprinkled with white papillæ and with a row of large medio-dorsal orange spots, and has spines much longer than the body segments. A curious butterfly of the Mississippi Valley and Great Plains is *Anæa andria*, the goatweed-butterfly (Pl. XI, Fig. 5). The larva, which is naked, gray-green, and studded with numerous paler points, feeds on species of Croton, the goatweeds. The American tortoise-shell, *Aglais milberti*, which occurs commonly in the North, has brownish-black wings with a broad orange fulvous band between the middle and outer margin; there are also two fulvous spots in the discal cell of the fore wing. The larva, which feeds on nettles, is spiny, velvety black above, greenish yellow below, and profusely dotted with whitish spots or points. Another northern butterfly is the Compton tortoise, *Eugonia j-album*, which resembles in general color and pattern the angle-wings (Polygonia), but has the hinder margin of the fore wings straight, the markings on these wings heavier, and a whitish spot on both fore and hind wings near the apex; there is also a small L-shaped silver spot on the under side of the hind wings. *Eugonia californica*, the California sister, is a beautiful butterfly common on the Pacific coast and found occasionally in the Rocky Mountains; it is velvety blackish brown with a broad white transverse bar across each wing, interrupted on the fore wings and tapering out on the hind wings, and with a conspicuous large orange-brown patch nearly filling the apex of the fore wings. Its larva feeds on oaks.

Two large groups of brush-footed butterflies, some of whose species occur in every locality, are the fritillaries, or silver-spots (genus Argynnis and allies) and the checker-spots (genus Melitaea and allies). The fritillaries, mostly medium-sized to large butterflies, are usually red-brown with numerous black spots scattered over the upper surface of both wings; the hind wings usually bear on the under side a number of striking silvery blotches, which give these butterflies their name of silver-spots. The regal fritillary, *Speyeria idalia*, of the Atlantic states, expands $2\frac{3}{4}$ to 4 inches and has the fore wings bright fulvous above spotted with black, and the hind wings blue-black with a marginal row of fulvous and submarginal row of cream-colored spots; both fore and hind wings have silver blotches on the under sides. The black, ocher, and red-banded caterpillars have six rows of fleshy black and white spines; they feed on violets and are nocturnal. The spangled fritillary, *Argynnis cybele*, is a good example of the more usual coloring and pattern of the group. It expands from 3 to 4 inches, has both wings fulvous above and thickly spotted with black; the under side of the hind wings is silver-blotched; in the female the basal half of the fore and hind wings above is dark chocolate-brown. The caterpillar is black with six rows of shining black branching spines, and feeds on violets. Numerous other smaller Argynnids are like *cybele* in color and pattern: it is difficult to distinguish the various species.

The checker-spots, small to medium size, blackish with red and yellowish spots, are represented by numerous species in the western mountain states, but by only two species in the east. The Baltimore, *Euphydryas phaeton*, expanding $1\frac{3}{4}$ to $2\frac{1}{2}$ inches, is the most familiar eastern checker-spot; it is black above with a marginal row of red spots followed by three rows of pale-yellow spots on the fore wings and two on the hind wings; besides there are some scattered red spots and some other yellow ones. The caterpillar is black, spiny, and banded with orange-red; it feeds chiefly on *Chelone glabera*, a kind of snakehead. On the Pacific coast the chalcedon, *Melitaea chalcedon*, is the most abundant checker-spot, although several other species are common. It has black wings spotted with red and ocher-yellow; the spiny black caterpillar feeds chiefly on Mimulus and Castilleja.

The satyrs or meadow-browns are a group of fifty or more beautiful velvet-brown butterflies whose markings consist chiefly of eye-spots, large and small, on both upper and under wing surfaces. A number of species are abundant and familiar, but a majority live exclusively in mountain states, and especially in the west. The common wood-nymph, or eyed grayling, *Cercyonis alope*, (Pl. X, Fig. 1), is the most familiar eastern and middle state species. A larger similarly patterned form, *C. pegala*, is common in the south. The larvæ of the meadow-browns feed on grasses, are pale green or light brown, and have the last abdominal segment forked. On the Pacific coast one of the most abundant autumn butterflies is the California ringlet, *Cœnonympha californica*, a small buffy-white member of this group with small eye-spots only on the under side of the wings. A number of interesting butterflies related to the meadow-browns are found only on mountain-tops or in high latitudes (arctic region) the equivalent in life conditions of high altitudes. In the Rocky Mountains on the peaks of the Front Range (13,000 feet altitude) I have struggled, gasping in the thin air, after beautiful frail little brown and grayish butterflies, Œneis and Erebia. Far above timber-line on bleak mountain-tops, masses of broken granite overspread for great spaces with lasting snow, these hardy little flutterers live successfully. At the edges of the great snow-fields are patches of alpine flowers, fragrant dwarf forget-me-nots and buttercups, which furnish food and interest for them in the solitude of the high peaks.

The mountain-top butterflies of the White Mountains, of the Rocky Mountains, and of the Sierra Nevada are closely allied; indeed individuals of the same species are found on the summit of Mt. Washington and on the crest of the Rockies, and nowhere between these two widely separated localities. The question as to how this interesting condition of things came about would be answered (by the student of distribution) as follows: In glacial times the species probably ranged clear across the continent. With the retreat of the great continental ice-sheet, while most of the butterflies followed it closely north, or became in successive generations slowly adapted to the temperate life conditions, some few probably followed up the slowly retreating local mountain glaciers. In time, therefore, the descendants of these arctic-loving species found themselves still under truly arctic conditions on the snow-covered mountain-tops, but isolated by the temperate lowlands from the rest of their kind on other mountain-tops or in arctic latitudes.

There are several excellent books about American butterflies which will help the nature student classify his specimens, and tell him of the distribution and habits of the various species. Among the best are Comstock's "How to Know the Butterflies," Holland's "The Butterfly Book," and Scudder's "Everyday Butterflies."

# CHAPTER XV

## THE SAW-FLIES, GALL-FLIES, ICHNEUMONS, WASPS, BEES, AND ANTS (Order Hymenoptera)

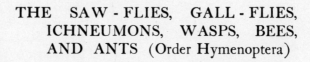

FIG. 645.—Mouth-parts of a honey-bee with maxilla and mandible of right side removed. *md.*, mandible; *mx.*, maxilla; *mx.p.*, maxillary palpus; *mx.l.*, maxillary lobe; *st.*, stipes of maxilla; *cd.*, cardo of maxilla; *li.*, labium; *sm.*, submentum of labium; *m.*, mentum of labium; *pg.*, paraglossa; *gl.*, glossa; *li.p.*, labial palpus.

**B**EES, ants, and wasps are the familiar Hymenoptera. They are the "intelligent" and the "social" insects, and therefore seem, of all the insect hosts, those living the most specialized or "highest" kind of life. As intelligence and social life are precisely those characteristics of our own which most distinctly set us off from other animals, we are quick to appreciate the worth of similar attributes in the "ant and bee people." But in actual degree of specialization of instinct and behavior the performances of the solitary wasps and bees are little less wonderful than those of the social kinds, and the amazing character of the life-history of many of the obscure and unfamiliar parasitic and gall-making Hymenoptera ought to incite as much interest and scientific curiosity as the marvels of the bee community. The Hymenoptera constitute a large order, 7500 species in this country, and one of endless variety of habit and structure. Few generalizations indeed can be made that will apply to all the members of the order, although there is no question concerning the true relationship of all the kinds of insects included in the order. Of the structural characteristics common to the Hymenoptera the clear, membranous condition of the two pairs of wings gives the name to the order (*hymen*, membrane; *pteron*, wing). The front wings are larger than the hind ones, and all are provided with comparatively few branched veins, whose homologies have not been fully worked out. The workers (infertile females) of all the ant species are wingless,

459

as are also the females of the Mutillid wasps and a few other exceptional forms. In many Hymenoptera (shown well in the honey-bee) the fore (costal) margin of the hind wings bears a series of small but strong recurved hooks which, when the wings are outspread, fit snugly over a ridge along the hind margin of the fore wing, the two wings of each side being thus fastened together so as to move synchronously. A structural characteristic not readily made out but of much morphological importance is the complete fusion of the true first abdominal segment with the thoracic mass, so that the small articulating segment between what are called thorax and abdomen is really the second abdominal segment.

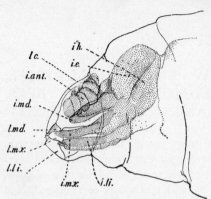

FIG. 646.—Lateral aspect of head of full-grown larva of honey-bee which has been cleared so as to show the forming adult head within. *ih.*, head of adult; *i.e.*, compound eye of adult; *lc.*, body-wall of larval head; *i ant.*, antenna of adult; *l.md.*, mandible of larva; *i.md.*, mandible of adult; *l.mx.*, maxilla of larva; *i.mx.*, maxilla of adult; *l.li.*, labium of larva; *i.li.*, labium of adult.

The mouth-parts are variously modified, but usually are fitted for both biting and sucking (or lapping). This is arranged for by having the maxillæ and labium more or less elongate and forming a sort of proboscis for taking up liquids, while the mandibles always retain their short, strong, toothed, jaw-like character. The mandibles of the honey-bee are modified into admirable little "trowels" for moulding wax and propolis. The females throughout the order are provided either with a saw-like or boring or pricking ovipositor, or with the same parts modified to be a sting. The sting is possessed by the wasps, bees, and ants (rudimentary in many ants), on which account these groups are often referred to collectively as the aculeate Hymenoptera. The sting of the honey-bee is shown in Fig. 650 and is a well-developed example of this characteristic hymenopterous weapon of defence and offence. The barb-tipped darts (*d*) extend down through the sheath (*s*) and are controlled by the chitinous bars called levers (*l*). The poison produced in the poison-gland (*p.gl.*) and stored in the

FIG. 647.—Mouth-parts of mud-wasp, with mandible and maxilla of right side removed. *md.*, mandible; *mx.*, maxilla; *mx.l.*, maxillary lobe; *mx.p.*, maxillary palpus; *li.*, labium; *m.*, mentum of labium; *pg.*, paraglossa; *gl.*, glossa; *li.p.*, labial palpus.

# PLATE XII.

## WASPS AND BEES.

1 = Sphærophthalmus californicus.
2 = Polistes aurifer.
3 = Elis sp.
4 = Psithyrus elatus.
5 = Bombus vagans.
6 = Agapostemon radiata.
7 = Xylocopa sp.
8 = Bembex spinolæ.
9 = Vespa germanica.
10 = Bombus californicus.
11 = Anthophora pacifica.
12 = Polybia flavitarsis.
13 = Chalybion cœruleum.
14 = Sphex ichneumonea.
15 = Pelopeus servilla.

PLATE XII

Mary Wellman, del.

sac (*p.s.*) flows from this into lesser reservoirs in the expanded base of the sheath and escapes through the valve (*v*) along the darts into the wound. The tactile (and perhaps olfactory) palpi (*p*) are used to explore the surface of the object to be stung. The modifications of the various appendage-like parts which compose the sting to form an egg-depositing organ (ovipositor) are extremely various and are described later in connection with various special groups. The number of separate parts or processes which compose the ovipositor or sting and which arise from the two abdominal segments next in front of the terminal one is six, and some entomologists consider these parts to be true appendages, homologous with the legs and mouth-parts.

In the development of all Hymenoptera the metamorphosis is complete, and the larvæ are, more than in any other order, helpless and dependent for their food and safety on the provision or care of the parents. With many

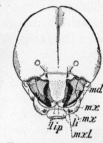

FIG. 648.—Frontal aspect of head of larva of mud-wasp. *md.*, mandible; *mx.*, maxilla; *mx.l.*, maxillary lobe; *li.*, labium; *li.p.*, labial palpus.

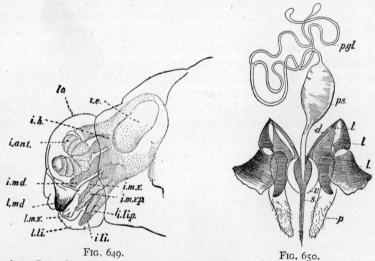

FIG. 649.

FIG. 650.

FIG. 649.—Lateral aspect of head of full-grown larva of mud-wasp cleared so as to show forming adult head within. *i.h.*, head of adult; *i.e.*, compound eye of adult; *l.c.*, body-wall of larval head; *i.ant.*, antennæ of adult; *l.md.*, mandible of larva; *i.md.*, mandible of adult; *l.mx.*, maxilla of larva; *i.mx.*, maxilla of adult; *i.mx.p.*, maxillary palpus of adult; *l.li.*, labium of larva; *i.li.*, labium of adult; *li.lip.*, labial palpus of adult.

FIG. 650.—Sting of the worker honey-bee. *p.gl.*, poison-gland; *p.s.*, poison-sac; *d.*, dart; *l.*, levers; *v.*, valve; *s.*, sheath; *p.*, palpus.

species, as the solitary wasps and bees, food is stored up in the cell in which the egg is deposited, so that the larva on hatching will find it ready to hand. With the social wasps and bees and all the ants, the workers bring food to the larva during its whole life. With the lower forms, the parasitic and gall-making kinds, the egg is deposited on or in a special and sufficient food-supply. All these unusual conditions are described in the discussion of the various groups. Indeed this whole chapter on the Hymenoptera is written especially with the aim of illustrating the biology, the special life conditions and relations of the various larger groups of these insects, rather than with the aim which determined the character of the chapters on the beetles (Coleoptera) and moths and butterflies (Lepidoptera), namely, that of presenting a systematic survey of the classification and individual habits of those members of the order most likely to be seen or captured by the collector. The beetles and the moths and the butterflies are the insects which fill the cabinets of the amateur and beginning student, and names and facts concerning particular species are likely to be the particular desiderata in connection with them. But it is the extraordinary and "wonderful" character of the ecological relations and physiological adaptations of the Hymenoptera which make these insects of such interest to nature-lovers, and which, indeed, is the subject that can most profitably be given special attention by any student of the order. Without, therefore, making any further attempt to formulate generalizations concerning this great complex of variously mannered insects, we may begin our study of its members arranged in subordinate groups, this grouping depending rather upon general biologic characteristics than strictly classific ones.

The classification of the Hymenoptera is a matter that interests but few amateurs; only a few families are at all well represented in general collections. Distinction among the more familiar larger groups, as the ants, bees, wasps, saw-flies, horn-tails, and ichneumons, is usually pretty well marked in the general habitus or *tout ensemble* of appearance. Certain other of the larger groups, composed of minute parasitic species, are almost unknown to the general collector; indeed but two or three American professional entomologists would attempt to distinguish species in these groups. In the following table, therefore, and in the later discussion of the various groups, I have lumped these little-known families together on a basis of commonness of habit, namely, of parasitic life, and devoted the space to a general account of the extraordinary life-history and habits which these parasitic Hymenoptera have adopted, with some reference to the special habits of certain particular species. Their classification into smaller groups is left undiscussed.

## KEY TO GROUPS OF HYMENOPTERA.

**A.** Trochanters (segment between the rounded basal coxa and the long femur) of the hind legs divided in two, i.e., two-segmented; female with a saw or borer at tip of body for depositing the eggs.

    **B.** Abdomen joined broadly to the thorax.

        **C.** Tibiæ of fore legs with two apical spurs; female with a pair of saw-like egg-depositing processes at tip of abdomen.

                (Saw-flies.) Family TENTHREDINIDÆ (p. 464).

        **CC.** Tibiæ of fore legs with one apical spur; female with elongate borer instead of saw...............(Horn-tails.) Family SIRICIDÆ (p. 466).

    **BB.** Base of abdomen constricted, so that it joins the thorax as if by a stem.

        **C.** Abdomen joined to the dorsum of the metathorax.

                (Ensign-flies.) Family EVANIIDÆ.

        **CC.** Abdomen joined to posterior aspect of metathorax.

            **D.** Fore wings with few veins and no closed cells (a few exceptions); very small parasitic Hymenoptera.

                Families CHALCIDIDÆ and PROCTOTRYPIDÆ (p. 476).

            **DD.** Fore wings with one or more closed cells (a few exceptions).

                **E.** Fore wings without a stigma (Fig. 655).

                    (Gall-flies.) Family CYNIPIDÆ (p. 467).

                **EE.** Fore wings with a stigma (Fig. 671); parasitic Hymenoptera, from very small to large.

                (The Ichneumons and other parasites.) Families BRACONIDÆ, STEPHANIDÆ, ICHNEUMONIDÆ, and TRIGONALIDÆ (p. 476).

**AA.** Trochanters of hind legs not divided, i.e., consisting of a single segment; female often with a sting.

    **B.** Fore wings with no closed submarginal cells (Fig. 683).

        **C.** Abdomen long and slender, and antennæ also long and filiform.

                Family PELECINIDÆ (p. 484).

        **CC.** Abdomen short, but little longer than head and thorax; antennæ short and elbowed............(Cuckoo-flies.) Family CHRYSIDIDÆ (p. 498).

    **BB.** Fore wings with at least one closed submarginal cell.

        **C.** First abdominal segment and sometimes the second segment in the shape of a small disk-like piece (Fig. 743).

                (Ants.) Superfamily FORMICINA (p. 533).

        **CC.** Basal segment (or segments) of abdomen normal or elongated to form a peduncle.

            **D.** First segment of tarsus of hind legs cylindrical and naked or with but little hair.

                **E.** Wings not folded longitudinally when at rest.

                    (Digger-wasps.) Superfamily SPHECINA (p. 490).

                **EE.** Wings folded longitudinally when at rest.

                    (True wasps.) Superfamily VESPINA (p. 503).

            **DD.** First segment of tarsus of hind legs expanded and flattened and furnished with numerous hairs, some rather long.

                (Bees.) Superfamily APINA (p. 510).

According to Ashmead our foremost American student of the classification of Hymenoptera, the above table gives in some respects false indications of relationship. For example, the Proctotrypidæ are held by Ashmead to be more nearly truly related to the wasps and to the gall-flies (Cynipidæ) than to the other parasitic Hymenoptera, as the Chalcididæ, Braconidæ, and Ichneumonidæ, with which this table groups them. The families composing the superfamilies Sphecina and Vespina, as separated by the character used in the key, are differently divided in Ashmead's superfamilies Sphecoidea and Vespoidea, and the families Tenthredinidæ and Siricidæ are replaced by the superfamilies Tenthredinidoidea and Siricicoidea, each containing several families. I only need to repeat what I have often said before, namely, that at best the keys and tables used in this book, as in most other insect manuals, to assist the student in his work of classifying insects are primarily things of convenience, taking advantage of obvious but often superficial and adaptively acquired likenesses and differences, rather than attempts to offer a true genealogical arrangement of the various groups.

The saw-flies, Tenthredinidæ, are the simplest Hymenoptera; they show no such extreme specialization in habit or structure as that possessed by the host of parasitic species, or by the "intelligent" groups, the ants, bees, and wasps. They compose a large family, 600 species being known in this country, but one of singular unity. The adults are much alike in appearance, and the larvæ all agree in their salient characters of structure and habit. Despite the large number of our species, comparatively few are known to the general observer, and these almost solely because of the injurious habits of their larvæ. These larvæ are the familiar rose-, currant-, pear-, larch-, and willow-slugs. They are soft bodied, naked, slug-like or caterpillar-like creatures, usually with six to eight pairs of prop-legs besides the three pairs of true thoracic legs, and are voracious devourers of green leaves. They may be distinguished from lepidopterous larvæ by their usual possession of more than five pairs of prop-legs and by their having but a single ocellus on each side of the head

Fig. 651.—A saw-fly, *Allantus basillaris*. (Twice natural size.)

instead of several. The eggs are laid by the females in little pockets cut in tender stems or in the leaf-tissue, usually on the under side, by means of the famous "saws" which have given the insects their vernacular name. These saws are a pair of small slightly chitinous pieces, finely serrate on the outer margins, which are carried by the last abdominal segment and can be thrust out and moved, saw-like, up and down. The larvæ, or slugs as they are often called because of their shape and the slimy secretion which covers the body of some kinds, usually "skeletonize" the leaves, i.e., eat away only the soft tissues, leaving the skeleton of tough, fibrous veins; often only the upper surface of the leaf is fed on. Some of them cover the body with a white, waxy secretion, and some, when disturbed, emit a malodorous fluid from the mouth or from pores in the skin. When full-grown, they crawl down to the ground, burrow into it, and pupate within a little cell sometimes lined with a thin silken cocoon. Some of the larvæ live in gall which develop about them; one such species is common on willows. The adults mostly have rather broad somewhat

FIG. 652.—The currant-slug, larva of the currant saw-fly, *Nematus ventricosus.* (Two and one-half times natural size.)

flattened bodies and head, are quietly colored, blackish, reddish, brownish, and usually quietly mannered, but fluttering about in the trees at egg-laying time.

It has been noted that numerous species of saw-flies can produce young

FIG. 653.—The currant-stem girdler, *Janus integer*, a saw-fly at work girdling a stem after having deposited an egg in the stem half an inch lower down. (Photograph by Slingerland; natural size.)

from unfertilized eggs (parthenogenetic reproduction), and in some species no males have yet been discovered.    It is indeed a general rule in the family that the females greatly outnumber the males.

Probably our most familiar saw-fly, at least in its larval stage, is the rose-slug, *Monostegia rosæ*, a soft-bodied, greenish-yellow, nocturnal larva that skeletonizes rose-leaves and often occurs in such numbers as practically to defoliate the bushes.    The adult fly is black with sooty wings and whitish fore and middle legs.    There are two generations a year.    Two currant-slugs are common:  one the imported currant-worm, *Nematus ventricosus* (Fig. 652), green with many small black spots (in its last stage only the head is black-spotted);  the other the native currant-worm, *Pristophora grossulariæ*, all pale green except the blackish head, which becomes partly green just before pupation.    Both of these slugs make slight cocoons of silk and leaves in which to pupate, the first-named one in or on the ground, the second one attached to the twigs or leaves of the currant-bush.

The pear-tree slug, *Eriocampa cerasi*, is half an inch long when full-grown, with the body expanded in front so as to be almost tadpole-shaped; it is greenish with a gummy slime over it.    It feeds in May and June on the upper surfaces of the leaves, and when full-grown crawls down to the ground and makes a little cell just below the surface in which to pupate.    The winged saw-fly is glossy black, about $\frac{1}{5}$ inch long.    The eggs are laid in slits cut on the under side of the leaves.    The larch is often seriously attacked by the larva of the saw-fly *Nematus erichsonii;* it is a glaucous green slug with jet-black head and two double rows of tiny black points around the abdomen; it is $\frac{3}{5}$ inch long and has seven pairs of prop-legs.    The adult, $\frac{2}{5}$ inch long, is thick-bodied, blackish with a broad bright resin-red band on the abdomen.    The eggs are laid in the young shoots in June or July, the larvæ feeding until late in July or early in August.    In California one of the most abundant saw-flies is a species of Lyda, which lays its eggs in the summer on the new growth of needles on pines.    The larvæ hatch out in fifteen days and feed on the needles for four months; then they transform to another larval stage, migrate to the tops of the trees, and just before winter spin a silken cocoon in which they pupate.    The adult flies issue in the spring.

A much smaller family than that of the saw-flies is the nearly related one of the horntails, the Siricidæ.    About fifty species are known in this country.    The females are provided with a boring ovipositor, which appears as a conspicuous, strong, long "horn," projecting from the tip of the abdomen;  Comstock describes this ovipositor as composed of five long slender pieces; the two outside pieces are grouped on the inner surface, and when joined make a sheath containing the other three pieces, two of which are furnished at the tip with fine transverse ridges like the teeth of a file.    With this boring ovipositor the female can drill holes into the solid wood of a tree and place an egg at the bottom of each.   One of the best-known horntails is the pigeon-tremex, *Tremex columba* (Fig. 654), 1½ inches long, with reddish head and thorax and black abdomen with yellow bands and spots along the sides.   The females bore holes ½ inch deep into elms, oaks, sycamore- or maple-trees, the ovipositor, in boring, being held bent at right angles with the abdomen.   The larvæ hatching from the eggs laid, one in each hole, burrow into the heart-wood of the tree, and grow to be cylindrical, blunt-ended, whitish grubs, 1½ inches long, with short thoracic legs and a short anal horn.   They pupate in their burrows within a cocoon made of silk and tiny chips.   The issuing winged adult gnaws its way out through the bark.   In

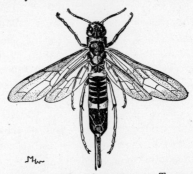

FIG. 654.—The pigeon-tremex, *Tremex columba*.  (After Jordan and Kellogg; natural size.)

some allied species (Sirex) the pupa may remain in the tree for several years.   Tremex is parasitized by an extraordinary ichneumon-fly, Thalessa, which has a slender, flexible ovipositor, four to five inches long, with which it bores into trees infested by Tremex and deposits its eggs in the Tremex-burrows.   The young Thalessa-grub (larva) moves along the burrow until it finds a Tremex-larva, to which it attaches itself, living parasitically.   (See account of Thalessa, p. 483.)   A small horntail sometimes abundant and injurious is the European grain-cephus, *Cephus pygmæus*, whose larvæ bore into wheat-stems.   The adult is ⅖ inch long, shining-black-banded and spotted with yellow.   It lays its eggs in tiny holes bored in the stems just about the time of the forming of the heads; the larvæ tunnel down through the stem, reaching the lowest part of the straw about harvest-time.   This part is left by the reaper, and in it the larva makes a silken cocoon within which it hibernates.   In March or April it pupates, and the adult issues in May.

Indications of the work of certain hymenopterous insects are familiar to even the most casual observers in the variously shaped "galls" that occur on many kinds of trees and smaller plants, especially abundantly, however, on oaks and rose-bushes.   Not all galls on plants are produced by insects, certain kinds of fungi giving rise to gall-like malformations on plants, nor are all the insect galls produced by members of that family of small hymenopterous insects called the Cynipidæ, or gall-flies.   But most of the closed plant-galls, and particularly those conspicuous, variously shaped, and most familiar ones found abundantly on oak-trees and rose-bushes, are abnormal growths due to the irritation of the plant-tissue by the minute larvæ of the

Cynipid gall-flies. These flies (Fig. 655) are all very small, the largest

species not being more than ⅓ inch long; they are short-bodied and have in most cases four clear wings with few veins. The females—and in numerous species there seem to be no males—have a long, slender, and flexible but strong, sharp-pointed ovipositor (Fig. 656), composed of several needle- or awl-like pieces, which is used to prick (pierce) the soft tissue of leaf or tender twig so that an egg may be deposited in this succulent growing plant-tissue.

Fig. 655.—A gall-fly, species undetermined.  (Much enlarged.)

Each female thus inserts into leaves or twigs many eggs, perhaps but two or three in one leaf or stem if the galls are going to be large ones, or perhaps a score or so if the galls will be so small as to draw but little on the plant-stores and be capable of crowding.  In two or three weeks the egg gives birth to a tiny footless maggot-like white larva which feeds, undoubtedly largely through the skin, on the sap abundantly flowing to the growing tissue in which it lies.  With the birth of the larva begins the development of the

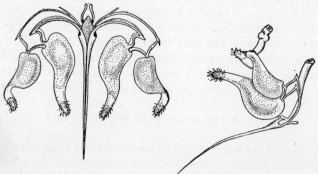

Fig. 656.—Ovipositor of a gall-fly, dorsal and lateral views; the long tapering part is the piercing portion; the other parts constitute levers and supports   (After Lacaze-Duthiers; greatly magnified.)

gall, which is an abnormal or hypertrophied growth of tissue about the point at which the larva lies.  The excitation or stimulus for the growth undoubtedly comes from the larva and probably consists of irritating special salivary excretions and perhaps also of physical irritation caused by the presence of the wriggling body. In some species the gall grows around and includes but a single larva, in others around several to many. The larva reaches its full development about coincidently with the full growth or end of the vitality of the gall, this period varying much with different galls. In the galls on deciduous leaves the vitality is shortest, ending in autumn; in twig-galls it may not end until winter or even until the following or indeed the second winter. When "dead" the gall dries and hardens, thus forming a firm protecting chamber in which the larva or larvæ pupate. The pupa undergoes its non-food-taking life securely housed in the dry gall, which may fall with the autumn leaves or cling to the bare twigs. From the galls the fully developed flies gnaw their way out when new leaves and tender shoots are appearing, ready to prick in new eggs for another life cycle.

FIG. 657.—Galls made by a Cynipid gall-fly. (Natural size.)

But, strange to say, with some species the new eggs may be deposited on plants of another kind and the hatching larvæ stimulate the growth of entirely different-shaped galls, and they themselves develop into gall-flies of markedly different appearance from their mothers. These new gall-flies in their turn lay eggs on the first host-plant; the forming galls are like those of the grandparent generation and the fully developed flies are of the grandparent kind. This alternation of generations— a condition in which a single species appears in two forms and produces two kinds of galls, usually on different host-plants—has been long known, but still remains a problem which interferes sadly with a number of popular biological generalizations. One of these generations appears exclusively in only one sex, the female, so that the other generation, composed of both males and females, is produced uniformly from unfertilized eggs. The adults and galls of the two generations were formerly described as belonging to two different Cynipid species. Not all gall-flies, however, show this dimorphic condition; some appear habitually in but one form and produce but one kind of gall; in most if not all of these cases the species is represented only by female individuals.

The great variety of the galls, the extraordinary instinct which leads the adult flies to the right selection of plant and position on twig or leaf for oviposition, and the interesting response or reaction of the plant to the growth-stimulating irritation of the gall-fly larva are subjects which have attracted much attention and study, but concerning which much remains to be discovered. In size and shape the galls present amazing variety; some are irregular little swellings on the leaves, others are like small trumpets, others like rosettes or star-like with radiating points; on the twigs some are spherical, some elongate, and some large and reniform. Figs. 657 to 665 show something of this variety. In their interior make-up they also differ much; some have a large hollow central space; some

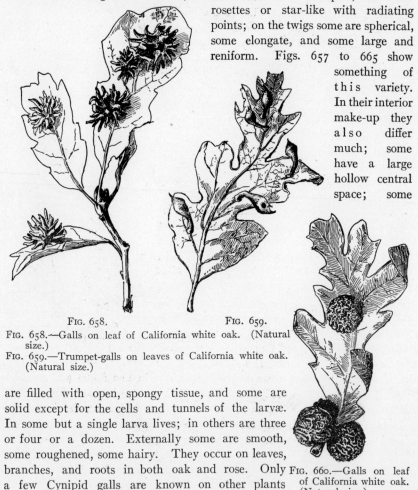

FIG. 658.　　　　　　　　　FIG. 659.

FIG. 658.—Galls on leaf of California white oak. (Natural size.)

FIG. 659.—Trumpet-galls on leaves of California white oak. (Natural size.)

are filled with open, spongy tissue, and some are solid except for the cells and tunnels of the larvæ. In some but a single larva lives; in others are three or four or a dozen. Externally some are smooth, some roughened, some hairy. They occur on leaves, branches, and roots in both oak and rose. Only a few Cynipid galls are known on other plants than these. In the face of the host of species of Cynipidæ found in this country—over 200 gall-making kinds are known, besides a score of parasitic species—and their small size and generally similar appearance, we shall not undertake to describe any of the various species. Comstock describes in his Manual several of the more common eastern galls, or

FIG. 660.—Galls on leaf of California white oak. (Natural size.)

"oak-apples." One of these is the fibrous oak-apple of the scarlet oak, 1 to 2 inches in diameter, produced by the gall-fly *Amphibolips coccineæ.*

FIG. 661.—Galls on leaf of California white oak. (Natural size.)

This gall is distinguished by having a small hollow kernel in the center of

the gall, in which the single larva lives, the space between the kernel and the dense outer layer of the gall being filled with fibers radiating out to the surface from the kernel. The spongy gall of the red and black oak, made by *Amphibolips spongifica*, has the space between kernel and outer wall filled by a porous, spongy mass. In the "empty oak-apples," the larger one of the scarlet and red oaks, *Holcaspis inanis*, 2 inches or more in diameter, and the smaller, of the post-oak, *H. centricola,* ¾ inch or less in diameter, and the space between kernel and outer wall contains

FIG. 663.        FIG. 662.

FIG. 662.—Galls on twigs of California white oak; upper figure, a gall split open longitudinally. (Natural size.)
FIG. 663.—Galls on leaf. (After Jordan and Kellogg; natural size.)

only a few slender silky filaments which suspend the kernel in place. The common bullet gall, *H. globulus*, of the small twigs, ½ to ⅔ inch in diameter, has the kernel surrounded by a hard woody substance.

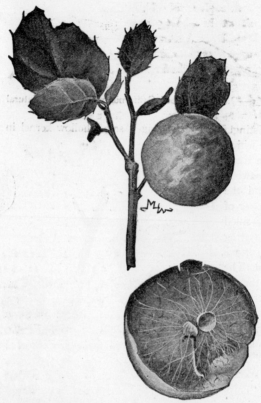

FIG. 664.—An oak-apple, or fibrous gall of the California live-oak; in upper figure the gall shown in position on the oak-twig; in lower, a gall cut open to show the inside. (Upper figure slightly reduced; lower figure natural size.)

In California the white or valley oaks bear very commonly conspicuous large white spherical to kidney-shaped galls (Fig. 665) which are attached to the branches, and often occur in such abundance as to make the injured tree look like some new kind of fruit-tree in heavy bearing.  This gall is caused by the gall-fly *Andricus californicus*, one of the largest of the Cynipidæ, and the gall itself attains a larger size than any other known to me. It begins as an elongate swelling underneath the bark of the fresh twigs, but soon breaks through as a shining, smooth excrescence rapidly increasing in size.   A single gall is inhabited by from six to a dozen larvæ.  A curious oak-leaf gall is the jumping seed-gall (Fig. 666), a small and shot-like gall which develops on the leaf, but which after reaching full growth falls off, when the

FIG. 665.—The giant gall of the California white oak, produced by *Andricus californicus;* at right a gall cut open to show inside structure. (After Jordan and Kellogg; one-half natural size.)

wriggling of the still active larva within causes it to roll about or even spring a quarter of an inch or more into the air.

Of the rose-galls Comstock mentions the mossy rose-gall, produced by *Rhodites rosæ*, as a very common one on the sweet-brier. It consists of a large number of hard kernels surrounding the branch and covered with reddish or green mossy filaments. In each kernel is a larva. The pith blackberry-gall, *Diastrophus nebulosus*, is a common, many-chambered, large, woody gall that occurs on black-berry-canes. It attains a length of 3 inches and a width of 1 inch to 1½ inches.

Regarding the wonderful instinct of the gall-fly, I quote the following from Stratton, an English student of galls:

"It is impossible that intelligence or memory can be of any use in guiding the Cynipidæ; no Cynips ever sees its young, and none ever pricks buds a second season, or lives to know the results that follow the act. Natural selection alone has preserved an impulse which is released by seasonally recurring feelings, sights, or smells, and by the simultaneous ripening of the eggs within the fly.

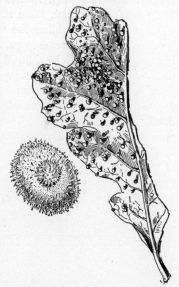

FIG. 666.—Jumping galls of the oak produced by *Cynips quercus-saltatrix*. (Galls on leaf of natural size; at left a single gall much enlarged.)

These set the whole physiological apparatus in motion, and secure the insertion of eggs at the right time and in the right place. The number of eggs placed is instinctively proportionate to the space suitable for oviposition, to the size of the fully grown galls, and to the food-supplies available for their nutrition. *Dryophanta scutellaris* will only place from one to six eggs on a leaf which *Neuroterus lenticularis* would probably prick a hundred times."

FIG. 667.—*Cynips quercus-saltatrix*, the gall-fly which produces the jumping galls. (Much enlarged.)

"Whatever form the gall takes, the potentialities of the tissue-growth exhibited by it must be present at the spot pricked by the fly."

"The potentialities of growth being present, they are called into activity by the larva, a result advantageous to the larva and sometimes described as disinterested and self-sacrificing on the part of the plant. We have just seen that, so far as the larva is concerned, the peculiar structures of the gall owe their origin to their success in feeding and defending it; and, so far as the plant is concerned, these structures have been evolved in consequence of their value in enabling the plant to repair injuries in general, and the injuries inflicted by larvæ in particular. If John Doe raises a cane to strike Richard Roe, and Richard throws up his arms intuitively to parry the stroke, the action does not indicate a prophetic arrangement of molecules to frustrate John in particular, but an inherited action of defence. The first act of an injured plant is to throw out a blastem, and only those larvæ survive to hand down their art which emerge from an egg so cunningly placed as to excite the growth of a nutritive blastem. It is not always possible to keep the besiegers from using the waters of the moat, although there is no disinterested thought of the besiegers' wants when the ditches are planned. So in the war-game that goes on between insect and plant, natural selection directs the moves of both players, but there is nothing generous or altruistic on either side."

The exact character of the plant's abnormal growth has been recently studied by several investigators. Cook, an American student, concludes from his studies that in the formation of all leaf-galls (except the Cecidomyid or dipterous midge-galls) the normal cell-structure of the leaf is first modified by the formation of a large number of small, compact, irregular-shaped cells. The mesophyll is subject to the greatest modification and many small fibro-vascular bundles form in this modified mesophyll. Both Adler and Sockeu consider that after the first stages of formation the gall becomes an independent organism growing upon the host-plant. Cook believes this to be true of the Cynipid galls. A surprising conclusion arrived at by Cook is that the morphological character of the gall depends upon the genus of the insect producing it rather than upon the plant on which it is produced; i.e., galls produced by insects of a particular genus show great similarity of structure even though on plants widely separated; while galls on a particular genus of plants and produced by insects of different genera show great differences. The formation of the gall is probably an effort on the part of the plant to protect itself from an injury which is not sufficient to cause death.

An additional interesting feature in the economy of Cynipid life is the presence in the galls of other insects besides the gall-makers. These others are on two footings, that is, some are guests or commensals, and some are true parasites, either on the gall-makers or on the guests! Curiously, among both guests and parasites are members of the same family, Cynipidæ, to which the makers and rightful owners of the galls belong. Others of the parasites may belong to the various well-known parasitic hymenopterous families, as the Ichneumonidæ, Chalcididæ, Braconidæ, etc., while others of the commensals may belong to entirely distinct orders, as the Coleoptera, Lepidoptera, etc. Kieffer (a famous French student of galls and gall-flies) gives the following amazingly large list of commensals and parasites bred from a common root-gall on oak, *Biorhiza pallida:* Commensals, the larvæ of five species of moths, of one fly, of one beetle, of one Neuropteron, and of two Cynipids; parasites, a total of 41 species, bred mostly from the various commensals.

The guest gall-flies, called inquilines, are often surprisingly similar to the species which actually produces the gall. A similar likeness between host and guest exists in the case of the bumblebee (Bombus) and its guest Psithyrus (closely related to Bombus). It may be that the guest species is a degenerate loafing scion of the working stock.

The group of gall-flies and their allies is looked on as a superfamily, the Cynipoidæ, in the latest authoritative classification (Ashmead) of the Hymenoptera, and divided into subfamilies, the Cynipidæ including the gall-makers, and the much smaller family, Figitidæ, including the parasitic species. Only about a score of parasitic Cynipoids are yet known in this country, while over 200 gall-making species and inquilines, or guest species, are known.

To collect gall-flies the galls should be gathered especially in the autumn, for with the end of the growing season the larvæ are mostly full-grown and ready to pupate. They should be separated according to kind, those of each kind being put into small closed bags of fine-meshed bobinet or tarlatan. In these the various gall-flies, inquilines, commensals of other orders, and the parasites will issue, and may be thus identified with their proper gall.

In the account of the Cynipidæ reference has been made to the division into gall-making species and parasitic species, the latter constituting but a small part of the whole family. The parasitic habit, only slightly indulged in among the Cynipidæ, is, however, the prevailing one of a majority of Hymenopterous insects. Although we commonly think of bees, ants, and wasps as the typical Hymenoptera and as constituting the bulk of the order, it is a fact that in point of numbers they are far outclassed by the parasitic forms whose life is, like that of the social Hymenoptera, also highly specialized,

Fig. 668.—Caterpillar of a moth killed by Hymenopterous parasites, the adult parasites having issued from the many small circular holes in the body-wall. (After Jordan and Kellogg; twice natural size.)

but along a radically different line. In a half-dozen families, including the largest in all the order, nearly every species is a parasite and a parasite of other insects. Indeed the chief agents in keeping the great insect host so checked that plants and other animals have some food and room on the earth are insects themselves. With all the artificial remedies man has devised and now uses against the attacks of insect pests, the all-important, constantly effective check on these pests is their parasitization by the host of species of the Hymenopterous families of Chalcididæ, Braconidæ, Proctotrypidæ, Ichneumonidæ, etc.

These parasitic Hymenoptera are only rarely collected by amateurs,

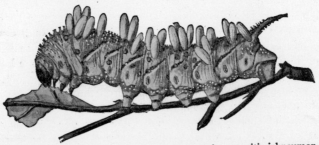

Fig. 669.—Larva of a sphinx-moth with cocoons of a parasitic ichneumon-fly. (Natural size.)

although caterpillar-breeders always get acquainted with some of them, to their dismay and disgust. But even if collected, the unsettled state of their classification, together with their (mostly) small size and the slight and hardly recognizable differences on which their scientific distinction rests, would make their systematic study nearly impossible for the amateur. On the other hand the interesting character and the biologic and economic importance of their habits of life make it desirable to know as much as may be about their life-history. I shall, therefore, give the little space which our book can afford to these insects almost exclusively to a consideration of the ecologic aspects of their study.

FIG. 670.—Hairy caterpillar killed by parasitic ichneumon-flies which have left the body through small holes in the skin. (Natural size.)

The superfamilies and families meant to be included among the insects referred to when the general term "parasitic Hymenoptera" is used are (using Ashmead's classification) the superfamily Proctotrypoidea, a great group of mostly minute species, many of which pass all their immature life within the eggs of other insects; the superfamily Chalcidoidea, an even larger group, also of small species, but with a few forms which are gall-makers and not parasites; and the superfamily Ichneumonoidea, including the larger parasitic Hymenoptera. Each of these superfamilies includes a number of families, and the three together comprise an enormous host of mostly little-known insect species. At the present time much diversity exists in the arrangement of the various parasitic families in entomological manuals. In the older books the parasitic habit has been looked to as indicating an affinity of relationship among them all; in more recent books and papers is adopted an arrangement proposed by Ashmead which indicates a nearer relationship on the part of

FIG. 671.—Caterpillar killed by Hymenopterous parasites which have issued from the cocoons attached to the skin of the caterpillar; upper figure one of the adult parasites. (After Jordan and Kellogg; caterpillar and cocoons natural size; adult parasite much enlarged.)

the Proctotrypoidea to the digger-wasps (Sphecoidea) and to the gall-flies (Cynipoidea) than to the other parasitic groups (Chalcidoidea and Ichneumonoidea). This latter arrangement is based on structural unlikeness among the parasitic groups to which Ashmead gives much classificatory importance.

Parasitism is a condition widely spread in the animal kingdom, parasitic species being found in most of the invertebrate phyla. The importance of these parasites in causing disease and death and their peculiar biological interest have led to much special study of them and of the particular phenomena of parasitic life. Parasites may be external or internal as they cling to the outer surface of their host or burrow within the body; permanent or temporary as they live their whole life or only part of it in or on the host; but in almost all cases except in those of our parasitic Hymenoptera the parasite shows a more or less marked degeneration or simplification by loss of parts of its body structure. Lice and fleas are the degenerate wingless descendants of winged ancestors; the intestinal worms are for the most part without sense-organs; the tumor-like Sacculina, parasite of crabs, has a body made up of feeding and reproductive organs and little else. But the parasitic hymenoptera show little or nothing of this insidious degeneration due to the adoption of a parasitic life. The reasons for this, however, are fairly obvious when the life-history and life-conditions of these insects are inspected.

The general course of the life and the character of the various stages of a parasitic hymenopteron are as follows: the winged, free-flying female (the males are winged and free-flying also) searches, often widely, for its special host species in that stage, egg or larval, on or in which its eggs are to be laid. This host may be always an individual of a particular species or may be one of any of several usually allied species. The hosts represent most of the larger insect orders, although caterpillars of moths and butterflies

FIG. 672.—A common parasite, *Merisus destructor*, female, of the Hessian fly. (After Lugger; natural size indicated by line.)

furnish the great majority of hosts for the parasitic Hymenoptera. On the surface of the body, or, more rarely, inserted beneath the skin, the parasite deposits one or several eggs. The footless, maggot-like larvæ soon hatch, and if not already inside the host's body very soon burrow into it. Here they lie, feeding on its body, tissues, growing and developing until ready to pupate. They may now eat their way out of the enfeebled and probably dying host to pupate in little silken cocoons or fluffy silken masses on or off its body-surface, or may pupate within the body. In the latter case the issuing winged adults have to bite their way out. The host usually dies before its time for pupation has arrived, but in some species it succeeds in pupating beforehand. The parasitic Hymenopterous larvæ, while degenerate in the same way as the footless,

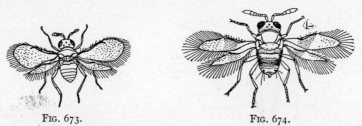

FIG. 673. FIG. 674.

FIG. 673.—A chalcid fly, *Pteroptrix flavimedia*. (After Howard; much enlarged.)
FIG. 674.—A chalcid parasite, *Aspidiotiphagus citrinus*, of one of the scale-insects of the orange. (After Howard; much enlarged.)

eyeless, antennaless maggots of house-flies, are not more so. Their parasitic habit has led to no such extraordinary structural specialization through degenerative loss or reduction of parts as is the usual condition in other parasites.

While Lepidopterous larvæ undoubtedly furnish the majority of hosts for the parasitic Hymenoptera, they are by no means the only ones. The eggs and pupæ of Lepidoptera as well as the larvæ, Diptera, Coleoptera, Hymenoptera in both egg and larval stages, some Hemiptera, especially

FIG. 675.—*Labeo longitarsis*, a parasite which lives in a sac in the abdomen of a Fulgorid, *Liburnia lentulenta*. (After Swazey; five times natural size.)

scale-insects (Coccidæ) and plant-lice (Aphididæ), the eggs of locusts and other Orthoptera, and some Neuroptera in egg and larval stage, may be infested; in fact the kinds of insects which may serve as hosts for the parasitic Hymenoptera strongly outnumber the kinds that do not.

While as a general rule each parasite confines its attacks to a single host-species, there are numerous exceptions; and on the other hand the host itself may be attacked by more than one parasitic species; most of our familiar Lepidoptera are parasitized by several different parasitic Hymenoptera.

For example, the American tent-caterpillar has been found by Fiske (New Hampshire) to be attacked by twelve species.

With regard to the number of parasitic individuals that may live at the expense of a single host individual no generalization can be made; the

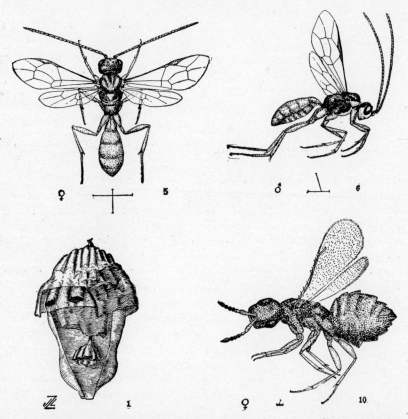

FIG. 676.—Hymenopterous parasites of a social-wasp. Fig. 1, nest of *Vespa* sp., portion of two envelopes cut away (two-thirds natural size); fig. 5, an adult parasite, *Sphecophagus* (?) *predator*, female; fig. 6, male of same species; fig. 10, *Melittobia* sp., female. (After Zabriskie; natural size indicated by lines.)

number varies, Howard says, from 1 to 3000. From a single caterpillar of the cabbage-moth, *Plusia brassica*, 2500 individuals of the parasite *Copidosoma truncatellum* have been bred. From large hosts are often bred large numbers of parasites, but with some parasitic species only one or a few eggs are ever laid on a single host, whether it be large or small. Small hosts cannot, of course, provide food for many parasites and hence the number in their case is always limited. Still, from a single scale-insect hardly more than ⅛ inch long a dozen and more tiny parasites have been bred.

A question of interest is that regarding how many individuals of a single host-species may, in a given locality, be parasitized. For the effectiveness of any parasite in keeping an injurious insect pest in check depends, of course, on its relative prevalence. Touching this may be quoted Fiske's estimate that less than 20 per cent of the American tent-caterpillars, which are attacked by a total of twelve species of parasites, are destroyed annually in the vicinity of Durham, N. H. On the other hand I have found a constant parasitization of about two-thirds of all the pupating individuals of the California oak-worm moth (*Phryganidia californica*) in years of its abundance in the vicinity of Stanford University, and this by the single ichneumon-fly, *Pimpla behrendsii*.

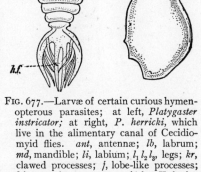

FIG. 677.—Larvæ of certain curious hymenopterous parasites; at left, *Platygaster instricator;* at right, *P. herricki*, which live in the alimentary canal of Cecidiomyid flies. *ant*, antennæ; *lb*, labrum; *md*, mandible; *li*, labium; $l_1 l_2 l_3$, legs; *kr*, clawed processes; *f*, lobe-like processes; *hf*, posterior processes. (After Kulagin; much enlarged.)

The success of any form of parasitism in any one locality in a given season brings up also the interesting matter of host and parasite "cycles." It is obvious that in the face of a scarcity of host individuals the dependent

FIG. 678.—*Pimpla* sp., an ichneumon-fly. (Twice natural size.)

parasitic species are bound to find difficulty in maintaining themselves; and conversely, that with the increase of the host in numbers "good hunting" arrives for the parasites. But the good times bring hard ones in their train, for when hosts are abundant the parasites increase so rapidly in numbers (having usually several generations to the host's one) as soon to overcome and sometimes almost extinguish in any given locality the host-species, which of course, means starvation for the parasite and a new lease of life for the host. Thus are brought about succeeding "cycles" of host and parasite abundance intimately associated with each other. In the case of the California oak-worm moth already referred to, a serious pest (when abundant) of the beautiful live and white oaks of California, the cycles are well marked, and we have come to rely on the effectiveness of the parasite species, *Pimpla behrendsii*, in overtaking by rapidly succeeding generations the increasing hosts of the pest, and in checking it before the actual realization of what is not infrequently threatened, the killing of all the live-oaks in certain regions of the state.

An interesting phenomenon in the biology of these parasites is that of hyperparasitism. It frequently happens that the parasites of a given host are themselves parasitized by other (usually smaller) parasitic Hymenoptera, while even these secondary parasites are not infrequently parasitized in their turn by still other species. Indeed some cases are known in which the tertiary parasites are infested by a fourth or quaternary species. An excellent example of hyperparasitism is revealed by Fiske's careful study, already referred to, of the hymenopterous parasites of the American tent-caterpillar. Twelve species of parasitic hymenoptera infest these caterpillars; of these twelve, six are themselves attacked by parasites (secondary), of which as many as six species may attack a single species of the primary parasites.

FIG. 679.—*Ophion purgatum*, an ichneumon-parasite of army-worms. (After Lugger; natural size.)

Among these secondary parasites are not only species distinct from the primary parasites, but some of the primaries parasitize each other as well as the caterpillars. Of the secondary parasites, four species are in turn parasitized by other (tertiary) parasites, of which three species have been noted, one occurring also as a secondary parasite; and finally, one of these tertiary parasites is infested by another of the tertiary group, which in this instance becomes a quaternary parasite. Thus the old rhyme of

> "Great fleas have little fleas
> Upon their backs to bite 'em,
> And little fleas have lesser fleas,
> And so *ad infinitum*,"

is often realized in the biology of the parasitic hymenoptera.

Most interesting questions are suggested when we consider the unusual life-conditions that may, and often do, obtain in parasitism. Lying immersed in the blood-lymph of the body-cavity of the host, how does the parasitic larva breathe, excrete, moult, etc.? The process of feeding consists probably for the most part simply in the taking up of the food from the host's blood, in many cases probably as much through the skin, by osmosis, as through the mouth itself. With some species, however, there seems to be a definite attack on certain of the solid tissues, as muscles, fat-body, etc. Such attacks necessarily avoid the vital organs or the host would be killed long before the parasitic larva is ready to pupate. With regard to the breathing it has been variously suggested that the larva applies itself to air-tubes (tracheæ) in the host-body in such a way as to effect an exchange of gases; that it needs no more oxygen than it obtains in the body fluid of the host; that its relation to the host is analogous to that of fœtus to mother among viviparous animals. Seurat's observations seem to indicate (for certain species at least) that solid food as well as blood-lymph is taken in; that respiration is effected through the skin by osmosis, that excretion from the intestine does not occur until after the pupal cocoon is formed, and that moulting actually occurs.

The host of species and the difficulties attending their determination, even (for amateurs) as regards their family classification, let alone their generic and specific identification, have led me to avoid any reference to the systematic study of these parasites. Certain particular species, especially among the larger forms, are of course more or less recognizable and familiar to observers. Among the larger species, most of which belong to the superfamily Ichneumonoidea, those of the genera Pimpla (Fig. 678) and Ophion (Fig. 679) are especially familiar. *P. conquisitor* (Fig. 680) is the commonest parasite of the tent-caterpillars (Clisiocampa), is also the chief one of the destructive cotton-worm, *Aletia argillacea*, of the south and has been bred from half a dozen other species of moths. It lays its eggs not on the larvæ of the tent-caterpillar moth, but on the pupæ (and perhaps on the caterpillars after spinning and just before pupating) inside the silken cocoon (Fig. 680). *P. inquisitor*, a common parasite of the tussock-caterpillars, is an ichneumon-fly whose life-history is given in much detail by Howard in the Insect Book. The Ophions are light brown or

FIG. 680. — *Pimpla conquisitor*, laying egg in cocoon of American tent-caterpillar moth. (After Fiske; about natural size.)

golden in color, with abdomen much compressed laterally. A common species parasitizes the giant larvæ of the polyphemus moth; but huge as this caterpillar is, only one egg is laid on it by the Ophion.

The wonderful Thalessa, with its flexible ovipositor six inches long, with which it drills a hole deep into a tree-trunk until it reaches a tunnel of the wood-boring larva of Tremex, has already been referred to (see p. 467). Comstock describes Thalessa as follows: "Its body is 2½ inches long and it measures nearly 10 inches from tip of antenna to tip of the ovipositor. When a female finds a tree infested by the Tremex she selects a place which she judges is opposite a Tremex-burrow, and, elevating her long ovipositor in a loop over her back, with its tip on the bark of the tree, she makes a derrick out of her body, and proceeds with great skill and precision to drill a hole into the tree. When the Tremex-burrow is reached she deposits an egg in it. The larva that hatches from this egg creeps along this burrow until it reaches its victim, and then fastens itself to the horntail larva, which it destroys by sucking its blood. The larva of Thalessa when full-grown changes to a pupa within the burrow of its host, and the adult gnaws a hole out through the bark if it does not find a hole already made by the Tremex. Sometimes the adult Thalessa, like the adult Tremex, gets her ovipositor wedged in the wood so tightly

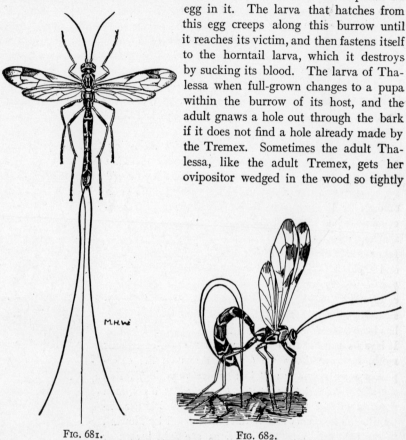

FIG. 681.                    FIG. 682.

FIG. 681.—*Thalessa* sp., ichneumon-parasite of the pigeon-tremex. (After Jordan and Kellogg; natural size.)

FIG. 682.—*Thalessa lunator* drilling a hole in a tree-trunk, in order to deposit its egg in burrow of the pigeon-tremex. (After Comstock; natural size.)

that it holds her a prisoner until she dies."

Another curious large parasitic Hymenopteron is *Pelecinus polyturator* (Figs. 683 and 684), the single American representative of the family Pelecinidæ, of whose habits little is known, but which has attracted much attention because of the strange discrepancy in size between male and female. The abdomen of the female is slender and 1½ inches or more in length, while that of the male is not more than ¼ inch. The males, only about ⅓ inch long, are much more rarely seen than the females.

Among the smaller parasitic Hymenoptera, the Chalcidids, Braconids, and Proctotrypids, but few complete life-histories are known. Many of the Proctotrypids, an enormous family in number of species, live, all but the winged adult stage of their life, in the eggs of other insects,

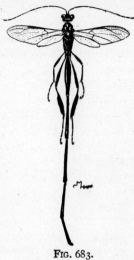

FIG. 683.

FIG. 684.

FIG. 683.—*Pelecinus polyturator*, female. (Natural size.)
FIG. 684.—*Pelecinus polyturator*, male. (After Packard; three and one-half times natural size.)

a half-dozen individuals perhaps in a single egg; needless to say they are among our smallest insects. Some are wingless, some show a marvelous hyper-

FIG. 685.—*Meteorus hyphantriæ*, parasite of the green-fruit worms, *Xylina* sp. (After Slingerland; much enlarged.)

metamorphosis in their life-history, and all present extremely interesting problems to biological students. Howard gives in his Insect Book an account of the life-history, as worked out by Schwarz, of a chalcis-fly, *Euplectrus*

*comstockii*, which infests various caterpillars. Its larvæ are external parasites clinging to the skin of the caterpillar. The chalcis-flies may usually be
recognized by the characteristic branched single vein of the fore wings (Fig.
673).

The economic importance of the hymenopterous parasites is obvious;
from the point of view of the economic entomologist there are no other

FIG. 686.—Larva of *Xylina lacticinerea*, green-fruit worm, killed by the parasitic grub
of *Mesochorus agilis*, which has spun its cocoon beneath the caterpillar, fastening
the latter to the leaf. (After Slingerland; natural size.)

insects outside of the pests of such interest as these natural pest-fighters.
Attempts have been made to make allies of them in man's warfare against
injurious insects by artificially disseminating them, even to the extent of

FIG. 687.—A caterpillar of *Xylina
lacticinerea*, green-fruit worm, from
which the parasitic larva of *Meteorus
hyphantriæ* has just emerged and
is spinning its cocoon. (After Slingerland; natural size.)

colonizing by importation from foreign
countries various new species in particularly pest-ridden localities. In California a constant and aggressive war has
to be maintained by the fruit-growers
against many insect pests, and particularly against the scale-insects. In this
warfare a number of attempts have been
made to introduce from other continents
parasitic enemies of the scales. Unquestionably considerable success has attended
some of these importations, although as
yet no other such signal overcoming of an
insect pest by the use of these Hessians
has occurred as attended the importation
from Australia, several years ago, of the predaceous ladybird-beetle (Vedalia),
enemy of the once dreaded fluted scale (see p. 189 for account of this).

Any discussion of the parasitic families of Hymenoptera would be incomplete if there were omitted all reference to certain species of Chalcidoidea which are exceptions to the general condition of parasitism obtaining in the group. A number—very small in proportion to the total number of species in the superfamily—of chalcidid species feed upon plants, producing small galls on the plants attacked. The wheat-joint worm, *Isosoma hordei*, whose larvæ live in small swellings —produced by their presence—in the stems of wheat and other grains, is a familiar example of these phy- tophagous Chalcidids. The most interesting species of this kind, however, is the "caprifying" fig-wasp, *Blastophaga grossorum*. There are several species of chalcidid fig-insects, but the species mentioned is the particular one on which depends the develop- ment of the Smyrna fig—by far the best of the food-figs. The male Blastophagas (Fig. 688) are grotesque, wingless, nearly eyeless creatures which never leave the fig in which they are bred, but the fe-

Fig. 688.—The fig-insect, *Blostophaga grossorum*, male. (After Howard; much enlarged.)

males (Fig. 689) are winged and fly freely about among the trees. A fig is a hollow, thick, and fleshy-walled receptacle in which are situated, thickly crowded over the inner surface, the minute flowers. The only entrance into the receptacle (or fig) is a tiny opening at the blunt free end of the young fig, and even this orifice is closely guarded by scales that nearly close it.

Fig. 689.—The fig-insect, *Blastophaga grossorum*, female. (After Howard; much enlarged.)

The eggs are laid by the females at the base of the little flowers in certain figs. The hatching larvæ produce little galls in which they lie, feeding and developing. They pupate within the galls, and the wingless males when they issue do not leave the interior of the fig, but crawl about over the galls, puncturing those in which females lie, and thrusting the tip of the abdomen through the puncture and fertilizing the females. The fertilized winged female gnaws out of the galls, and leaves the fig through the small opening at the blunt free end. She flies among the trees seeking young figs, into which she crawls, and where she lays her eggs at the bases of as many flowers as possible. But it is only the wild, inedible, or "caprifigs" that serve her purpose. The flowers of the cultivated Smyrna seem to offer no suitable egg-laying ground and in them no eggs are laid. But as the female walks anxiously about inside the fig, seeking for a suitable place, she dusts all the female flowers with pollen brought on her body from the male flowers of the caprifig from which she came, and thus fertilizes them.   This process is called *caprification*.*   Without it no Smyrna fig has its flowers fertilized and its seeds "set."   It is the development of the seeds with the accompanying swelling of the fleshy receptacle and the storing of sugar in it that makes the Smyrna fig so pleasant to the palate.   The trees may grow large and bear quantities of fruit, but if the figs (really the fig-flowers) are not

Fig. 690.—Figs on a branch; the two lower ones are mammæ, winter figs, from which
   Blastophaga are about to issue; the others are profichi, spring figs, ready to receive the
   Blastophaga.   (After Howard; natural size.)

caprified, the size, sweetness, and nutty flavor of the perfect fruit are lacking. To insure caprification, branches laden with caprifigs containing Blastophagas just about to issue are suspended artificially among the branches of the

* For an account of the important rôle played by insects in the fertilization of flowers
see Chapter XVI.

Smyrna fig. Of course the female Blastophaga entering a Smyrna fig and dying there leaves no progeny, for she lays no eggs. It is therefore necessary to maintain a plantation of caprifigs in or near the Smyrna orchard. These bear three crops or generations of figs: one, the "profichi," ripening in the

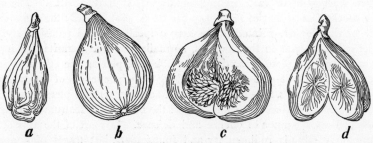

FIG. 691.—Figs showing effect of non-caprification and of caprification. *a*, outside appearance of non-caprified fig; *b*, outside of caprified fig; *c*, interior of caprified fig; *d*, interior of non-caprified fig. (After Howard; natural size.)

spring; another, the "mammoni," ripening in the late summer; and the third, or "mammæ" generation, which hangs on the trees through the winter. By means of these successive generations of caprifigs a series of three generations (or sometimes four) of Blastophaga appear each year.

In this country California fruit-growers have long grown figs, but they were of a quality very inferior to the well-known Smyrna, whose home is in Asia Minor. But the persistent efforts of an orchard-owner of the San Joaquin Valley, Mr. George Roeding, with the assistance of expert entomologists of the United States Division of Entomology, have resulted, after numerous unsuccessful trials extending over ten years, in establishing by direct importation from Algeria the Blastophaga in California, and the production of figs of the same quality as that of the Asiatic fruit. From caprifig-trees (grown from cuttings originally imported from Smyrna) scattered through a sixty-acre orchard of Smyrna fig-trees (also obtained from imported cuttings and which Mr. Roeding maintained for fourteen years without any financial return) figs containing Blastophagas ready to issue are taken off, strung on short raffia strings, and hung on the branches of the Smyrna fig-trees when the Smyrna fruit is ready for fertilization. In 1900 the first crop of California Smyrna figs was obtained—sixty tons, all from this orchard— and it is now practically certain that the colonization of the tiny chalcidid fly, *Blastophaga grossorum*, in California has added another important fruit to the list of horticultural products of that State.

## WASPS.

We have now to take up the more familiar groups of wasps, bees, and ants, in all of which the females (and the sterile workers in those species in which such kind or caste of individuals exists) have a sting. The sting (see description of that of the honey-bee on p. 460) is really the same structure as the slender, pointed, often long ovipositor of the parasitic Hymenoptera; but whereas in the saw-flies, horntails, and true Parasita this instrument is used for piercing or drilling a hole and placing the egg in it or on the body of the host—the egg passing along the whole length of the ovipositor and issuing from its tip—in the so-called aculeate Hymenoptera, that is, the stingers, the egg issues from the body at the base of the instrument which is itself used as a weapon of offence and defence. In most of the ants of our country the sting is rudimentary and functionless, but traces of it and its poison can be found.

The Hymenopterous insects referred to by the generic term wasps are many and various, and their multiplicity and variety have led to the formulation of many contradictory schemes of classification for them. That adopted by Comstock in his Manual groups them in two superfamilies: one, the Sphecina, or digger-wasps, including fourteen families; the other, the Vespina, or so-called true wasps, including but three. The Vespina include the social forms, as the yellow-jackets and the hornets, composing the family Vespidæ, one family of solitary parasitic wasps, the Masaridæ, and one other family of solitary mason, carpenter, leaf-cutting, mining, and digging wasps, the Eumenidæ. The Sphecina include wasps all solitary (not social), but some of them parasitic, some inquiline, some earth-diggers, and some carpenters and wood miners. The structural character separating these two superfamilies is the longitudinal folding or plaiting of the wings in the Vespina, a condition not present in the Sphecina. Some systematists refuse to recognize so many distinct families while others would perhaps subdivide them into a still larger number. The latest classification, that of Ashmead, recognizes two superfamilies, the Sphecoidea, or insect-catching wasps, including twelve families whose species are all solitary, none parasitic, and all diggers or miners, and the Vespoidea, including sixteen families of social, parasitic, guest, and mason wasps, together with a few diggers. The structural character separating these two great groups of wasps is the extension of the pronotum back to the tegulæ or shoulder-tippets (or the absence of the latter) in the Vespoidea, and the failure of the pronotum to extend back as far as the tegulæ in the Sphecoidea. All the bees agree with the Sphecoidea in this character, so that Ashmead thinks the Sphecoidea more nearly related to the Apoidea or bees than the Vespoidea are, despite the fact that all the wasps that live a communal life, like that of the bumble- and honey-bees, belong to the Vespoidea. The Sphecoidea may be distinguished from the bees by their slender undilated tarsi, as contrasted with the swollen, pollen-carrying tarsi of the bees.

The eggs of wasps are usually deposited in a nest (burrow in soil, tunnel in wood, receptacle built of clay, cells made of wasp-paper, etc.) in which food, consisting of killed or paralyzed insects, is stored for the use of the larva, or to which, after the larva's birth, insect food is brought by the mother or by sterile workers. The parasitic wasps deposit their eggs on the paralyzed body of some insect, while the guest wasps lay their eggs in the nests of other wasps or bees, where the hatching larva can feed on the food stored up by the host for its own young. The larvæ are white, footless, soft-bodied grubs, which lie in their cells feeding on the food stored up or brought them and pupating in the same cell. The adults on issuing

FIG. 692. — Nest-burrow of *Oxybelus quadri-notatus*. (After Peckham; one-half natural size.)

from the pupal cuticle gnaw their way out of the cell by means of their strong jaws. With the social wasps all the eggs are laid by a queen or fertile female in each community; with the solitary ones each female lays eggs.

The general external structural characters of wasps are familiar: the elongate but compact and trim body with usually smooth, shining surface, variously colored and patterned, steely blue, jet black, yellow, and rusty reddish being the commoner colors and the pattern usually consisting of narrow or broad transverse bands or rings. All have four clear membranous wings (excepting the female Mutillidæ), and all the females and workers have strong stings. The mouth-parts consist of strong toothed jaws, of jaw-like maxillæ and lobed under lip, the last two usually closely joined by membranes and specially fitted for lapping up sweetish liquids or soft viscous or solid substances. The killing or paralyzing of the prey (food for the young) is accomplished by the sting, while the digging and mining and the transporting of materials for the nest are done by the strong mandibles. The antennæ are rather long and slender, the compound eyes large and many-faceted.

The digger-wasps differ from the social kinds, such as the yellow-jackets and hornets, by not living together in communities, composed of a queen, males, and sterile workers, but by living solitarily. There are no sterile worker digger-wasps, but each female makes a separate nest and provisions it by her own labor. The stored food consists of paralyzed or, more rarely, killed insects or spiders. "The nests may be of mud, and attached, for shelter, under leaves, rocks, or eaves of buildings, or may be burrows hollowed out in the ground, in trees, or in the stems of plants. The adult wasp lives upon fruit or nectar, but the young grub or larva must have animal food, and here the parent wasp shows a rigid conservatism, each species providing the sort of food that has been approved by its family for generations, one taking flies, another bugs, and another beetles, caterpillars, grasshoppers, crickets, locusts, spiders, cockroaches, aphids, or other creatures, as the case may be.

"The solitary wasps mate shortly after leaving the nest, in the spring or summer. The males are irresponsible creatures, aiding little, if at all,

FIG. 693.—A solitary wasp, *Sphex occitanica*, dragging a large wingless locustid (Ephippiger) to nest. (After Fabre; natural size.)

in the care of the family. When the egg-laying time arrives the female secures her prey, which she either kills or paralyzes, places it in the nest, lays the egg upon it, and then, in most cases, closes the hole, and takes no further interest in it, going on to make new nests from day to day. In some genera the female maintains a longer connection with her offspring, not bringing all the provisions at once, but returning to feed the larva as it grows, and only leaving the nest permanently when the grub has spun its cocoon and becomes a pupa.

"The egg develops in from one to three days into a footless maggot-like creature, which feeds upon the store provided for it, increasing rapidly in size, and entering the pupal stage in from three days to two weeks. In the cocoon it passes through its final metamorphosis, emerging as a perfect insect perhaps in two or three weeks, or, in many cases, after the winter months have passed and summer has come again. Probably no solitary wasp lives through the winter, those that come out in the spring or summer perishing in the autumn."

The nest-making habits of any solitary wasp, when carefully observed, will prove to be of absorbing interest. On the broad salt marshes of the

Fig. 694.—Nesting-grounds of the solitary wasp, *Ammophila* sp., in the salt marshes of San Francisco Bay.

western shore of San Francisco Bay near Stanford University I have often watched an interesting species of wasp at work. This is one of the genus Ammophila, the thread-waisted sand-diggers. The marshes are nearly covered with a dense growth of a low fleshy-leaved plant, the samphire or pickle-weed (Salicornia), but here and there are small, perfectly bare, level, sandy places, which shine white and sparkling in the sun because of a thin incrustation of salt. In September these bare places are taken possession

Fig. 695.—Ammophila putting inchworm into nest-burrow. (From life; natural size.)

of by many female Ammophilas, which make short vertical nest-burrows all over the ground. An Ammophila having chosen a site for its nest bites out a small circular piece of the salty crust, and with its strong jaws digs out bit by bit a little well. Each pellet dug out is carried away by the wasp, flying a foot or two from the mouth of the tunnel, and dropped. To emerge from the hole the wasp always backs upward out of it and while digging keeps up a low humming sound.  After the tunnel is dug about three inches deep she covers up the mouth with a bit of salt crust or little pebbles, and flies away.  Some minutes later she comes back carrying a limp inchworm about an inch long, which she drags down into the nest.  Away she goes again and soon returns with another inchworm; repeating the process until from five to ten caterpillars have been stored in the tunnel.  All these are alive, but each has been stung in one of its nerve-centers (ganglia) so that it is paralyzed.  Finally, down she goes and lays a single egg, attaching

FIG. 696.　　　　　　　　　　　　FIG. 697.

FIG. 696.—Nest-burrow of Ammophila, with food for the young; paralyzed inchworms in bottom and burrow nearly filled.  (Natural size.)

FIG. 697.—Ammophila bringing covering bit of salt incrustation to put over the stored and filled nest-burrow.  (From life; natural size.)

it to one of the paralyzed caterpillars.  She then fills the tunnel with pellets of earth, carefully chewing up the larger pieces so as to make a close, well-packed filling.  Lastly, she carefully smooths off the surface and puts a small flat piece of salt crust on top, so that the site of the tunnel shall be as nearly indistinguishable as possible.

Ammophilas are common all over the country, and the nest-building of various species has been watched by other observers.  The use by an individual Ammophila of a small pebble, held in the jaws, as a tool to pound down and smooth off the earth has been twice recorded, once in Wisconsin and once in Kansas.  These are perhaps our only records of the use of a tool by an insect.

The habits of the Ammophila described above are typical of the interesting life-history which, varying indeed in many details, is common to nearly all of the solitary wasps, whether belonging to the Sphecoidea or Vespoidea.

Exceptions are those species which live as guests of other wasps, or as parasites on other insects.

The habit common to almost all of the solitary wasps of so stinging the prey, caterpillars, spiders, beetles, flies, bugs, or whatever other insects are used to provision the nests, as not to kill but only to paralyze it, is perhaps the most amazing part of all the interesting behavior of all these wasps. The advantage is obvious: killed, the prey would quickly decompose, and the hatching carnivorous wasp larva would have only a mass of, to it, inedible, decaying flesh instead of the fresh live animal substance it demands. But if stored unhurt, the prey would, if a cricket or spider or similarly active animal, quickly escape from the burrow, or if a caterpillar or weak bug, at least succeed, albeit unwittingly, in crushing the tender wasp egg by wriggling about in the underground prison-cell. More than that, unhurt, some insects could not live without food the many days that are necessary for the development of the wasp larva, especially in the face of the frantic and exhausting efforts they would be impelled to in their attempts to escape. But paralyzed, there is no exertion, metabolism is slight, and life without food is capable of being prolonged many days. The paralysis is due to the stinging by the wasp of one or more of the ganglia (nerve-centers)

FIG. 698.—*Cerceris tuberculata*, dragging weevil (*Cleonus* sp.) to nest.
(After Fabre; natural size.)

of the ventral nerve-cord. With a wasp species (*Sphex flavipennis*) observed by Fabre,* which provisions its nest with crickets, each cricket was stung

* Fabre, J. H., Insect Life, 1901.

three times, once in each thoracic ganglion which resulted in immediate complete paralysis. *Cerceris tuberculata* hunts weevils (Cleonus) (Fig. 698) and stings them exactly in the large central ganglion formed by the fusion of the three thoracic ganglia, paralyzing them immediately. Insects thus paralyzed will keep alive, flexible, and fresh, but immovable, as Fabre has observed, for six weeks, a much longer time than is necessary for the development of any of the wasp larvæ. The amazing expertness and accuracy displayed in plunging the sting into exactly those spots where injury will give rise to exactly that physiological phenomenon in the prey that will make it available for the special conditions attending the wasp larva's sustenance— this adroitness and this seeming knowledge of the structure and the physiology of the prey have led some entomologists to credit the solitary wasp with anthropomorphic qualities that are quite unwarranted. The whole behavior is probably explicable as a complex and advantageous reflex or instinct, developed by selection.

Similarly the whole course of the nest-building and provisioning is an elaborate performance wholly for the sake of the young which the mother will likely never see; and these young in turn will if females do the same thing, perfectly and in essentially if not exactly the same manner without ever previously seeing such remarkable processes performed. All these complex and altruistic habits have naturally led to much speculation concerning their origin and their relation to psychical conditions. Whether a consciousness of what is being done and an intelligence is brought to bear upon its doing; whether we may attribute to the wasp a psychical state, with its attributes of cognizance, reason, and emotion—these are questions which are debated warmly. The consensus of opinion, however, is distinctly adverse to the reading into the behavior of Ammophila or any of its allies anthropormorphic attributes of reason, consciousness, and emotion.

The fixity and inevitableness which is, despite the slight variations of practice noted by the Peckhams,* pre-eminently characteristic of the behavior of the wasps, and the fact that each female is *ab ovo* adequate to carry through the complex train of actions without teaching, experience, or opportunity for imitation, practically prove all this seeming marvel of reasoned care for the future young to be an inherited instinct incapable of essential modification except by the slow process of selection through successive generations.

Nevertheless, as Sharp well says, the great variety in the habits of the species, the extreme industry, skill, and self-denial they display in carrying out their voluntary labors, render the solitary wasps one of the most instructive groups of the animal kingdom "The individuals of one generation

* Peckham, Geo. W. and Eliz G., On the Instincts and Habits of the Solitary Wasps, Bull. 2, Wis. Geol. and Nat. Hist. Survey, 1898.

only in rare cases see even the commencement of the life of the next; the progeny for the benefit of which they labor with unsurpassable skill and industry being unknown to them.    Were such a solicitude displayed by ourselves we should connect it with a high sense of duty, and poets and moralists would vie in its laudation.    But having dubbed ourselves the higher animals, we ascribe the eagerness of the solitary wasp to an impulse or instinct, and we exterminate their numerous species from the face of the earth for ever, without even seeking to make a prior acquaintance with them. Meanwhile our economists and moralists devote their volumes to admiration of the progress of the civilization that effects this destruction and tolerates this negligence.''

Sharp divides the solitary wasps, according to their habits, roughly into four groups: (1) those that form no special receptacles (nests) for their young, but are either of parasitic or subparasitic habits or take advantage of the abodes of other insects, holes, etc.; (2) constructors of cells of clay formed into pottery by the saliva of the insect, and by drying; (3) excavators of burrows in the ground; (4) makers of tunnels in wood or stems of plants. · Several species make use of both of the last two methods.

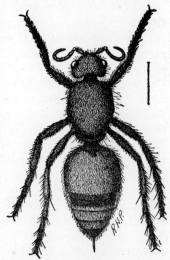

Some of the parasitic wasps dig into the ground until they find some underground insect, usually a larva, for example a beetle-grub, which they sting (paralyze) and on which they then deposit an egg.    There is no attempt to make a nest or to remove the prey from its position as found.    The hatching wasp larva feeds on the grub but in such a way as not to kill it before its own development is complete.    A common parasitic wasp of this habit is *Tiphia inornata*, $\frac{3}{5}$ inch long, shining black, which paralyzes white grubs, the larvæ of June-beetles. Other allied species, some yellow and black and much larger, prey on other larvæ of Scarabæid beetles    From the nests of other

FIG. 699.—A cow-killer, or wingless wasp, *Sphærophthalma similima*, female. (After Lugger; natural size indicated by line.)

wasps, and of both solitary and communal bees, have been bred several kinds of solitary wasps which live either parasitically or as guests (inquilines) in these nests.    If guests, their larvæ feed on the stored food of the host; if parasites, they feed on the actual larval or adult bodies of their hosts themselves.    Interesting wasps living habitually in nests of other wasps or bees are the Mutillidæ, popularly known as velvet-ants, cow-ants, or cow-killers.  The females (Figs. 699 and 700) are wingless and rather like ants in appearance, although readily distinguishable from them by their covering of white, red, black, or golden hair and of course by the absence of the scale-like expansion of the basal abdominal segments characteristic of the true ants.  The males are winged and much less frequently

collected or seen.  It is believed that all Mutillids live as guests or parasites in the nests of other wasps or bees.  They are strong stingers and swift runners. Nearly two hundred species have been found in the United States, the center of abundance being in the southwest.  They are common in California.  *Sphærophthalma californica* (Pl. XII, Fig. 1) is ½ inch long, with brick-red hair, black on bases of abdomen and thorax;  *S. pacifica* is similarly colored but much

FIG. 700.—*Sphærophthalma pacifica.* (One and one-half times natural size.)

larger, ¾ inch long;  *S. aureola*, ½ inch long, has head, most of thorax, and posterior half of abdomen with yellow hair, elsewhere black.

The brilliant metallic-green little bee-like cuckoo-flies (Chrysididæ) are not unfamiliar to collectors, and belong, because of their habits, in the group of parasitic wasps.  "Although these insects are handsome," says Comstock, "they have very ugly morals, resembling those of the bird whose name has been applied to them.  A cuckoo-fly seeks until it finds one of the digger-wasps, or a solitary true wasp or a solitary bee, building a nest, and when the owner of the nest is off collecting provisions steals in and lays its egg, which the unconscious owner walls in with her own egg.  Sometimes the cuckoo-fly larva eats the rightful occupant of the nest, and sometimes starves it by eating up the food provided for it.  The bees and wasps know this foe very well, and tender it so warm a reception that the brilliant-coated little rascal has reason enough to double itself up so that the righteous sting of its assailant can find no hole in its armor.  There is one instance on record where an outraged wasp, unable to sting one of the cuckoo-flies to death, gnawed off her wings and pitched her out on the ground.  But the undaunted invader waited until the wasp departed for provisions, and then crawled up the post and laid her egg in the nest before she died."

Of mason- or potter-wasps, that is, solitary wasps that make a nest of clay or mud worked up with saliva, there are numerous species belonging to several different families.  The daintiest mud-nests are the little vases of Eumenes (Fig. 701), which are said to have served as models for early Indian pottery.  Eumenes is a neat little black-and-yellow wasp with the abdomen shaped like an old-fashioned tear-drop earring.  It belongs to the family Eumenidæ, which is the only family of solitary wasps (besides the rarely seen parasitic Masaridæ) which fold their front wings longitudinally as the social wasps (yellow-jackets and hornets) do. In this family are found diggers, and miners in the earth, carpenters making their nests in twigs or boards, as well as masons or clay-handlers. The species of the genus Odynerus are numerous; in appearance they resemble the yellow-jackets, but are smaller and more slender. They are given to taking advantage of any deserted nest of another wasp, or of some already existing hole or tunnel, to save themselves the trouble of mining or moulding a nest of their own. Riley found an Odynerus cell in the tunnel through a spool, and Ashmead found one in the keyhole of a door-lock. The familiar, long, thread-

Fig. 701.              Fig. 702.

Fig. 701.—A vase mud-nest of *Eumenes* sp. (Natural size.)
Fig. 702.—Nest of a mud-dauber wasp. (Natural size.)

waisted, nervous, black-and-yellow or steel-blue mud-daubers that build several tubular cells an inch or more long side by side of mud, plastered to the under side of a porch roof, on ceilings, under eaves, or under flat stones, belong to the genus Pelopœus (Pl. XII, Fig. 15) of the large family Sphecidæ. These cells are provisioned with paralyzed or dead spiders. Another smaller kind of mud-dauber is Agenius, a genus of the Pompilidiæ. The tiny mud-cells of these wasps, built in crevices or on stones, are also provisioned with little spiders, often with their legs torn off. Originally the mud-daubers built their nests in hollow trees or under overhanging rocks, as they do yet sometimes; but they mostly nowadays take advantage of the safe and convenient places man arranges for them.

Of Sharp's fourth group, the true diggers or miners in the ground, I have already described a typical species in the Ammophila of the San Francisco Bay salt marshes. There are many species of this genus, and they are found all over the country. The great golden digger, *Sphex ichneu-*

*monea* (Pl. XII, Fig. 14), a brilliant and powerful Sphecid, is a common and widely distributed species, which makes a burrow from 4 to 8 inches deep, provisioning it with green grasshoppers. The Peckhams have described in detail in their fascinating book, "The Solitary Wasps," the life and habits

of two species of Astata, wasps of the family Larridæ, which make nests with funnel-like openings (Fig. 703) in sandy soil and provision them with bugs (Hemiptera), most of which are killed, not paralyzed. The Bembecidæ, distinguished by the projecting, even beak-like upper lip, are all diggers, and include our largest solitary-wasp species. *Bembex spinolæ* (Pl. XII, Fig. 8), a large black and bluish-white banded form, shows an interesting variation from the usual digger-wasp habits of feeding the young. Throughout their entire larval life (two weeks) the female catches flies and brings them to the covered nest, having to dig away each time the loose soil

FIG. 703.—Nest-burrow of *Astata unicolor*. (After Peckham; natural size.)

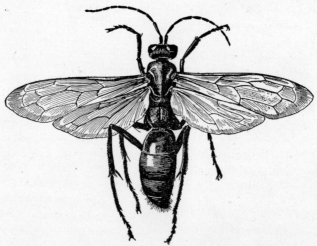

FIG. 704.—Tarantula-killer, *Pepsis formosa*. (Natural size.)

and to scrape it in again as she leaves the nest. One of the giant solitary wasps of our country is the powerful cicada-killer, *Sphecius speciosus*, $1\frac{1}{4}$ inches long, rusty black with yellow-banded abdomen. The wasp, attracted to its prey by its shrill singing, pounces upon a cicada, paralyzes it by a swift stab, and then laboriously flies with or drags the heavy body to the burrow. This burrow may be a foot or even more in depth, usually consisting of a nearly vertical tunnel for 6 inches, with a sharply diverging nearly horizontal part as long as or longer than the entrance one. Sometimes instead of a single terminal cell there are several lateral cells, in each of which one or two cicadas are stored. Another familiar group of diggers are the spider-wasps, Pompilidæ, mostly black or steely-blue with bluish or light-bronzy wings (Pl. XII, Fig. 13). This is a large family including a few guest-wasps (Ceropales) and a few mud-daubers or mason-wasps (Agenia), as well as true diggers, but all of the members of the family which make their own nests provision them with spiders. The giant tarantula-killer, *Pepsis formosa* (Fig. 704), largest of all our wasps, belongs to this family. It is common in California and the southwest, where its sensational combats with the great hairy tarantulas (Mygale) are often seen. It does not always come off victor in these fights, or at least conquers the tarantula only at the expense of its own life. After one such long and fierce battle I found both fighters *hors du combat*, the tarantula paralyzed by the wasp's sting, but the wasp dying from the poisonous wounds made by the great fangs of the spider.

It is a matter of much speculation how the digger-wasps find their nests again after carefully covering them and going off to search for caterpillars, spiders, bugs, or whatever are to be stored up for the larvæ. The Peckhams have made many interesting observations touching the problem, tracing carefully the movements (Figs. 705 and 706) and behavior of individuals

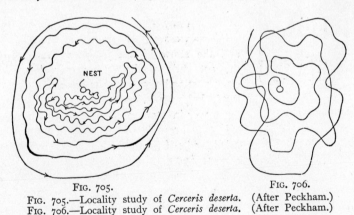

FIG. 705.    FIG. 706.

FIG. 705.—Locality study of *Cerceris deserta*. (After Peckham.)
FIG. 706.—Locality study of *Cerceris deserta*. (After Peckham.)

after finishing a burrow and making ready to provision it. From these observations they conclude "that wasps are guided in their movements by their memory of localities. They go from place to place quite readily because they are familiar with the details of the landscape in the district they inhabit. Fair eyesight and a moderately good memory on their part are all that need be assumed in this simple explanation of the problem."

In the last of Sharp's divisions, on the basis of habit, are those solitary wasps that make nest-tunnels in wood or the stems of plants. In the pith of various kinds of cane-bearing plants, as brambles, blackberries, etc., may often be found the tunnels (Fig. 707), provisioned with plant-lice or other small homopterous bugs, of various small wasps of the families Mimesidæ and Pemphredonidæ. The Mimesids have a petioled abdomen and look like little Sphecids; the Pemphredonids are shining black. The family Crabronidæ, a rather large group of solitary wasps distinguished by having only one closed submarginal cell in the fore wings, includes many wood-borers. Very common in sumac-branches, according to Comstock, are the nests of slender yellow-banded *Tripoxylon frigidum;* the cells are separated by mud partitions. The Peckhams found two slender-waisted, black species of Tripoxylon common near Milwaukee, namely, *T. albopilosum,* ¾ inch long, with tufts of snowy-white hairs on the fore legs, and *T. rubrocinctum,* a little smaller and with a red band about the body. Although these wasps are normally wood-borers, they will use convenient cavities in any material; *rubrocinctum* was found using crevices in the mortar of a brick house, and the straw of a stack where thousands of the cut ends of the straws offered attractive clean nesting-holes; *albopilosum* was found nest-

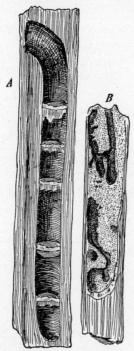

FIG. 707.—Nest-tunnels of two carpenter-wasps. *A, Monobia quadridens* (Eumenidæ); *B, Stigmus fraternes* (Pemphredonidæ). (After Comstock; natural size.)

ing in holes made by beetles in posts and trees, but never in straws; a third common species, *bidentatum,* seemed to nest only in burrows tunneled by itself in the stems of plants. Another carpenter-wasp, common in the eastern states, is the large Eumenid species, *Monobia quadridens,* which drills a tunnel in solid wood, dividing it into cells by transverse partitions (Fig. 707, *A*). The species of the genus *Crabro* make their nests especially in the canes of blackberry- and raspberry-bushes. The Peckhams found that *Crabro stirpicola* did much of its work at night, something not observed in the case of any other solitary wasp. This species provisioned its cells with various species of flies.

The social wasps all belong to the single family Vespidæ, which includes but three genera of American wasps, of which one is limited to the Pacific coast. These three genera may be distinguished by the following characters:

Social wasps with abdomen broad and truncate at base (next to thorax) . . Vespa.
Social wasps with abdomen spindle-shaped, tapering at both ends . . . . . . . Polistes.
Social wasps with abdomen pedunculate, i.e., basal segment elongated to form a stem
or peduncle; occurring only on Pacific coast . . . . . . . . . . . . . . . . . . . . Polybia.

All these wasps fold the wings longitudinally when at rest, and in all there exist three castes or kinds of individuals in each species, namely, males, females, and sterile workers. Like the worker bees, worker wasps are winged, not wingless, as the worker ants are.

The "social" habit, as distinguished from the "solitary" habit characteristic of all the wasps we have so far studied, consists of the founding and maintenance of communities by the living together in a single group through the spring, summer, and autumn of all the offspring, males, females, and workers, of a single fertilized female, the queen. This community is thus a single family, often indeed very large, which busies itself about the care of a family nest. The nest may be underground or suspended from the branch of a tree, placed under the eaves of a building or otherwise supported above ground. It is built of paper made by moistening bits of old wood with saliva and chewing them into pulp, and consists of one or more horizontally placed tiers or combs of cells, exposed or enclosed by paper envelopes, in which a single entrance and exit opening is left.

The castes or kinds of individuals are not so distinctly recognizable by structural differences as with the social bees and the ants, but the sexual forms, males and females, are always obviously larger than the workers (Fig. 709). The special functions of the different castes are (1) the mating with the females by the males; (2) the building of the queen-nest (the miniature early spring nest, see next paragraph), the gathering of food for the first, early spring generation, and the laying of eggs for all the broods by the females; (3) the bringing of food, and the enlarging and building and care of the nest and of the young by the workers.

It has already been mentioned that a community holds together through part of the year only. The life-history of a community is in general outline as follows: In the early spring fertilized females (queens) which have hibernated (as adults) in sheltered places, as crevices in stone walls, under logs, stones, etc., come out from their winter hiding-places and each makes a small nest (of the kind characteristic of its species, see later) containing a few brood-cells. In each cell an egg is laid, and food, consisting of insects, killed and somewhat masticated, is hunted for and brought to the larvæ throughout their brief life by the queen. The larvæ soon pupate in the cells and in a

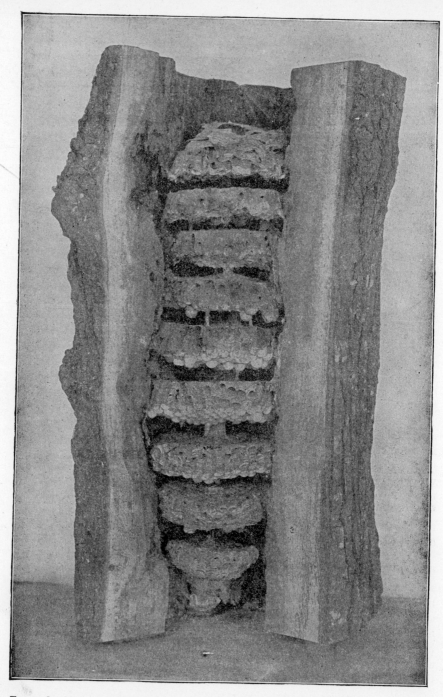

FIG. 708.—Nest of *Vespa crabro*, found in hollow oak-tree on Long Island. (After Beutenmüller. Natural size, 2 feet long by 7 inches wide.)

few days issue as winged wasps. They are exclusively workers. These

FIG. 709.—*Vespa* sp.  *a*, worker; *b*, female or queen.  (After Jordan and Kellogg; natural size.)

workers now enlarge the nest, adding more brood-cells in which the queen deposits eggs. The bringing of food and care of the young now devolve on the workers. The new or second brood is also composed of workers only, and these immediately reinforce the first brood in the work of enlarging the nest and building new brood-cells. Thus through the summer several broods of workers are reared, until in the late summer or early fall a brood containing males

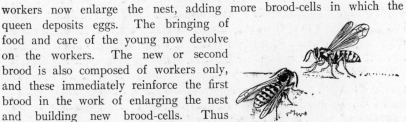

FIG. 710.—Two workers of the yellow-jacket, *Vespa* sp.  (From life; natural size.)

and females as well as workers appears. The community is now at its maximum both as regards population and size of nest. In the species (Vespa sp.) which make the great ball-like aerial nests the community may grow to number several thousand individuals. The males and females mate (presumably with members of other communities), but no more eggs are laid, and with the gradual coming on of winter the males and workers and many of the females die. There persist only as survivors of each community a few fertilized females; these crawl into safe places to pass the winter. Any social wasp found in winter-time is thus, almost certainly, a queen. Those of the queens which come safely through the long winter found the communities which live through the following season.

FIG. 711.—Communal nest of the yellow-jacket, *Vespa* sp. (Much reduced.)

The social wasps of the genus Vespa, the familiar yellow-jackets and hornets, are the ones which build the large subspherical nests familiar to all outdoor observers and related to much boyish adventure. Inside the great globe are several horizontal combs of brood-cells in tiers, all enclosed by several layers of wasp-paper (Figs. 711 and 712). The large bald-faced hornet, *V. maculata*, is the best-known builder of the globe nests. The smaller

FIG. 712.—Nest of yellow-jacket, *Vespa* sp., cut open to show combs within.
(About one-third natural size.)

yellow-jackets, *V. germanica* (Pl. XII, Fig. 9) and *V. cuneata*, build in hollows in stumps or stone fences or underground. Such protected or underground nests are not as thoroughly and thickly enveloped in paper as are the exposed arboreal globe nests. The miniature queen-nests (Fig. 713) of the Vespæ, with the single little brood-comb inside, may often be found by careful searching in spring.

The long-bodied blackish social wasps of the genus Polistes (Pl. XII, Fig. 2; also Fig. 714) build single exposed horizontal combs out of wasp-paper (chewed wood) which are attached to the under side of porch roofs, eaves, ceilings of outbuildings, etc., by a short central stem. The little comb made by the queen may contain but half a dozen cells, but after the workers hatch many other cells are added around the margin. But the nest and community never compare in size and numbers with the large communities of Vespa. The hibernating queens of Polistes often seek hiding-places in our houses. Wasps of this genus are not infrequently parasitized by the remarkable Stylopid beetles (Fig. 403) Xenos, of which an account is given on p. 295.

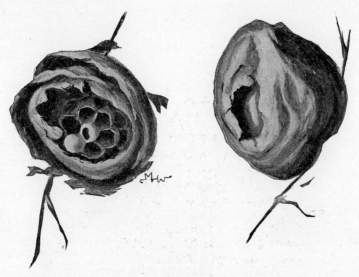

FIG. 713.—Queen-nest of yellow-jacket, *Vespa* sp.; specimen at right in normal condition; at left cut open to show brood-cells. (Natural size.)

Only one species of Polybia occurs in the United States, and that one, *P. flavitarsis* (Pl. XII, Fig. 12), is found only on the Pacific coast. It is common in California. It is readily distinguishable from the other social wasps by its slender pedunculate basal abdominal segment and the small button-like shape of the rest of the abdomen. It builds a single-comb, unenveloped nest, like that of Polistes, but not reaching the diameter of the broad disk-like Polistes comb.

It has been mentioned that the social wasps feed their young (larvæ) chewed insects. Differing from most of the solitary wasps, the social kinds do not store up food for the young, but collect and bring it constantly through the life of the larvæ, a period of from eight to fifteen days. This food consists of the partially masticated remains of various insects pursued and killed by the queen or workers. The queen brings food only for the larvæ of the first small spring brood.

The adult wasps are more catholic as regards the palate; they feed on insects or decomposing animal substances—fish especially attract them—and on exposed sweet substances, as sirups, preserved fruits, etc.

The paper-making and nest-building are industries whose details can only be touched on in our limited space. The paper is not only made of chewed-up bits of weathered wood gathered from old fences or outbuildings; "round the swampy edges of ponds or in wet ditches wasps may be seen gathering tough herbaceous filaments which they felt up into a texture stronger and better able to resist the wind and rain than a paper made of wood scrapings." The moulding

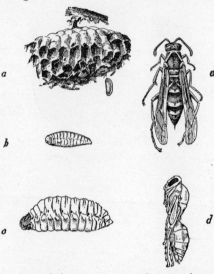

of the pulp at the nest has been observed carefully by Ormerod in the case of two English species of Vespa "It appeared," says Ormerod, "that when a wasp came home laden with building materials she did not immediately apply these, but flew into the nest for about half a minute, for what purpose I could not ascertain. Then emerging she promptly set to work. Mounted astride on the edge of one of the covering sheets, she pressed her pellet firmly down with her fore legs till it adhered to the edge, and, walking backwards, continued this same process of pressing and kneading till the pellet was used up, and her

FIG. 714.—*Polistes* sp. *a*, nest; *b*, young larva; *c*, older larva; *d*, pupa; *e*, adult. (All one and one-half times natural size except nest, which is much reduced.)

track was marked by a short dark cord lying along the thin edge to which she had fastened it. Then she ran forwards, and, as she returned again back-

FIG. 715.—The single-comb nest of a hornet, *Polistes* sp. (One-half natural size.)

wards over the same ground, she drew the cord through her mandibles, repeating this process two or three times till it was flattened out into a little strip or ribbon of paper, which only needed drying to be undistinguishable from the rest of the sheet to which it had been attached. And then she gravely retired into the nest again.

"By this means of marking different wasps it was evident that each wasp had not a place of her own to work at, but that all worked anywhere and anyhow. And this whether they were engaged in adding to the structure or in removing what had been built previously. So, a wasp which had been collecting white fibers joined her quota to what had been built by a wasp who had gathered materials of a darker color, giving a variegated appearance to the work. Further, it seemed clear that only the young wasps built. probably because they only had the power of secreting mucus in sufficient quantity for working up the dry fibers into a pulp. This was inferred from the generally larger size, and the smooth ends of the wings, of the wasps which were examined while thus engaged. Wasps grow smaller as they grow older, and the ends of their wings get tattered with advancing days.

"By the conjoint labors of all these busy workers, here a little and there a little, the nest grows. The work of one week may have to be removed the next week, to make way for modern improvements and for the requirements of the growing city; and, as we have seen, it has nearly all to be done twice over. But wasps work very hard, and the nest grows visibly day by day. The little egg-shell in which it began is lost in the changes which the top of the nest undergoes. The slight strap from which it hung is now quite inadequate to sustain the daily increasing weight, and new points of attachment are sought to projecting roots, or stones, or branches. Sometimes a branch runs all through a nest, materially adding to the difficulty of its capture. Or, failing these, the original point of support is strengthened by layer upon layer of paper, rubbed smooth, and thickly coated with wasp-gum, to preserve so vital a point from all accidents of wind and weather. The regular arrangement of the upper part of the nest is much disturbed in the course of these events, and the top of one nest comes to look very like the top of another. But at the bottom, at the growing part of the nest, the different architectural instincts of the several species are displayed quite to the last. The number of layers of paper employed to form the nest-cover varies with the species, with the season, and with the circumstances under which the nest has been built. Sometimes the case is so thin that the comb shows an edge through the wall, while sometimes it is composed of as many as a dozen layers. But. however the thickness of the walls may vary, as a rule so invariable as to have been adopted as a means of classification, the combs of the nests of the Vespæ have no connection with the outer case, except at the top of the nest. The comb and the case are mutually independent and separate from each other.

"The combs, unlike those of the honey-bee, are laid horizontally, stage below stage, each hanging from the one immediately above it, without any reference to the rest of the series.  The two or three uppermost stages of comb, into which the first rudimentary cells have been expanded, are, in course of time, worked into the case of the nest at their edges.  And the cells are cut down to allow room for the wasps to camp on the upper surface of the comb beneath.  Wasps do not stand cold and wet, so a shelter is here provided for them, where they may be kept dry and warm, without interfering with the comfort and safety of the larvæ in the lower stages.  Incidentally another advantage is gained by this arrangement.  For the fabric of the nest is thus materially strengthened, by substituting, at this vital point, a hard, dry, light flooring for the loose, damp comb, which is almost ready to fall to pieces by its own weight.

"When a new stage is to be constructed, the wasps begin by raising the walls of two or three adjoining cells in the center of the lowest comb.  From these diverging roots a round cord is drawn out, as it were, on the end of which little cells are made, just as on the end of the footstalk from which the nest originally sprung.  As each cell takes shape an egg is deposited in it, so as to lose no time; and while its walls are gradually rising the comb is gradually spreading, by concentric rings of cells.  The mother wasp follows close on the traces of the worker, and the circles of larvæ of the same age show the system on which the comb has been made.  As the comb spreads, new stays are let down to support the weight increasing with the width.  Meanwhile the expansion of the case keeps exact pace with the lateral growth of the comb; the old case is nibbled away within, and new paper is laid on outside, so as to make room all around the edge.  And before each stage has attained its full dimensions, another has been commenced below it, just in the same manner."

## BEES.

In popular repute there are just two kinds of bees, honey-bees and bumble-bees.  Actually there is a host of kinds, many of them small and hardly noticeable, and perhaps even when seen mistaken for other insects.  Still, all the bees have such a "bee-y" manner and general appearance that such mistakes can only be made by the most casual of observers.  There are indeed a few slender-bodied small bees that suggest wasp more than bee perhaps in general seeming; and there are not a few kinds of flies (Diptera), especially the flower-flies (Syrphidæ), bee-flies (Bombyliidæ), and certain robber-flies (Asilidæ) that resemble bees quite sufficiently to be often mistaken for them.  Careful inspection will quickly reveal the deception, by showing the presence of but a single pair of wings on all these bee-mimicking flies.

While bumblebees and honey-bees are the everywhere common, conspicuous, and familiar representatives of the great superfamily of bees, the Apoidea, they include but a fraction of the nearly one thousand different kinds of bees so far recorded as occurring in this country. Indeed, all of our social honey-bees, although variously called German, Italian, Carniolans, etc., belong to a single species, and that not a native but an imported one. Of the bumblebees a few more than fifty native species are known. Besides the hive-bee and the bumblebee, then, there are nearly a thousand other bees in the American fauna to be taken into account. As among the wasps, there are parasitic, guest, solitary, and social kinds of bees; and as among the solitary wasps there are diggers, miners, carpenters, and masons, so also there are miner-, carpenter-, and mason-bees. There are bees which lay their eggs in the nests of other bees, so that their young feed on the stored food of the hosts; there are bees which make nest-burrows in the ground, others that tunnel in stems of plants and wood, others that mould clay cells, others that cut leaves and line their nest bored into the pith of canes, others that live in communities underground which break up each year, and finally, most conspicuous among them all, there is the familiar species that lives in great persistent communities in hives and hollow trees.

All these thousand bee kinds can be conveniently and naturally primarily grouped into two divisions, the short-tongued bees (Fig. 716) (those with a short, broad, flattened, spoon-like tongue) and the long-tongued bees (Fig. 717) (those with a slender, elongate, subcylindrical flexible tongue). In the older books these groups were called families, namely the Andrenidæ (short-tongued bees) and the Apidæ (long-tongued bees), but modern systematists, while still recognizing the convenience of this primary grouping, classify bees into a dozen families or more. For the purposes of this book, however, we shall recognize a grouping on structural characters into simply two main divisions, short-tongued and long-tongued, and another grouping, on a basis of habit and of psychologic development, into three general groups, namely, solitary bees, gregarious bees, and communal bees.

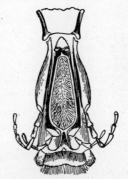

Fig. 716.—Mouth-parts of a short-tongued bee, *Prosopis pubescens*. Note short, broad, flap-like tongue (glossa of labium). (After Sharp; much enlarged.)

The structural characters in which all bees agree among themselves and differ from the other Hymenoptera are the possession of branched or feathery hairs on the head and thorax and of swollen or expanded and flattened tarsal segments: the pronotum does not extend back to the tegulæ of the wings as is the case with the Sphecoid wasps, but not with the Vespoid wasps, including the social kinds.  The mouth in all bees is provided with a well-developed pair of strong mandibles, either sharp and toothed for digging in the ground or tunneling in wood, or smooth and spoon-like for moulding wax.  The food of both adults and larva is always flower-nectar (made into honey) and pollen (for the very young larvæ a predigested food, bee-jelly, is regurgitated by the nurse workers) and never insects, paralyzed, killed, or chewed, as with the wasps.  The bee mouth is therefore fitted for the lapping or sucking up of nectar, as well as for scraping off and crushing pollen.  The maxillæ and labium are more or less intimately joined by membranes and chitinous bars and are capable of much variety of movement in the way of folding, retraction, and extension.  The antennæ are elbowed and their terminal, smooth, cylindrical segments are provided with numerous sense-pits and papillæ, special organs of olfactory and tactile perception.  The compound eyes are large and sight is undoubtedly better than in most insects. There are only male and female individuals in the solitary species, both winged, and the females provided with a sting; in the social species (bumble- and honey-bees) there are in addition worker individuals (females of arrested sexual development but with special structural development) which are also winged and furnished with a sting.  The eggs are laid in cells in the ground, in plant-stems, in logs or posts, or made of wax (hive-bee) or hollowed out of a food-mass of pollen (bumblebees), and the hatching larvæ find stored up for them a sufficient food-supply for their larval life, or they are brought food constantly during this life. · These larvæ are footless, white, soft-bodied grubs, which pupate in their cells.  The issuing imagines gnaw their way out of the cells.

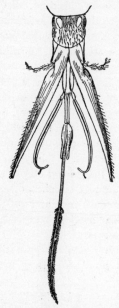

Fig. 717.—Mouth-parts of a long-tongued bee, *Anthophora pilipes*.  Note greatly extended tongue (glossa of labium).  (After Sharp; much enlarged.)

Of the short-tongued bees all are solitary or gregarious; of the long-tongued most are solitary, but a few, the bumble- and the honey-bee, live in communities.  I shall give an account of a few of the more interesting or more familiar kinds of bees, illustrating the various typical habits of nest-building as well as the gradually progressive tendency toward that specialization of life, communism, exemplified in its extreme condition by the hive-bee.

The hairy, medium-sized mining-bees of the short-tongued genus Colletes dig short vertical burrows in the ground which they line internally with a sort of slime that dries to a substance like gold-beater's skin; they partition the burrow into six to ten cells in each of which is deposited an egg, together with a store of food, pollen, and honey mixed. Colletes has the under-lip bilobed like that of wasps and is evidently one of the lowest of the bees.

Prosopis is a short-tongued genus of nearly hairless, small, coal-black bees which tunnel into the stems of brambles and other plants, or dig burrows in the ground, or make cells in crevices in walls; the cells are always lined with a silken membrane, and the stored food is more liquid than usual with bees.

The dainty little blue or green carpenter-bees of the long-tongued genus Ceratina are common and widespread; their nests are tunnels in twigs and canes of sumac, brambles, and other plants (Fig. 718). Comstock writes of the nest-building of the species, *C. dupla*, as follows: "She always selects a twig with a soft pith which she excavates with her mandibles, and so makes a long tunnel. Then she gathers pollen and puts it in the bottom of the nest, lays an egg on it, and then makes a partition out of pith chips, which serves as a roof to this cell and a floor to the one above it. This process she repeats until the tunnel is nearly full, then she rests in the space above the last cell, and waits for her children to grow up. The lower one hatches first; and, after it has attained its growth, it tears down the partition above it, and then waits patiently for the one above to do the same. Finally, after the last one in the top cell has matured, the mother leads forth her full-fledged family in a flight into the sunshine. This is the only case known to the writer where a solitary bee watches her nest till her young mature. After

FIG. 718.—Nest-tunnel of carpenter-bee. (Natural size.)

the last of the brood has emerged from its cell, the substance of which the partitions were made, and which has been forced to the bottom of the nest by the young bees when making their escape, is cleaned out by the family, the old bee and the young ones all working together. Then the nest is used again by one of the bees. We have collected hundreds of these nests, and, by opening different nests at different seasons have gained an idea of what goes on in a single nest. There are two broods each year. The mature bees of the fall brood winter in the nests."

Other familiar carpenter-bees are the great black Xylocopas (Pl. XII,

Fig. 7). They are as large as bumblebees and with their heavy thick body and black color look much like them; they have the body more flattened and less hairy, however, and the hind legs of the females are never provided with a "corbiculum," or pollen-basket (a concave smooth place bounded on each side by a row of long stiff curving hairs), but are covered by a stiff brush of short hairs. These giant bee-carpenters tunnel into solid wood for a foot or more, dividing the burrow into a series of cells by partitions made of small chips stuck together. They are common all over the country, "choosing in civilized regions fence-posts and boards." Certain very large species make their nests in the great fallen sugar-pines and yellow pines of the Sierran forests and are among the most characteristic insects of the giant-tree forests.

FIG. 719.—Nest of leaf-cutter bee, *Megachile anthracina*. (After Sharp; somewhat enlarged.)

The long-tongued family Megachilidæ includes a number of common and interesting bees, most familiar, perhaps, being the mason-bees (Osmia), the potter-bees (Anthidium), and the leaf-cutters (Megachile). The Osmias are metallic, black, blue, or green, and make their nests of clay and sand, moulded into cells, and built in already existing cavities in stone walls, old posts, tree-trunks, etc., or in tunnels bored by the bee in plant-stems and twigs. The various species of Anthidium are black and rufous, or rufous and yellow, with the abdomen always banded or spotted with yellow, white or rufous. The females normally construct globular cells rather like the earthen vases of Eumenes (Fig. 701), but made of the resinous exudations of pine-trees and other plants, or dig burrows in the soil which they line with down stripped from pudescent or woolly-leafed plants. Both Osmia and Anthidium sometimes make their nests in deserted snail-shells! The leaf-cutting bees (Figs 719 and 720) are usually carpenters as well as tailors; that is, they first bore a tunnel in some plant-stem or in wood, and then cut out pieces of green leaves with which they line the tunnel and partition in such a way as to form a series of thimble-shaped cells each partially filled with a paste of pollen and nectar on which an egg is deposited. The

FIG. 720.—Single cell in nest of leaf-cutter bee, *Megachile anthracina*. (After Sharp; somewhat enlarged.)

pieces of leaf are fastened together with a gummy secretion from the mouth of the bee. Comstock has found leaf-cutter nests in a "crack between shingles on a roof, beneath stones lying on the ground, and in Florida in the tubular leaves of a pitcher-plant."

Other common genera of solitary long-tongued bees are Anthophora (Pl. XII, Fig. 11), the species of which are hairy and robust-bodied, looking indeed much like small bumblebees, Melissodes and Synhalonia with very long antennæ, rather like honey-bees in general appearance, and others of the great family Anthophoridæ. All these bees agree in general habits with those already described, but every species presents an opportunity for interesting and valuable work by amateurs and nature-lovers in observing precisely its nest-building habits and life-history. No more attractive opportunity for outdoor observers offers than that of the field study of the solitary bees.

As mentioned at the beginning of the discussion of the solitary bees, some species are parasitic or, more properly named, guest or inquiline in habit. That is, the females of these species, instead of building a nest-burrow of their own and storing it with food, lay their eggs in the nest-burrows of other bees, so that the larvæ on hatching will be able to feed on the supplies stored up by the host-bee. This habit is not confined to a few species, but is common to a surprisingly large number of solitary bees. Two entire families, including a hundred species of North American bees, are exclusively composed of parasitic bees (in addition a third parasitic family, an offshoot of the bumblebees, is mentioned in connection with the account, later, of the social bees). These two families are the cuckoo-bees, Nomadidæ, mostly bright-colored species, metallic blue or green with the abdomen spotted or banded with yellow or white, and the Stelidæ, differing structurally from the cuckoo-bees by having only two, instead of three, submarginal cells in the wings. Ashmead believes that the Nomadidæ are descended from the Anthophoridæ, and the Stelidæ from the Megachilidæ, the parasitic habit having arisen independently in the two groups. Howard mentions the interesting fact that the cuckoo-bees seem not only to be tolerated by their hosts, but that in some cases it has been observed that enough food is stored by the host-bee to enable the larvæ of both host and guest to complete their development side by side and to issue simultaneously as adult bees. It may indeed be found, as has been discovered in numerous other cases of commensal life, that the cuckoo-bee gives, in some way, aid to the host, so that the living together is mutually advantageous.

With the wasps there are no transition stages, among living forms, between a strictly solitary life, where each female makes her own independent nest-burrow, lays an egg in it and stores it with food, or brings food to the larva through its life, and the social or communal life exhibited by the yellow-jackets and hornets, where many females (of arrested sexual development, although not always to such a degree as to be actually incapable of producing fertile eggs) called workers combine to build a common nest and numerous brood-cells, in which eggs are deposited by a single queen female, the mother of the whole community. With this division of labor has come to exist a certain differentiation of structure, manifest in a difference in size and in some anatomical details between the working females and the egg-laying female.

But with the bees certain interesting gradations in domestic economy or insectean sociology exist which throw some light on the possible line of progression or specialization from strictly solitary to strictly communal life. Numerous technically "solitary" bees show a marked gregariousness, a fondness, as it were, for the company and society of other individuals of their kind. This is chiefly manifested in the building of many nest-burrows close together, forming a sort of village or colony of homes, each home belonging to a single female, built by her, provisioned by her, and the young issuing from it her own offspring, but all these homes belonging to individuals of one species of gregarious or social inclination. Near Stanford University,

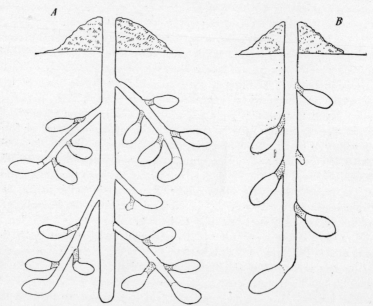

FIG. 721.—Diagrams of nest-burrows of short-tongued mining-bees. B, nest of Andrena; A, compound nest of Halictus.

in a roadside cutting exposing a clayey bank, lived a few years ago a great colony of the large mining-bee *Anthophora stanjordiana*, the vertical, open-mouth nest-burrows set about as closely as they could be without breaking into each other. This bee does not store up food in the nest, but brings it to the larva, the burrow not being closed. The whole colony covered but a few square yards of the many yards of exposed surface. The nest-tunnels were capped by curious little chimneys, mostly curving so as to present the opening not directly upward, exposed to rain, but to one side or almost downward, thus preventing the flooding of the open burrows by water. Similar villages or colonies are made by the little short-tongued mining-bees of the genus Andrena. Comstock has noted Andrena villages covering only one square rod of ground that included several thousand nests, and he received from a correspondent "a description of a collection of nests of this kind which was fifteen feet in diameter, and in the destruction of which about 2000 bees were killed—a terrible slaughter of innocent creatures."

A step farther in this social tendency is exhibited by the smallest of all our mining-bees, the tiny little short-tongued bees of the genus Halictus, the various species measuring from $\frac{1}{10}$ to $\frac{3}{10}$ of an inch in length. While each female forms her own nest-cells, lays eggs in them, and provisions them, she is one of a number of females that work together to build a common vertical tunnel with single external opening, along the sides of which the various cells are arranged. In this way one entrance and one corridor, built and used by several individuals in common, serve to give access to several distinct homes, i.e., nest-cells. These groups of homes with common corridors and openings are placed thickly together in populous sand-bank colonies. Thus, as Comstock aptly puts it, "while Andrena builds villages composed of individual houses, Halictus makes cities composed of apartment-houses."

The next stage exhibited among present-day bees in this progressive specializing of the gregarious tendency is the condition under which the bumblebee lives. This is a long leap from the apartment-house life of Halictus, and does not explain how the differentiation into castes, i.e., the establishment of the worker (rudimentary female) caste, composed in some cases of two distinct sizes, worker majors and worker minors, has come about. If we could but know the intermediate sociologic stages which were exhibited by bees now extinct (or, if living, not yet discovered), but that certainly existed not very long ago (as geologic time-reckoning goes), the marvelous division of labor, differentiation of structure, and commensal interdependence of individuals displayed by the honey-bees would be divested of much of its mystery.

The bumblebees possess a domestic economy wholly like that of the social wasps (yellow-jackets and hornets). In each species there are three kinds of individuals, males, fertile females, and workers (infertile females) which are sometimes of two constant sizes, called worker majors and worker minors. The workers are all distinctly smaller than the fertile females and usually differ somewhat in marking (Fig. 723). The only individuals to over-winter are fertilized females, queens, which hibernate as queen wasps do in sheltered places, as crevices in stone walls, holes in the ground, in hollow trees or under leaves, etc.  When spring comes, each queen finds some deserted mouse's hole, mole's burrow, or other cavity in the ground, or digs one herself;  she then gathers some pollen and honey which she brings to the hole, making there a ball-like mixed pasty mass of it.  On this lump of food she deposits a few eggs, from half a dozen to a score, and then, while waiting for their hatching, brings more food and deposits more eggs.  The hatching larvæ feed on the pollen and honey paste, sepa-rating and eating out one or more considerable cavities in it.  When full-grown each spins a silken cocoon within which it pupates.  The issuing bees are all workers.  They enlarge the nest-burrow, if necessary bring more food, the queen lays more eggs, and so for several broods.  The larvæ ready to pupate are enclosed in waxen cells, sometimes several in a single cell, by the workers (except in the first brood, when there are no workers to make the cells).  A full-sized bumblebee's nest may be as large as one's head, composed of a cluster of large irregular waxen cells, mostly containing brood (larvæ or pupæ), but some containing pollen and a few honey.  All may be enclosed in a loose covering of

FIG. 722.—Bumblebee at clover-blossom.  (From life; natural size.)

hay or bits of stems and roots, the whole lying at the bottom of a deep or shallow tunnel.  There are usually two or more openings to the nest. In the late summer and fall males and females are reared, issue from the nest and mate.  With the oncoming of cold weather the males and workers gradually die, leaving a few fertilized young queens to live through the winter.  These are the founders of next year's communities.

All the bumblebees belong to the genus Bombus (family Bombidæ), long-tongued bees with two apical spurs on the hind tibiæ and with a single submarginal cell in the front wings.  Their big velvety black-and-yellow bodies and their deep-toned buzz are the more familiar characters

FIG. 723.—Worker (A) and queen (B) bumblebees, *Bombus* sp. (After Jordan and Kellogg; natural size.)

which distinguish them.  Over fifty species of bumblebees occur in this country; they differ in size and in the arrangement and relative amounts of the black and yellow markings (Pl. XII, Figs. 5 and 10). A common eastern species is *B. ferviotus* (the "boiling bumblebee" is good!), which has the body of the workers almost all yellow above, only a narrow median band across the thorax and the tip of the abdomen being black; *B. affinis* has (workers) the base of the abdomen, its posterior half, and a median band across the thorax black, the rest yellow; *B. terricola* has the anterior half of the thorax, a band across the posterior third of the abdomen, and another one on the next to the last segment yellow, the rest black; *B. californicus*, the most abundant species in California, has the anterior half of thorax and a single narrow band near tip of abdomen yellow; *B. edwardsii*, another species common on the Pacific coast, has a median band across the thorax and a broad anterior one across the abdomen and the very tip of the abdomen black, the rest yellow.

FIG. 724.—Nest of bumblebee, *Bombus* sp., showing opening at surface of ground and brood-cells in cavity underneath. (Adapted from McCook.)

The strange case of the guest bumblebee, species of the genus Psithyrus (Pl. XII, Fig. 4), is almost sure to come to the attention of any observer of bumblebee-nests. In all general characters and total seeming truly bumblebee-like, found always in and about bumblebee-nests, these insidious guests, cleverly living at the bountiful table of their host, present to us an interesting problem touching their deceptively Bombus-like make-up. Are they really bumblebees, that is, bees directly descended from bumblebee stock, which have become degenerate and adopted a parasitic life, or are they bees of another stock, which, for the sake of successfully deceiving the bumblebees and thus gaining access to their nests, have gradually acquired (through long selection) the bumblebee dress and general appearance? The former supposition is the more probable. They are like bumblebees in so many structural details unnecessary for such deception that they must be looked on as a degenerate offshoot from the Bombidæ. Having given up the gathering and carrying of pollen, their tarsi are no longer provided with a pollen-basket (concave smooth surface bounded by lines of long stiff incurving hairs) and by the absence of this arrangement they may always be distinguished from the true bumble-bees. There is no working caste, infertile female workers, with these Psithyridæ, each species being represented by males and females only.

At the head of this line of specialization among the bees, that is, the development of the communistic tendency, stand the two genera of honey-bees, Melipona and Apis. The numerous species of Melipona are restricted

Fig. 725.—Comb of the tiny East Indian honey-bee, *Apis florea*.
(After Benton; one-third natural size.)

to tropical regions; some are very small, the so-called "mosquito-bees," and in all the sting is blunted and apparently never used as a weapon. The life-history of no one of the species has been fully made out, and there is some doubt as to whether each community—some of the nests are known to include an enormous number of individuals—has but a single queen—that is, single egg-laying female—or not. Of the other genus, Apis, there are but few species, the best known being the common hive-bee, *A. mellifica*, which extends naturally over all the northern half of the Old World and from there has been introduced into nearly all the countries of the globe. In its long domestication several varieties or races have been created by artificial selection, the more familiar ones being the German or black race, the Italian or amber race, and the Carniolan or striped race.

A community of the hive-bee, which may live, of course, not in a hive at all, but in a hollow tree, as undoubtedly was the habit of the species in wild state (the "bee-trees" of America, however, are inhabited by bee colonies which have swarmed away from domesticated ones and are only wild by virtue of escaping from the slave-yards of their human masters), consists normally of about 10,000 (winter) to 50,000 (summer) individuals, of which one is a fertile female, the queen; a few score to several hundred are

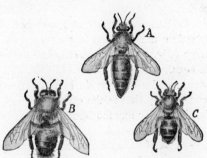

FIG. 726.        FIG. 727.

FIG. 726.—The honey-bee, *Apis mellifica*. *A*, queen; *B*, drone; *C*, worker. (Natural size.)

FIG. 727.—Hind leg of worker honey-bee, *Apis mellifica*, showing pollen-basket. (Much enlarged.)

males, the drones; and the rest are infertile females, the workers. These three kinds of individuals are readily distinguishable by structural charac-

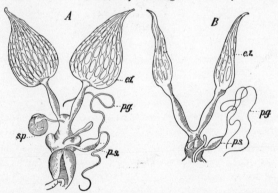

FIG. 728.—Ovaries of queen (*A*) and worker (*B*) honey-bee, *Apis mellifica*. *et*, egg-tubes; *sp*, spermatheca; *pg*, poison-gland; *ps*, poison-sac. (After Leuckart; much enlarged.)

ters. The queen (Fig. 726) has a slender abdomen one-half longer than that of a worker, she has no wax-plates on the under side of the abdominal segments, and no transverse series of comb-like hairs, the planta (Fig. 734), on the under side of the broad first tarsal segment of the hind feet, and no pollen-basket (Fig. 727) on the outer surface of the hind tibia.   The drones, males, (Fig. 726), have a heavy broad body excessively hairy on the thorax, and lack pollen-basket, planta, wax-plates, and other special structures of the workers.   The workers are smaller than queen or drones, and possess certain special structures or body modifications to enable them to perform certain special functions connected with their performance of the various industries characteristic of the species.   These special structures will be described in some detail later when the various special industries are particularly considered.   In internal organization the workers differ from the queen in having the ovaries rudimentary (Fig. 728), so that only in exceptional cases can a worker produce fertile eggs.

In functions the three castes differ as they do in the social wasps and the bumblebees, only more constantly; that is, the queen lays the eggs, never, as with Bombus and the Vespids, doing any food-gathering or nest-building;

FIG. 729.—Honey-bees gathering pollen and nectar.   (From life.)

the males act simply as consorts for the queen, which means that only one of every thousand, perhaps, performs any necessary function at all in the communal economy; the workers build brood- and food-cells, gather, prepare, and store food, feed and otherwise care for the young, repair, clean, ventilate, and warm the hive, guard the entrance and repel invaders, feed the queen, control the production of new queens, and distribute the species, founding new communities, by swarming.

The life-history of a community is as follows: A "swarm" (how and when a swarm is formed will be explained later), consisting of a queen (fertile female) and a number of workers (from two to twenty thousand or more), issues from a community nest (hive, hollow tree, or elsewhere) and finds, through the efforts of a few of the workers, a place for a new nest (in another sheltered hollow place, usually, through the intervention of the bee-keeper, another hive). Taking possession of this new nesting-place, the workers immediately begin to secrete wax (method described later) and to build "comb," i.e., double-tiered layers of waxen cells, usually as "curtains" or plates hanging down from the ceiling of the nest (the bee-keepers supply artificially made "foundations" or beginnings of these curtains in vertical frames set parallel and lengthwise of the hive, so that the combs will be built symmetrically and conveniently for the bee-keeper's handling). In many of these cells the queen, which has received the fertilizing sperm-cells

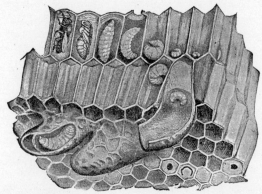

FIG. 730.—Brood-cells from honey-bee comb showing different stages in the metamorphosis of the honey-bee; worker brood at top and three queen-cells below; beginning at right end of upper row of cells and going to left, note egg, young larva, old larva, pupa, and adult ready to issue; of the large curving queen-cells, two are cut open to show larva within. (After Benton; natural size.)

from a male during a mating flight high in the air, lays fertilized eggs, one at the very bottom of each cell. In other cells, pollen and honey brought by workers (the honey brought as flower-nectar and made from this, as explained later) are stored for food. In three days the eggs hatch, the tiny larvæ being footless, white, soft-bodied, helpless grubs. They are fed at first exclusively with "bee-jelly," a highly nutritious, predigested substance elaborated in the bodies of the nurse workers and regurgitated by them into the mouths of the larvæ. After a couple of days of feeding with this substance, the larvæ are fed, in addition to bee-jelly, pollen and honey taken by the nurses from the cells stored with these food-substances. After three days of this mixed feeding, the larvæ having grown so as to fill half or two-thirds of the cell, lying curled in it (Fig. 730), a small mass of mixed pollen and honey is put into each cell, which is then capped, i.e., sealed over with a thin layer of wax. The larva feeds itself for a day or so longer on the "bee-bread" and then pupates in the cell. The quiescent non-feeding pupal stage lasts for thirteen days, when the fully developed bee issues from the thin pupal cuticle, gnaws away the wax cap and emerges from the cell. For from ten days to two weeks the bee does not leave the hive; it busies itself with indoor work, particularly nurse work, the feeding and care of the young. Then it takes its place with the fully competent bees, makes foraging expeditions or undertakes capably any other of the varied industries of the worker caste.

After numerous workers have been added to the community, egg-laying by the queen going on constantly day after day, so that the young come to maturity, not in broods, but consecutively, day after day, certain hexagonal cells of plainly larger diameter are made by the comb-building workers, and in these the queen lays *unfertilized* eggs. This extraordinary capacity for producing either fertilized or unfertilized eggs, as demanded, depends upon the queen's control of the male fertilizing cells held in the spermatheca. This reservoir of fertilizing cells can be kept open as eggs pass down the oviduct and by it on their way out of the body, thus allowing the spermatozoids to swim out, penetrate (through the micropyle in the egg-envelopes) and fertilize the eggs, or it may be kept closed, preventing the issuance of the spermatozoids and, consequently, fertilization. From the unfertilized eggs laid in the larger cells hatch larvæ which are fed and cared for in the same way as the worker larvæ, but which require six days for full growth, the pupal stage lasting fifteen days. When finally the fully developed bees issue from these cells it will be found that all are males (drones). This parthenogenetic production of drones, discovered about 1840 by Dzierzon, and long accepted as proved, was recently questioned by Dickel and one or two other naturalists and was therefore reinvestigated by Petrunkewitsch and others, with the result of confirming, on new evidence and by new methods of investigation, the declarations of the discoverer of the fact.

If, now, our community has increased so largely in numbers that its quarters begin to be insufficient for further expansion, certain excited groups of workers will be seen tearing down certain cells and replacing them by a new giant cell which is usually built up around one of the fertilized eggs laid in a small hexagonal cell. The egg hatches before the cell is finished, and the larva lies in the large open cavity of the growing cell, on which numerous nurses are in constant attendance. Often several of these unusual giant cells may be built at one time. The larva which hatches from the fertilized egg in one of these cells is fed the nutritious bee-jelly through all of its life, little or no pollen or honey being given it. When the larva is five days old a quantity of the milky semi-fluid jelly is put into the cell, which is then capped, the opening being at the bottom of the hanging, nut-shaped cell, and in only seven days more the fully developed bee issues. This bee is a queen. Very rarely a worker and not a queen issues from a queen-cell. That is, a larva hatching from a fertilized egg laid by the queen in a small hexagonal cell, if fed bee-jelly for two or three days and then pollen and honey, will develop into a worker; that larva from the same egg, if fed bee-jelly all its life, and reared in a large roomy cell, will develop into a queen. The difference between a queen honey-bee and a worker honey-bee, both structural and physiological, are, as already pointed out, conspicuous. The influence of a varying food-supply is something mysteriously potent, and this case of the queen bee gives great comfort to those biologists who believe that the external or extrinsic factors surrounding an animal during development have much influence in determining its outcome.

As there is by immemorial honey-bee tradition but one queen in a community at one time, when new queens issue from the great cells something has to happen. This may be one of three things: either the old and new queens battle to death, and it is believed that in such battles only does a queen bee ever use her sting, or the workers interfere and kill either the old or new queen by "balling" her (gathering in a tight suffocating mass about her), or either old (usually old) or new queen leaves the hive with a swarm, and a new community is founded. If several new queens are to issue, the workers usually, by thickening from the outside the walls of one or more of the cells, compel the issuing to be successive and not simultaneous. This results in a series of royal battles, or a series of swarmings, or a combination of the two. A queen ready to issue from a cell makes a curious piping audible some yards from the hive, which is answered by a louder piping, a trumpeting, from the old queen. At these times there is great excitement in the hive, as indeed there is during all of the queen-raising season.

The swarming out, it is apparent, does not break up the old community; in fact only accident, or the successful attacks of such insidious enemies as the bee-moth, and various contagious diseases, break up the parent colony. In this respect is to be noted an important difference between the other social bees and wasps with their communities annually destroyed and refounded, and the honey-bee with its persistent one. Of course workers die and so do drones and queens. The tireless workers which hatch and labor in the spring and summer months rarely live more than six or eight weeks, while the workers born in the late autumn and remaining quietly in the shelter of the hive through the winter live for several months. Queens live, usually, if no accident befalls, two or three years; an age of four or five years is occasionally attained. Most of the drones in each community either die naturally before winter comes or are killed by the workers. Feeble workers and larvæ and pupæ are also sometimes killed just before winter, if the food-stores which are to carry the community through the long flowerless season are for any reason not likely to prove sufficient for so large a number of individuals. In all these matters, that is, the making of queens and when, the swarming out and when, and the reduction of the community to safe winter numbers, the decision is made by the workers and not the queen. The queen is no ruler; she is the mother, or, better, simply the egg-layer for the whole community.

The drones, we have seen, have one particular function to perform in the community life, the queen another single particular function; but the workers have numerous varied performances to achieve if the community shall live successfully. It might be expected, from analogous conditions elsewhere existing in animal life, that with the division of labor in the honey-bee economy there should be a corresponding differentiation of structure or polymorphism inside the species. This polymorphism or existence of structurally different kinds of individuals occurs in bees only to the extent already pointed out; there are three kinds of individuals: the queens, with a special function, the drones, with a single special function, and the workers, each capable of performing, and, for the time of the performance, doing it exclusively, any of the varied industries necessary to the community life. All worker honey-bees are alike, each possessing all the special structural specializations, as pollen-basket, wax-plates, wax-shears, trowel-like jaws, etc., which have been developed for the special performance of particular industries. In some other communal insects a differentiation or polymorphism among the workers exists; many ant species have two or even three kinds of workers, the termites have soldiers as well as workers, etc. I purpose now to describe briefly each of the principal special industries achieved by the workers, at the same time describing the structural specialization connected with each of these industries.

The wax produced by the workers is a secretion which issues as a liquid, soon hardening, from pairs of thin five-sided plates, one pair on the ventral surface of each of the last four abdominal segments (Fig. 731). It is secreted by modified cells of the skin lying under the chitinized cuticle of the plates, and oozes out through fine pores in the plates. To produce it certain workers eat a large amount of honey, then massing together form a curtain or festoon hanging down from the ceiling of the hive or frame, and increase the temperature of their bodies by some strong internal exertion; after the lapse of several hours, sometimes indeed two or three days, fine, thin, glistening, nearly transparent scales of wax appear on the "wax-plates." These wax-scales continue to increase in area and soon project beyond the margin of the segment, when they either fall off or are plucked off by other workers or by the wax-producing worker itself. They are then taken in the mouth,

sometimes chewed and mixed with some saliva, and carried to the seat of
the comb-building operation. Here the wax is pressed against the frame roof
(or artificial foundation) and by means of the trowel-like mandibles moulded
into the familiar hexagonal cells; each comb being composed of a double

Fig. 731.

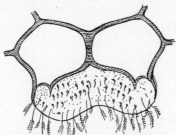

Fig. 732.

Fig. 731.—Ventral aspect of abdomen of worker honey-bee, showing wax-plates. (Three
times natural size.)

Fig. 732.—Wax-plate from ventral aspect of abdomen of honey-bee. (Much enlarged.)

layer of these cells, a common partition serving as base or bottom of each
tier. Although most bee books speak rather glibly of the comb-building
operations, it is still undetermined whether the wax-producers leave the curtain and carry their own wax to the new comb and help mould it, or whether

Fig. 733.—Honey-bees building comb. (After Benton.)

the scales are taken away by other (building) workers, or whether they are
nipped off with the wax-shears (Fig. 734) of the hind legs, and if so, whether
by the wax-maker or a helper or builder, or whether they fall off to the bot-

tom of the hive and are there gathered up by helpers or builders, or whether all or most of these various performances occur—which from my own observations and those of my students seems true. In building cells for storing honey, new wax is almost exclusively used; for brood-cells old wax and

wax mixed with pollen may be used. Any comb or part of a comb not needed is torn down and the wax used to build other comb- or cap-cells.

The seeking and collection of pollen and honey is not undertaken by a bee until from ten to fifteen days after its emergence from the pupal cuticle, these first days being spent in the hive at nurse or other indoor work. Then short orienting flights begin to be made, and soon the long-distance flights (a mile or more sometimes), which are often necessary for successful foraging, are undertaken. The pollen is taken up or brushed off from the ripe anthers of the flowers with the mouth-parts, fore legs, or ventral body-wall, the pollen-grains being readily entangled in the numerous branching hairs, and then, by clever manipulation of the fore, middle, and hind legs aided by special pollen-brushes (plantæ) (Fig. 734) on the inner side of the front tarsal segments of the hind feet, transferred to and packed into the pollen-baskets (Fig. 734), one in the outer face of

FIG. 734.—First tarsal segment of hind legs, front and back view, of honey-bee. 1, drone; 2, worker; and 3, queen. *a*, distal tip of tibia; *b*, first tarsal segment; *c*, proximal end of second tarsal segment. (After Sharp; much enlarged.)

each hind tibia. A forager loaded with pollen returns to the hive, and, seeking an empty cell near the brood-cells, stands over and with his hind legs partly in it and thrusts off the two masses, with the aid of the middle legs (the spurs of the middle tibiæ being apparently often used as pries). This pollen is tamped down in the cell by inside workers and receives no further manipulation.

The "honey" which is collected by the foragers is not yet bee-honey, but is nectar of flowers, too watery and too likely not to "keep" to be stored in the cells without further treatment. It is sucked and lapped up by the complicated elongate flexible mouth-proboscis, swallowed into the fore stomach or honey-sac (Fig. 735), and carried in this to the hive Bees have been seen to exude drops of water on their return flight when honey-laden, and it is possible that it comes from the nectar in the honey-stomach. At any rate, some ten or twelve per cent. of the water content of the nectar has to be evaporated before this nectar becomes honey. When the foraging worker with honey-sac full returns to the hive it regurgitates its nectar either into the mouth of another bee or into a clean (new wax) cell, usually near the margin of the comb. At the bottom of the honey-sac is the so-called stomach-mouth, a little pea-like protuberance with two cross-slits, making four lips. These lips can be opened or closed voluntarily; if the bee drinking nectar wishes to bring it back to the hive to store it, she keeps them closed, thus making a sac of the honey-stomach, open only through the mouth; whenever she wishes to feed herself she opens them, thus allowing the honey or pollen to pass on into the true or digesting stomach. This arrangement also permits of the regurgitation of the bee-jelly or bee-milk (fed the larvæ by the nurse workers), which is believed to be prepared in the true stomach, pressed past the lips forward into the honey-stomach and on through the œsophagus into the mouth.

Fig. 735. — Alimentary canal of worker honey-bee showing (hs) honey-sac lying directly behind (œ) œsophagus. (Much enlarged.)

When the nectar is put into the honey-cells it has still to have much water evaporated from it. To accomplish this an effective system of ventilation (see p. 530) is now set up in the hive, so that air-currents pass constantly over the open nectar-containing cells; moreover, by the very vigor of this activity on the part of the bees the temperature of their bodies is raised; by radiation of heat from the bodies the temperature in the hive is sensibly increased, and the currents of warm air soon carry off the excess water. To make the honey "keep," that is, to make it antiseptic, formic acid is added to it, probably from glands in the head whose secretions distinctly show its presence. It is just possible that the formic acid is supplied by the poison-sacs, the poison introduced by the bee's sting being largely composed of formic acid. But it is much more probable that at the time of the regurgitation of the nectar from the honey-stomach through the mouth the formic-acid secretions from the head-glands are mixed with it.

Nectar for honey-making is obtained by bees from a great many different plants, but that from some makes honey better, to our taste, than that from others. Among the most important producers of the best honey in the east and north are white clover, basswood, buckwheat, and the fruit-trees and small fruits; in the middle states are the tulip-tree, sorrel-tree, sweet clover, and alfalfa; in the south are the mangrove, cabbage- and saw-palmettos, and sorrel-tree; while in the west are alfalfa and white sage. The best and most of the California honey is from the wild white sage.

Besides pollen and nectar, two other substances are collected and brought to the hive by the foraging workers. At some seasons of the year when many larvæ are being reared, and the supply of water derived by condensation of the moisture in the warm hive atmosphere as this air strikes the cooler hive-walls is insufficient, the workers drink up dew from leaves, or water from puddles, which they hold in the honey-sac and bring to the hive, regurgitating it into the thirsty larval mouths. For the filling in of crevices, the stopping up of holes, the fastening together of loose parts, etc., the bees use a substance called propolis, which is simply the resinous exudations of various plants. This propolis is collected and packed into the pollen-baskets as pollen is and brought in by the foragers. Some of my bees, needing propolis, discovered a house just in course of painting, and made a gallant though hopeless struggle to bring in all the fresh paint as fast as it was put on by the painters! This house must have seemed a remarkable sort of propolis-producing plant! Propolis is not packed in cells, but is used as soon as brought in, the trowel-mandibles being the instruments used in putting and moulding it in the needed place.

Of the indoors work there is much besides those industries already referred to, namely, wax-making, comb-building, honey-making, crevice-chinking. Because the queen and nurses (bees less than two weeks old) do not leave the hive their excreta are voided within doors; there are also bits of old, dirty wax, occasional dead bees, and various other waste substances constantly accumulating in the hive. Or, rather, this detritus would accumulate if the workers were not always keenly careful to carry out all such stuff; the hive is constantly being cleaned, and is on any day in the week a model of good housekeeping.

Besides keeping the hive clean the workers must keep it ventilated, that is, clean of atmosphere as well as clean of floor and wall. This is done by setting up air-currents through the hive which carry out constantly the vitiated air and thus compel fresh air to enter. Always near the exit and scattered through the hive, especially along its floor, may be seen bees standing with head down and body diagonally up and wings steadily vibrating with great rapidity. These are the ventilating agents, and they have an exhausting and tedious work.

About the entrance may be also always seen bees which seem neither to be leaving the hive nor entering it, but which move about constantly and meet and touch antennæ with all incomers. These are the warders of the gate. There are never wanting enemies of the industrious, well-stocked honey-bee community, whose entrance into the hive must be vigorously guarded against. Yellow-jackets hover tentatively around the opening; they are arrant robbers and are ready to take any chance to get at the full honey-cells. But more dangerous because of the habit of attacking *en masse* are honey-bees of other hives. Not infrequently a desperate foray by hundreds of other bees will be made into a hive, especially a weak one, and a pitched battle will occur in and about the entrance and inside the hive itself, resulting in the death of hundreds, even thousands, of bees. More insidious and even more dangerous are the stealthy invasions of a small dusty-winged moth, the bee-moth (*Galleria mellonella*), which, slipping in at night unobserved, lays its eggs in cracks; the larvæ which hatch from the eggs feed on the wax of the combs, and as they spin a silken net over them wherever they go, the presence of many such works great injury both in the actual destruction of comb and in the felting and cobwebbing of the interior of the hive with the tough silken netting. Other still more insidious enemies there are, as the minute bee-lice (Braula), which attach themselves to the bees and suck out their body-juices, and the invisible bacterial germs of foul-brood and other characteristic bee diseases. But all these are beyond the sensitiveness of the guards to recognize, and for the successful fighting of them the aid of the bee-keeper is necessary.

The feeding and care of the young bees, the larvæ, have already been partly described in the account of the life-history of the different kinds of

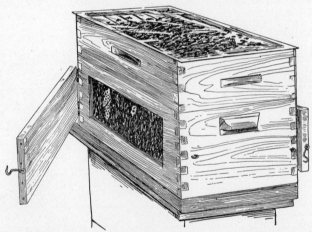

FIG. 736.—An ordinary beehive made into an observation-hive by inserting glass panes in sides and putting a glass sheet under the wooden cover. (Drawn from hive in the author's laboratory.)

individuals in the community and cannot be further referred to in this brief history of the honey-bees' domestic economy. Of course only the more conspicuous features in this economy have been described at all; a host of interesting details cannot even be mentioned. But enough has been said, surely, to indicate the fascinating field for observation afforded by a honey-bee community. If such a community be kept in an observation-hive and this hive be placed conveniently near the house, or, better, *inside one's room*, it will prove a never-failing source of interest and pleasure.

Perhaps it had better be explained how an observation-hive can be kept in one's room without interfering with coincident human occupancy. The observation-hive, in the first place, may be, as shown in Fig. 736, simply an ordinary outdoors hive into each side of which a large pane of glass has been let, with swinging outer wooden doors, one on each side, which, when shut, keep the hive in normal darkness, but opened, allow "observing" to go on. In addition to the side glasses a loose sheet of glass is inserted just under the ordinary "honey-board" or removable top of the hive. Or the observation-hive may be, as shown in Fig. 737, a special, narrow, two-frame

FIG. 737.—An observation-hive holding only two frames, with the two sides wholly of glass, so that any single bee can be continuously watched. (Drawn from hive in author's laboratory.)

hive, with both sides wholly composed of glass held in the narrow wooden frame which forms the ends and the top and bottom of the hive. A black cloth jacket should be kept on the hive when "observing" is not going on. In such a hive, which will obviously hold but a small community (one of not over 10,000 individuals) any single bee can be kept continuously under observation, as there are no side-by-side frames between which it can crawl and thus be hidden from view. To keep either of such hives in the house it is only necessary to substitute for a pane of glass in a window a thin wooden pane in which is cut a narrow horizontal opening, the size of the regular hive-opening (if the latter is too broad it can be closed for a few inches at each end). Or a narrow board strip of the full width of the window can be inserted so that the lower sash of the window, when closed, will rest on this strip. In the strip cut a narrow opening of the width or less of the hive-opening. Set the observation-hive on a table or shelf against the window so that the hive-opening corresponds with that in the window-pane or window-strip. Or, better, place it six or seven inches from the window and connect hive and window-opening by a shallow broad tunnel of wooden bottom and sides but glass top. Over the glass top of this tunnel lay a sheet of black cardboard, which will keep the tunnel dark normally, but which can be simply lifted off whenever it is desired to see what is going on at the entrance. Here can be seen the departure of the foragers and their arrival with pollen, propolis, or honey, the alertness of the guards, the repelling of robbers and enemies, the killing of drones, the ventilating, etc., etc. Through the glass sides of the hive itself can be seen all the varied indoors businesses in their very undertaking; the life-history of each kind of individual can be followed in detail; the wax-making and comb-building, the storing of the food-cells, the feeding of the young by the nurses, the excitements, the joys, and the discouragements, the whole course of life in this microcosm.

The natural questions of the thoughtful observers of honey-bee life touching the probable origin and causal factors of this elaborate train of behavior will be found, not answered, to be sure, but discussed, at the end of this chapter. For before undertaking any consideration of the much-discussed problem of reflexes, instincts, and intelligence in the communal-living insects, we should examine the life and ways of the ants, the most specialized of all the social animals.

## ANTS.

Unlike the wasps and bees, the two other great groups of Hymenoptera that contain communal-living species, the ants (superfamily Formicina) include no solitary species at all, every one of the twenty-five hundred or more known ant species living in communities. The development or evolution of social life in persistent communities is accomplished for the whole group; no connecting or gradatory forms living in annually destroyed communities (like those of the bumblebees and social wasps) or in simple colonies of gregarious individuals (like Halictus and other mining-bees) exist to connect the ants with the solitary or independent life common to the great majority of insects.* And the division of labor, establishment of castes or kinds of individuals, and marked differentiation of structure are developed to the extreme among the ants. The variety of habits and the special adaptations to different conditions are also represented in their widest range and most complex stage of development among the ants. Obviously the ants are at the head, the extreme forefront of this kind of specialization in insect life.

No insects are more familiar. They live in all lands and regions; they exist in enormous numbers; they are not driven away by the changes in primitive nature imposed by man's occupancy of the soil; they mine and tunnel his fields and invade his dwellings. And many things which man attempts they do more successfully than he does, and may be his teachers!

But few other insects can be mistaken for ants even by the most superficial observer; the wingless Mutillid wasps, so-called velvet ants, are rather like them in general appearance, and the smaller termites, or white ants, bear just a slight superficial resemblance to true ants, especially in the case of the sexual individuals with their long narrow wings. /But ants may be at once definitely distinguished from all other insects by the readily made out structural character of the basal segments or peduncle of the abdomen. One or two of these segments are expanded dorsally to form a little scale or flat button-like knot—a characteristic exhibited by no other insects. For the rest, ants show a body structure like that, in general, of the wasps and bees: compact and well-distinguished thorax and abdomen; wings (present only in males and fertile females, and in them easily removable) with a few sparsely branching veins and few cells; the mouth furnished with strong biting-jaws, which in most species can be used without the opening or even the moving of the other mouth-parts (maxillæ and lips); antennæ slender, cylindrical, and sharply elbowed at the end of the rather long basal segment; legs long and strong and fitted for running, and the body-wall firm and smooth. Many ants have a stridulating (sound-making) organ situated on the articulating surface of one of the peduncular abdominal segments, which are always extremely mobile. Ants show few special structures of the kind so characteristic of the honey-bee; that is, modifications of the body to suit the various particular industries undertaken by the insect. They seem to use the strong mandibles as universal tools to dig and tunnel, to obtain food, carry it and manipulate it, to fight, to carry tenderly their eggs and young from place to place, to cut leaves, husk seeds, and what not else. While some ants have the sting well developed and capable of inflicting a wound even more painful than that of a honey-bee, in most of our species

* Wheeler's recent studies of the Ponerine ants of Texas, referred to later in this chapter, seem to show that this long-believed generalization must be modified: the communities of some of these ants seem to be annual growths.

the sting is rudimentary, short and blunted, and no longer a weapon. The mandibles are relied on by the stingless ants as means of defence and offence.

An ant species always includes at least three kinds of individuals, as a social wasp or bee species does, and may include several more (Fig. 738). There are always winged males, which die soon after their issuance from the nest to take part in the mating-flight swarm, and winged females, or queens, which pull off their wings immediately after this flight. Thus winged ants are to be seen only at certain seasons of the year, the fertile females when found in the nest being almost always in wingless condition. In addition to the winged individuals there are wingless workers which are infertile females, i.e., with rudimentary egg-glands and lacking also the spermatheca. These workers in many species, probably most, are of two sizes, worker minors and worker majors; the two are not wholly distinct,

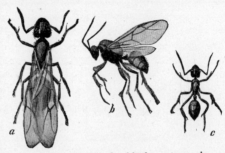

FIG. 738.—A California black ant, species undetermined, showing winged forms and wingless worker. (After Jordan and Kellogg; twice natural size.)

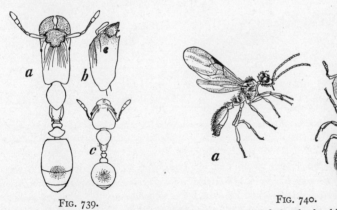

FIG. 739.

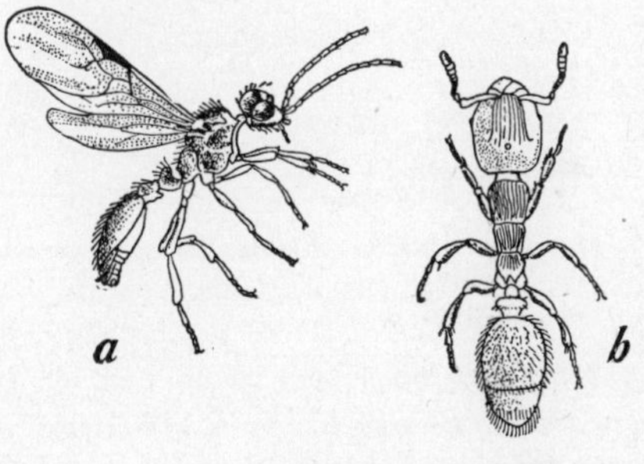

FIG. 740.

FIG. 739.—Soldier (a) and worker (c) of *Pheidole lamia*; b, head of soldier in profile. (After Wheeler; much enlarged.)

FIG. 740.—Male (a) and ergatoid female (b) of *Tomognathus sublævis*. (After Wheeler; much enlarged.)

however, as intermediate sizes are occasionally to be noted. In addition there may exist workers with extra-large heads and jaws which are known as soldiers (Fig. 739), but also between these and ordinary workers intermediate stages are sometimes seen. Finally there may exist ergatoid (worker-like) wingless but fertile females and males. Wheeler finds among the ants of the family Poneridæ, which includes the most generalized or simplest of the ant kinds, that the "queen and worker differ but little in size and structure; ergatoid females or forms intermediate between the queens and workers are of normal and comparatively frequent occurrence in some species; the habits of the queen and workers are very similar; the female is not an individual on whom special attention is bestowed by the workers, and the

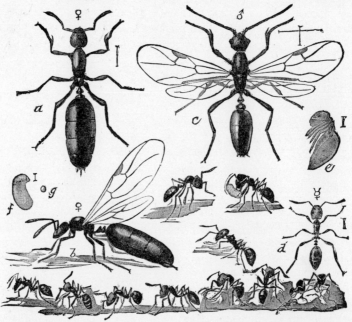

FIG. 741.—The little black ant, *Monomorium minutum*. *a*, female; *b*, female with wings; *c*, male; *d*, workers; *e*, pupa; *f*, larva; *g*, egg of worker. (After Marlatt; natural size indicated by line.)

workers show no tendency to differentiate into major and minor castes." This investigator has also noted at the other extreme a dimorphism of the queens (winged females) in *Lasius latipes*, a member of the specialized family Camponotidæ, and in two genera, Leptogenys and Tomagnathus, the absence of any winged female, the queens having become degenerate to the extent of losing their wings. Hand in hand with this differentiation into castes and the accompanying differences in structure goes, of course, a division of labor or specialization of function, as will soon be pointed out.

We have no such detailed and complete knowledge of the community life of ants as we have of the social wasps and bees; in particular we are lacking in knowledge concerning the exact mode or modes of the establishment and beginning life of new colonies. Whether after the mating flight a fertilized queen unaccompanied by workers can found a new community, or whether such fertilized queens are found after they come to the ground and remove their wings and are taken charge of by a group of workers which then take the queen into an already existing community or with her establish a new one; or whether, as seems probable, most of these modes of procedure are represented in the life-history of various different ant species—all these questions are by no means well answered on a basis of careful observation and experimentation. Most of the observations which have been made on the founding of new communities seem to show that a fertilized queen begins alone the establishment of a new community by building a little nest, laying a few eggs, caring for the hatching larvæ herself, and thus

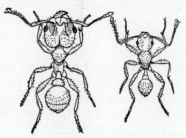

FIG. 742.—Soldier and worker of *Pheidole commutata*. (After Wheeler; enlarged.)

raising by her unaided exertions a small brood of neuter workers which are always normally undersized, probably from insufficient nourishment. This mode of community founding is just like that obtaining among the social wasps and the bumblebees. Leidy and Comstock have observed such a mode of founding new colonies by the common carpenter-ant of the East, *Camponotus pennsylvanicus*, and in Europe *Myrmica ruginodis*, *Camponotus ligniperdus*, and *Lasius alienus* have been noted to follow the same procedure. An interesting fact in these cases is that the food given the larvæ by the queen is supplied from her own body, by regurgitation through the mouth, no food whatever being brought into the nest from the time that the queen first begins to lay eggs until this first brood is matured. Wheeler, whose admirable recent studies of American ants have revealed many important and intensely interesting facts in the life of our American ant communities, finds among the Ponerine species, undoubtedly in most respects the least specialized of the ants, that the colonies, all of which are small, "appear to be annual growths, formed by swarming as in the bees, and not by single fertilized female ants unaccompanied by workers."

The workers of the first brood begin immediately to take on themselves the work of the little community, the queen from now on having only to produce eggs. First of all comes the enlarging of the nest. Ants' nests, comprising a sum of irregular chambers and galleries, are mostly built underground, although some have a considerable part above the normal ground surface, built up as a mound or hillside, of more or less symmetry and greater or less size. This part above ground may be composed chiefly or wholly of soil brought up from below surface, or may be partly or wholly made up of bits of wood, grass and weed stems, chaff or pine-needles. The nest may be made under a stone or log, or be placed in a wholly exposed place. Most ants keep their nests fairly near the surface, but a few are deeply subterranean miners. Still other species tunnel out their corridors and rooms in wood—an old log or stump, dry branches, or what not—while yet others live in the stems of plants, in old plant-galls, in hollow thorns and spines; finally, a few make nests of delicate paper or tie leaves together with silken threads. Very wonderful are some of the interrelations between certain plants and certain ant species in tropic regions, whereby the plant seems to have developed suitable cavities for the accommodation of the ants, whose presence is in turn advantageous to the plant by the protection it affords against the ravages of certain leaf-eating insects which are repelled, or rather attacked as prey, by the ants. In many cases two ant species will live together in a compound or mixed nest, the relation between the two species being (a) simply that of two close neighbors, friendly or unfriendly; (b) that of two species having their nests with "inosculating galleries" and their "households strangely intermingled but not actually blended"; (c) that of one species, usually with workers of minute size, which lives in or near the nests of other species and preys on the larvæ or pupæ or surreptitiously consumes certain substances in the nests of their hosts—some different larger species—that is, the relation of thief and householder; (d) that of two species living in one nest but with independent households, one of these species living as a guest or inquiline at the expense of the food-stores of the other, but consorting freely with their hosts and living with them on terms of mutual toleration or even friendship; and (e) that of slave-maker and slave, a relation not at all rare and readily observed all over our country. In addition certain other as yet little studied cases of the living together of distinct ant species occur which, when understood, may reveal yet other symbiotic relations.

Inside the nest the eggs are laid by the queen or queens in large numbers, not in separate cells as with the wasps and bees, but in little piles heaped together in various rooms and sometimes moved about by the workers. The hatching larvæ, tiny, white, footless, helpless, soft-bodied grubs, are fed by the workers either a predigested food regurgitated from the mouth, or chewed fresh insects, caught and killed by the workers, or dry seeds or other vegetable matter brought into the hive and stored in the "granary" rooms. A single species of ant may use all these different kinds of food, but for the most part the ants belonging to one species habitually do not. The primitive food consists of seeds and cut-up insects. The importance of knowing the exact facts with regard to this matter will be appreciated when the reader comes to the later discussion of the probable origin of the various castes in the communal insect species. The adult ants feed on a variety of substances, both animal and vegetable, almost all, however, having a special taste for sweetish liquids, such as the secreted honey-dew of plant-lice, scale-insects, certain small beetles and others, and the sugary sap of certain trees. The males and fertile females are fed by the workers.

Besides feeding the larvæ, the nurses have to see that the young enjoy suitable temperature and humidity of the atmosphere; this is accomplished by moving the larvæ or pupæ from room to room, farther below the surface, up nearer the surface, or even out into the warm sunshine above ground. The carrying about of ants' "eggs," which are not eggs but usually the cocooned pupæ, by the workers, is a familiar sight around any ant-nest, particularly a disturbed one. The various special industries undertaken by ants, as the attendance on and care of honey-dew-secreting plant-lice, the fungus-growing in their nests, the harvesting (but not planting!) of food-seeds, the waging of wars for pillage or slave-making, the long migrations, etc., etc., all more or less familiar through much true and some inaccurate popular writing, will be referred to in what detail our space permits in the later descriptions of the life of certain interesting species of American ants.

In any community there may live at one time several (two to thirty) queens with wings removed. In small colonies there is, however, usually but one. As already mentioned, winged ants are to be seen only at certain times in the year. When a brood of sexual individuals (males and females) is matured in the community, these winged forms issue on a sudden impulse (comparable in a way with the outwinging ecstasy of bees at swarming-time) from all the openings of the nest and take wing. The air may be swarming with them, flights from neighboring nests intermingling and joining. This is the mating flight, and after it is over and those ants which have escaped the bird attacks and other dangers attending this bold essay into the outer world alight or fall exhausted to the ground, the males soon die, while the females pull the wings from the body and get under cover. In the communal nest, therefore, winged ants are rarely found. The life of the workers of most ant species is conspicuously longer than that of other social insect workers: they live for from one to three or four or even five years. Lubbock has kept workers until six years old, and queens until seven. The males all die young, but both other kinds of individuals are exceptionally long-lived for insects.

About two hundred species of North American ants constituting the superfamily Formicina or Formicoidea are comprised in three principal families. Some authors recognize five or six families, but it is doubtful if such a division of the group can be fairly made. These three families can be distinguished by the following key:

Basal peduncle of the abdomen composed of a single segment (the first) (Fig. 743).
Abdomen not constricted between the second and third segments (Fig. 743, 1).
                                                                CAMPONOTIDÆ.
Abdomen constricted between the second and third segments (Fig. 743, 2). PONERIDÆ.
Basal peduncle of the abdomen composed of two segments (Fig. 743, 3)..MYRMICIDÆ.

Of these families that of the Poneridæ is the smallest in number of species, and includes the least specialized (as regards sharply marked division of labor, differentiation into castes, and complexity of the communal life) of all the ants. In the following brief accounts of a few of the better known American ants the family relationship of each of the species referred to is indicated.

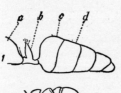

FIG. 743.—Diagrams of lateral aspect of abdomen of representatives of the three families of ants: 1, Camponotidæ; 2, Poneridæ; 3, Myrmicidæ. *a*, thorax; *b*, first abdominal segment; *c*, second abdominal segment; *d*, third abdominal segment.

Of the Poneridæ only about 25 species are so far known in this country; all are stingers, although not very strong ones, and but a few species are at all common. Little was known of their habits and life-history before the recent studies of Professor Wheeler on three species occurring in Texas, namely, *Odontomachus hæmatodes*, *Pachycondyla harpax*, and *Leptogenys elongata*. The nests, made under stones or logs, are primitive structures, composed of a few simple and irregular burrows or galleries, some of which run along the surface of the soil immediately beneath the stone or log, while others extend obliquely or vertically downwards for from 8 to 10 inches. There are no widened chambers. The nests of *L. elongata* comprise ten to fifty individuals, those of *P. harpax* fifteen to one hundred, and those of *O. hæmatodes* one hundred to two hundred. Ergatoid (worker-like) females, no larger than and almost exactly like the true workers, existed in all the nests; the workers of none of the species fed each other or the males and females, and the larvæ were fed simply by giving them pieces of freshly killed insects, which they chewed and devoured by means of their unusually well-developed mandibles. This method of larval feeding is more primitive (demands less care and manipulation on the part of the workers) than in the case of any other ants,—indeed of any other social insects, for even the wasps, which also feed their young pieces of insects, masticate these insect morsels thoroughly before turning them over to the tender larvæ. The feeding of the Ponerine larvæ is also very irregular and capricious both as to quantity and time. If the regulation by the workers of the kind and quantity of food given the larva is the cause or one of several influencing factors in determining the caste or kind of individual into which the larva shall develop, as is believed by most students of social insects, then the unmanipulated food of the Ponerine larvæ and the inequality of its control as to quantity and time of feeding may explain how it is that the caste distinctions are so much less marked in this primitive ant family than in the Myrmicidæ and Camponotidæ, where, as we shall see, the character and amount of the food given the larvæ is carefully controlled by the workers.

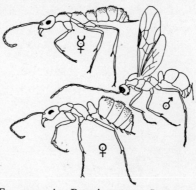

FIG. 744.—A Ponerine ant, *Leptogenys elongata*. (After Wheeler; enlarged.)

The family Myrmicidæ includes a large number of our most interesting ants; almost all are stingers, and all are readily distinguished from members of either of the other families by having the basal two abdominal segments knot-like, and forming the peduncle. Some of the Myrmicids are well known because of their abundance, wide distribution, and troublesome tendency to invade our houses, like the common little red ant, *Monomorium pharaonis*, while others are familiar through the accounts which have been written by various authors of their specialized habits. Among the latter are the harvesting or agricultural ants (Pogonomyrmex), a single species of which, the large harvester of Texas, *P. barbatus* var. *molifaciens*, has had a three-hundred-page book devoted to it, and the fierce marauding ants of the genera Eciton and Atta best known through certain famous tropic kinds, but represented in this country by several thoroughly interesting and characteristic species.

FIG. 745.—An agricultural-ant worker, *Pogonomyrmex imberbicolus*. (After Wheeler; much enlarged.)

Nine species of harvesters (Pogonomyrmex) (Fig. 745) occur in this country (in the southern, southwestern, and Pacific coast states) all (except one small retiring species) as far as known forming small or large communities in nests partly underground and partly heaped up in conspicuous mounds (Figs. 746 and 747) in open, sunny, and usually grassy places. They live specially abundantly in the great western plains and indeed in nearly desert regions. Into the nest they bring great stores of seeds and grains, gathered from the neighboring grasses, and their well-marked runways make distinct paths through the dense grass surrounding the nest. Immediately

FIG. 746.—Mound-nest of the western agricultural ant, *Pogonomyrmex occidentalis.* (After photograph by G. A. Dean, Wallace, Kans.)

around the nest this grass is cleanly cut away. The widespread popular belief that these ants plant or sow (with purpose or intention) the seeds of a

FIG. 747.—Vertical section of mound-nest of the western agricultural ant, *Pogonomyrmex occidentalis;* this nest about 5 feet deep by 6 feet in diameter. (After photograph by G. A. Dean, Wallace, Kans.)

favorite grass, Aristida, is shown by Wheeler to be untrue; what does often happen is that the carrying out of the chaff and sometimes sprouted seeds (unfit for food) from the nest, and dropping them at the edge of the cleared circle, results in a kind of unintentional planting of grain and grass, and as Aristida seeds make up an exceptionally large part of the food-stores, a majority of the plants in the ring about the nest may often be Aristida. A common Californian agricultural ant, *P. subdentatus*, found abundantly by Professor Heath at Monterey, is a splendid fighter as well as provident grain-storer, its stings being declared by Heath to be more painful than those of the honey-bee.

Eciton, the driver-ant, a genus long famous for the marauding and pillaging habits of certain Brazilian species — in these marches the great procession is said to be marshaled by big-headed officers and led by scouts! —is represented in the southwestern part of our country by a few species, *E. cæcum, E. schmitti, E. opacitheræ,* and others. These show in their life the characteristic habit of indulging in maurauding expeditions to the nests of other ants for the purpose of seizing and carrying off the larvæ and pupæ, which are used for food by the Ecitons. Not all the booty is devoured at once; some of it may be stored in the Eciton nest (which is usually but a temporary habitation) and gradually used through several days after the expedition.

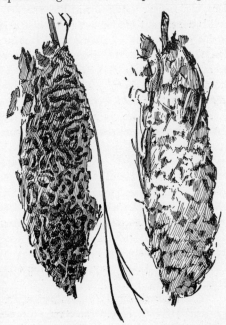

FIG. 748.—Shed-nest of *Cremastogaster lineolata*, 18 inches long by 12 inches in circumference, taken several feet from the ground in a burrow in Hyde County, North Carolina; this ant usually nests under sticks and logs. (After Atkinson.)

The Ecitons are restless ants, and have a great predilection for moving about on long marches or migrations. On these marches they carry with them stored booty, which may consist of the dead bodies of various small insects, as well as the living larvæ and pupæ of pillaged ant communities. The nests of Eciton are entirely subterranean, and are usually simply a cavity, partly natural, partly dug out by the ants under some sheltering stone or other object lying in the ground. The males and females differ remarkably from the workers and from each other in appearance, so much so indeed that the few sexual Eciton forms that have already been discovered have mostly been first described as members of new genera. A flourishing Eciton colony may comprise several thousand individuals.

Interesting and common Myrmicids are the little Cremastogasters, of which one of the most abundant Eastern species is *C. lineolata*, the shed-builder ant. It is a small black and yellowish-brown species, the workers measuring from $\frac{1}{4}$ to $\frac{3}{16}$ inch in length, which usually lives in nests in decaying logs or stumps or in the ground under stones. But sometimes it builds a nest out of chewed wood, like a large rough gall attached to some bush above ground. Atkinson describes such a nest (Fig. 748) 18 inches long and 12 inches in circumference which contained adults, larvæ, and pupæ. In addition to these nest-sheds, small temporary sheds are sometimes built at some distance from the nest "over the herds of Aphids, or scale-insects, from which they obtain honey-dew."

Another interesting and abundant Myrmicid is the minute yellow "thief-ant," *Solenopsis molesta*. Although it sometimes lives in independent nests, more often by far it is to be found living in association with some larger ant species—it consorts with many different hosts—feeding almost exclusively on the live larvæ and pupæ of the host. The thief-ant is so small and obscurely colored that it seems to live in the nest of its host practically unperceived. The Solenopsis nest may be found by the side of the host-nest, around it, or partly in it, the tiny Solenopsis galleries ramifying through the nest-mass of the host, and often opening boldly into these larger galleries. Through their narrower passages, too narrow to be traversed by the hosts, the tiny thief-ants thread their way through the other nest in their burglarious excursions.

As an example of Myrmicids which live in compound or mixed nests the species *Myrmica brevinodes*, a common red-brown ant that lives under stones in the East, and the smaller *Leptothorax emersoni* may be referred to. The interesting symbiotic life of these ants has been studied and carefully described by Wheeler (*American Naturalist*, June, 1901). The little Lep-tothorax ants live in the Myrmica nests, building one or more chambers with entrances from the Myrmica galleries, so narrow that the larger Myrmicas cannot get through them. When needing food the Leptothorax workers come into the Myrmica galleries and chambers and, climbing on to the backs of the Myrmica workers, proceed to lick the face and the back of the head of each host. A Myrmica thus treated "paused," says Wheeler, "as if spellbound by this shampooing and occasionally folded its antennæ as if in sensuous enjoyment. The Leptothorax, after licking the Myrmica's pate, moved its head around to the side and began to lick the cheeks, mandibles, and labium of the Myrmica. Such ardent osculation was not bestowed in vain, for a minute drop of liquid—evidently some of the recently imbibed sugar-water—appeared on the Myrmica's lower lip and was promptly lapped up by the Leptothorax. The latter then dismounted, ran to another Myrmica, climbed onto its back, and repeated the very same performance. Again it took toll and passed on to still another Myrmica. On looking about in the nest I observed that nearly all the Leptothorax workers were similarly employed." Wheeler believes that the Leptothorax get food only in this way; they feed their queen and larvæ by regurgitation. The Myrmicas seem not to resent at all the presence of the Leptothorax guests, and indeed may derive some benefit from the constant cleansing licking of their bodies by the sham-pooers. But the Leptothorax workers are careful to keep their queen and young in a separate chamber, not accessible to their hosts. This is probably the part of wisdom, as the thoughtless habit of eating any conveniently accessible pupæ of another species is wide-spread among ants.

FIG. 749.—Galleries and chambers in wood of the Eastern large black carpenter-ant, *Camponotus pennsylvanicus*. (After McCook.)

The third family, Camponotidæ, a large one, includes a majority of the familiar ants of eastern North America. The large black carpenter-ant, *Camponotus pennsylvanicus* (Fig. 749), which builds extensive nests in logs, stumps, building timbers, and even living trees; the large black-and-red mound-builder, *Formica exsectoides*, whose ant-hills are from five to ten feet in diameter; and *Lasius brunneus*, the little brown ant "whose nests abound along the borders of roads, in pastures, and in meadows," are all familiar Camponotid species. The last-named one is known in the middle states as the corn-louse ant because of its interesting association with the wide-spread corn-root louse, *Aphis maidi-radicis*. In the Mississippi valley this aphid deposits in autumn its eggs in the ground in corn-fields, often in the galleries of the little brown ant. The following spring, before the corn is planted, these eggs hatch. Now the little brown ant is especially fond of the honey-dew secreted by the corn-root lice. So when the latter hatch in the spring, before there are corn-roots for them to feed on, the ants with great solicitude carefully place them on the roots of certain kinds of knotweed (Setaria and Polygonum) which grow in the field, and there protect them until the corn germinates. They are then removed to the roots of the corn.

A curious Camponotid is the honey-ant, *Myrmecocystus melliger*, found in the southwestern semi-arid states. McCook studied these ants in the

Garden of the Gods near Colorado Springs, where he found hundreds of the low-mounded nests in the gravelly soil. The name honey-ant is derived from the curious structural modification and habits of certain workers, whereby these become simply the containers of stored honey, which fills out the

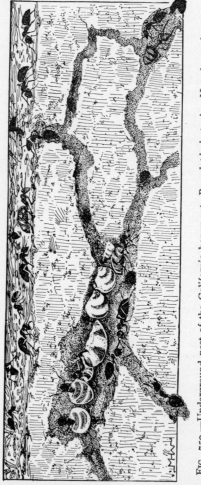

FIG. 750.—Underground nest of the California honey-ant, *Prenolepis imparis*. Note honey-bearers with swollen abdomen in the largest chamber. (Twice natural size.)

abdomen to the size and shape of a currant or small grape. These honey-bearers hang by their feet from the ceiling of small dome-shaped chambers in the nest; their yellow bodies stretch along the ceiling, but the rotund abdomens hang down as almost perfect globules of transparent tissue through which the amber honey shines. The honey is obtained by the workers from fresh (growing) Cynipid galls on oak-trees, which exude a sweetish sticky liquid which is brought in by the foraging workers and fed to the sedentary honey-holders by regurgitation. It is held in the crop of the honey-bearer, the distention of which produces the great dilation of the abdomen. The stored honey is fed on demand to the other workers by regurgitation; a large drop of honey issues from the mouth of the honey-bearer, resting on the palpi and lips, and is eagerly lapped up by the feeding individuals, two or three often feeding together. A somewhat similar honey-ant, *Prenolepis imparis* (Fig. 750), is common in California.

The most interesting, however, of the familiar American ants are the "slave-makers" and their "slaves." Three species of slave-makers occur in North America, of which two belong to the family under present discussion. These are *Formica sanguinea*, represented by five subspecies, and *Polyergus rufescens*, the shining slave-maker, represented by two subspecies. The third slave-making species, *Tomognathus americanus*, is a rare Myrmicid. The slaves of *F. sanguinea* are other smaller species of the same genus, especially *F. subsericea*, *F. nitidiventris*, and *F. subœnescens*, while the slaves of Polyergus are the same species of Formica and the additional one, particularly common as a slave form, *F. schaufussi*. Communities of the slave-making species are occasionally found in which there are no slaves; when slaves are present they may be few or many; usually they are more numerous, proportionally, the smaller the numbers of the slave-makers in any community. The slaves are captured by the attack, by a body of slave-making workers, on a slave-ant community and of the pillage of the attacked nest of larvæ and pupæ; some of these may be eaten, but others are brought back unharmed to the slave-makers' nest. Here more yet may be eaten, but most are cared for and soon hatch to become the slaves of their captors. Never are adults enslaved; they are killed or driven off during the attack. The slaves undertake unhesitatingly all the varied work of bringing in food, nest-building, and caring for the young in the community. Indeed in some cases the slave-makers come to be very dependent on the slaves, which ought really then to be called auxiliaries or helpers, for the slave-maker workers also assist in all the community undertakings, while the "slaves" often seem to dominate, or at least to be quite as important as, their would-be rulers in the determination of the course of events in the compound community. So far does this dependence go in the case of certain foreign ants that the originally dominant species loses its workers, and is thus absolutely dependent on the auxiliary species for the maintenance of the community. In the general division of labor in the compound community the fighting is always done, at any rate chiefly, by the slave-makers. McCook has described in some detail the community life of the shining slave-maker, *Polyergus lucidus*, and its auxiliary, *Formica schaujussi* (Proc. Phil. Acad. Sci., 1880, p. 376 et seq.).

The observation and study of ants' ways must be partly done in the field, but, thanks to the obliging manner in which most species will readily live in artificial nests prepared for them indoors, much intensely interesting work in the study of ants can be done on one's own reading-table. Several types of artificial formicaries (ants' nests) have been devised, one by Lubbock, another by Forel, another by Janet, another by White, etc., any one of which seems to give good results. Professor Comstock gives the following directions for making a Lubbock nest: "The principal materials needed for the construction of a nest of this kind are two panes of window-glass ten inches square, a sheet of tin 11 inches square, and a piece of plank 1¼ inches thick, 20 inches long, and at least 16 inches wide.

"To make the nest, proceed as follows: Cut a triangular piece about 1 inch long on its two short sides from one corner of one of the panes of glass. From the sheet of tin make a tray ⅜ of an inch in depth. This tray will be a little wider than the panes of glass and will contain them easily. On the upper side of the plank a short distance from the edge cut a deep furrow. This plank is to form the base of the nest, and the furrow is to serve as a moat, which is to be kept filled with water in order to prevent the escape of the ants. It is necessary to paint the base with several coats of paint to protect it from water and thus prevent its warping.

"To prepare the nest for use, place the tin tray on the base, put in the tray the square pane of glass, lay on the edges of the glass four strips of wood about ½ inch wide and a little thicker than the height of the ants which are to be kept in the nest, cover the glass with a layer of fine earth of the same thickness as the strips of wood, place upon this layer of earth and the strips of wood the pane of glass from which one corner has been cut, and cover the whole with a cover of the same size and shape as the upper pane of glass. In the nest figured the cover is made of blackened tin, and one-half of it is covered by a board. This gives a variation in temperature in different parts of the nest when it stands in the sunlight.

"The ants when established in the nest are to mine in the earth between the two plates of glass. The removal of one corner from the upper pane provides an opening to the nest. The thickness of the strips of wood between the edges of the two panes of glass determines the depth of the layer of earth in which the ants live. This should not be much thicker than the ants are high; for, if it is, the ants will be able to conceal themselves so that they cannot be observed.

" The nest being prepared, the next step is to transfer a colony of ants to it. The things needed with which to do this are a two-quart glass fruit-can, or some similar vessel that can be closed tightly, a clean vial, and a garden trowel. With these in hand find a small colony of ants, such as are common under stones in most parts of the country. Collect as many of the ants and of the eggs, larvæ, and pupæ as possible, and put them in a fruit-can, together with the dirt that is scooped up in collecting them with the trowel. Search carefully for the queen; sometimes she is found immediately beneath the stone covering the nest, but often it is necessary to dig a considerable distance in order to find her. She can be recognized by her large size. If the queen is not found, empty the contents of the can back into the nest, and take up another colony; without a queen the experiment will be a failure. Wh.n the queen is found place her in the vial so that she shall not be injured while b.ing carried to the schoolroom.

"Having obtained a queen and a large part of her family, old and young, return to the schoolroom and empty the contents of the fruit-can onto the board covering the upper pane of glass, and place the queen there with her family. If much dirt and rubbish has been collected with the ants, remove some of it so that not more than half a pint of it remains. When this is done leave the ants undisturbed for a day or two. Of course the moat should be filled with water so that they cannot escape.

"Usually within twenty-four hours the ants will find the opening leading into the space between the two panes of glass and will make a mine into the layer or earth which is there, and will remove their queen and young to this place. This process can be hastened by gradually removing the dirt placed on the cover of the nest with the ants.

"After the ants have made a nest between the panes of glass they can be observed when desired by merely lifting the board forming the cover of the nest.

"With proper care a colony can be kept in a nest of this kind as long as the queen lives, which may be several years. The food for the ants can be placed on the base of the nest anywhere within the moat, and may consist of sugar, minute bits of meat, fruits, etc. With a little care the kinds of food preferred by the colony can be easily determined. The pupæ of ants, which can be collected from nests in the field during the summer months, will be greedily devoured. The soil in the nest should be kept from becoming too dry by putting a little water into one side of the tin tray from time to time."

White prefers for a formicarium an inverted bell-glass (Fig. 751) mounted on a wooden block which is set like an island in a shallow pan of water. "Enough of the contents of a nest should be removed and transferred to the bell-glass to occupy about half of its available space. A cover either of baize or brown paper should be placed over the sides of the glass so as to conceal the contained earth and to allow the light to filter only through the surface, so that the ants may be thus induced to work against the transparent sides of the formicarium. The darkness occasioned by the screen leads them to believe that they are working underground, at certain distances from the surface, and thus induces them to construct many tiers of chambers and connecting corridors within the range of practical observation. This

FIG. 751.—A convenient bell-jar formicary. The dish in which the bell-jar stands is surrounded by water held in the large zinc pan.

we may judge to our satisfaction when, after a few days, the screen is withdrawn for a short season, and the marvels of the constructive instinct of the little people revealed to our wondering gaze."

Janet, a distinguished French student of ant life, uses a block of porous earthenware in which several little chambers or hollows have been made,

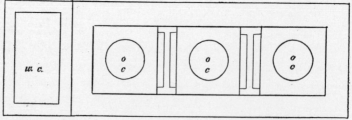

FIG 752.—Plan of a Janet nest. *o*, opening covered by opaque cover, *c*; *wc*, wet chamber. (After Janet.)

connecting with each other by little surface grooves, the whole covered with a glass plate, and over that an opaque cover (Fig. 753). Into a cavity at one end of the block he puts water which soaks some distance along the length of the block, thus rendering some chambers humid, while others at the far end are dry. He gives the ants no soil, forcing them to use the already made chambers. This formicarium reveals, therefore, none of the secrets of nest-building, but it does reveal admirably a host of those interesting processes connected part cularly with the life-history of the individuals of the colony. Miss Fielde uses still another kind of nest, also like Janet's with

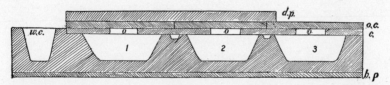

FIG. 753.—A Janet nest in vertical section. *w.c.*, wet chamber; 1, 2, 3, brood-chambers; *o.*, circular openings for brood-chambers made in *c.*, a transparent cover; *o.c.*, glass cover in three removable pieces; *d.p.*, opaque cover; *b.p.*, base plate. (After Janet.)

fixed chambers, but made wholly of glass, the requisite moisture being furnished by a bit of sponge kept soaked with water and placed in one of the communicating chambers. Fig. 754 with its caption explains the make-up of a Fielde nest.

In the study of the life of ants by means of such formicaries as have just been described, as well as through observations in the field, the student, amateur or professional, should keep in mind certain particular desiderata in formicology. It is highly desirable to determine for as many species as possible the exact method of founding a new colony: isolate a queen in a small artificial formicary, well provided with food, and see if she can and will begin one; isolate a small group of workers with some eggs or young larvæ, but without a queen, and see if they can and do produce a queen and establish themselves as a permanent community. The characteristic habits of feeding the young should be

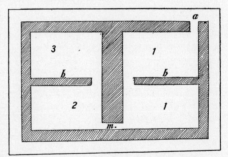

FIG. 754.—Plan of the Fielde ant-nest, 10 inches by 6 inches. *a*, entrance and exit to food-rooms (1); 2, nursery; 3, sponge-room; *b*, screens; *m*, passage.

determined for various species; the presence of or possibility of producing ergatoid (wingless, worker-like) fertile females and males in the case of various species should be noted; and special attention should be given in all observations to determining in how far the behavior in general, and single processes in particular, can be explained as machine-like reflexes of unintelligent organisms, or make necessary the assumption that ants have a choice-making and generally adaptive and teachable intelligence. Can ants dislocate in time their reactions to stimuli? Are ants conscious?

Curious interrelations of ants with some other animals have already

been referred to, as their care of plant-lice (Aphididæ) from which they obtain the much-liked honey-dew, and their association with various species of their own general kind in the relations of slave-maker and slave, host and parasite, or host and guest. But still another kind of intimate association with other animal species is common in ant-life, namely, that of the occurrence in their nests of many different species of other insects (as well as certain mites, spiders, and myriapods) which force their presence on their ant hosts by cleverness or deception, or are tolerated or even encouraged by the hosts. A few of these arthropods which inhabit ants' nests are true parasites or predaceous enemies, such as have to be endured by almost all other insect kinds, but the large majority of these so-called *myrmecophiles* do little or no injury to their ant hosts, while a few even return in some degree the advantages which

FIG. 755.—*Ecitoxenia brevipes*, a rove-beetle (Staphylinidæ), which lives in the nests of the robber-ant, *Eciton schmittii*, in Texas. Note absence of wings and curiously modified shape. (After Brues; natural length one-eighth inch.)

they receive by the association. These advantages are (*a*) ready-made subterranean cavities and lodging-places, defended against most enemies by the fierce and capable owners of the nest; (*b*) a pleasant and favorable temperature maintained despite the frigidity of the outer atmosphere; (*c*) stores of vegetable food, as seeds, etc., garnered by the ants, and supplies of animal food, as bits of freshly killed insects, etc., collected by the hosts, as well as the larvæ and pupæ, and even the dead bodies of the ants themselves; (*d*) the sweetish liquid food readily regurgitated by most

FIG. 756.  FIG. 757.

FIG. 756. — *Termitogaster texana*, a rove-beetle (Staphylinidæ), which lives in the nests of the termite, *Eutermes cinereus*, in Texas. (After Brues; natural length $1\frac{1}{2}$ mm.)

FIG. 757.—*Ænigmatis blattoides*, a Phorid fly, which lives in the nests of the ant, *Formica fusca*, in Denmark. (After Meinert; thirteen times natural size.)

ant workers in response to certain stimuli, and normally used for feeding the queens, males, and occasionally other workers; and finally (*e*) means of safe transportation due to the migrating habits of many of their host species.

The myrmecophilous (ant's-nest-inhabiting) insects are limited to no single order. Of the total of 1177 insect species recorded by Wasmann in 1900 as living for part or all of their life in ants' nests, 993 are beetles, of

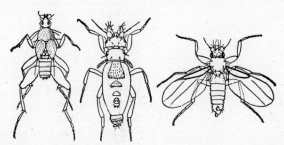

FIG. 758.—Ant-guests; at left, *Psyllomyia testacea*, female; next at right, *Ecitomyia wheeleri*, female; at extreme right, male of last-named species. These two insects are species of flies of the family Phoridæ, the females of which have become extremely degenerate because of their myrmecophilous life. (After Wheeler; much enlarged.)

which the families Staphylinidæ (rove-beetles), Pselaphidæ, Paussidæ, Clavigeridæ, Histeridæ, Silphidæ, Thorictidæ, Lathridictidæ, and Scydmænidæ make up all but 100 species, these latter representing 22 other families; 76 are Hemiptera, of which 15 are plant-lice and scale-insects; 39 are Hymenoptera, of which 22 are other ant species; 26 are Lepidopterous larvæ, 20 are Thysanura, 18 Diptera, 7 Orthoptera, 1 a Pseudo-Neuropteron, 34 are mites, 26 are spiders, and 9 are isopod crustaceans. While most of these only derive advantage from this commensalism with ants, some, and notably the small Paussid, Clavigerid, Pselaphid, and other beetles, live truly symbiotically with their hosts, — being of immediate reciprocal benefit to them. These little beetles, many of which show most amazing modifications of body structure (Figs. 755, 756) (such modifications, usually degenerative, are displayed also by numerous other ant guests, particularly Phorid flies (Figs. 757, 758), in adaptation to this extraordinary life, secrete a sweet substance which is greedily eaten by the ants. The hosts in return care for, clean, and feed by regurgitation the curious little beetles.

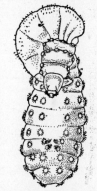

FIG. 759.—Larva of a Phorid fly attached to the larva of the ant, *Pachycondyla harpax*. (After Wheeler; much enlarged.)

The "wonderful" and "marvelous" character of the behavior of the ants, bees, and wasps has long been a subject of popular interest and an object of much scientific observation and experimentation more or less rigorously conducted. Speculation, both popular and scientific, concerning the causal factors concerned has run a wide gamut, from the declaration of Bethe that ants are simply complex machines responding mechanically, with fixed strictly reflex reactions, to physico-chemical stimuli, to the anthropomorphic comparisons of the natural-history popularizer, who reads into the behavior of the "wonderful little ant people" human emotions, human reason, intelligent discrimination, and volitional action.

A difficulty met with at the very beginning of any discussion of the behavior of social insects is the lack of precise definitions of three presumably classificatory terms distinguishing, on a basis of cause, three kinds of behavior or action, viz., reflexes, instincts, and intelligence. Another more fundamental difficulty in the actual study and interpretation of animal behavior is the absolute lack in ourselves of any criterion or means of interpretation of action other than our experience of our own sensation and psychology. Nevertheless the matter can be, and is now being, undertaken in a rational and unbiased spirit, and is attaining important positive results based on observation and experiment conducted with rigorously scientific method and expressed with scientific caution. Although little more than an appreciable beginning has been made in this work, we can already distinguish some of the springs or factors, both intrinsic and extrinsic, which determine the actions of these insects, and we can define scientifically some of the limitations as well as some of the possibilities of their purposeful behavior.

Between the cleanly mechanical or reflex theory of Bethe, Uexkull, and others, and the reflexes plus instincts and animal-memory theory of Wasmann, Loeb, and Wheeler, or between this and the instincts plus intelligence theory of Lubbock and Forel, there is no sharp line, although between Bethe and Forel there is a wide gulf. What modern investigation has clearly and positively done is to cut away the anthropomorphism of the careless popularizer, and to compel a strong leaning toward a belief in the efficiency of reflex and instinct to explain most if not all of ant behavior. What would not have been heard with any patience at all a few years ago, that is, a purely mechanical, i.e., reflexive reaction to physico-chemical stimuli, explanation of many of the "wonderful" actions of ants, as their perception of paths, their recognition of nest-mates, and swift attack on strangers, their refrain from attack on other species living in symbiotic relations with them, etc., etc., is now heard with careful attention. Couple with this purely reflexive theory the theory of inherited specialized instincts developed by natural selection from widely diffused generalized instincts and most of us are inclined to find in the combination the springs of most if not all ant behavior; and what will explain the complex activities of ants will certainly explain those of all the other so-called "intelligent insects," namely, bees and wasps, both solitary and social.

A final problem in the life of the social insects is that touching the origin and establishment of the various castes or kinds of individuals inside the single species. The presence of two, often widely differing kinds of individuals, namely, male and female, is so familiar as to lose, for some of us, part of its significance and importance. But why the young produced by the union of male and female can differ so widely as they may, that is, to the extent of the difference between male and female, seems to us explicable by the fact that just such two differing parent individuals take part in the production of the new individuals, and by the fact that such a phenomenon is the usual and ordinary one of heredity. (However little we may understand the natural phenomenon or law of heredity just as little do we understand gravitation, which we habitually are content to assign as an ultimate cause for certain effects). But with the social insects we have always one, and often more than one, still different individual among the offspring, and one which takes no part whatever in the (embryonic) production of new individuals; it can hand on nothing to the offspring by heredity. The question is, then, how are two kinds of individuals (male and female) able to produce not only their own kinds, but a third kind which has no part in producing or fertilizing the egg-cell from which it develops?

And on the heels of this question comes a second. How is it that if the present-day forms and kinds of animals are due to the results of the combined influences of variation, natural selection, and heredity—that is, that the inevitably appearing slight congenital differences as they are of advantage or disadvantage in the life of the animal are preserved or destroyed in the species by natural selection—how, it may be asked, have the characters of the worker castes been thus determined by selection, for in this case the modified individuals have no part in the transmission of their characteristics by heredity?

The first question is answered as far as it at present can be in terms not wholly agnostic, by the statement that it is probably true among ants, as has been shown actually to be true with certain other social insects, namely, the termites (p. 111) and the honey-bee (p. 525), that the difference between queen (fertile female) and worker (infertile female) is brought about during postembryonal development by differences regulated by the nurses in the quality and quantity of food supplied the developing individuals. Sharp says: "There is a considerable body of evidence suggesting that the quality or quantity of the food or both combined are important factors in the treatment by which the differences are produced. The fact that the social insects in which the phenomena of caste or polymorphism occur, though belonging to very diverse groups, all feed their young, is of itself very suggestive. When we add to this the fact that in ants, where the phenomena of polymorphism reach their highest complexity, the food is elaborated in their own organs by the feeders that administer it, it appears probable that the means of producing the diversity may be found herein."

The answer to the second query—a query anticipated by the keen-minded Darwin as voicing an apparently insuperable objection to the selection theory—as made in the Origin of Species at the end of the chapter on Instinct has, by the investigation of modern students of ants, only been strengthened. This answer made by Darwin, and repeated with new supporting observations and ingenious arguments by the present-day Neo-Darwinians, is briefly: that the differences between the queens and the various worker castes are quantitative rather than qualitative, that gradatory conditions exist between the extreme points of the various lines of structural and physiological specialization, individuals being found in almost every ant species, so far carefully studied, standing as connecting links between queen and highly specialized infertile worker (or soldier); that there has been a gradual achievement of this differentiation of structure through the advantage to the species of the slight congenital tendencies toward sterility on the part of some of the young, and by consequence their special devotion to the nest industries, leaving the fertile individuals freer for reproductive activity; that the evolution has been one of communities rather than of individuals; that those fertile males and females have persisted which have shown a tendency to produce some sterile individuals among their progeny which, living in consociation with the fertile individuals of the brood, were of special advantage to the community more and more as they possessed such variations of structure as would fit some for general work and others for the special defence of the colony; and, finally, that such advantages to the community have been quite sufficient as handles for the action of natural selection, with the final result as seen to-day in developing ant species in which there is a fairly sharp division between fertile and sterile forms, and between two or three different castes of the sterile individuals. Those species are the modern ones whose fertile females produce several well-modified kinds of individuals. Darwin and the Neo-Darwinians of to-day not only find in this answer an adequate explanation of the development of the modern highly specialized ant community by the action of natural selection, but find the existence of such communities a convincing fact telling against the belief of Lamarckians and Neo-Lamarckians in evolution by the accumulation of inherited structural and physiological characters acquired in the lifetime of individuals. As

Darwin says: "The case (of ant communities with worker castes) also is very interesting, as it proves that with animals, as with plants, any amount of modification may be effected by the accumulation of numerous, slight, spontaneous variations, which are in any way profitable, without exercise or habit having been brought into play. For peculiar habits, confined to the workers of sterile females, however long they might be followed, could not possibly affect the males and fertile females, which alone leave descendants. I am surprised that no one has hitherto advanced this demonstrative case of neuter insects against the well-known doctrine of inherited habit as advanced by Lamarck."

It will be noted that the answer to the first question as to how the marked differences between the fertile and the sterile forms of ants in any nest are brought about during individual development, and the answer of Darwin to the second question as to how these differences have been brought about in the species itself, are not thoroughly in harmony. Darwin's answer would at first glance seem to assume differences in the eggs laid by a single queen capable of determining the difference in the individuals developed from these eggs; so that no special treatment (feeding) of an individual would be necessary to produce the ultimate differences in the matured individuals. But the congenital differences may be potential and not definitive; the feeding treatment, namely, the addition of certain extrinsic or environmental factors, might be necessary to discover or make actual the latent or potential differences congenitally resident in the eggs.

Still a third question arises in connection with the specialized conditions obtaining in modern ant communities. It is this: How have the compound and mixed communities, in which two ant species live in some kind or degree of symbiosis, arisen? How has it come about that two species of ants which normally are deadly enemies ready to do battle with each other at any meeting—a condition which seems to be curiously general throughout the group of ants, not only different species being always ready to attack one another, but members of different communities of the same species showing a deadly animosity for each other—how is it that these two species have come to live peaceably together in a mixed community?

In the first place in some of the cases the animosity still exists; the "thief" ants which live in other ants' nests escape with their lives only because of their minute size and obscure coloring, their careful avoidance of detection, and the care with which they keep the galleries of their own part of the nest too small for the entrance of the hosts; they appear to manage this double household arrangement by vigilance, cleverness, and deceit. Cases of true symbiosis with mutual benefit are readily explicable by the selection theory. Their beginning is a little hard to understand, but an association with reciprocal advantages, once begun, could readily be developed into such a curious condition as that, for example, of *Myrmica* and *Leptothorax* described on p. 544. The beginning of such an association requires the assumption, of course, that the apparent general rule of mutual animosity existing among ants shall have its natural exceptions; that their instincts are not wholly immutable or all embracing. To take a particular case, Wheeler has admirably shown the remarkable differences of instinct exhibited by the species of the single genus Leptothorax. While systematists agree that this large and widely distributed genus is unusually homogeneous, Wheeler shows that in habits its species are singularly diverse: "Many of the forms have no tendency to consort with ants of other species, but differ considerably in the stations which they inhabit. Some prefer to live under stones, others in moss, others under bark or in dead wood, and still others, like one of the Texan species, in cynipid galls, or, like our New England *L. longispinosus* Rog., in the worm-eaten hickory-nuts among the dead leaves under the trees. Many species, however, have a pronounced *penchant* for entering into more or less intimate symbiotic relations with other Formicidæ, as shown in the following conspectus:

"1. The European *L. muscorum* often lives in plesiobiosis [double nest] with *Formica rufa*.

"2. A similar tendency is undoubtedly exhibited by our American *L. canadensis* Provancher, which I have had occasion to observe since the second part of this paper was written." [Here Wheeler describes in detail the symbiosis of *L. canadensis* and *Cremastogaster lineolata*, the common shed-builder ant of the north and east.]

"3. *L. pergandei* lives, probably as a guest, in the nests of *Monomorium minutum*, var. *minimum*.

"4. The single colony of the Mexican *L. petiolatus* which I have seen was living in parabiosis [interlacing nest] with species of Cryptocerus and Cremastogaster.

"5. *L. tuberum*, var. *unifasciatus*, lives with the European *Formicoxenus ravouxi*, the relations between the species being, perhaps, the same as those which obtain between *Formica rufa* and *Formicoxenus nitidulus*.

"6. *L. muscorum*, *L. acervorum*, and *L. tuberum* live as slaves or auxiliaries with the European *Tomognathus sublœvis*.

"7. *L. curvispinosus* probably performs the same rôle in the nests of *T. Americanus*.

"8. *L. tuberum* has been found associated with *Strongylognathus testaceus*. Here, too, the Leptothorax probably acts as the slave of the dulotic species.

"9. *L. emersoni* lives with *Myrmica brevinodis* as described [on p. 544]."

It is evident, therefore, says Wheeler, that the ants of this genus have originally possessed certain traits which made it specially easy for them to enter into symbiotic relations with other species of ants. Some of these fundamental or original traits may still be recognized in the genus, to wit:

"1. The genus has a very wide geographical distribution, a prerequisite to the establishment of such numerous and varied relations with other ants.

"2. The species are all of small size. This must undoubtedly facilitate their association with other ants.

"3. The colonies consist of a relatively small number of individuals. This, too, must greatly facilitate life as guests or parasites in the nests of other ants.

"4. Most of the species are rather timid, or at any rate not belligerent. They are, therefore, of a more adaptable temperament than many other ants even of the same size (e.g., *Tetramorium cæspitum*). Forel has shown that *L. tubero-affinis* will rear pupæ of *L. mylanderi* and even of *Tetramorium cæspitum* and live on good terms with the imagines when they hatch.

"5. There is no very sharp differentiation in habits between the queens and workers of Leptothorax. This, too, should facilitate symbiosis. The queens, as I have shown in the case of *L. emersoni*, may retain the excavating instinct and the instincts which relate to the care of the larvæ.

"6. The similarity in instinct between the queens and workers of Leptothorax finds its physical expression in the frequent occurrence of intermediate or ergatogynous forms. So-called microgynic individuals, or winged queens no larger than the workers, have been frequently observed by Forel and Wasmann in *L. acervorum*. Those observed by the latter author also showed color transitions between the normal queens and workers."

Finally, Wheeler points out that this heterogeneity of habit and these existing gradatory steps between strictly non-working fertile queen and strictly non-fertile working-worker, are evidence for the selection theory as explaining the division of labor and differentiation of structure in the specialized ant communities. "Viewed as a whole, these different symbiotic relations cannot be said to bear the ear-marks of internal developmental causes operating in a perfectly determinate manner. Indeed, appearances are quite otherwise and seem rather to point to indeterminate variations which have been and are still in process of being seized on a fixed by natural selection. It must also be admitted that the same appearance is presented by the whole complex of conditions in compound and mixed nests, but the demonstration is more cogent when it can be shown that we have relations as different as those of dominant species (*L. emersoni*) and slaves (*L. acer-*

*vorum*) not only in the same genus but among closely allied forms. *This fact also suggests that the instincts of the same species may be so generalized as to enable it to function like man, either as a slave or master, according to the circumstances."*

And this leads us to consider briefly that extremest form of consociation between two ant species, namely, the so-called dulosis, the living together of slave-makers and slaves. To put summarily the result of various careful studies of dulotic communities made by both European and American observers, it may be said that this condition has grown out of the general instinct that most ants show, to obtain when and where possible the larvæ and pupæ of other ant species for food. From a raid on a neighboring community and the immediate devouring of as many larvæ and pupæ as possible to a similar attack and feast plus the bringing home of a supply of this choice food to be stored for eating through the next few days is a natural, and as exemplified by numerous observed cases, an actual s'ep. Then if the booty be large in amount, it is inevitable that some of the pupæ shall transform in the new nest. Now, are these newly issued workers to be at once attacked and eaten? This depends on whether the proper stimulus is present or not. As practically certainly determined by numerous observations and experiments the stimulus for attack and war among ants (as well as bees) is odor; recognition of nest mate and perception of intruder or foreigner depends probably solely on the sense of smell, and the stimulation of this sense has come during the evolution of the instincts of ants to be a stimulus to direct reflexive action; the odor of the home community determines friendly behavior, the odor of any other community gives direct rise to attack. Now, this odor has several component elements; one, for example, inherited (by the inheritance of a characteristic metabolism) from the queen, so that descendants of a common mother, or of sister-mothers (common grand-maternal inheritance), have an odor with something in common; another element and a strong one is, however, the nest odor compounded of all the individual odors in a community and *gradually* taken on by each hatching young. If the young be removed from one community and be hatched in another they seem to take on the odor of the second community. And so the living booty brought back by the raiders, issuing in the new nest, becomes endowed with the odor of the new community and is unmolested. But the instinct of the hatched workers is to work; and so work they do. If their work is of advantage to the raider community, natural selection will do the rest. In the beginning there were no slave-makers; raiders there were which raided other nests, not for slaves, but for food. But bringing home extra supplies of this food, which hatched and lived and worked in the new nest, evolution from food to slaves and from raiders to slave-holders has naturally taken place. Now such an extreme in this specialization has been reached as shown by *Polyergus* which is abjectly dependent on its slaves. It is no longer capable of digging, is unable to take enough food, unaided by its slaves, to keep it from starvation in a nest stored to repletion, nor can it care for its own young. Specialization is leading *Polyergus* to its end!

# CHAPTER XVI

## INSECTS AND FLOWERS

HE nectar of flowers is a favorite food with many insects; all the moths and butterflies, all the bees and many kinds of flies are nectar-drinkers. Flower-pollen, too, is food for other hosts of insects, as well as for many of those which take nectar. The hundreds of bee kinds are the most familiar and conspicuous of the pollen-eaters, but many little beetles and some other obscure small insects feed largely on the rich pollen-grains. But the flowers do not provide nectar and pollen to these hosts of insect guests without demanding and receiving a payment which fully requites their apparent hospitality. And several particular things about this payment are of especial interest to us: these are, first, the unusual character of the payment received; second, the great value of it to the plants; and finally, the strange shifts and devices which the plants exhibit for making the payment certain.

In the course of this book, so far chiefly devoted to a systematic consideration of various kinds of insects and their habits, several interesting ecological relations between plants and insects have been referred to. That plants furnish the nesting-grounds, or "homes," of many insects has been shown: the wood-borers pass their long, immature life concealed and protected in burrows in the bark or wood of trees and bushes; the delicate little leaf-mining caterpillars wind their devious tunnels safely in the soft tissues of even the thinnest of leaves; while in more specialized manner the extraordinary galls developed on the oaks and roses and other plants serve as safe houses for the soft-bodied Cynipid larvæ enclosed by them. The making of homes like these often, indeed usually, serves the double purpose of both housing and feeding the insect; as it gnaws or bites out its protecting burrow in stem or leaf it is getting the very food it most prefers; as the plant swiftly builds up about the gall-making larva masses of succulent tender tissue, it is supplying in unstinted quantity the very food (plant-sap) which the larva has to have or starve.

But the food relation may and mostly does exist between plant and insect without combination with the nest or home relation. To the countless hosts of plant-feeding insects, the leaf-eating beetles and locusts and caterpillars, the sap-sucking bugs and plant-lice, the plant furnishes food alone; and in furnishing it, under a rough compulsion, is nearly always the loser, even, often enough, to death. The special relation between insects and plants to which this chapter is devoted is also a kind of food relation, but with the

unusual character of being one in which the plant is not at all a loser but a gainer, and in as great measure as the insect itself. Only plants with flowers and mostly only those with bright-colored, odorous, and nectar-secreting flowers, have any part in this relation, which is, as the reader has already recognized, that interesting phenomenon, the cross-pollination of flowers by their insect visitors. As this interrelation of flowers and insects is one of very large importance in the life of many insect kinds, profound modifications of their structure and habits depending on it, and as popular knowledge of the subject is likely to be extremely general in its scope, I have thought it advisable to present a brief special account of this phenomenon.

The agency of insects in effecting the cross-pollination of flowers has long been recognized. Credit is given to Sprengel for first publishing accounts of the interesting modifications of flowers due to their interrelation with insects, and for discovering that the insects were instrumental in pollinating the flowers. (Das entdeckte Geheimniss der Natur im Bau und in der Befruchtung der Blumen, von Christian Konrad Sprengel, Berlin, 1793).

FIG. 760 —Snapdragon being visited by honey-bees. (From nature.)

But that this pollination by insects was (nearly) exclusively cross-pollination he did not apparently fully understand, or at least he did not fully understand the significance of cross-pollination. It was reserved for Darwin (On the Fertilization of Orchids by Insects, London, 1862), on a basis not merely of his acquaintance with the observations of Sprengel, Waechter, Delpino, Hooker, and others, but of characteristically keen and careful investigations of his own (particularly on orchids) to reveal the wide diffusion and great specialization of this interrelation, and to explain the causal factors in determining the marvelous phenomena attending its development. These causal factors are (1) the real advantage to the plant species of cross-fertilization, and (2) the action of natural selection in modifying both flowers and insects for the sake, or by reason of, this advantage.

Fertilization among plants is like fertilization among animals; a germ- (sperm-) cell from one individual (male or hermaphrodite) fuses with a germ- (egg-) cell from another (female or hermaphrodite) individual or from the same (hermaphrodite) individual. The sperm-cells are contained in pollen produced in the anthers of stamens; the egg-cells lie in the ovaries at the

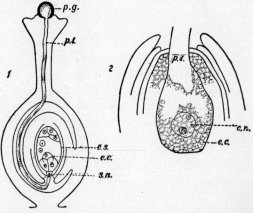

FIG. 761.—Diagram of section of pistil and ovary of a flower, showing the descent of the pollen-tube and its entrance into the ovule. *p.g.*, pollen-grain; *p.t.*, pollen-tube; *e.s.*, embryo-sac; *e.c.*, egg-cell; *s.n.*, sperm-nucleus. Left-hand figure (1) shows the pollen-tube grown down around and up into the ovary with the sperm-nucleus just entering the ovule; right-hand figure (2) shows the fusion of the sperm-nucleus and egg-nucleus. (After Stevens.)

base of the pistils, these pistils having an exposed pollen-catching surface (stigma) at their free tip. Before actual fertilization can occur pollination must take place; pollination being the bringing and applying of ripe pollen-grains to the ripe surface of the stigma. How fertilization then takes place is succinctly explained by Fig. 761 and its caption, which is copied from Stevens (Introduction to Botany, Boston, 1902).

Cross-pollination is simply the bringing of pollen from one plant individual to the stigmas of another individual of the same species. Self-pollination is the getting of pollen from the stamens of one flower onto the stigma of the same flower. The advantage of cross-pollination, as first experimentally proved by Darwin, and since then confirmed by other experimenters and, without scientific intention but none the less effectively, by hosts of economic plant-breeders (horticulturists, florists, etc.), lies in the fact that the seeds produced when the ovules of one plant are fertilized by the sperm-cells (in the pollen) of another develop plant individuals of markedly stronger growth (shown in size of plant and its fruits, in number of seeds, etc.) than seeds produced by the fertilization of ovules by sperm-cells of the same plant. To effect this advantageous cross-pollination two lines of specialization or modification of floral structures have arisen (presumably through the action of natural selection): (1) modifications such as to attract insects and insure cross-pollination as the result of their visits (and to much less extent to attract other animals, particularly humming-birds), and (2) modifications tending to prevent self-pollination. Coupled with both these general lines of modification are others to effect certain auxiliary or accessory conditions the necessity for which grows out of the larger needs; such are, for example, modifications to prevent the stealing of nectar and pollen by other animals (insects particularly) than those on which cross-pollination specially depends, and to make possible self-pollination in cases where cross-pollination, although probable, may for some accidental or other rare cause not take place. Coincidently, and reciprocally with the development of modifications of the flower structures, has occurred the specialization of certain structures and habits among those insects which are the cross-pollinating agents. These modifications occur chiefly in the structure of the mouth-parts and legs of bees, wasps, flies, and a few other insects and in their food and flight habits, and the care of their young. The reciprocal modifications of flowers and insects have gone so far in some cases that certain species of plants and certain species of insects cannot now live except by virtue of their inter-relation. Many flowers are not fertile when pollinated by their own pollen, and yet have no other possible means of getting pollen from other plants except that of insect visits.

The principal means which have been developed to avoid self-fertilization are the following: (a) the having each flower unisexual instead of bisexual, that is, producing either pollen (staminate) or ovules (pistillate) but not both; these unisexual flowers may occur on the same plant individual (monœcious) or on separate individuals (diœcious); (b) the having both pistils and stamens on each flower, but with the anthers and the stigma not maturing coincidently (dichogamous), either the anthers breaking open and discharging the pollen before the stigmas are ready to receive it (proterandrous) or the stigmas maturing before the pollen ripens and is discharged (proterogynous); (c) the having the stamens and pistils (in the same flower) different in length so that the pollen would be unlikely to fall on the stigmas, or (*d*) the having the stamens and pistils so situate with regard to each other that it is difficult or very unusual for the pollen to reach a stigma. All these devices are familiar to every student of botany, and to gardeners, florists, and flower-lovers generally, and examples of them all can readily be found among our common garden and field plants. Any simple manual of botany will put one in the way of hunting them out for one's self.

To recur now to the first of the two principal lines of specialization referred to as those which have arisen in connection with the advantage of cross-pollination, namely, the modification of the floral structures, we shall find these modifications to consist of (*a*) the secretion of nectar to attract the insects, (*b*) the development of odor, color, pattern, and shape to guide them to the flower and when there to the nectar and pollen in such a way as to insure their brushing against both, or either, pollen and stigma, (*c*) the modification of shape so as to prevent the stealing of nectar and pollen by non-helpful insects, and (*d*) the blossoming at those times in the year (seasonal flowering) when the particularly helpful insects are most numerous, and the opening of the flowers at such times, in daylight, twilight, or at night, as specifically accords with the food-seeking flights of these insects. The manifold variety of these modifications will be indicated and illustrated by accounts of a few specific cases exemplifying certain more or less distinct kinds of modification and reciprocal relation with insects, but a few general statements may first be made.

The pollen collected for food by the bees and a few other insects is, of course, a normal product of the flower, and it is only necessary that there be enough of it to supply the insects and yet suffice for the plant's own uses, i.e., in fertilization. As the oldest, the most primitive, means developed among plants to effect cross-pollination, a means still used by all the conifers, the grasses, and many other plants mostly characterized by the total absence of colored floral envelopes (petals and sepals), is the production of vast quantities of light, non-adherent, pollen grains to be distributed by the wind, the more specialized entomophilous flowers (those depending on insects to carry their pollen) probably started with enough and more of pollen to supply their own needs as well as the demands of their visitors.

The nectar, however, is a special product, developed in direct connection with the insect pollinating specialization. It is a "more or less watery solution of sugar and of certain salts and aromatic substances secreted by a special tissue known as the nectary and expelled at the surface through the epidermis by breaking down of the tissues, or through a special opening of the nature of a stoma. The nectar either remains clinging to the surface of the nectary or it gathers in large drops and falls into a nectar receptacle provided for it, as in the case of violets, where horn-like outgrowths from the two lower stamens secrete the nectar and pour it into a cup formed by the base of the lower petal.

"The nectaries may occur on any part of the flower, but they are most frequently found at the bases of the stamens, petals, and ovaries, and rarely on the calyx. In the plum and peach they form a thick inner lining of the cup-shaped receptacle. In nasturtiums the nectar is secreted in a long spur from the calyx.

"Some flowers of simple construction expose their nectar freely to all sorts of insects, but others conceal it in various ways so that it is accessible only to insects of certain kinds. A frequent device is to have some parts of the corolla close over the way to the nectar so that small insects which would not assist in cross-pollination are excluded, and only those which are strong enough to push aside the barrier or have proboscides of proper construction to thrust past it can obtain the nectar and accomplish the transference of the pollen."

With nectar and pollen ready for the insect the plant has yet to advertise its sweets, and for that brilliant colors and attractive odors are relied on. An attractive odor for insects is not always pleasing to us: certain Araceæ, some Trilliums, and others have a carrion-like odor, combined with "dull colors often marked with livid blotches or veins like dead animal bodies, and these flowers attract flesh-flies and carrion-beetles which are the pollinating agents." It appears from various experiments that odor is the chief factor in attracting insects from a considerable distance, and that with the nearer approach of the insect color becomes an important guide. Despite the poor sight (formation of incomplete images, and this possible only within certain limited focal distances) of insects they appear to distinguish colors at distances where the forms of objects must be very indistinct to them. Once attracted to the flower by odor or color, or by both, the pattern and fine color streaks and spots play their part in guiding them to the nectaries. (See discussion on p. 580 of the sight and color recognition of insects.) The shape of the flower now has also its influence; this it is which compels the visitor, in order to get at the nectar, to brush against the pollen, or the stigma, or both as the case demands, and thus to render fairly its payment for the special food provided. The particular shape and make-up, too, often have reference to the necessity of keeping away illegitimate visitors, who would drain the secreted stores without recompense. Small creeping insects, as ants (very fond of nectar), thrips, and others may be shut out of the nectaries by fine, stiff little hairs densely set in the throat of the flower-cup, like those on the stamens of spiderwort or at the bases of the stamens of *Cobœa scandens*, or may be denied access even to the flower itself by sticky glandular hairs on the stem and leaves. I once counted nearly a hundred dead or hopelessly entangled small insects on the tall sticky stem of a single Salpo-glossus plant.  But sometimes the burglars are successful.  Needham, in a careful study of the insect visitors on the blue flag (*Iris versicolor*) near Lake Forest, Ill., found a dozen or more successful pollen and nectar thieves among them, while several other would-be thieves were deceived by the curious markings of the flower as to the proper entrance and so failed to

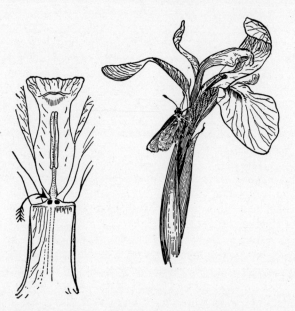

FIG. 762.—Blue flag, *Iris* sp., being robbed of nectar by skipper-butterfly; at left diagram showing position of butterfly's proboscis (represented by the arrow) with reference to openings of the nectaries.  (After Needham; natural size.)

make entry and get to the stores.  The most persistent nectar thieves were several species of Pamphilas (skipper-butterflies) which stood outside the flower and inserted the proboscis obliquely between the sepal and the base of the style, plying and thrusting with it until one of the two holes leading to the nectary is found (Fig. 762).  The actual pollinating visitors were chiefly small Andrenid bees.

It will also be well to note, before taking up the special examples to be described, the general character of the modifications which have arisen among the regular visitors whose advantage in the way of getting food sup-plies of nectar and pollen has been sufficient to impose, on some of them at least, very considerable adaptive structural changes.  The great majority of nectar-drinking insects are bees, moths, and butterflies and two-winged flies (of these especially the Syrphidæ).  The pollen collectors are mostly bees, who use pollen not only directly themselves, but carry it in quantities to their nests as food for their young, and in the case of honey-bees for the other workers busy indoors. To show the affinities and the number of species of the insect visitors to entomophilous flowers I have compiled the following figures from Robertson's records of his observations on flowers in the neighborhood of Carlinville, Ill. In twenty-six observing days 275 insect species visited the flowers of *Pastinaca sativa*, of which 1 was a Neuropteron, 6 were Hemiptera, 9 were moths and butterflies, 14 were beetles, 72 were Diptera, and the rest Hymenoptera, of which 21 were bees, 39 sawflies and parasitica, and the remainder wasps, solitary and social. Of 115 species visiting the milkweed *Asclepias verticillata*, 52 were Hymenoptera, 42 Diptera, 16 Lepidoptera, and 3 Coleoptera; of 52 species visiting *Rhamnus lanceolata*, 23 were various solitary bees; of 87 species found at the flowers of the willow *Salix cordata* in seven days, 43 were Hymenoptera, 39 Diptera, 4 Coleoptera, and 1 Hemipteron; 112 species of insects visited *Ceanothus americanus* in five days; 79 species visited sweet-clover in two days; 71 species visited the little spring beauty, *Claytonia Virginica*, in twenty-six days, while 18 species visited the yellow violet in seven days. The hivebee and the bumblebees are the pre-eminent cross-pollinating insect agents, some flowers, as clover for example, having its pollen distributed by bumblebees alone (although Robertson found 13 different species of butterflies robbing nectar from red clover). The willow *Salix humilis*, watched for eleven days, had its staminate flowers wholly monopolized by honey-bees, although 51 kinds of nectar-feeding insects visited its pistillate flowers. Of the 488 species of American entomophilous flowers which have been studied by Robertson I find by going through his records that the honey-bee visits nearly all, while bumblebees are recorded from a large number.

The adaptations for pollen-gathering are mostly limited to bees and consist of (*a*) the development of hairs, simple and branched or feathery, specially situated to brush up and hold the pollen grains as the bee clambers over the stamens, and (*b*) in the honey-bees and bumblebees the development of the well-known pollen-basket, or corbiculum (see description and figure on p. 528). The adaptations for nectar-drinking consist in the elongation and tube-forming modification of the mouth-parts of bees, flies, and moths and butterflies. While in the less specialized bees the mouth-parts are short, with the labium in the condition of a short broad flap-like lip (Fig. 716), in the specialized nectar-drinkers, as the bumbles, the hive-bee, and the other so-called long-tongued forms, the maxillæ and labium are long and slender and the various parts can be so held together as to form a very effective lapping and sucking proboscis (Fig. 717). Similar conditions exist among the two-winged flies (Diptera); the proboscis of a flower-fly (Syrphid) or bee-fly (Bombiliid), for example, is a long, slender, sucking beak very different from the broad-ended labellum of a house-fly.  But it is in the Lepidoptera that this specialization of the mouth structure in connection with the nectar-feeding habit reaches its widest application and the extreme of its specialization.  Almost no other food than nectar is taken by the whole great host of moths and butterflies (Lepidoptera), and throughout the order the mouth-parts are greatly modified, so as to form a perfect flexible, often very long, slender sucking proboscis (Fig. 510).  (Some moths and butterflies, however, take no food at all in the imago (winged) stage and these mostly have only rudimentary mouth-parts.)  This proboscis is composed of the two greatly elongated maxillæ with their grooved inner faces so opposed and locked together as to form a closed perfect tube open at its two ends, the tip of the proboscis and its base, the mouth (see p. 361).  By means of an expansion of the pharynx, to whose upper wall muscles running to the dorsal wall of the head are attached, an effective pumping arrangement is obtained, so that when the proboscis is thrust down a flower-cup into the nectary a stream of nectar may be drawn up into the throat.  The proboscis of some moths is very long so as to enable them to drink from the deepest tubular corollas; for example that in our larger sphinx-moths, like the common tomato-worm moth (five-spotted sphinx), is 6 inches long (Fig. 509); in Brazil there lives a sphinx-moth, *Macroxilia cluentius*, with proboscis 8 inches long.  An orchid grows in Madagascar with nectary 12 inches long, with almost an inch of nectar in the bottom, but the sphinx-moth, which almost certainly exists, with a proboscis long enough to reach this sweet store has not yet been found.

The following few examples, showing varying degrees of specialization, illustrate specifically many of the already generally described adaptations due to the reciprocal relation between flowers and insects.

The simpler entomophilous flowers, such as those of the apple, cherry, wild rose, ranunculus, etc., brightly colored and fragrant, are mostly wide open and accessible to a large variety of insect visitors.  They are all abundant pollen providers and some secrete nectar which is easily got at.  But to get either nectar or pollen the insects have to scramble over and among the many crowded stamens of the center, dusting themselves well during the process with pollen, which is carried on to the next flower visited and there probably rubbed off on to the stigma.  In such simple forms the stigma of the first flower visited is likely to be fertilized with its own pollen by the scrambling visitors, if both anthers and stigma are coincidently mature (which in many of these flowers is not the case).  But even then if the stigma is also pollinated by foreign pollen grains, it seems to be more strongly affected by them than by its own pollen.  Experiments have demonstrated the superior potency of the foreign pollen in actually effecting fertilization.

Open flowers of more specialization in general botanical relations, although of little more as concerns the particular one under discussion, are the Umbelliferæ and the numerous Compositæ. In the umbels and flower-heads, often rather inconspicuous but nearly always well provided with nectar, the sweet drink is easily got at even by short-tongued insects, so that some of the species have a surprising host of visitors. For example, Robertson found 275 different insect species visiting *Pastinaca sativa* (an umbellifer with exposed nectar) in the neighborhood of Carlinville, Ill.; 238 visiting *Cicuta maculata*, and 191 visiting *Sium cicutæfolium;* observing some of the composites, more specialized, Robertson noted 146 insect species at goldenrod (*Solidago canadensis*) in eleven days during August, September, and October, and 100 at *Aster paniculatus* in four days in October.

Of course not all the insect visitors to a flower are cross-pollinating agents; some are deliberate thieves, some may or may not help in cross-pollination, and some are reliable, although, of course, unwitting, pollinators. As an interesting test of the proportion of actual pollinators to the whole number of insect visitors may be taken Robertson's observations on the milkweed (Asclepias) and its visitors (see account of the conditions in Asclepias on p. 573). Of 115 insect species which visited flowers of *Asclepias verticillata* (Carlinville, Ill.) in fifteen days, representatives of 58 of these actually got pollinia (pollen-masses) attached to themselves; while of 80 species visiting *A. incarnata* in twenty-four days, 63 carried off pollinia. I do not know of any other records which show the proportion of actual pollination to total number of visitors, but it is highly desirable that such observations be made for other flowers. Asclepias obviously offers a particularly favorable opportunity for such tests (on account of the conspicuousness of the pollinia), but an ingenious observer will be able to study the matter successfully with other plants.

With the flowers of tubular corolla the pollinating insects are of course neither so many nor do they represent such varied insect groups. The long-tongued bees and flies can get nectar from a flower-cup not too deep, but in the deeper cups the moths and butterflies are the only insects which can reach the nectar. The common jimson-weed, *Datura stramonium*, is, as Stevens says, an excellent illustration of this. "The corolla is about five centimeters long, and the cavity of the tube is nearly closed at about the middle of its length by the insertion of the filaments there. When the flower opens in the evening it emits a strong musky odor, and a large drop of nectar is already present in the bottom of the tube; so that large sphinx-moths, leaving the places of seclusion occupied by them during the day, are attracted by the strong odor and white color of the flowers.

"Flying swiftly from flower to flower, the moth thrusts its long proboscis to the bottom of the tube and secures the nectar; and while it is tarrying briefly at each flower, keeping itself poised by the swift vibration of its wings, it is pretty certain to touch with its proboscis both anthers and stigmas, which stand close together at about the same height near the mouth of the corolla. Both cross- and self-pollination might be brought about in this way, but, as Darwin has shown, the foreign pollen would probably possess

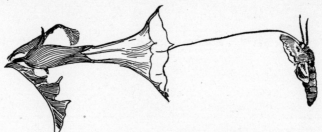

FIG. 763.—Hawk-moth posed before a jimson-weed, *Datura stramonium*. (After Stevens; one-half natural size.)

the greater potency, and cross-fertilization would be apt to result. Fig. 763 is a photograph of a sphinx moth and Datura-flower, posed to show the relative lengths of the moth's proboscis and the corolla tube."

Another kind of specialization in flower structure which tends to preserve the nectar for certain specific insect visitors is well illustrated by the salvias, the snapdragon, and other similarly irregularly tubular flowers (Labiatæ, Leguminosæ, Scrophulariaceæ, etc.). Probably all such flowers are pollinated by insects (a few species by humming-birds). The irregularity in corolla is accompanied by a specific disposition of the stamens and pistil, so that the insect visitors are compelled to visit the nectary in one particular manner, a manner devised to insure their touching, or being touched by, the anthers or stigma or both. In the snapdragon (Fig. 760) the opening of the flower-cup is normally closed, but when a bee alights on the broad keel or platform (composed of two petals grown together) its weight so depresses this platform as to open the way into the flower-cup, which closes at once when the bee goes in and drinks the nectar. Scrambling and twisting about in the narrow chamber it thus thoroughly dusts itself with pollen, or thoroughly dusts the

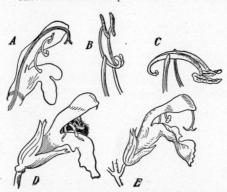

FIG. 764.—Salvia-flower. *A*, showing position of pistil and stamens; *B*, anthers of stamens in normal position; *C*, anthers of stamens tipped down; *D*, bee entering flower; *E*, flower, natural condition. (After Lubbock; natural size.)

stigma with pollen acquired from a previous visit to another flower. Miscellaneous small insects alighting on the keel are not heavy enough to depress it, and thus are prevented from entering and stealing the nectar. In the salvias (sages) the corolla is similarly tubular below and two-lipped above, the lower lip serving as an alighting-platform for the insect visitors (usually bees), while the arched upper lip covers and protects the stamens and pistil. In *Salvia officinalis* (Fig. 764) the stamens do not come immediately into contact with the bee as it enters, but they have to be moved in a particular manner, which is accomplished as follows: "Two of the stamens are minute and rudimentary. In the other pair the two anther-cells, instead of being, as usual, close together, are separated by a long connective. Moreover, the lower anther-cells contain very little pollen; sometimes, indeed, none at all. This portion of the stamen, as shown in Fig. 764, hangs down and partially stops up the mouth of the corolla-tube. When, however, a bee thrusts its head into the tube in search of the honey, this part of the stamen is pushed into the arch, the connectives of the two large stamens revolve on their axis, and consequently the fertile anther-cells are brought down onto the back of the bee."

In the scarlet sage (*Salvia* sp.) cross-pollination is accomplished by humming-birds, which, hovering in front of the narrow mouth of the flower-cup, thrust deeply into it their long bills in the search for small insects which may have entered for nectar. Other flowers regularly visited and cross-pollinated by humming-birds are the scarlet currant, various painted cups (Castilleias), the scarlet mimulus, the wild columbine, the trumpet-creeper, the spotted touch-me-not, the cardinal-flowers, cannas, and fuchsias. Red seems to be the attractive color for humming-birds. As the only humming-bird species east of the Rocky Mountains is the ruby-throat (*Trochilus ruber*), this one species is to be credited with being the chief pollinating agent of a considerable number of flowers; in California and the southwest there are several species to do the work.

Another marked and easily seen variant in this specialization of flowers to insure cross-pollination by insects is that shown by the milkweeds of the genus Asclepias. Stevens has described this so well (Introduction to Botany, p. 191 et seq.) that I simply quote here most of his account. "*Asclepias cornuti*, common everywhere in this country, is perhaps the best species for demonstrating this [peculiar specialization of the milkweeds]. As shown in Fig. 765, the sepals and petals are reflexed; the stamens are joined throughout their length, and are united to a thick and flat structure at their apices, known as the stigmatic disk, which is also united with the top of the two pistils. The pistils are entirely enclosed by the stamens and the stigmatic disk. Five spreading, hollow receptacles for the nectar grow out and upward from the bases of the stamens.

"Each pollen-sac contains a compact mass of pollen-grains which never become separated from one another, and so constitute what is termed a pollinium. The two contiguous pollinia of adjacent anthers are united by horny rods which converge upward and join with a horny dark body known as the corpusculum, which is hollow and has a slit along its outer face. This slit is relatively broad at the bottom, and tapers toward the top, thus forming a clip in which the feet of the insects get caught. Between each pair of anthers there is a deep recess closed by two vertical lips which stand wider open at the bottom than at the top, and the recess also narrows at the top. The opening between the lips at the top stands exactly beneath the slit in the corpusculum.

FIG. 765. — Honey-bee at Asclepias - flowers, with legs still fast in a stigmatic chamber of the flower last visited. (After Stevens; natural size.)

"The surface of the flower is slippery, so that when a bee, for instance, visits it, a good foothold is not obtained until the bee slips its foot into the recess between the anthers, termed the stigmatic chamber. Having obtained a foothold, the bee thrusts its sucking-apparatus into the hollow nectar-receptacle and obtains the nectar which has invited it to the flower. When the bee, however, seeks to go to another flower, its foot slips upward and becomes caught in the slit in the corpusculum. A struggle now ensues which usually results in the bee pulling the two pollen-masses, united to the corpusculum, through the narrow slits at the tops of the pollen-sacs; and thus laden, it seeks another flower, and there slips its foot, together with the pollen-masses, into the stigmatic chamber.

"Now when the bee attempts to leave the flower, the pollen-masses become tightly wedged at the narrow apex of the chamber, and a hard pull is required to break them loose from the foot. Finally, as the foot is being drawn from the stigmatic chamber it catches into the corpusculum directly above and pulls out a second pair of pollen-masses. Thus the bee goes from flower to flower and from plant to plant, repeatedly pulling pollen-masses from their sacs and depositing them in the stigmatic chamber. Fig. 765 is from a photograph of a honey-bee gathering nectar from Asclepias-flowers. One of the hind legs is still

FIG. 766.—Cabbage-butter-fly caught by legs in corpuscula of two Asclepias - flowers. (After Stevens; natural size.)

held in the stigmatic chamber of the flower, which the bee has just deserted."

Hive-bees, although common visitors to Asclepias, are really hardly strong enough to insure pulling loose from the flowers, and many of them, besides numerous flies and small butterflies, get caught and die on the flower-heads. Robertson has noted nine species of insects thus killed by *A. cornuti*. Bumblebees and large wasps and large butterflies are the most certain milkweed pollinators.

Still another markedly different kind of specialization to effect cross-pollination by insects is that shown by many Araceæ and Aristolochiaceæ. The flower (Fig. 767) in these plants consists of a long tubular perianth (spathe) with a constriction near the base, the narrow opening into the cavity below being nearly closed by stiff downward-pointing hairs, so as to make a sort of floral eel-trap. It really is an insect-trap: small flies crawl down the long tube and through the narrow opening in search of nectar; but when ready to return find themselves imprisoned by the downward-point-ing hairs. After a while the stigmas which mature before the anthers and have likely been pollinated (with pollen brought from other flowers) by the entering insects, wither, a drop of nectar is secreted for the benefit of the captured insects, and the anthers mature, exposing their ripe pollen-grains. The hairs in the throat of the flower gradually shrivel up and release the insects, which are now well showered with pollen falling on them from the anthers above. Visiting another Arum-flower, they hardly fail to rub off some of this pollen on the mature stigmas. Sometimes more than a hundred small flies will be found imprisoned in a single Arum.

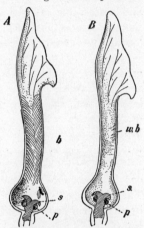

FIG. 767.—Flower of *Aristolochia clematitis* in longitudinal section: *A*, before fertilization by little fly; *B*, after fertilization. *p*, pollen-masses; *s*, stigma; *b*, bristly hairs; *wb*, without bristly hairs. (After H. Müller.)

Classic examples of apparently the wildest vagaries in flower structure are those presented by the orchids. But Darwin's fine work revealed the method in all this floral madness. Orchids are pollinated almost exclu-sively by insects, and the extravagant shapes and color-patterns are all means for accomplishing cross-pollination. Any one interested at all in the inter-relation between flowers and insects should read Darwin's account of the orchids and their insect visitors, in his book "On the Fertilization of Orchids by Insects." As this book is generally accessible, I will here only call atten-tion to one new and peculiar feature generally characteristic of the specialization in orchids, namely, the development of sensitive parts in the flower, so that with a proper stimulus certain purposeful motions or movements are performed by certain of the floral parts. Most of the orchids offer their pollen in masses, pollinia, which adhere to the insect and are carried around by it during its visits to other flowers. The stalks of these pollinia bend (by contracting) after they are attached to the insect so as to bring the pollen-masses into the most effective position for insuring contact with the stigmatic surfaces of the flowers visited. In the remarkable orchid Catasetum, a certain part of the flower is endowed with such sensitiveness and is normally restrained in such a tense position that when it is touched by an insect (or any foreign body) it springs in such a way as to throw the pollinia at and against the intruder. Darwin once irritated one of these flowers in the presence of Lubbock, who was amazed to see the pollinium thrown "nearly three feet, when it struck and adhered to the pane of a window."

Some other flowers, not orchids, also possess sensitive parts; familiar examples are various species of Berberis, whose stamens "when touched near the base, as happens when a bee is probing for honey, will spring violently inward, shaking off the pollen and scattering it upon the insect visitors." Kalmia presents a somewhat similar case "where the stamens are bent over into little pockets, from which they spring out when touched, throwing the pollen to some distance."

In the examples thus far chosen the flower has been the more conspicuous beneficiary in the partnership, and has shown the chief adaptations. The advantage to the insect visitor is almost exclusively a food advantage, and its adaptation has been usually simply one of the structure of its mouth-parts. But there is known at least one case in which the insect pollinator does much more for itself by its flower visits than find food for immediate use, and in which an amazing adaptation of habit has arisen on its part. On the other hand the plants concerned depend solely on the one insect kind for pollination. This is the famous case of the cross-pollination of Yuccas by the small moths of the genus Pronuba. There are several species of Yuccas (Spanish bayonets) in this country, and several Pronubas, but a brief account (taken largely from Stevens's Introduction to Botany) of the relations between the common Yucca grown in gardens (*Y. filamentosa*) and the moth species, *Pronuba yuccasella*, will be typical of the interrelations of all.

The Yucca has a lily-like flower composed of three sepals and three petals, all creamy white, six stamens with fleshy outward-curving filaments surrounded by small anthers, and a pistil extending much above the tops of the stamens with three carpels imperfectly united at the top, and thus leaving a tube entirely open at the apex. "The inner surface of this tube is stigmatic. This stigmatic tube does not open directly into the cavities of the ovary, but sends off three very narrow branches, each of which communicates with the cavity of a carpel. Accordingly, when pollen is once deposited on the inner surface of the main stigmatic tube, the pollen-tubes find easy access to the ovules in each of the three carpels. The pollen is sticky and hangs together in masses, so that it is not adapted to being carried by the wind, and it is apparently impossible for it to get to the stigmatic tube without some outside agent.

"A small amount of nectar is secreted, but it is excreted at the very base of the pistil, so that insects seeking it would be far removed from the stigmas. Indeed, the low position of the nectar would seem rather to lead insects away from the stigmas. The flowers are borne in compound racemes high aloft on a strong woody shaft, and, because of their rather strong odor when new buds are opening in the evening and their white color, they are quite certain to make their presence known to insects flying in the twilight.

"If we take these facts as our clew and attentively watch these flowers about eight o'clock in the evening, the method of cross-pollination will be made clear. A white moth, known as the Pronuba-moth, is seen to mount a stamen, scrape together the sticky pollen, and pack it against the under side of its head by means of a spinous structure known as the maxillary tentacle, which seems to have been specially developed for this purpose, for in other moths it is a mere vestige. In gathering the pollen it hooks its tongue over the end of the stamen, evidently to secure a better hold. Having become well loaded with pollen, as shown in the photomicrograph of the moth's head, it descends the stamen and flies to another flower. There it places itself on the pistil between two of the stamens

Fig. 768.—Pronuba-moth depositing eggs in ovary of Yucca. (After Stevens; natural size.)

(see Fig. 768) and thrusts a slender ovipositor through the wall of the ovary and into the cavity occupied by the ovules.

"Having deposited an egg, it ascends the pistil, and by means of the maxillary tentacles and tongue, which at other times are coiled around the load of pollen, it rubs pollen down the inner surface of the stigmatic tube. Fig. 769 is a [drawing made from a] flashlight photograph of a moth performing this act. The moth then descends the pistil, and standing between another pair of stamens it deposits another egg within the ovary; then it ascends the pistil and rubs pollen on the stigmatic surface as before. This process is repeated until it may be that each of the six lines of ovules is provided with an egg, and the process of pollination has been as many times accomplished.

"The full meaning of this wonderful series of operations will not be understood until subsequent developments have been followed. Since the process of pollination has been so thoroughly done, most of the numerous ovules become fertilized and the seeds begin their development. In the mean time the moth eggs hatch into larvæ, which find their food in the developing seeds. But the seeds are so numerous that the larvæ reach their growth, gnaw a hole in the seed-pod and escape, while many uninjured seeds still remain in the pod. The larva spins a thread by which it descends to the ground, and, burrowing beneath the surface, it passes the winter in its pupal state, emerging as a fully developed moth at the time of the flowering of the Yucca the following summer.

Fig. 769. — Pronuba-moth rubbing pollen down the stigmatic tube of Yucca. (After flash-light photograph by Stevens; natural size.)

"It appears that the mature moth takes no food, unless it secures some of the nectar of the Yucca blossoms in which it is wont to pass the day, with its head close to the bottom of the flower where the nectar is excreted. It does not eat the pollen which it gathers, and it seems certain that it is prompted to place the pollen in the stigmatic tube after each act of oviposition solely by the instinct to provide for its young; for it is readily understood that if the ovules are not fertilized the seeds would not develop and the larvæ would be without food.

"The Yucca flower, instead of having elaborate devices to secure cross-pollination, simply prohibits self-pollination by its tubular stigmas and its relatively short and reflexed stamens; and then, the sticky pollen and an abundance of ovules being provided, the performance of pollination is intrusted to the wise instinct of the Pronuba-moth; and not pollination simply, but cross-pollination, for it has been noticed that it is the habit of the moth after securing the pollen to fly to another flower before it begins to lay its eggs." (This extraordinary interrelation between Yucca and Pronuba was discovered and carefully studied by C. V. Riley in 1872, and his intensely interesting detailed accounts of his observations are to be found in Vol. 3 Trans. St. Louis Acad. Sci., his 5th and 6th reports as state entomologist of Missouri, and in the 3d Ann. Rept. of the Missouri Botanical Garden).

The above various and interesting examples of the interrelations between flowers and insects are not exceptional cases; indeed this state of affairs with its accompanying mutual adaptation is the rule throughout the families of flowering plants, the Spermatophyta. The absence of it is the exception; cross-pollination is far more abundant than self-pollination. And the devices by which it is brought about are in their details almost as many and as various as are the different shapes and color-patterns of flowers. The student who may be interested to learn what flowers have been studied to discover the kinds of insect visitors and the character of the modifications that have arisen for the sake of cross-pollination should refer to the many papers (published in the Botanical Gazette, Trans. St. Louis Acad. Sci., and elsewhere) of Robertson, who between 1886 and 1895 studied 488 species of American insect-pollinated flowers; to Lubbock's "British Wild Flowers in Relation to Insects," in which similar studies on English flowers are recorded; to H. Müller's "Fertilization of Flowers," a bulky volume of observations on European insect-pollinated flowers together with much more general discussion, and a detailed consideration of the structure of the most important insect pollinators; to the same author's "Alpenblumen," an account of the relation between insects and the flowers of the Alps; and to Darwin's book, already mentioned, on the fertilization of orchids by insects.

It is plain that this fact of the adaptation of flower structure and pattern for the sake of cross-pollination by insects explains a great deal of the manifold variety of form and color-marking which exists among flowers. The adaptation of the flower to its insect visitors goes even farther: to a certain extent the flowering season of many plants is determined by the time of the appearance in winged stage of its more important insect visitors. Robertson sums up his interesting observations concerning this fact (based on the study of nearly 500 plant species and their insect visitors) as follows: "We have reviewed the principal groups of insect-pollinated plants and have noted a correspondence more or less well marked between their blooming seasons and the seasons of the insects upon which they depend." But it is only fair to presume that the insects, at least those which get a large amount of food from the flowers, may have become adapted as to their flight-time in some degree to the blossom-time of their host-flower. That this is true of the bees, which get practically all of their food (pollen and nectar), both for themselves and for their young, from flowers, seems certain.

But the easy and sweeping way in which this theory has been made to explain the immense variety and often intricate condition of floral structure and pattern has, naturally and wisely, led to a more rigid scrutiny of its all-sufficiency for the explanation of floral variety. It is apparent of course that flowers in their fundamental structural character are controlled largely by heredity, and this heredity is largely an expression of phylogeny, that is, ancestral history. Flowers of close natural relationship are bound to be more alike than those widely separated genealogically. But beyond this there really seems to be no other explanation of flower shape and appearance having the same validity as that of adaptation to insect visitors.

The most effective criticism of this explanation is one against its effectiveness in explaining color, and particularly color-pattern. It is based on the general consensus of belief among zoologists and entomologists concerning the poorness of insect vision. The general character of this vision, with an account of the eye structure, is explained on pp. 30–33 of this book. The fixed short focal distance, the incompleteness and lack of detail incident to a mosaic image, and the lack of accommodation (only partly provided for by the shifting of the peripheral pigment) to varying light intensity, which are admitted conditions of insect vision, make it seem difficult to account for the intricacy in pattern common to many flowers on a basis of adaptation to animal visitors of such poor seeing capacity as insects.

Experimental evidence touching this criticism is singularly meager when one considers the importance of the subject. If insects can accurately distinguish colors, and at some distance, and can perceive fine and intricate details of color-pattern at very short distance, then the explanation of floral structure and pattern or adaptation to insect visitors has solid foundation for even the amazingly large and varied results which it attempts to explain; if not, it is hard to understand how the explanation is valid (at least in any such all-sufficient degree as commonly held), despite its logical character (in the light of our knowledge of the nearly limitless capacity for modification of natural selection) and the abundant confirmatory evidence.

Most of the experimental evidence so far offered is that included in Darwin's account (" On the Fertilization of Flowers by Insects "); in Lubbock's account of his experiments on honey-bees, familiar because of its presentation in his readable book, " Ants, Bees, and Wasps "; and in Plateau's account of his more recent but less familiarly known experiments with various insects, including bees. Both Lubbock and Plateau are investigators ingenious in device, keen in deduction, and of unquestioned scientific honesty. Yet their conclusions are in direct contradiction. Lubbock believes that bees recognize colors at a considerable distance, that they "prefer one color to another, and that blue is distinctly their favorite." Plateau finds that neither the form nor the brilliant colors of flowers seem to have any important attractive rôle, "as insects visit flowers whose colors and forms are masked by green leaves, as well as continue to visit flowers which have been almost totally denuded of the colored parts"; that insects show no preference or antipathy for different colors which flowers of different varieties of the same or of allied species may show; that flowers concealed by foliage are readily discovered and visited; that insects ordinarily pay no attention to flowers artificially made of colored paper or cloth whether these artifacts are provided or not with honey, while, on the contrary, flowers artificially made of living green leaves and provided with honey are visited (from the attraction of the "natural vegetable odor"). From these observations Plateau concludes that "insects are guided with certainty to flowers with pollen or nectar *by a sense other than that of vision and which can only be that of smell,*" and finds particular proof of this in the facts, according to his observations, (1) that insects tend, without hesitation, towards flowers usually neglected by reason of the absence or poverty of nectar, from the moment that one supplies these flowers with artificial nectar, represented by honey; (2) that insects cease their visits when one cuts out the nectary without injuring the colored parts, and re-begin their visits if one replaces the destroyed nectary by honey; (3) that it suffices to attract numerous insects if one puts honey on or in normally anemophilous flowers, simply green or brown in color, which are normally practically invisible and almost never visited by insects; and (4) that the visiting of flowers artificially made of fresh green leaves and containing honey demonstrates plainly the rôle of the sense of smell.

It must be said that, despite many just criticisms which may be made on the character of his experiments, Plateau has made necessary more experimentation for the relief of the general theory that floral adaptation of color is due to the color preferences of insect visitors. It seems to me probable that the truth of the matter is in a large degree expressed by the statement that the distant attraction is exerted by the odors of flowers working on a very sensitive sense of smell in insects (chemotropism, in the language of the modern believers in reflexes), while the intimate guiding to the particular flower and the nectary is controlled chiefly by the color and pattern.

Finally we come to the question of the origin of this mutually advantageous interrelation and its many-branched course of development or specialization. Advantage and natural selection are looked on as the chief factors in this development. "It is extremely probable," says the botanist Campbell, "that all the primitive flowers were anemophilous (cross-pollinated by the wind), and that from these have been derived the more specialized entomophilous and ornithophilous forms. It is evidently of advantage to the plant to have the great waste of pollen necessitated by wind-pollination reduced, and this is possible when insects or birds are the agents in its transfer. It is probable that entomophily began by the casual visits of insects to flowers, attracted by the pollen, which is still the principal object of visits by many insects, serving as an important source of food. Flowers which had more conspicuous stamens or perianth would stand a better chance of visits from insects, and from the slight variations thus started may have proceeded the development of the conspicuous flowers of the modern entomophilous plants." To attract insects not pollen-eaters the development of the nectar has been necessary. However sweet-smelling or beautiful, flowers would not be visited by insects unless they had some inducements more substantial to offer. These inducements are the pollen and, to the great majority of flower-visiting insects, the nectar.

It is of distinct interest to note that no plants with colored flower-parts or special floral envelopes existed (in geological time) before the time of winged insects. The oldest fossil Angiosperms, monocotyledons as well as dicotyledons, are from the lower Cretaceous rock strata; in Tertiary times there was a great increase in the number and variety of the dicotyledons, and most of the present families were probably in existence in those times. Winged insects are known from Devonian rocks, and much more numerously from Carboniferous strata; but all these early Paleozoic insects belong to the lower more generalized kinds, which to-day take little part in cross-pollination. Not until Jurassic times did the higher orders appear, the Hymenoptera, Lepidoptera, and Diptera, which include the great majority of the cross-pollinating insect agents. Thus the insects which we know to-day as the pollen- and nectar-feeders, hence flower-visitors, began to be abundant coincidently with or a little in advance of the flowering plants. Reciprocally helpful and mutually adapting themselves to the growing interrelation, the flies, bees, moths, and butterflies on the animal side and the dicotyledonous plants with varied flower-shapes, color, and pattern on the vegetable side have developed so successfully that in present times both flower-visiting insects and insect-attracting flowers have come to be the most specialized and notable members of each of their respective groups of organisms.

# CHAPTER XVII

## COLOR AND PATTERN AND THEIR USES

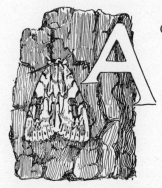 CONSPICUOUS characteristic of the insect body is its color-pattern. The painted butterflies, the great moths, the burnished beetles, the flashing dragon-flies, the green katydids and brown locusts, all attract attention first by the variety or intensity of their colors and the arrangement of these colors in simple or intricate symmetry of pattern. Even the small and, at casual glance, obscure and monochrome insects reveal on careful examination a large degree of color development and an ofttimes amazing intricacy and beauty of pattern. So uniformly well developed is color-pattern among insects that no thoughtful collector or observer of these animals escapes the self-put question, What special cause is it that results in such a high degree of specialization of color and its arrangement throughout the insect class? and if he be an observer who has taken seriously the teachings of Darwin and the utilitarian school of naturalists, his question becomes couched in the form, What is the use to the insects of all this color and pattern?

For the attitude of any modern student of Nature, confronted by such a phenomenon, is that of the seeker for the significance of the phenomenon. And the key to significance in such a case is to be sought in utility. The usefulness of color in animate Nature as an inspirer and satisfier of our own æsthetic needs and capacities, or of color-patterns as means whereby we may distinguish and recognize various sorts of animals and plants, is a usefulness which may be answer enough to the passing poet on the one hand, and the old-line Linnean systematist on the other, but is, of course, no answer to science. Science demands a usefulness to the color-bearing organisms themselves; and a usefulness large and serious enough to be the sufficient cause for so highly specialized and amazing a development.

The explanations of some of the color phenomena of insects are obvious; some uses we recognize quickly as certain, some as probable, some as possible,

Some colors are obviously there simply because of the chemical make-up of parts of the insect body. That gold is yellow, cinnabar red, and certain copper ores green or blue are facts which lead us to no special inquiry after significance; at least significance based on utility. And if an insect has part of its body composed of or containing a substance that is by its very chemical and physical constitution always red or blue or green, we may be content with knowing it and not be too insistent in our demand to the insect to show cause, on a basis of utility, for being partly red or blue or green. And even if this red or blue be disposed with some symmetry, some regularity of repetition, either segmentally or bilaterally, this we may well attribute to the natural segmental and bilaterally symmetrical repetition of similar body parts. Some color and some color-pattern, then, may be explicable on the same basis as the color of a mineral specimen or of a tier of bricks.

But no such explanation will for a moment satisfy us as to the presence and arrangement of colors in the wing of Kallima, the dead-leaf butterfly (Pl. XIII, Fig. 1), or in Phyllium, the green-leaf Phasmid (Pl. XIII, Fig. 2). We demand an explanation based on direct and large usefulness to the insect.

Certain uses seem pretty apparent: the brown and blackish pigments in the compound eyes have the function of absorbing light-rays so that these rays may be prevented from passing through the walls of adjacent ommatidia, and thus confusing the mosaic vision; the pigment of the simple eye-flecks of some insect larvæ serves, as in the eye-spots of other simple animals, to absorb light at a certain spot especially sensitive and thus make possible a recognition of light intensity, a low grade, not of seeing, but of simple appreciation of the presence or absence of light. Some color in the skin of insects may serve, too, as is pretty certainly the case with many vertebrates, to absorb heat or prevent its radiation, or, on the other hand, to reflect it, or to allow it to radiate freely. In view of the cold-bloodedness of insects this must be a use, in this class of animals, extremely restricted and infrequent. But such uses as these are at best explanatory of but little of the wealth of color and pattern manifest in the insect class. A utility more important, and common to many more individuals and capable of explaining a specialization of color and pattern much more complex, is needed as a basis for color significance.

The green katydid singing in the tree-top or shubbery is readily known to be there by its music, but just which bit of green that we see is katydid and which is leaf is a matter to be decided by unusually discriminating eyes. The clacking locust, beating its black wings in the air, is conspicuous enough, but after it has alighted on the ground it is invisible, or, rather, visible but indistinguishable; its gray and brown mottled color-pattern is simply continuous with that of the soil. The green larvæ of the Pierid butterflies

# PLATE XIII.

## PROTECTIVE RESEMBLANCE.

1. Kallima sp.

2. Phyllium sp.

3, 4, 5. Larvæ of Lycæna pseudargiolus piasus Bdvl. on California buckeye, Æsculus californicus.

PLATE XIII

Mary Wellman, del

lying longitudinally along green grasses simply merge into the color scheme of their environment. The gray moth rests unperceived on the bark of the tree-trunk. Hosts of insect kinds do really thoroughly harmonize with the color-pattern of their usual environment, and by this correspondence in shade and marking are difficult to perceive for what they are. Now if the eyes that survey the green foliage or run over the gray bark are those of a preying bird, lizard, or other enemy of the insect, it is quite certain— our reason tells us so insistently—that this possession by the insect of color and pattern tending to make it indistinguishable from its immediate environment is advantageous to it: advantageous to the degree of often saving its life. Now such a use of color and pattern is obviously one which can be wide-spread through the insect class, and may be to many species which lead lives exposed to the attacks of insectivorous animals of large—even of life and death—importance. And naturalists, most of them at least, believe that this kind of usefulness is real, and that it is the principal clue to the chief significance of color and pattern. And this not alone in the case of insects, but of most other animals as well.

From this point of view, namely, that color-patterns may be of advantage in the struggle for existence, just as strength, swiftness, and other capacities and conditions are, the specialization and refinement, all the wide modification and variety of colors and patterns, are explicable by the hypothesis of their gradual development in time through the natural selection of naturally occurring advantageous variations. On this basis, such special instances of resemblance to particular parts of the environment, as that shown by Kallima in its likeness to a dead leaf, and Diapheromera in its simulation of a dry, leafless twig, are simply the logical extremes of such a line of specialization.

But the nature observer may be inclined to ask how such brilliant and bizarre color-patterns as those of the swallowtail-butterflies and the tiger-banded caterpillars of Anosia can be included in any category of "protective resemblance" patterns. They are not so included, but are explained ingeniously by an added hypothesis called that of "warning colors," while for the striking similarities of pattern often noted between two unrelated conspicuously colored species still another clever hypothesis is proposed. In these cases it is not concealment that the color-pattern effects, but indeed just the opposite. Since the pioneer studies of Bates and Wallace and Belt, naturalists have been observing and experimenting and pondering these exposing as well as these concealing conditions of color and pattern, and they have proposed several theories or hypotheses explanatory of the various conditions. These hypotheses are plausible; but they are much more than that; they are each more or less well backed up by observation and experiment, and some of them have gained a large acceptance among naturalists.

Both the reasoning and the observed facts on which these hypotheses rest are based on the usefulness of the colors and patterns to the animals in their relation to the outside world. And the influence of advantage and natural selection is given the chief credit for determining the present-day conditions of these colors and patterns.

Before, however, we take up these hypotheses, defining them and looking over some of the evidence adduced for their support, as well as some of the criticism leveled at them, we may advisedly look to the actual physical causation of color in insects. Whatever the use or significance of color, our understanding of this use must be based on a knowledge of the method or modes of the actual production of color.

Color in organisms is produced as color in inorganic Nature is. Certain substances have the capacity of selective absorption of light-rays so that when white light falls on them, certain colors (light-waves of certain length) are absorbed, while certain others (light-waves of certain other lengths) are reflected. An object is red because the substance of which it is (superficially) composed reflects the red rays and absorbs the others. Certain other objects or substances may produce color (be colored) because of their physical rather than their chemical constitution: their surfaces may be so composed of superposed lamellæ, or so striated or scaled, that the various component rays of white light are reflected, refracted, and diffracted in such varying manner (at different angles and from different depths) that complex interference effects are produced, resulting in the practical extinguishing of certain colors (waves of certain length), or the reflection of some at angles so as not to fall on the eye of the observer, and so on. Such colors will change with changes in the angle of observation, and are the so-called metallic or iridescent colors. These two categories of color have been aptly called chemical and physical: chemical color depending on the chemical make-up of the body, physical on its structural or physical make-up. As a matter of fact we shall find that most insect colors are due to a combination of these two kinds.

Substances that produce color by virtue of their capacity to absorb certain colors and reflect only one or more others we may call, in our discussion of color production, pigments, and pigmental may be used as practically synonymous with chemical in referring to colors thus produced, while structural may be sometimes used as synonymous with physical in referring to colors dependent on superficial structural character of the insect body. For colors produced by the co-operation of both pigment and structure, combination or chemico-physical may be used as a defining name. In a recent valuable paper by Tower * the history of and authority for the adoption of these various names is given.

* Tower, W. L. Colors and Color-patterns of Coleoptera. Decennial Pubs. of Univ. of Chicago, 1903, vol. X, pp. 33–70.

Tower finds, on the basis of his own researches and those of various other investigators of insect colors, that among insects the chemical colors are yellow, orange, red, buff, brown, black, and rarely green-blue and black; physical colors are the pearly colors, almost all whites, and rarely violet-greens, reds, and some metallic and iridescent colors; while chemico-physical colors are violet, greens, reds, and iridescent and almost all metallic colors. Tower believes it probable that but few really pure physical colors will be found in insects, by far the larger part of those now classed as such falling into the category of the chemico-physical. Tower finds white to be the only purely physical color occurring among the Coleoptera (the insect group whose colors he has specially studied).

With regard to the situation of the pigments on which chemical and, partly, physico-chem cal colors depend, these colors may be divided into cuticular and hypodermal (first defined by Hagen) and subhypodermal (defined by Tower). The cuticular colors are produced by coloring substances situated in the chitinized cuticle that overlies the whole insect body; they are permanent colors, not fading after death, and are insoluble, without actual dissolution of the cuticle, in water, acids, alkalies, ether, or essential oils; they are browns, blackish, drab, some yellows, and possibly some reds. The hypodermal colors are produced by pigments lying in the hypoderm (cellular layer of the skin, just underneath the cuticle) and are of two sub-categories, viz., first some yellows and green which are due to xyanthophyll and chlorophyll taken from plant-food, and which are not permanent, fading after death and on exposure, and soluble in the usual organic solvents; and second, certain permanent colors, reds and chrome yellows, due to definite pigment granules imbedded in the cytoplasm of the hypodermal cells. The subhypodermal colors, found practically only in larvæ, are due to various substances, as derived plant pigments and others, in the hæmolymph (blood) which show through the skin (hypoderm and cuticle).

The structural or physical colors, and the combination or physico-chemical colors, to which two classes belong all white and all metallic, pearly and iridescent colors, including most blues, greens, violet, and golden, depend for their production on a superficial or surface structural condition of the insect body or part consisting either of the superposition of one or more thin transparent or translucent lamellæ over a darker layer, or the fine roughening of the surface by means of striæ, pits, or minute hair-like processes. Tower has offered a graphic classification of these colors (together with the one already explained of chemical colors) in the table which follows. The classification is sufficiently explained in the table to make unnecessary any further discussion of the various kinds of structures involved in color production among insects.

## TABLE OF INSECT COLORS.
### By W. L. Tower.

**Chemical colors**

Cuticular colors — Black, Dark brown, Brown, Straw yellows — Located in primary cuticula — Permanent. Insoluble in water, alcohol, ether, oils, weak acids, or alkalies. Soluble in strong concentrated mineral acids with dissolution of the cuticula

Hypodermal colors
1 — Chrome yellows, Red, Vermilion, Scarlet, Blue — Located in hypodermal cells as granules — Lipochromes — Permanent. Insoluble in water, oils, alcohol, weak acids, or alkalies. Soluble in ether or other fatty solvents
2 — Green, Yellow, White — Located in or between the hypodermal cells — Derived pigments — Not permanent. Fade at death or on exposure. Soluble in water, alcohol, etc. Are chlorophyll or xyanthophyll derivatives largely

Sub-hypodermal colors — Green, Yellow, White — Located in the body-cavity in hæmolymph or fat-body — Derived pigments — Not permanent. Fade at death or on exposure. Soluble in usual organic solvents

**Physical colors**

Reflection colors — White — Caused by air included within scales, etc. The most common, and perhaps the only true physical, color

Refraction colors — Metallic colors — Opalescent colors — Caused by combining white and some metallic refraction color, usually with pigment present. Frequently caused by thin irregular lamellæ over pigment, giving effect of Newton's rings

Diffraction colors — Iridescent colors — See next class

**Chemico-physical colors**

Reflection pigmental colors (a) — Colored surfaces with polished appearance — Blacks, Browns, Yellows, Reds — Caused by a polished lamellar surface over layer of pigment.

Refraction pigmental colors (b) — Almost all metallic colors — Cause—polished refractive lamella overlying a layer of pigment

Diffraction pigmental colors (c) — Almost all iridescent colors — Cause—surface structures, pits, ridges on refractive lamella overlying a layer of pigment

Combination colors — Various iridescent metallic and opalescent metallic colors, etc., in which colors of groups a, b, and c combine to produce color effects — This class of color is confined largely to Lepidoptera and almost exclusively to scaled insects or areas bearing scales

That our discussion of insect colors may be made more explicit we may, with the foregoing account of the causes and kinds of colors in mind, endeavor to see just how the color-pattern of a certain single group of insects is produced. This group is that of the moths and butterflies, in which color and pattern obviously reach a maximum of development and specialization.

If the wing of a moth or butterfly be rubbed gently between finger and thumb, a spot on the wing will soon lose its color and become transparent, while on finger and thumb will be found a fine sparkling powder, the "flour" of the miller-moth, the jewel-dust of the butterfly. This dust, rubbed on a glass slide and examined under the microscope, will be seen to be com-

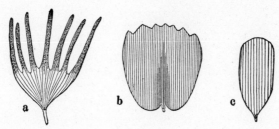

FIG. 770.—Single scale from moths and butterflies.  *a*, from *Tolype velleda; b*, from *Castnia* sp.; *c*, from *Micropteryx aruncella.* (Greatly magnified.)

posed of symmetrical tiny scales, each composed of a flattened blade and short stem or pedicel (Fig. 770). A considerable variety of shape will be noticeable among these scales, and if scales are rubbed from other moths and butterflies, many new shapes will be found. But through all this diversity of appearance, a fundamental plan of make-up may be recognized in each of these minute structures. Most commonly the scales are more or less ovate in outline with the little stem projecting from the narrower end. The broader end has its margin entire or with dentations of varying depth and number. These dentations may be so deep that the scale looks like a several-fingered little hand. In size the scales vary from .07 mm. ($\frac{1}{350}$ inch) to .8 mm. ($\frac{1}{30}$ inch) if we exclude the long hair-like forms common near the base of each wing, and also the slender elongate ones which project from the wing-margins. In width the scales vary from hair-like to a breadth of .4 mm. ($\frac{1}{60}$ inch).

FIG. 771.—Scale of *Hepialus mcglashani*, showing primary and secondary striation. (Greatly magnified.)

Some scales are as broad as long, or even broader than long. Running longitudinally from base to outer margin are many fine little subparallel lines or striæ. These striæ vary in distance apart, on different scales, from .0007 mm., as in the scales of the great blue Morpho butterflies, to .004 mm., as in the sulphur-yellow butterfly, *Catopsila eubule*.

The scales cover (in all but the few "clear-winged" moths) the wings

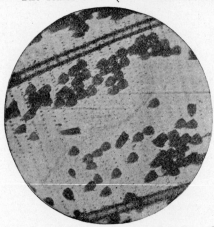

on both upper and lower sides, being insecurely attached to the wing membrane by having their short pedicels inserted in little pockets or cups on the wing surface. They show an interesting and varying manner of arrangement. This arrangement varies from an extremely uniform one in the butterflies and higher moths to one of much less regularity of disposition in the lower moths. On the wings of a butterfly the scales are inserted with their pedicels directed toward the base of the wing in subparallel rows running transversely across the wing, i.e., from anterior to posterior margin, and the scales in each row are at approximately equal distances apart. Their distance is less than the width

Fig. 772.—A small, partly denuded part of the wing of a butterfly, *Lycena* sp., showing the scales and pits in a wing membrane, into which the tiny stems of the scales are inserted. (Photomicrograph by George O. Mitchell; greatly magnified.)

of each scale, so that adjoining scales overlap laterally and thus make each row to be composed of two tiers of scales, an upper and an under one: the insertion-cups of one tier are very slightly but perceptibly advanced beyond those of the other tier. The scales of the upper tier alternate with those of the lower tier, and each upper scale overlaps laterally two under ones. But in addition to this lateral overlapping, the distance between the rows of insertion-cups is less than the length of the scales, so that there is an overlapping of the tip of the scales of one row over the bases of the scales in the next row in front. By this

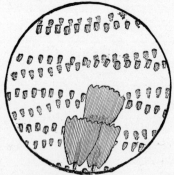

Fig. 773.—Bits of denuded wing of a butterfly, *Grapta* sp., to show rows of insertion-pits on upper and lower sides, with three scales in position. (Greatly magnified.)

double overlapping there is formed a complete shingled covering of scales over each surface (upper and under) of each wing.

This close placing and overlapping, and the small size of the scales, bring it about that the number of scales on a single wing is truly prodigious.

FIG. 774.—Diagram to show shingled arrangement of scales over surface of butterfly's wing; the short black bars indicate scales in cross-section; the broad central bar, the wing in cross-section.

In *Morpho* sp., for example, the distance apart of the lines of insertion-pits on a bit of the upper wing surface taken from the middle of the fore wing is .151 mm.; the distance apart of the pits in a line is .043 mm. (on the under surface the pits are .05 mm. apart); so that in a space 25 mm. by 25 mm. (1 square inch *circa*) there would be 165 lines of scales with 600 scales in each line, or 99,000 scales to each square inch of wing-surface. As the upper and under surfaces of the fore and hind wings combined equal about 15 square inches, the total number of scales on the wings of Morpho may be roughly approximated at 1,500,000.

The pedicels of the scales are of slightly varying shapes and of different lengths, corresponding with the pockets into which they fit. Those which enter insertion-cups which are expanded at the base, or at some point between the base and the mouth, present at the tip or between the tip and the point of merging into the blade of the scale, respectively, a slight expansion, so that they are pretty firmly held in the cup by a sort of ball-and-socket attachment. The scales are held in position by the elasticity of the cups which closely clasp the pedicels. After death of the moth or butterfly this elasticity is largely lost, by desiccation of the wing membrane, and the pedicels are more easily brushed from the wing than when the insect is alive.

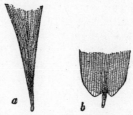

FIG. 775.—Base of scales: *a*, of *Gloveria arizonesis*; *b*, of *Morpho* sp. (Greatly magnified.)

Now to pay attention to the actual structure or make-up of individual scales. When studied carefully under the microscope singly and in cross-sections of the wing the scales are seen to be tiny flattened sacs, composed of two membrances, enclosing sometimes only air, sometimes pigment granules attached to the inner face of one of the membranes, and sometimes (as observed in cabinet specimens) the dry remains of what may have been during life an internal pulp. The striæ are confined to the outer membrane (that farthest from the wing-membrane) and are probably folds in this outer membrane. These striæ are plainly elevated above the interstrial space. All scales, excepting some androconia (scent-scales on male butterflies) (Fig. 777), possess these longitudinal striæ, which traverse the scale

from base to outer margin and are very sharp, and separated from one another by equal distances. The striæ sometimes curve in at the lower angles of the blade, converging toward the origin of the pedicel; in other cases they fade out at these angles. In scales of *Anosia plexippus* from 33 to 46 striæ, averaging .002 mm. apart, are present on each scale. There would thus be 12,500 of these striæ to the inch. On transparent scales from *Morpho* sp. the striæ were .0015 mm. to .002 mm. apart; on opaque (pigment-bearing) scales from the same specimen the striæ were from .0007 to .00072 mm. apart, or at the rate of about 35,000 to the inch.

FIG. 776.—Scale of *Lycomorpha constans*, showing cross-striæ. (Greatly magnified.)

If we examine a long series of scales brushed off from different parts of a wing of moth or butterfly, we can always note a series of gradating forms running from slender hair-like form to typical short, broad, flat scale. The significance of this, when we come to inquire about the origin of scales, is plain. Scales are unusual structures among insects: besides the moths and butterflies, only a few beetles, the mosquitoes, the fish-moths, and a few other scattering insects have them. But all insects have hairs. Hairs are structures common throughout the class. And it is certain that scales are derived or developed from hairs. They are a specialized, a highly modified sort of hair. On the lower, the more generalized moths, the hair-like scales are the more abundant. The wings show a thick intermixing of loose, fluffy hair-scales or scale-hairs with more typical scales irregularly arranged. In the higher Lepidoptera, the specialized sort of hairs, namely the scales, compose almost exclusively the wing-covering, and these scales are arranged in the specialized uniform shingling manner previously described. But even on the wings of a butterfly all the gradations from hair to scale can be found by going from base out to discal area of the wing. These gradation series vary in character in different families, as shown in Figs. 778, 779, 780, and 781. In some the

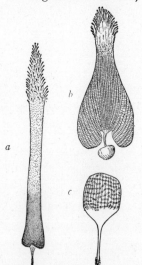

FIG. 777. Androconia from wings of male butterflies. *a*, from wing of Nymphalid butterfly; *b*, from wing of Pierid butterfly; *c*, from wing of Lycænid butterfly. (All greatly magnified.)

hair becomes a scale by shortening and broadening, keeping its free
tip entire; in others the hair splits distally and then each branch splits

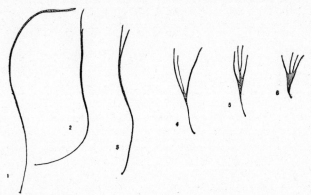

FIG. 778.—Scales taken from a single fore wing of *Megalopyge crispata*, showing gradations from true hair to specialized scale.   (Greatly magnified.)

again, and so on, while the base is continually shortening and broadening
so that the scale form finally reached is a fingered or deeply-toothed

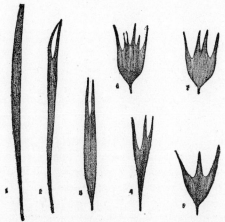

FIG. 779.—Scales from a single fore wing of *Gloveria arizonesis*, showing gradations from
scale-hair to specialized hair.   (Greatly magnified.)

one.   But in all the series the final result is that from a long, slender, subcylindrical hair is evolved a short, broad, flattened, little scale.   A study
of the actual development of an individual scale on the forming wing of a
butterfly during the pupal or chrysalid stage confirms the hypothesis of the
evolution of the scales.   In the growing developing wing the scales begin
as hairs, arising by the extension of certain hypodermal cells in the wing-

membrane which gradually change in the few or many days of pupal development into typical scales (Figs. 782 and 783).

FIG. 780.—Scales from a single fore wing of *Heliconia* sp., showing gradations from scale-
hair to specialized scale. (Greatly magnified.)

We have studied now with some care the general character of the scale-
covering of moths and butterflies, and the actual structural make-up and
the origin of the indi-
vidual scales. And we
learned at the very beginning of our study that
it is the scale-covering
which is the producer or
carrier of all the brilliant
and varied color and
pattern which character-
ize the moths and butter-
flies. When we rub off
the myriad little scales
the wings themselves are

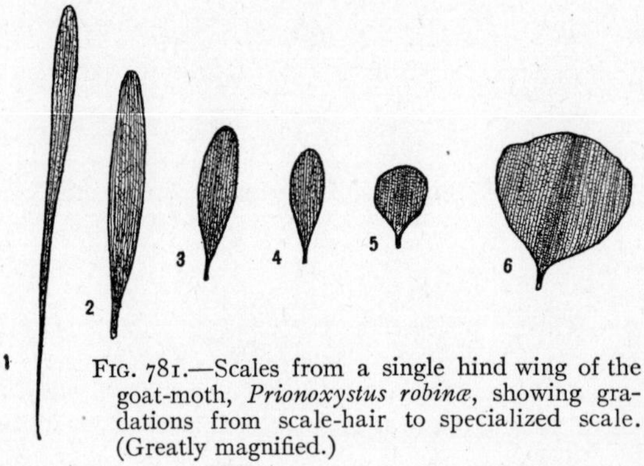

FIG. 781.—Scales from a single hind wing of the
goat-moth, *Prionoxystus robinæ*, showing gradations from scale-hair to specialized scale.
(Greatly magnified.)

found to be colorless, transparent. We have now to note how it is that
the scales, the color-carrying organs, actually produce the colors.

The scales in their fully
developed dry condition are
chiefly cuticular in structure,
but they may contain pig-
ment granules and various
substances left by the hypodermal cell-layer in drying.
The colors of the scales are
to be classified then as both
cuticular and hypodermal in
character, and both chemical
and physical in origin. For
the most part they are strictly
combination colors due to

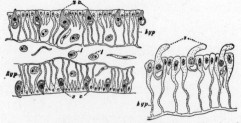

FIG. 782.—Diagrammatic figures showing the development of the scales on a wing of *Euvanessa antiopa;* at left, cross-section of bit of pupal wing showing the two wing-membranes and intervening space
or wing-cavity; at right, cross-section of a single
wing-membrane in older pupal wing. *s.c.*, scale-
cells; *hyp.*, hypodermal cells; *l*, leucocytes; *s*, developing scales. (After Mayer; greatly magnified.)

chemical (pigmental) substances within the scale and to the structural character of the scale-walls. The pigment granules within the scales are brown, yellowish, or reddish, and as they mostly transmit the same colors as they reflect, the colors of strongly pigmented scales are the same by transmitted light (light shining through them) as by reflected light. But with

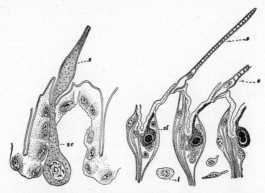

FIG. 783.—Diagrammatic figures showing late stages in development of scales of the wing of *Anosia plexippus;* figure at right showing older stage than figure at left. *s,* scale; *sc,* scale-cell; *l,* leucocyte. (After Mayer; greatly magnified.)

the physical colors this is not the case. Scales which produce brilliant blues and other colors are often empty, and these when viewed by transmitted light are nearly colorless. Or they may contain pigment and then when viewed by transmitted light show a dull brownish or yellowish color entirely different from the metallic iridescence which they show by reflected light.

The physical color effects produced by scales are due to their (*a*) lamination and (*b*) striation. Each scale is composed of a pair of thin subtransparent laminæ (lamellæ), the thin dry sides of the flattened sac, and when arranged in the shingling sheath over the wing-membrane, overlapping each other at sides and ends, they produce a layer of superposed thin transparent lamellæ which is exactly the structural condition necessary to the production of varied refraction (interference) effects of color. This scale layer produces color by virtue of its structure just as a piece of laminated mica or bit of old weathered glass or film of soap-bubble produces color (Newton's rings). In addition the striæ-bearing outer surface of each scale is essentially the same as a ruled surface or grating, producing color by diffraction and interference just as do the well-known Rowland's and Rutherford's gratings, familiar to students in physical laboratories. In the finest of these artificially striated gratings the lines are about .0006 mm. apart: in butterfly scales the striæ are from .002 to .0007 mm. apart.

The blacks, browns, yellows, and dull reds of butterflies and moths, then, are produced chiefly by pigment; while all the brilliant metallic colors, the iridescent blues and greens, and hosts of allied shades, are due to the structural or physical make-up of the scale-covering. The patterns, varied and intricate, with lines and spots and bars, sharply deliminated or softly merging into the ground color or into one another, depend on the fact that the color-units, the scales, are so small that by the juxtaposition of scales containing different pigments, or varying slightly in structure, different colors may be produced abruptly or gradually, depending upon the degree of differences in pigment and structure of adjacent scales. By the extremely regular arrangement, in the higher moths and butterflies, of the short, rigid, little scales, definite lines and sharp limits to spots and bars are possible. In the lower, fluffy moths where the scales are hair-like and irregularly arranged such sharp delimitations of pattern parts are not possible. Thus the specialization of the scales, both as to structure and arrangement, in the brilliantly colored and complexly patterned day-flying Lepidoptera is seen to be exactly connected with the specialization of color and pattern.

The studies that have so far been made upon the character and origin of types of pattern have brought some aspect of orderliness into what seems at first glance a chaos of complexity, but our knowledge of this matter is yet too little organized to make it available in such a brief general account of insect color and pattern as this one necessarily is. In the actual develop-

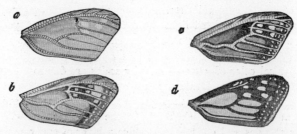

Fig. 784.—Diagrammatic series showing development of color-pattern in pupal wings of the monarch butterfly, *Anosia plexippus*. (After Mayer; one-half natural size.)

ment or course of appearance of the color-pattern in the wings of any individual moth or butterfly certain conditions regularly obtain, as shown by Van Bemmeln, Urech, Haase, Mayer, and others. Mayer's account and figures of the development of color in the fore wings of the monarch butterfly, *Anosia plexippus*, show a typical case. The pupal stage of Anosia lasts from one to two weeks. "For the first few days," says Mayer, "the wings are perfectly transparent, but about five days before the butterfly issues they become pure white. An examination of the scales at this period shows that they are completely formed and merely lack pigment. In about forty-eight hours after this (see Fig. 784, *a*) the ground-color of the wings changes to a dirty yellow. It is interesting to note that the white spots which adorn the mature wings remain pure white. Fig. 784, *b*, illustrates the next stage, where the black has begun to appear in the region beyond the cell. The nervures

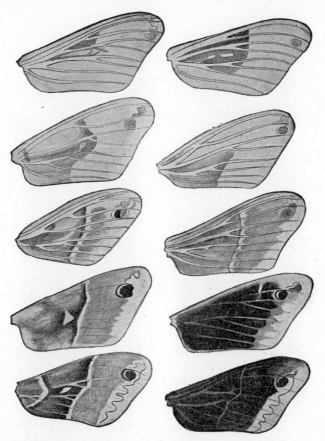

FIG. 785.—Diagrammatic series showing development of color-pattern in pupal wings of the promethea moth, *Callosamia promethea;* female wings in vertical series at left, male at right. (After Mayer; one-half natural size.)

themselves, however, remain white. Fig. 784, *c*, shows a still later condition, where the dirty yellow ground-color has deepened into rufous, and the black has deepened and increased in area and has also begun to appear along the edges of the nervures. In Fig. 784, *d*, the black has finally suffused the nervures, the base of the wing and the submedian nervure being the only parts that still remain dull yellow. It is apparent that in *Anosia plexippus*, as in *Callosamia promethea*, the central areas of the wings are the first to exhibit the mature colors, and that the nervures and costal edges of the wings are the last to be suffused.''

The development of the wing-patterns in the male and the female of the promethea moth, as worked out by Mayer, is shown by Fig. 785.

Other butterflies and moths which have been thus followed through the pupal life show a similar possession of color-appearance. Tower has similarly followed the color-development in certain beetles. Tower's figures illustrating the development in the large blackish-brown Prionid beetle,

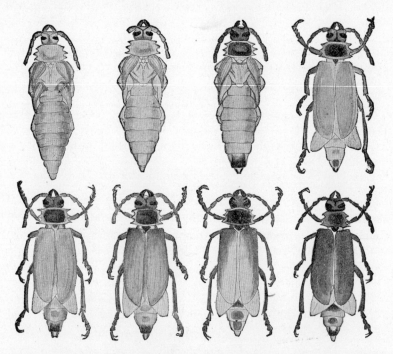

Fig. 786.—Diagrammatic series showing development of color-pattern in pupæ and young adults of the giant wood-boring beetle, *Orthosoma brunnea*. The first three figures in the upper line, counting from the left, are pupæ of successive ages, the rest of the figures adults of successive ages. (After Tower; natural size.)

*Orthosoma brunnea*, are shown in Fig. 786. Tower finds that in all the insects so far studied the chemical colors of the body follow the general course illustrated by Orthosoma. The color begins to form on the head and anterior parts first and gradually spreads posteriorly.

Now that we have got in some degree acquainted with the ways in which colors are actually produced among insects, we may come back to the question asked in the first paragraph of this chapter, namely, "What is the use to the insect of all this variety of color and pattern?" We may attempt now to get some clue to the significance of the color phenomenon. So wide-spread and well developed are color and pattern among insects that the presumption is strong that the utility of color-pattern is large.

The only hypothesis that gives to colors and markings a value in the life of insects at all comparable with the degree of specialization reached by these colors and markings and by the special structures developed to make them possible, is that already referred to as the theory of protective and aggressive resemblances, of warning and directive patterns, and of mimicry. These various uses of color-patterns are all concerned with the relation of the insect to its environment; they are means of protecting the insect from its enemies or of enabling it to capture its prey. They are uses obviously concerned with the "struggle for existence"; they are "shifts for a living." For the sake of clearness in the discussion of these various uses—a discussion which must by the limitations of space be most unsatisfactorily condensed—the uses will be rather arbitrarily classified into several categories which in Nature are not as sharply distinguished as the paragraph treatment of them might suggest.

**General protective resemblance.**—The general harmonizing in color and pattern with the color scheme of the usual environment is a condition which every field student of insects recognizes as widely existing. The difficulty of distinguishing a resting moth from the bark on which it is resting, a green caterpillar or leaf-hopper or meadow grasshopper from the leaf to which it clings, a roadside locust or bug from the soil on which it alights, is a difficulty which has to be reckoned with by every collector. Now while there are few human collectors of insects, there are hosts of bird and toad and lizard insect-hunters, to say nothing of the many kinds of predaceous insects themselves who use their own cousins for chief food. So that where this difficulty of distinguishing the resting insect from its environment is sufficient to postpone success on the part of the insect-hunting bird or lizard, the life of the protectively-colored insect is obviously saved, for the time, by its dress. This is a utility of color and pattern than which there can be, from the insect point of view, nothing higher.

**Variable protective resemblance.**—While with most insects all the individuals of one species show a similar color and pattern, it is noticeable that with a few species there is a marked variability or difference in color and sometimes in markings. Locusts of various species of the genus Trimerotropis show a variability in color of individuals ranging through gray, brown, reddish, plumbeous, and bluish, and such accompanying variability in marking as to result in producing much variety of appearance in a single series of collected individuals. I have noted in collecting these locusts in Colorado and California that this variability of coloration is directly associated with the color-differences in the soil of the localities in which these locusts live; the reddish individuals are taken from spots where the soil is reddish, the grayish where it is sand-colored, and the plumbeous and bluish from soil formed by decomposing bluish rock.

On the campus of Stanford University there is a little pond whose shores are covered in some places with bits of bluish rock, in other places with bits of reddish rock, and in still others with sand. The toad-bug, *Galgulus oculatus*, lives abundantly on the banks of this little lake. Specimens collected from the blue rocks are bluish in ground-color, those from the red rocks are reddish, and those from the sand are sand-colored. But the colors of these insects are fixed; they cannot, like the chameleon and certain other lizards, or like numerous small fishes and some tree-frogs, change color, quickly or slowly, with changes in position, that is, movements from green to brown or to other colored environment. Variable protective resemblance in insects is, as far as known, a variability directly induced, to be sure, by varying environment, but all acquired during the development of the individual insects, and fixed by the time they reach the adult stage.

The well-known experiments of Trimen, Müller, and Poulton with the pupating larvæ of swallow-tailed butterflies, *Papilio* sp., and Poulton on other butterflies with naked chrysalids, show that the chrysalids of numerous butterfly kinds take on the color, or a shade approaching it, of the substance surrounding the pupating larvæ, and show also that the result is due to a stimulus of the skin by the enclosing color, and not to a stimulus received through the eyes, and carried to the skin by the nerves. Larvæ just ready to pupate were enclosed in boxes lined with paper of different colors; the chrysalids when formed were found to be colored to harmonize with that particular color of paper by which they were surrounded while pupating. As these chrysalids in Nature hang exposed on bark and in other unsheltered places, without protecting cocoon or cover of any kind, the actual protective value of this harmonious coloration is obvious.

The larvæ (caterpillars) of various moths, particularly Geometrid and Sphingid species, often appear in two color types, one brown and the other green. Poulton has shown by experiment and observation with some of these species that those larvæ reared among green leaves and twigs and branches become brown. This variable protective resemblance, like that of Trimerotropis, Galgulus, and the Papilio chrysalids, also is fixed after being once acquired.

An interesting example of color harmony which may be classified under the head of variable protective resemblance that has come under my obser-

vation while writing this chapter is the case of the larvæ of *Lycæna* sp.,
abundant on the flower-heads of the just-blossoming (May) California
buckeye, *Æsculus californicus*.  The buds of the buckeye are green, or green

FIG. 787.—The dead-leaf butterfly, *Kallima* sp., a remarkable case of special protective
resemblance.  (Natural size.)

and rose, or even all rose externally.  The quiet slug-like Lycænid larvæ
lie longitudinally along the buds and their short stems, and are either green

with faint rosy tinge, especially along the dorsi-meson, or are distinctly rosy all over, depending strictly upon the color-tone of the particular inflorescence serving as habitat for the larva (Pl. XIII, Figs. 3, 4, and 5). The correspondence in shade of color is strikingly exact: the utter invisibility, or rather indistinguishability, of the larvæ is something that needs to be experienced as my artist, my students, and I have experienced it in the last few weeks, to be fairly realized. We have watched the larvæ through their whole life, and all the time the safe position along the bud and the immobility are maintained.

**Special protective resemblance.**—The figures of Kallima (Pl. XIII, Fig. 1, also text Fig. 787) and of Phyllium (Pl. XIII, Fig. 2, also text Fig. 788), referred to in an early paragraph in this chapter, illustrate extreme and

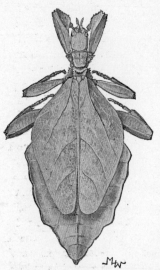

often-referred-to examples of a protective resemblance which may be called "special" in that the insect's appearance simulates in more or less nearly exact way some particular part of the habitual environment, this being, in the case of Kallima, a dead leaf, in the case of Phyllium a green leaf. The details of this simulation are extreme: in Kallima the projections or tails of the hind wings represent the leaf-stem, the long central midrib of the leaf is represented by a brown line continuously across both wings, the lateral leaf-veins corresponding on one side to the actual course of the wing-veins, but on the other being represented by brown lines running at right angles, nearly, to the wing-veins; in Phyllium the flattened and expanded head, thorax, legs, and abdomen with the broad green wing-covers, leaf-veined and spotted with yellow like a fungus-attacked or insect-punctured leaf compose a false picture of great effectiveness. Are not these details of deceit almost past belief?

FIG. 788.—The green-leaf insect, *Phyllium* sp. This insect is bright green with scattered yellowish marks, the color and pattern combining with the shape to make the insect almost indistinguishable when at rest among green leaves.

The slender grass-green larvæ of many moths and butterflies are much like green grass-leaves; their slimness and, if Weismann's interpretation be accepted, the few longitudinal whitish lines which serve as air-lines to divide the body into two or three (apparent) grass-blades, are special characters of importance. The inch-worms or larvæ of Geometrid moths are familiar examples of special protective resemblance. Abundant as these larvæ are, they are only occasionally seen, and then usually when "loop-ing" along on the ground or sidewalk. When in their habitual haunts in trees and bushes, the slightest disturbance, as the approach of bird or lizard or human observer, causes them to "go stiff," holding the body (Fig. 789)

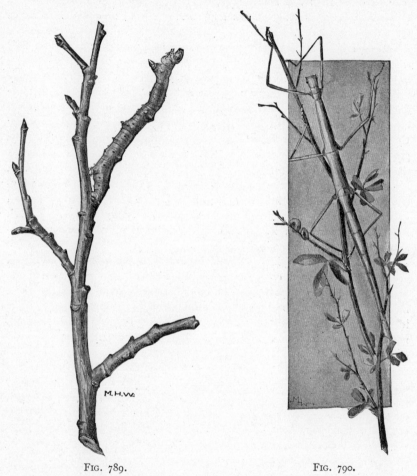

FIG. 789.                    FIG. 790.

FIG. 789.—An inch-worm, larva of geometrid moth, in protective position. (After Jor-dan and Kellogg; natural size.)
FIG. 790.—The walking-stick, or twig-insect, *Diapheromera femorata*. (Slightly enlarged.)

rigidly out from the branch or stem to which they cling by the posterior two pairs of prop-legs, and looking so like a short twig, or broken one, that they are only rarely recognized for what they really are. The skin is brown or green (variable resemblance, depending on their nurture) and roughened and tubercled like a bud-scarred bit of twig. The absence of the middle prop-legs prevents the harm to this illusion that would come from their presence. An interesting point in this simulation—and one which is commoner in such cases than has been generally referred to—is the combining of a habit or kind of behavior with the structural and color modification to make the illusion successful.

Another familiar and extreme case of special protective resemblance is that of the walking-stick, or twig-insect, *Diapheromera femorata* (Fig. 790), a Phasmid wide-spread over the whole of our country. The absence of wings, the extreme elongation and slenderness of body and legs, and the dichromatic condition, individuals being either green or brown, all combine to make this insect a masterpiece of deceit. The moths of the genus Cymatophora and their larvæ also mostly harmonize excellently with the gray bark on which they rest; the moths adding to their general simulation the curious habit of resting often with folded wings at an angle of 45° with the tree-trunk, head downwards, with the curiously blunt and uneven wing-tips projecting, so as to imitate with great fidelity a short broken-off branch or chip of bark. Numerous other moths and caterpillars resemble bark and habitually rest on it. The Catocalas, Schizura, and others are examples familiar to the moth-collector.

Any field student of insects by paying attention to the matter of special protective resemblance can soon make up a formidable list of examples. Some of these may appeal more to him than to persons seeing his specimens in the collecting-boxes, and some indeed will probably be questionable to other naturalists. But nevertheless no collector or field student but has noted many examples of this clever artifice of Nature to protect her children.

**Warning colors.**—If the field student may be relied on to note and record a long list of insects colored and marked so as to harmonize well with their general environment or with some specific part of it, he may also be relied on to bring in a list of opposites: a record of bizarre and conspicuous forms, colored with brilliant blues and greens and streaked and spotted in a manner utterly at variance and in contrast with the foliage or soil or bark or whatever is the usual environment of the insect. The great red-brown monarch butterfly and its black-striped green and yellowish larva, the tiger-banded swallowtails, the black and yellow wasps and bees, the ladybird-beetles with their sharply contrasting colors, the brilliant green blister-beetles, the striped and spotted Chrysomelids—in all these and many others there can be no talk of protective resemblance: if only such a paradoxical theory as protective conspicuousness could be established, then these colors and markings might well be explained by it.

Exactly such an explanation of brilliant color and contrasting markings is afforded by the theory of warning colors. It has been conclusively shown, by observation and experiment, by several naturalists,* that many insects are distasteful to birds, lizards, and other predaceous enemies of the insect class.

The blood-lymph or some specially secreted body fluid of these insects contains an acrid or ill-tasting substance so that birds will not, if they can recognize the kind of insect, make any attempt to catch or eat them. This letting alone is undoubtedly the result of previously made trials, that is, has been learned. Now it would obviously be of advantage to those species of insects that are ill-tasting if their coloring and pattern were so distinctive and conspicuous as to make them readily learned by birds, and once learned

FIG. 791.—Larva of the monarch butterfly, *Anosia plexippus*, conspicuously marked with black and whitish yellow rings, and distasteful to birds. (Natural size.)

easily seen. A distasteful caterpillar needs to advertise its unpalatability so effectively that the swooping bird will recognize it before making that single sharp cutting stroke or peck that would be about as fatal to a caterpillar as being wholly eaten. Hence the need and the utility of warning colors. And indeed the distasteful insects as far as recognized are mostly of conspicuous color and pattern.

Such warning colors are presumably possessed not only by unpalatable insects, but also by many that have certain special means of defence. The wasps and bees, provided with stings, dangerous to most of their enemies, are almost all conspicuously marked with yellow and black. Many bugs, well defended by sharp beaks, possess conspicuous color-patterns.

**Terrifying appearances.**—Certain other insects which are without special means of defence and are not at all formidable or dangerous are yet so marked or shaped and so behave as to present a curiously threatening or terrifying appearance. The large green caterpillars of the sphinx-moths have a curious rearing-up habit which seems to simulate threatened attack (Fig. 792). They have, too, a great pointed spine or horn on the back of the posterior

* A most interesting recent account of a long series of such observations and experiments is presented in "The Bionomics of South African Insects," by G. K. Marshall and E. B. Poulton, Trans. Ent. Soc. Lond., 1902. This paper contains the records of five years of careful study in the field of the phenomena relating to the theories of warning colors and mimicry.

tip of the body which has a most formidable appearance, but is, as a matter of fact, not at all a weapon of defence, being quite harmless. Numerous stingless insects when disturbed wave about the hind part of the body or curl it over or under much as stinging insects do, and seem to be threatening to sting. The striking eye-spots of many insects are believed by some entomologists to be of the nature of terrifying markings. Marshall tried feeding baboons a full-grown larva (about 7 in. long) of the sphinx-moth,

FIG. 792.—Larva of the pen-marked sphinx-moth, *Sphinx chersis*, showing threatening attitude. (After Comstock.)

*Chærocampa osiris*. The larva has large strongly colored eye-spots and is "remarkably snake-like, the general coloring somewhat recalling that of the common puff-adder, *Bitis arietans*. The female baboon ran forward expecting a titbit, but when she saw what I had brought she flicked it out of my hand on to the ground, at the same time jumping back suspiciously; she then approached it very cautiously, and after peering carefully at it from the distance of about a foot she withdrew in alarm, being clearly much impressed by the large blue eye-like markings. The male baboon, which has a much more nervous temperament, had meanwhile remained at a distance surveying the proceedings, so I picked up a caterpillar and brought

it towards them, but they would not let me approach, and kept running
away round and round their pole, so I threw the insect at them. Their
fright was ludicrous to see; with loud cries they jumped aside and clambered
up the pole as fast as they could go, into their box, where they sat peering
over the edge watching the uncanny object below." (Marshall.) Marshall
also writes concerning the eye-like markings on the wings of the mantis,
*Pseudocreobotra wahlbergi:* "They are, I think, almost certainly of a terrifying character. When the insect is irritated the wings are raised over its
back in such a manner that the tegmina stand side by side, and the markings

FIG. 793.—Larva of the puss-moth, *Cerura* sp.; upper figure showing larva in normal
attitude; lower figure showing larva when disturbed. (After Poulton; enlarged.)
(See description of this larva on p. 394.)

on them then present a very striking resemblance to the great yellow eyes
of a bird of prey or some feline animal, which might well deter an insectivorous enemy. It is noticeable that the insect is always careful to keep
the wings directed towards the point of attack, and this is often done without
altering the position of the body."

**Directive coloration.**—Still another use is believed by some entomologists
to be afforded by such markings as ocelli and other specially conspicuous
spots and flecks on the wings of butterflies and moths, and by such apparently
useless parts as the "tails" of the hind wings of the swallowtail and Lycænid
butterflies, and others. Marshall busied himself for a long time with collecting butterflies which had evidently been snapped at by birds (in some cases
he observed the actual attack) and suffered the loss of a part of a wing.
Examining these specimens when brought together, Poulton and Marshall

noted that the "great majority [of these injuries to the wings] are inflicted at the anal angle and adjacent hind margin of the hind wing, a considerable number at or near the apical angle of the fore wing, and comparatively few between the points." In this fact, coupled with the fact that the apical and hind angles of the fore and hind wings respectively are precisely those regions of the wings most usually specially marked and prolonged as angular processes or tails, Poulton sees a special significance in the patterns of these wing-parts: he thinks they are "directive marks which tend to divert the attention of an enemy from more vital parts." It is obvious that a butterfly can very well afford to lose the tip or tail of a wing if that loss will save losing a head or abdomen. Poulton sees a "remarkable resemblance of the marks and structures at the anal angle of the hind wing, under side, in many Lycænidæ to a head with antennæ and eyes," and recalls that this has been independently noticed by many other observers. "The movements of the hind wings by which the 'tails,' the apparent antennæ, are made continually to pass and repass each other add very greatly to this resemblance."

**Mimicry.**—Of all the theories accounting for the utility of color and pattern, that of mimicry demands at first thought the largest degree of credulity. As a matter of fact, however, the observation and evidence on which it rests are as convincing as are those for almost any of the offered explanations of the usefulness of color-pattern. Although the word mimicry could often have been used aptly in the account of special protective resemblance, it has been reserved for use in connection with a specific kind of imitation, namely, the imitation by an otherwise defenceless insect, one without poison, beak, or sting, and without acrid and distasteful body fluids, of some other specially defended or inedible kind, so that the mimicker is mistaken for the mimicked form and, like this defended or distasteful form, relieved from attack. Many cases of this mimicry may be noted by any field student of entomology.

Buzzing about flowers are to be found various kinds of bees, and also various other kinds of insects, thoroughly bee-like in appearance, but in reality not bees nor, like them, defended by stings. These bee-mimickers are mostly flies of various families (Syrphidæ, Asilidæ, Bombyliidæ), and their resemblance to bees is sufficient to and does constantly deceive collectors. We presume, then, that it equally deceives birds and other insect enemies. Wasps, too, are mimicked by other insects; the wasp-like flies, Conopidæ, and some of the clear-winged moths, Sesiidæ (Fig. 794), are extremely wasp-like in general seeming.

The distasteful monarch butterfly, *Anosia plexippus*, wide-spread and abundant—a "successful" butterfly, whose success undoubtedly largely depends on its inedibility in both larval and imaginal stage—is mimicked with extraordinary fidelity of detail by the viceroy, *Basilarchia archippus*

(Plate XI, Figs. 1, 4, also text Fig. 795). The Basilarchias, constituting a genus of numerous species, are with but two or three exceptions not at all of the color or pattern of Anosia, but in the case of the particular species *archippus* not only the red-brown ground-color but the fine pattern details in black and whitish copy faithfully the details in Anosia; only in the addi-

FIG. 794.—Various moths and wasps, the moths having the appearance of wasps, probably through mimicry, and protected by being mistaken for the stinging insects. (Photograph by author; natural size.)

tion of a thin blackish line across the discal area of the hind wings does *archippus* show any noticeable difference. Viceroy is believed not to be distasteful to birds, but its close mimicry of the distasteful monarch undoubtedly leads to its being constantly mistaken for it by the birds and thus left unmolested.

The subject of mimicry has not been studied largely among the insects of our country, but in the tropics and subtropics numerous striking examples of mimetic forms have been noted and written about. The members of two large families of butterflies, the Danaidæ and Heliconidæ, are distasteful to birds, and are mimicked by many species of other butterfly families, especially the Pieridæ, and by the swallowtails, Papilionidæ. Many plates illustrating such cases have been published by Poulton and Marshall, Haase,

Weismann, and others. Shelford,* in an extended account of mimicry as exemplified among the insects of Borneo, refers to and illustrates many striking examples among the beetles, the Hemiptera, Diptera, Orthoptera, Neuroptera, and moths: distasteful Lycid beetles are closely mimicked by other beetles, by Hemiptera, and by moths; distasteful ladybird-beetles are mimicked by Hemiptera, Orthoptera, and by other beetles; stinging Hymen-

FIG. 795.—The monarch butterfly, *Anosia plexippus* (above), distasteful to birds, and the viceroy, *Basilarchia archippus* (below), which mimics it.

optera are mimicked by stingless Hymenoptera, by beetles, flies, bugs, and moths. Poulton and Marshall, in their account of mimicry among South African insects, publish many colored plates revealing most striking resemblances between insects, well defended by inedibility or defensive weapons, and their mimickers.

Our space unfortunately prevents any specific consideration of these various interesting cases.

The special conditions under which mimicry exists have been studied and are of extreme interest. It is obvious that the inedible or defended mimicked form must be more abundant than the mimicker, so that the experimenting young bird or lizard may have several chances to one of getting an

* Shelford, R. Observations on some Mimetic Insects and Spiders from Borneo and Singapore, Proc. Zool. Soc. Lond., 1902, pp. 230 et seq.

ill taste or a sting when he attacks an insect of certain type or pattern. This requirement of relative abundance of mimicker and mimicked seems actually met, as proved by observation. In some cases only females of a species indulge in mimicry, the males being unmodified. This is explained on the ground of the particular necessity for protection of the egg-laden, heavy-flying, and long-lived and hence more exposed females, as compared with the lighter, swifter, shorter-lived males.

It has been found that individuals of a single species may mimic several different species of defended insects, this polymorphism of pattern existing in different localities, or indeed in a single one. Marshall believes that the seasonal polychromatism of certain butterfly species is associated with the mimicry of certain defended butterflies of different species, these different species appearing at different times of the year.

**Criticisms and general consideration of the foregoing hypotheses of color use.**—It is needless to say that such hypotheses and theories of the utility of color and pattern have been subjected to much criticism, both adverse and favorable. The necessity for limiting results within the working range of efficient causes has been the soundest basis, to my mind, for the adverse criticism of the theories of special protective resemblance, warning colors, and mimicry. Until recently most of the observations on which the theories are based have been simply observations proving the existence of remarkable similarities in appearance or equally striking contrasts and *bizarrerie*. The usefulness of these similarities and contrasts had been deduced logically, but not proved experimentally nor by direct observation. In recent years, however, a much sounder basis for these theories has been laid by experimental work. There is now on record a large amount of strong evidence for the validity of the hypothesis of mimicry. Certainly no other hypothesis of equal validity with those of protective resemblance and mimicry has been proposed to explain the numerous striking cases of similarity and the significant conditions of life accompanying the existence of these cases, which have been recorded as the result of much laborious and indefatigable study by certain naturalists.

Plateau and Wheeler have tasted so-called inedible or distasteful insects and found nothing particularly disagreeable about them. But as Poulton suggests, the question is not as to the palate of Plateau and Wheeler nor of any men: it concerns the tastes of birds, lizards, etc. Better evidence is that afforded by actual observation of feeding birds and lizards; of experimental offering under natural conditions of alleged distasteful insects to their natural enemies. Marshall's observations and experiments on the point are suggestive and undoubtedly reliable. Much more work of the same kind is needed.

The efficient cause for bringing color and pattern up to such a high degree of specialization has been assumed, by nearly all upholders of the use hypotheses, to be natural selection. This agent can account for purposefulness, which is obviously an inherent part of all the hypotheses. And no other suggested agent can. Weismann makes, indeed, of this fact, by inverting the problem, one of his most effective arguments for the potency and *Allmacht* of natural selection. He declares that the existence of special protective resemblance, warning colors, and mimicry proves the reality of selection. But it must be asked, while admitting the cogency of much of the argument for natural selection as the efficient cause of high specialization of color and pattern as we have seen it actually to exist, how such a condition as that shown by the mimicking viceroy butterfly has come to be gradually developed, gradual development being confessedly selection's

FIG. 796.—The owl-butterfly, *Caligo* sp., under side. (Two-thirds natural size; photograph by the author.)

only mode of working. Could the viceroy have had any protection for itself, any advantage at all, until it actually so nearly resembled the inedible monarch as to be mistaken for it? No slight tinge of brown on the black and white wings (typical color scheme of the genus), no slight change of marking would be of any service in making the viceroy a mimic of the monarch. The whole leap from typical Basilarchia to (apparently) typical Anosia had to be made practically at once. On the other hand is it necessary for Kallima, the simulator of dead leaves, to go so far as it has in its modification? Such minute points of detail are there as will never be noted by bird or lizard. The simple necessity is the effect of a dead leaf; that is all. Kallima certainly does that and more. Kallima goes too far, and proves too much. And there are other cases like it. Natural selection alone could never carry the simulation past the point of full advantage.

But whatever other factors or agents have played a part in bringing about this specialization of color and pattern, exemplified by insects showing protective resemblances, warning colors, terrifying manners, and mimicry, natural selection has undoubtedly been the chief factor, and the basis of

FIG. 797.—The death's-head sphinx-moth.  (Photograph by the author.)

utility the chief foundation, for the development of the specialized conditions.

If any readers of this brief discussion of color and its uses among the insects care to refer to more detailed accounts of the general subject of color and pattern, or to parts of it, they will find the following books and papers useful: Poulton's "The Colour of Animals"; Beddard's "Animal Coloration"; Newbigin's "Color in Nature"; Wallace's "Darwinism," Chaps. VIII, IX, and X; papers by Mayer on "The Development of the Wing-scales and their Pigment in Butterflies and Moths" (Bull. Mus. Comp. Zool., Vol. XXIX, No. 5, 1896), on "The Color and Color-patterns of Moths and Butterflies" (Bull. Mus. Comp. Zool., Vol. XXX, No. 4, 1897), and on "Effects of Natural Selection and Race-tendency upon the Color-patterns of Lepidoptera" (Bull.

Brooklyn Inst. Arts and Sci., Vol. I, No. 2, 1902); a paper by Tower on "Color and Color-patterns of Coleoptera" (Decenn. Pubs. Univ. of Chicago, Vol. X, 1903); a paper by Kellogg on "The Taxonomic Value of the Scales of the Lepidoptera" (Kansas Univ. Quar., Vol. III, No. 1, 1894); the papers by Poulton and Marshall referred to on page 605, and that by Shelford referred to on page 610.

# CHAPTER XVIII

## INSECTS AND DISEASE

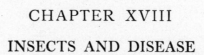

THROUGHOUT this book reference is constantly made to the injuries done by insects to our forest-trees, flowers, fruits, vegetables, and grains. The millions of dollars lost annually because of the sap-sucking of the San José scale, the grape-phylloxera, the chinch-bug, and the Hessian fly, and the biting and chewing of beetles and caterpillars, grubs and borers, are a sort of direct tax paid by farmers and fruit-growers for the privilege of farming and growing fruit. If this tax were levied by government and collected by agents with two feet instead of being levied by Nature and collected by six-footed agents, what a swift revolt there would be! But we have, most of us, a curious inertia that leads us to suffer with some protesting complaint but little protesting action the "ways of Providence," even when we fairly well recognize that Providence is chiefly ourselves.

When we reflect on the four hundred millions of dollars a year lost to our pockets by insect ravages we may incline to believe that the only kind of insect study which should claim our attention is the study of how to rid our lands of these pests. We may be excused for affirming of bugs, as was said of Indians by some epigrammatist, that the only good ones are the dead ones. When, however, we learn, as we are learning in these present days, that insects are not simply serious enemies of our crops and purses, but are truly dangerous to our very health and life, we must become still more extravagant in our condemnatory expressions concerning them.

We have long looked on mosquitoes, house-flies, and fleas as annoyances and even torments, but that each of these pests actually acts as an intermediate host for, and is an active disseminator of, one or more wide-spread and fatal diseases is knowledge that has been got only recently. Mosquitoes help to propagate, and are, almost certainly, the exclusive disseminating agents of malaria, yellow fever, and the various forms of filariasis; house-flies aid in spreading typhoid fever and other diseases; fleas are agents in distributing the germs of bubonic plague. Other insects are known to spread other diseases. Howard says: "While in malaria and typhoid we have two principal diseases common to the United States which may be conveyed by insects, the agency of these little creatures in the transfer of the disease-germs is by no means confined to human beings. In Egypt and in the Fiji Islands there is a destructive eye-disease of human beings the germs of which are carried by the common house-fly. In our southern states an eye-disease known as pinkeye is carried by certain very minute flies of the genus Hippelates. The so-called Texas fever of cattle is unquestionably transferred by the common cattle-tick, and this was the earliest of the clearly demonstrated cases of the transfer of disease by insects. In Africa a similar disease of cattle is transferred by the bite of the famous biting fly known as the tsetse-fly. The germs of the disease of cattle known as anthrax are carried by gadflies, or horse-flies, and when these flies subsequently bite human beings malignant pustules may result. And other discoveries of this nature are constantly being made. Even the common bedbug is strongly suspected in this connection."

These statements are not guesses; they are proved facts of science. It will be some time before these facts and their significance receive their full recognition in medical practice; the knowledge of medicine is always in advance of its practical recognition. But modern medical practice is much swifter to incorporate the new facts of biology than was the practice of even a decade or two ago, and in such lines of work as army and other governmental service the new methods of preventive medicine are quickly adopted. Already there are organized movements all over the world to make use of the new knowledge concerning the relation of insects to human disease. As I write these pages comes the report of the work of Major Ronald Ross, one of the discoverers of the malaria-disseminating capacity of the mosquito and one of the leaders in the anti-mosquito crusade, in nearly stamping out malaria in the long notorious pest-hole of Ismailia. Malarial cases have been reduced there from 300,000 cases annually to 300, by effective war on mosquitoes. Dr. Cruz reports that Rio Janeiro has abolished its old-fashioned quarantine regulations, and vessels with yellow fever on board will hereafter simply be disinfected and supervised. In October, 1903, Cruz directed the operations of twelve hundred men specially employed in destroying the larvæ of the mosquito in their breeding-places in and around the city, and as a result only nine cases of yellow fever developed in the midsummer months of January and February (1904), as against 275 cases in the same months in 1903. In the period from 1850 to 1896, 51,600 deaths occurred in Rio Janeiro from this disease, and at times as many as 2000 patients have been cared for in the isolation hospital, which is now closed. The benefits of the war waged on the mosquito at Rio Janeiro have been as great as those obtained at Havana, where the vigorous work of the American authorities during our occupation of the islands practically stamped out yellow fever in a city long notorious the world over as a plague-center.

**Mosquitoes and malaria.**—First of these known cases of the dissemination of human disease by insects to be worked out in detail was the relation of mosquitoes to the breeding and distribution of the causative germs of malaria. Malarial fevers occur the world over and have long been associated in the popular mind with low wet localities or with localities near marsh or swamp. Mosquitoes live in great abundance precisely in such regions, but for a long time no association between mosquitoes and malaria was even suspected. Miasma, the effluvia from low wet ground, was held to be the causative, or at least carrying, agent of malaria. It was not until 1880, when Laveran discovered and described the actual parasitic sporozoon (minute one-celled amœba-like animal) of malaria, that the actual cause of the disease was recognized.

Malaria as we know it in the United States is a wide-spread and serious disease, but not commonly a fatal one. But in India five million deaths occurred in a single year, 1897, from malarial fever. Giles declares that the malarial parasite is responsible for by far the greatest proportion of all sickness and death in the tropics. "Cholera and plague," he says, "are the insignificant enemies that perhaps kill a few thousands a year—in an impressive way, it is true; but the quiet insidious malaria sweeps off its millions." The serious state of affairs in India, as well as on the Gold Coast of Africa, on the Roman Campagna, and in other notoriously malaria-stricken regions, finally led to careful scientific study of the life-history of the malaria-producing sporozoon by well-trained English and Italian physicians and naturalists, with the result that we now know in definite and accurate detail the whole marvelous story of the interrelations of the malarial parasite, the mosquito, and the human host.

Lankester was the first to find an amœba-like parasite living in the blood of animals, *Drepanidium ranarum* of frog's blood, but since his discovery numerous other similar protozoon blood-parasites, collectively called Hæmatozoa, have been found in reptiles, birds, bats, cattle, and monkeys. The hæmatozoon infesting cattle discovered by Theobald Smith, an American investigator, produces the disease known as Texas fever, and is spread from animal to animal by ticks. The particular blood-parasites, called Hæmamœbæ, which produce malarial fevers, are not restricted to man alone, but infest birds, bats, and monkeys as well.

In 1885 Golgi discovered that the malaria-producing Hæmamœbæ of the human body exist in three varieties, each apparently responsible for one of the three well-known types of malarial fever, namely, quartan, tertian, and remittent.   And soon after 1885, Golgi and other investigators, Italian, English, and American (Celli, Grassi, Mannaberg, Bignami, Danielewsky, Carter, Osler, Labbé, Koch, Manson, Councilman, Thayer, MacCallum, and others), succeeded in working out in minute detail the behavior, development, and pathological effects, direct and indirect, of the parasites in the human blood.   From these researches I may summarize the life of the malaria-producing Hæmamœbæ in the human body as follows: The youngest parasites, or amœbulæ, are found living within the red blood-corpuscles; here they grow at the expense of the corpuscle substance.   They increase rapidly in size, while the blood-corpuscle begins to degenerate.   From the breaking down of the hæmoglobin of the corpuscle, due to the metabolism of the

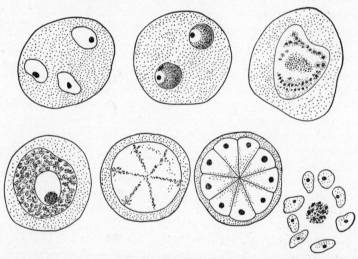

Fig. 798.—Diagrammatic figure of stages in the development of the malaria-producing Hæmamœba (Plasmodium) in a red blood-corpuscle of the human body.

parasite, granules of a blackish pigment are formed; this is the melanin long known as a regular diagnostic characteristic of malaria.   After a few days, from one to several depending on the variety of the Hæmamœba, the amoebulæ reach maturity.   They begin now to sporulate; that is, the nucleus and cytoplasm divide into many small parts, each nuclear part having aggregated about it part of the cytoplasm.   The walls of the blood-corpuscle then break, and these many Hæmamœba spores are released into the blood-plasma. Each of these spores soon attaches itself to a fresh blood-corpuscle, penetrates it, and begins a new life-cycle.   It is obvious that such a parasitic life in the blood-corpuscles, using up their substance and breaking them down, must work much harm to the human body. This harm is exactly that which we recognize as the result of malaria. The fever and other ills that are a part of malaria are the direct and indirect pathological effects of the growth and metabolism and multiplication of the Hæmamœbæ in our blood. From a single infection the sporulation or escape of the myriads of spores from the breaking-down corpuscles into the blood-plasma takes place practically simultaneously and makes the beginning of the malarial spasm. This kind of multiplication of the Hæmamœbæ, by sporulation, is termed asexual; there is no participation of individuals of two kinds, or sexes, in the reproduction. It is a sort of multiplication common to a great many minute, simple animals and plants, but it does not seem in any of these to be the only mode of multiplication. Scores, even hundreds, of successive generations may be produced asexually, but finally there occurs another kind of reproduction, which has for its essential characteristic the meeting and fusing of the nuclei or parts of them, and sometimes the body protoplasm or parts of it, of two individuals of the species. In all but the very simplest organisms these two conjugating individuals differ somewhat in size, shape, and manner of behavior. Scientists began to ask when and how and where conjugation occurred in the Hæmamœbæ of malaria; their questioning was made more insistent by the discovery that some of the amœbulæ in the blood-corpuscles did not sporulate, but continued to circulate in the blood without any particular function at all. More than that, it was noted that whenever they were withdrawn from the circulation, as when a drop of blood was taken out of the skin with a pipette for examination under the microscope, these traveling amœbulæ would swell up and liberate themselves from their enclosing corpuscle, and that some of them would emit a number of long motile filaments; these filaments could be seen lashing about strongly, and often succeeded in breaking away from the parent cell, and darting away among the corpuscles. This phenomenon can always be observed in the blood drawn from a malarial patient, in from ten to fifteen minutes after its withdrawal from the circulation. What is the meaning of it? A further insistent question came up at this time. And that is, If the Hæmamœbæ are the actual and sole cause of malaria, how do they get from man to man? How is the malaria disseminated?

The explanation of the significance of the phenomenon of the formation of the motile filaments from amœbulæ in blood withdrawn from circulation, and the answer to the question as to the mode of transmissibility of malaria, are closely connected, and were reached chiefly through the brilliant work of Manson and Ross, two English investigators of tropical diseases. Especially interesting is the work of Ross in establishing the actual fact of the carrying by the mosquito of the Hæmamœbæ from man to man. The following long quotation from Ross, taken from a lecture delivered by him on March 2, 1900, before the Royal Institution of Great Britain, gives a detailed account of this work, answers both the questions asked above, and at the same time serves to reveal a typical instance of the faith and persistence of the men to whom we owe scientific progress.

"It was reserved for Manson," says Ross, "to detect the ultimate (though not the immediate) functions of these bodies [the motile filaments]. He asked why the escape of the motile filaments occurs only after the blood is abstracted from the host (a fact agreed upon by many observers). From his study of these filaments, of their form and their characteristic movements, he rejected the Italian view that they are regressive forms; he was convinced that they are living elements. Hence he felt that the fact of their appearance only *after* abstraction from the blood (about fifteen minutes afterwards) must have some definite purpose in the life-scheme of the parasites. What is that purpose? It is evident that these parasites, like all others, must pass from host to host; all known parasites are capable of not only entering the host, but, either in themselves or their progeny, of leaving him. Manson himself had already pushed such methods of inductive reasoning to a brilliantly successful issue in discovering by their means the development of *Filaria nocturna* in the gnat. He now applied the same methods to the study of the parasites of malaria. Why should the motile filaments appear only after abstraction of the blood? There could be only one explanation. The phenomenon, though it is usually observed in a preparation for the microscope, is really meant to occur *within the stomach-cavity of some suctorial insect, and constitutes the first step in the life-history of the parasite outside the vertebrate host.*

"It is perhaps impossible for any one, except one who has spent years in revolving the subject, to understand the full value and force of this remarkable induction. To my mind the reasoning is complete and exigent. It was from the first impossible to consider the subject in the light which Manson placed it without feeling convinced that the parasite requires a suctorial insect for its further development. And subsequent events have proved Manson to have been right.

"The most evident reasoning—the connection between malarial fever and low-lying water-logged areas in warm countries—suggested at once that the suctorial insect must be the *gnat* (called *mosquito* in the tropics); and this view was fortified by numerous analogies which must occur at once to any one who considers the subject at all, and which it is not necessary to discuss in this place.

"Needless to say, since Manson's theory was proved to be the right one it has been shown to be not entirely original. Nuttall, in his admirable history of the mosquito theory, demonstrates its antiquity. Eleven years before Manson wrote, King had already accumulated much evidence, based on epidemiological data, in favor of the theory. A year later (1884), Laveran himself briefly enunciated the same views, on the analogy with *Filaria nocturna*. Koch and, later, Bignami and Mendini were also advocates of the theory—partly on epidemiological grounds and partly because of a possible analogy with the protozoal parasites of Texas cattle-fever which Smith and Kilborne had shown to be carried by a *tick*. Hence many observers had independently arrived at the same theory by different routes. . . .

"To leave these interesting theories and to return to actual observations—I should begin by remarking that Manson thought the motile filaments to be of the nature of zoospores—that is, motile spores which escape from the gametocytes in the stomach-cavity of the gnat, and then occupy and infest the tissues of the insect. In this he was proved, two years later, to have been wrong. The motile filaments are not spores, but *microgametes*—that is, bodies of the nature of spermatozoa. I have said that some of the amœbulæ in the blood-corpuscles of the host become sporocytes, which produce asexual spores (nomospores); while other amœbulæ become gametocytes, which have no function within the vertebrate host. As soon, however, as these gametocytes are ingested by a suctorial insect they commence their proper functions. As their name indicates, they are sexual cells—male and female. About fifteen minutes after ingestion (in some species) the male gametocytes emit a variable number of microgametes—the motile filaments—which presently escape and wander in search of the female gametocytes. These contain a single *macrogamete*, or ovum, which is now fertilized by one of the microgametes, and becomes a zygote. We owe this beautiful discovery to the direct observation of MacCallum (1897), confirmed by Koch and Marchoux, and indirectly by Bignami. . . . Directly MacCallum's discovery was announced Manson saw the important bearing of it on the mosquito. Admitting that the motile filaments themselves do not infect the gnat, he at once observed that it was probably the function of the zygote to do so—and this time he was perfectly right.

"I must now turn to my own researches. Dr. Manson told me of his theory at the end of 1894, and I then undertook to investigate the subject as far as possible. I began work in Secunderabad, India, in April, 1895; and should take the present opportunity for acknowledging the continuous assistance and advice which I received from Dr. Manson and from Dr. Laveran, and later from the Government of India. Even with the aid of the induction the task so lightly commenced was, as a matter of fact, one of so arduous a nature that we must attribute its accomplishment largely to good fortune. The method adopted—the only method which could be adopted—was to feed gnats of various species on persons whose blood contained the gametocytes, and then to examine the insects carefully for the parasites which by hypothesis the gametocytes were expected to develop into. This required not only familiarity with the histology of gnats, but a laborious search for a minute organism throughout the whole tissues of each individual insect examined—a work of at least two or three hours for each gnat. But the actual labor involved was the smallest part of the difficulty. Both the form and appearance of the object which I was in search of, and the species of the gnat in which I might expect to find it, were absolutely unknown quantities. We could make no attempt to predict the appearance which the parasite would assume in the gnat; while owing to the general distribution of malarial fever in India, the species of insect concerned in the propagation of the disease could scarcely be determined by a comparison of the prevalence of different kinds of gnat at different spots with the prevalence of fever at those spots. In short, I was forced to rely simply on the careful examinations of hundreds of gnats, first of one species and then of another, all fed on patients suffering from malarial fever—in the hope of one day finding the clue I was in search of. Needless to say, nothing but the most convincing theory, such as Manson's theory was, would have supported or justified so difficult an enterprise.

"As a matter of fact, for nearly two and a half years my researches were almost entirely negative. I could not obtain the correct scientific names of the various species of gnats employed by me in these researches, and consequently used names of my own. Gnats of the genus *Culex* (which abound almost everywhere in India) I called 'gray' and 'brindled' mosquitoes; and it was these insects which I studied during the period referred to. At last, the particular nugatory results which had been obtained with gnats of this genus determined me to try other methods. I went to a very malarious locality, called the Sigur Ghat, near Ootacamund, and examined the mosquitoes there in the hope of finding within them parasites like those of malaria in man. The results were practically worthless (except that I observed a new kind of mosquito with spotted wings); and I saw that I must return to the exact methods laid down by Manson. The experiments with the two commonest kinds of Culex were once more repeated—only to prove once more negative. The insects, fed mostly on cases containing the crescentic gametocytes of *Hæmomenas præcox*, were examined cell by cell—not even their excrement being neglected. Although they were known to have swallowed Hæmamœbidæ, no living parasites like these could be detected in their tissues—the ingested Hæmamœbidæ had in fact perished in the stomach-cavity of the insects. I began to ask whether after all there was not some flaw in Manson's induction; but no—I still felt his conclusion to be an inevitable one. And it was at this moment that good fortune gave me what I was in search of.

"In a collecting-bottle full of larvæ brought in by a native from unknown source I found a number of newly hatched mosquitoes like those first observed by me in Sigur Ghat—namely, mosquitoes with *spotted wings* and *boat-shaped* eggs. Eight of these were fed on a patient whose blood contained crescentic gametocytes. Unfortunately I dissected six of them either prematurely or otherwise unsatisfactorily. The seventh was examined, on August 20, cell by cell; the tissues of the stomach (which was now empty owing to the meal of malarial blood taken by the insect four days previously being digested) were reserved to the last. On turning to this organ I was struck by observing, scattered on its outer surface, certain oval or round cells of about two or three times the diameter of a red blood-corpuscle—cells which I had never before seen in any of the hundreds of mosquitoes examined by me. My surprise was complete when I next detected within each of these cells *a few granules of the characteristic coal-black melanin of malarial fever*—a substance quite unlike anything usually found in mosquitoes. Next day the last of the remaining spotted-winged mosquitoes was dissected. It contained precisely similar cells, each of which possessed the same melanin; only the cells in the second mosquito *were somewhat larger than those in the first.*

"These fortunate observations practically solve the malarial problem. As a matter of fact, the cells were the *zygotes of the parasite of remittent fever growing in the tissues of the gnat;* and the gnat with spotted wings and boat-shaped eggs in which I had found them belonged (as I subsequently ascertained) to the genus *Anopheles*. Of course it was impossible absolutely to prove at the time, on the strength of these two observations alone, that the cells found by me in the gnats were indeed derived from Hæmamœbidæ sucked up by the insects in the blood of the patients on whom they had been fed—this proof was obtained by subsequent investigations of mine; but, guided by the presence of the typical and almost unique melanin in the cells, and by numerous other circumstances, I myself had no doubt of the fact. The clue was obtained; it was necessary only to follow it up—an easy matter. . . .

"Early in 1898, mainly through the influence of Dr. Manson, Sir H. W. Bliss, and the United Planters' Association of Southern India, I was placed by the Government of India on special duty in Calcutta to continue my investigations. Unable to work with human malaria—chiefly on account of the plague-scare in Calcutta—I turned my attention to the Hæmamœbidæ of birds. Birds have at least two species of Hæmamœbidæ. I subjected a number of birds containing one or the other of these parasites to the bites of various species of mosquitoes. The result was a repetition of that previously obtained with the human parasites. Pigmented cells precisely similar to those seen in the *Anopheles* were found to appear in gnats of the species called *Culex fatigans* Wiedemann, when these had been fed on sparrows and larks containing *Hæmamœba relicta*. On the other hand, these cells were never found in insects of the same species when fed on healthy birds or on birds containing the other parasite, called *Hæmamæba danilewskii*.

"It will be evident that this fact was the crucial test both as regards the parastic nature of these cells and as regards their development from the hæmocytozoa of the birds; and it was not accepted by me without very close and laborious experiment. The actual results obtained were as follows:

"Out of 245 *Culex fatigans* fed on birds containing *H. relicta* 178, or 72 per cent., contained 'pigmented cells.' But, out of 41 *Culex fatigans* fed on a man containing crescentic gametocytes, 5 on a man containing immature tertian parasites, 154 on birds containing *H. danilewskii*, 25 on healthy sparrows, and 24 on birds with immature *H. relicta*—or a total of 249 insects, all carefully examined—not one contained a single 'pigmented cell.'

"Another experiment was as follows: Three sparrows, one containing no parasites, another containing a moderate number of *H. relicta*, and the third containing numerous *H. relicta*, were placed in separate cages within three separate mosquito-curtains. A number of *Culex fatigans*, all bred simultaneously from larvæ in the same breeding-bottle, were now liberated on the same evening partly within the first mosquito-netting, partly within the second, and partly within the third. Next morning many of these gnats were found to have fed themselves on the birds during the night. Ten of each lot of gnats were dissected after a few days, with the following result:

"The ten gnats fed on the healthy sparrow contained no 'pigmented cells.' The ten gnats fed on the sparrow with a moderate number of parasites were found to contain altogether 202 'pigmented cells,' or an average of 29 in each gnat. The ten gnats fed on the sparrow with numerous parasites contained 1009 'pigmented cells,' or an average of 100 cells in each gnat. These thirty specimens were sent to Manson in England, who made a similar count of the cells.

"I may mention one more out of several experiments of the same kind. A stock of *Culex fatigans*, all bred from the larva, were fed on the same night partly on two sparrows containing *H. relicta*, and partly on a crow containing *H. danilewskii* (placed, of course, under separate mosquito-nettings). Out of 23 of the former lot, 22 were found to have pigmented cells; while out of 16 of the latter, none had them.

"Hence no doubt remained that the 'pigmented cells' really constitute a developmental stage in the mosquito of these parasites; and this view was accepted both by Laveran and Manson, to whom specimens had been sent. In June, 1898, Manson published an illustrated paper concerning my researches, and showed that the pigmented cells must in fact be the zygotes resulting from the process of fertilization discovered by MacCallum.

"It remained to follow out the life-history of the zygotes. For this purpose it was immaterial whether I worked with the avian or the human parasites, since these are so extremely like each other. I elected to work with the avian species, chiefly because the plague-scare in Bengal still rendered observations with the human species almost impossible. By feeding *Culex fatigans* on birds with *H. relicta* and then examining the insects one, two, three or more days afterwards, it was easy to trace the gradual growth of the zygotes. Their development briefly is as follows: After the fertilization of the macrogamete has taken place in the stomach-cavity of the gnat, the fertilized parasite or zygote has the power of working its way through the mass of blood contained in the stomach, of penetrating the wall of the organ, and of affixing itself on, or just under, its *outer coat*. Here it first appears about thirty-six hours after the insect was fed, and is found as a 'pigmented cell'—that is, a little oval body, about the size of a large red corpuscle, and containing the granules of melanin possessed by the parent gametocyte from which the macrogamete originally proceeded. In this position it shows no sign of movement, but begins to grow rapidly, to acquire a thickened capsule, and to project from the outer wall of the stomach, to which it is attached, into the *body-cavity* of the insect-host. At the end of six days, if the temperature of the air be sufficiently high (about 80° F.), the diameter of the zygote has increased to about eight times what it was at first; that is, to about 60 microns. If the stomach of an infected insect be extracted at this stage, it can be seen, by a low power of the microscope, to be studded with a number of attached spheres, which have something of the appearance of warts on a finger. These are the large zygotes, which have now reached maturity and which project prominently into the mosquito's body-cavity.

"All this could be ascertained with facility by the method I have mentioned: and it should be understood that gnats can be kept alive for weeks or even months by feeding them every few days on blood, or, as Bancroft does, on bananas. But a most important point still required study. What happens after the zygotes reach maturity? I found that each zygote as it increases in size divides into *meres*, each of which next becomes a *blastophore* carrying a number of *blasts* attached to its surface. Finally, the blastophore vanishes, leaving the thick capsule of the zygote packed with thousands of the blasts. The capsule now *ruptures*, and allows the blasts to escape into the body-fluids of the insect.

"These blasts, when mature, are seen to be minute filamentous bodies, about 12–6$\mu$ in length, of extreme delicacy, and somewhat spindle-shaped— that is, tapering at each extremity. Prof. Herdman and I have adopted this word 'blast' for these bodies after careful consideration, but others prefer other names. They are, of course, *spores;* but spores which have been produced by a previous sexual process, and are in fact the result of a kind of *polembryony*. Just as a fertilized ovum gives rise to blasts, which produce the cluster of cells constituting a multicellular animal, so, in this case, the fertilized ovum, or zygote, gives rise to blasts, each of which, however, becomes a separate animal. Prof. Ray Lankester suggests for the blasts of the Hæmamœbidæ the simple term 'filiform young.'

"At this point the investigations took a turn of extreme interest and importance, scarcely second even to that attached to the first study of the zygotes. Since the blasts are evidently the progeny of the zygotes, they must carry on the life-history of the parasites to a further stage. How do they do so? What is their function? Do they escape from the mosquito, and in some manner, direct or indirect, set up infection in healthy men or birds? Or, if not, what other purpose do they subserve? It was evident that our knowledge of the mode of infection in malarial fever—and perhaps even the prevention of the disease—depended on a reply to these questions.

"As I have said, the zygotes become ripe and rupture about a week after the insect was first infected—scattering the blasts into the body-cavity of the host. What happens next? It was next seen that by some process, apparently owing to the circulation of the insect's body-fluids (for the blasts themselves appear to be almost without movement), these little bodies find their way into every part of the mosquito—into the juices of its head, thorax, and even legs. Beyond this it was difficult to go. All theory—at least all theory which I felt I could depend upon—had been long left behind, and I could rely only on direct observation. Gnat after gnat was sacrificed in the attempt to follow these bodies. At last, while examining the head and thorax of one insect, I found a large gland consisting of a central duct surrounded by large grape-like cells. My astonishment was great when I found that many of these cells were closely packed with the blasts (which I may add are not in the least like any normal structures in the mosquito). Now I did not know at that time what this gland was. It was speedily found, however, to be a large racemose gland consisting of six lobes, three lying in each side of the insect's neck. The ducts of the lobes finally unite in a common channel which runs along the under surface of the head and enters the middle stylet, or lancet, of the insect's proboscis.

"It was impossible to avoid the obvious conclusion. Observation after observation always showed that the blasts invariably collect within the cells of this gland. It is the salivary or poison gland of the insect, similar to the salivary gland found in many insects, the function of which, in the gnat, had already been discovered—although I was not aware of the fact. The function is to secrete the fluid which is injected by the insect when it punctures the skin—the fluid which causes the well-known irritation of the puncture, and which is probably meant either to prevent the contraction of the torn capillaries or the coagulation of the ingested blood. The position of the blasts in the cells of this gland could have only one interpretation—

wonderful as that interpretation is. The blast must evidently pass down the ducts of the salivary gland into the wound made by the proboscis of the insect, and thus cause infection in a fresh vertebrate host.

"That this actually happens could, fortunately, be proved without difficulty. As I had now been studying the parasites of birds for some months, I possess a number of birds of different species, the blood of which I had examined from time to time (by pricking the toes with a fine needle). Some of them were infected, and some, of course, were not. Out of 111 wild sparrows examined by me in Calcutta, I had found *H. relicta*—the parasite which I had just cultivated in *Culex fatigans*—in 15, or 13.5 per cent. As a rule, non-infected birds were released; but I generally kept a few for the control experiments mentioned above, and the blood of these birds had consequently been examined on several occasions, and had always been found free from parasites. At the end of June I possessed five of these healthy control birds— four sparrows and one weaver-bird. All of them were now carefully examined again and found healthy. They were placed in their cages within mosquito- nets, and at the same time a large stock of old infected mosquitoes were released within the same nets. By 'old infected mosquitoes' I mean mosquitoes which had been previously repeatedly fed on infected birds, and many of which on dissection had been shown to have a very large number of blasts in their salivary glands. Next morning numbers of these infected gnats were found gorged with blood, proving that they had indeed bitten the healthy birds during the night. The operation was repeated on several succeeding nights, until each bird had probably been bitten by at least a dozen of the mosquitoes. On July 9 the blood of the birds was examined again. I scarcely expected any result so complete and decisive. Every one of the five birds was now found to contain parasites—and not merely to contain them, but to possess such immense numbers of them as I had never before seen in any bird (with *H. relicta*) in India. While wild sparrows in Calcutta seldom contain more than one parasite in every field of the micro- scope, those which I had just succeeded in infecting contained ten, fifteen, and even more in each field—a fact due probably to the infecting gnats having been previously fed over and over again on infected birds, a thing which can rarely happen in nature.

"The experiment was repeated many times—generally on two or three healthy birds put together. But now I improved on the original experiment by also employing controls in the following manner: A stock of wild sparrows would be examined, and the infected birds eliminated. The remainder would then be kept apart, and at night would be carefully excluded from the bites of gnats by being placed within mosquito-nets. These constituted my stock of healthy birds. From time to time two or three of these would be separated, examined again to insure their being absolutely free from parasites, and then subjected to the bites of 'old infected mosquitoes,' and, of course, kept apart afterwards for daily study. Thus my stock of healthy birds was also my stock of control birds. Until they were bitten by gnats, I found that they never became infected (except in a single case in which I think I had overlooked the parasites on the first occasion), although large numbers of healthy birds were kept in this manner. The results in the case of the sparrows which were subjected to the bite of the infected gnats were different, indeed. Out of 28 of these, dealt with from time to time, no less than 22, or 79 per cent., became infected in from five to eight days. And, as in the first experiment, all the infected birds finally contained very numerous parasites.

"It was most interesting to watch the gradual development of the parasitic invasion in these birds; and this development presented such constant characters that, apart from other reasons, it was quite impossible to doubt that the infection was really caused by mosquitoes. The course of events was always as follows: The blood would remain entirely free from parasites for four, five, six, or even seven days. Next day one or perhaps two parasites would be found in a whole specimen. The following day it was invariably observed that the number of organisms had largely increased; and this increase continued until in a few days immense numbers were present—so that, finally, I often observed as many as seven distinct parasites contained within a single corpuscle! Later on many of the birds died; and their organs were found to be loaded with the characteristic melanin of malarial fever.

"I also succeeded in infecting on a second trial one of the six sparrows which had escaped the first experiment; and also a crow and four weaver-birds; and, lastly, gave a new and more copious infection to four sparrows which had previously contained only a few parasites.

"These experiments completed the original and fundamental observations on the life-history of the Hæmamœbidæ in mosquitoes. The parasites had been carried from the vertebrate host into the gnat, and had finally been carried back from the gnat to the vertebrate host. The theories of King, Laveran, Koch, and Bignami, and the great induction of Manson, were justified by the event: and I have given a detailed historical and critical account of these theories, and of my own difficulties, in the hope of bringing conviction to those who might perhaps otherwise think the story to be too wonderful for credence."

Since Ross's work, a host of new observations and facts have been made known by various investigators. All of these studies only add to the certainty that the malaria parasite depends absolutely upon mosquitoes for its full development and for its dissemination. Many of these observations and experiments have to do with actual tests of malaria prevention. Conspicuous among these tests was that of two English physicians, Sambon and Low, in 1900, in the "malaria-house" in the Roman Campagna. This experiment is described by Howard as follows: "Doctors Sambon and Low had constructed a comfortable little five-roomed wooden house about three hours' drive from Ostia, in one of the most malarious portions of the Campagna. The house was tightly built and was thoroughly screened. The experimenters lived in this house through the period when malaria is most prevalent. They took no quinine and no health precautions beyond the fact that at sundown each day they entered the house and remained there until daylight the next morning. Dr. Rees, of the London School, visited them and occupied the house with them for a portion of the time, and all three conducted laboratory work in one of the rooms, which was fully equipped for such a purpose, and led a busy and contented life. They visited the neighboring villages and investigated outbreaks of the fever in men and cattle. They received and entertained many visitors who were interested in the experiment. They turned indoors before six o'clock and then stood at the windows and timed the first appearance of Anopheles, which would come at a certain hour each evening and try to enter the screened windows and doors. As Dr. Rees expressed it, 'It must have been very tantalizing for them to be unable to get at us.' When the rains set in, every one said that that was the critical time of the experiment. The people in the surrounding country generally became feverish and ill, which meant simply that they were all full of malaria, and the chilling caused by the rain brought about an explosion of the fever. The experimenters, however, went out into the rain and got soaked to the skin, but their health remained perfect. Not the slightest trace of malaria developed in either of them; as above stated, the spot where the house was built was probably the most malarious one in the whole Campagna, and it was situated on the banks of one of the canals, which was literally swarming with Anopheles larvæ. The prevalent idea that the night air of the Campagna is in itself so dangerous was included in the experiments, and the windows were always left open at night, so that if the marsh air had anything to do with malaria they would have contracted it.

"A check experiment was carried on at the same time. Anopheles mosquitoes which had been fed on the blood of a sufferer from malaria in Rome, under the direction of the Italian authority Bastianelli, were sent to London early in July. A son of Dr. Patrick Manson, the famous investigator who first proved the transfer of filariæ by mosquitoes, offered himself as a subject for experiment, and allowed himself to be bitten by the mosquitoes. He had never been in a malarious country since he was a child, but in due time was taken with a well-marked malarial infection of the double tertian type, and microscopical examination showed the presence of numerous parasites in his blood."

Another test in the same year was made by Professor Grassi near Salerno. "The objects of this experiment were," writes Howard, "(1) to afford absolute proof of the fact that malaria is transmitted exclusively by the bite of Anopheles mosquitoes; (2) to found, on the results of recent research, a code of rules to be adopted for freeing Italy from malaria in a few years. The experiment consisted in protecting from malaria railway employees and their families, living in ten cottages, at the stations of St. Nicolo, Varco, and Albanella, situated along the Battipaglia-Reggio Railway. They numbered one hundred and four persons, including thirty-three children under ten years of age. Of these one hundred and four individuals, at least eleven, including four children, had never suffered from the disease, not having previously lived in a malarious district; a certain number, it appeared, had not suffered from it in two or three years, and all the others, that is to say, the large majority, had suffered from it during the last malarial season, some of them even in the winter. During the malarial season the health of the protected individuals was good, with the exception of a few cases of bronchitis and a case of acute gastro-enteritis. None of these cases was treated with quinine. The one hundred and four persons, with three exceptions, had remained free from malaria up to September 16th, the date of the report."

These two experiments alone would be conclusive. Since 1900, however, the brilliantly successful results of actual practical measures undertaken on a large scale in Africa under the supervision of English experts, and in many European and American localities by army, governmental, and municipal authorities, have settled the matter of malaria infection for all time. It only remains now to adopt in medical practice everywhere and in the work of boards of health, other municipal and country boards of supervision, the efficacious methods, well proved, of fighting malaria by fighting mosquitoes. An account of some of these methods, together with the facts of the life-history of mosquitoes, and information regarding the distinguishing characters of the malaria-bearers (Anopheles) and the non-malarial kinds (Culex and others), are given on pp. 305 et seq. of this book. In addition I may simply say, *when in malarial regions avoid the bite of a mosquito as you would that of a rattlesnake.* One can be quite as serious in its results as the other.

**Mosquitoes and yellow fever.**—So much space has been given to the account of the relation of mosquitoes to the propagation and dissemination of malaria that we can do only scant justice to the mosquitoes in their rôle as disseminators of other diseases.

Although yellow fever is a plague long known and one much studied, so that its diagnosis and its treatment are well understood and are the necessary knowledge of every physician practicing in tropical regions, and although we know certainly that it is the result of the growth in the body of a parasitic organism, and that this organism is disseminated by mosquitoes, infection being accomplished only by the puncture of a mosquito, it is a curious fact that the causative germ or parasite has not yet been isolated; in other words, is not yet specifically known. Whether bacterium or sporozoon, whether inhabiting the blood solely or occurring also in other tissues, answers to these questions remain to be discovered. Numerous claims have been made by various physicians of the discovery of the parasite; the latest claim has been published within the last few months, but so far none of these reputed determinations of the yellow-fever parasite has been proved to the satisfaction of scientific men. That the yellow-fever germ, whatever it is, is however actually carried by mosquitoes, *and apparently in no other way*, and that the dissemination of the disease thus depends upon the intervention and aid of mosquitoes, are facts that have been proved largely through the able and courageous work of American investigators.

An early suggestion that mosquitoes might be the agents in spreading yellow fever came from an Havana physician, Dr. Carlos Finlay. His theory was based chiefly on observations of the correspondence between an abundance of mosquitoes and a period of increase of yellow fever. In 1900 an Army Yellow Fever Commission, composed of Major Walter C. Reed, surgeon, U. S. A., and three acting assistant surgeons was appointed by Surgeon-General Sternberg to investigate the disease. Two members of the Commission, Major Reed and Dr. Lazear, lost their lives from the attacks of the disease they were studying. The Commission was soon able to report that yellow fever followed the bite of mosquitoes of the species *Stegomyia fasciata*, after the mosquitoes had first been allowed to suck blood from yellow-fever patients. Soon after it was able to report that yellow fever did not follow as a result of exposing non-immune subjects to contact with clothes or bedding or other belongings of patients actually suffering and dying from yellow fever. On the basis of these discoveries the Commission made certain crucial experiments whose outcome is convincing proof of the facts of the transmission of the disease by mosquitoes, and that it is transmitted in no other way.

A small house was built, thoroughly screened against mosquitoes. In this house seven non-immune persons lived during sixty-three days; three of them occupied the room each night for twenty days, sleeping on sheets, pillow-cases, and blankets brought from beds occupied by yellow-fever patients in Havana, soiled by their discharges. Some of the bedding and clothing worn by the subjects in the yellow-fever house were purposely infected with the discharges of a fatal case of yellow fever. During all the sixty-three days the average temperature of the house was kept at 76.2° F., a considerable amount of humidity was maintained, and little sunlight or freely circulating air was admitted, all of these conditions being highly favorable for the development of yellow fever. Not a single one of the seven inhabitants of the house was attacked by the disease.

Another similar building was erected near by, well provided with doors and windows for thorough ventilation. It was divided into two rooms by a wire-screen partition extending from floor to ceiling. All articles admitted to the building were carefully disinfected by steam before being placed therein. Into the large room of this building mosquitoes which had been previously contaminated by biting yellow-fever patients were admitted. Non-immunes were placed in both rooms. In the room in which mosquitoes were not admitted the experimentalists remained in perfect health. In the other room six out of seven persons bitten by infested mosquitoes came down with yellow fever. In all, of persons bitten by infested mosquitoes that had been kept twelve days or more after biting yellow-fever patients before being allowed to bite them, 80 per cent. were taken with the disease.

Other similar crucial tests were made by the Commission and have been made by other investigators working in other places. The conclusions are positive. Yellow fever is caused by a germ, as yet undetermined, which lives for part of its life in the blood of human beings, and is carried from man to man by mosquitoes, being sucked up with blood by mosquitoes which find access to yellow-fever patients, and transmitted to the blood of new subjects from the beak during puncturing. An interval of about two weeks after the mosquito is affected is necessary before the mosquito is capable of conveying the infection, which means that the yellow-fever germ is undergoing a certain necessary part of its development in the mosquito's body.

As I have already mentioned (p. 308), the mosquito species *Stegomyia fasciata*, the carrier of the yellow fever in the West Indies, is the most abundant mosquito species in the Hawaiian Islands and also in the Samoan Islands. In neither of these groups of tropic islands has yellow fever yet found a footing, but is it not possible that with the cutting of the Panama Canal and the direct passage of ships from the West Indies to these islands, the whole passage being made within tropical regions, yellow-fever-infested mosquitoes will be carried alive to the Pacific islands? It is certainly a matter which must receive scientific attention.

**Mosquitoes and filariasis.**—Filariasis is the rather generic term for a number of diseases, or for one disease which manifests itself in several ways, due to the presence in the body of the infected patient of filariæ or thread-worms.

These organisms are of much higher organization than the minute unicellular Hæmamœbæ that cause malaria; they belong to the group of round-worms, the Nematoda, and in fully developed condition some species of filariæ are very long, the notorious guinea-worm, *Filaria medinensis*, which parasitizes the human body in the tropics of the Old World, attaining a length of three feet. Other species vary from an inch to a foot in length. All the species of the genus Filaria are parasites of other animals living mostly in the stomach and intestine, sometimes in the connecting tissue and elsewhere in the body. One species lives in the heart of dogs, another in the body-cavity of the horse, donkey, and ox, still another in the eyes of negroes in West Africa, while *Filaria bancrofti*, the particular species which is the cause of filariasis, lives in the blood and lymphatic vessels of men in tropic lands of both Old and New World. The young or larval filariæ (sometimes called *F. sanguinis-hominis*) live in the blood, but they finally lodge in the lymphatic glands and there mature.

The most common form of filariasis is called elephantiasis. The presence of the parasite in the lymphatic glands and vessels leads to a subcutaneous hypertrophy of tissue which often results in a most frightful malformation of parts of the body. The legs and arms are particularly affected, and such a member may become of enormous size and be hideously repulsive in appearance. A single leg may come to weigh as much as all the rest of the body. An arm may become a foot thick, the fingers being mere papillar-like processes at the end of it. In Samoa fully one-third of the natives are attacked by this disease, which is incurable, and, though slow in development and nearly painless, certainly fatal.

Manson, to whose keen inductions much of the credit for the discovery of the relation between the mosquito and malaria is due, was the first to suggest, on a basis of some observation and special investigation, that the mosquito is the secondary or intermediate host of the elephantiasis-producing filariæ and that the mosquito is probably responsible for the dissemination of the disease.

The subsequent researches of Manson, Bancroft, and others have proved that the filariæ actually do live in the bodies of mosquitoes, being taken into the alimentary canal with the blood sucked from men affected by the disease. These filariæ work their way through the walls of the alimentary canal and gather in the thoracic muscles. Here they live for some time, two or three weeks probably, and are then ready for their further development in the blood and lymph of man. Exactly how this transfer is made is not definitely proved as yet, although much evidence has been secured to show that the transmission is made by the mosquito-bite. Manson suggested that the female mosquitoes coming to reservoirs, ponds, or puddles of water to lay their eggs would often die there so that their bodies would fall on to the surface of the water. As they disintegrated by rapid decay, the larval filariæ in the thoracic muscles would escape into the water, and live there until taken into the alimentary canal of people drinking some of the water from the reservoir or pond. Bancroft believes, however, that the filariæ are transmitted by the bite or puncture of the mosquito, and has actually observed the migration of the filariæ from the thoracic muscles forward into the head and "beak" of the mosquito. He has seen a filaria larva issuing from a fine opening near the tip of the labium. According to Bancroft's theory the filaria escapes from the beak of a puncturing mosquito into the skin of a man, finishes its development and growth in the skin, becomes adult, pairs and produces embryos which get into the lymphatic spaces or vessels, and are carried by the lymph into the blood. Here they circulate over the body, finally lodging in the lymphatic glands and causing the characteristic hypertrophy of tissue. Further investigation is necessary, however, before the question of transmission is fully understood. That the mosquito is the actual disseminating agent of the disease is, however, certain.

The species of mosquito which acts as intermediate host and distributing agent of the filariæ in Australia is *Culex fatigans*, var. *skusii*. *Anopheles rossii* is also known to carry the filariæ. In Samoa, where elephantiasis is more prevalent than anywhere else in the world, I have found the most abundant mosquito to be *Stegomyia fasciata*, the same species that spreads yellow fever. This species is also the most abundant mosquito in the Hawaiian Islands, and is indeed wide-spread over the tropics and subtropics of the whole world. If, as is probable, it is the principal carrier in Samoa of the filariæ that cause elephantiasis, it is the most formidable single species among all the insect scourges of mankind.

In this brief account of the rôle played by certain insects in the propagation and dissemination of certain human diseases only a small part of the story, as already known, has been told. Cockroaches, bedbugs, and other household insects are being found to be hosts for the germs of other familiar diseases. A host of investigators is at work; reports of discoveries are being published constantly, and in a few years our knowledge of this causal relation of insects to human disease will fill books instead of chapters.

# CHAPTER XIX

## REFLEXES, INSTINCTS, AND INTELLIGENCE

IN recent years many biologists have come to believe that most of the behavior of the simplest animals and some of the actions of the higher are controlled in a much more rigidly mechanical way than has usually been admitted; that, in a word, much of the action, and apparent instinctive or intelligent response of animals to external conditions, is an immediate physico-chemical rather than an inexplicable vital phenomenon; that the animal body in its relation to the external world is much more like a passive, senseless, although very complex, machine, stimulated and controlled by external factors and conditions, than like the percipient, determining, purposeful creature that our usual conception of the organism makes it out to be.

Clever experimenters, as Loeb, Lucas, Radl, Bethe, Uexkull, and numerous others, believe themselves justified in explaining a host of the simpler actions or modes of behavior of animals on a thoroughly mechanical basis, as rigorous, inevitable reactions to the influence or stimulus of light, heat, contact, gravity, galvanism, etc. Phototropism, stereotropism, geotropism, etc., are the names given to these phenomena of response by action and behavior to stimuli of light, contact, gravity, etc., respectively.

Some of these biologists are ready to carry their giving up of other than mechanical behavior among animals to great lengths. Loeb introduces a paper written in 1890 on instinct and will in animals as follows:

"In the biological literature one still finds authors who treat the 'instinct' or the 'will' of animals as a circumstance which determines motions, so that the scientist who enters the region of animated nature encounters an entirely new category of causes, such as are said continually to produce before our eyes great effects, without it being possible for an engineer ever to make use of these causes in the physical world. 'Instinct' and 'will' in animals, as causes which determine movements, stand upon the same plane as the supernatural powers of the theologians, which are also said to determine motions, but upon which an engineer could not well rely.

635

"My investigations on the heliotropism of animals led me to analyze in a few cases the conditions which determine the apparently accidental direction of animal movements which, according to traditional notions, are called voluntary or instinctive. Wherever I have thus far investigated the cause of such 'voluntary' or 'instinctive' movements in animals, I have without exception discovered such circumstances at work as are known in inanimate nature as determinate movements. By the help of these causes it is possible to control the 'voluntary' movements of a living animal just as securely and unequivocally as the engineer has been able to control the movements in inanimate nature. What has been taken for the effect of 'will' or 'instinct' is in reality the effect of light, of gravity, of friction, of chemical forces, etc."

But Jennings, a very careful and tireless investigator of the behavior of the protozoa, closes a fascinating volume on his work with the following paragraph:

"The present paper may be considered as the summing up of the general results of several years' work by the author on the behavior of the lowest organisms. This work has shown that in these creatures the behavior is not as a rule on the tropism plan—a set, forced method of reacting to each particular agent—but takes place in a much more flexible, less directly machine-like way, by the method of trial and error. This method involves many of the fundamental qualities which we find in the behavior of higher animals, yet with the simplest possible basis in ways of action; a great portion of the behavior consisting often of but one or two definite movements, movements that are stereotyped in their relation to the environment. This method leads upward, offering at every point opportunity for development, and showing even in the unicellular organisms what must be considered the beginnings of intelligence and of many other qualities found in higher animals. Tropic action doubtless occurs, but the main basis of behavior is in these organisms the method of trial and error."

In a rough way the responses or reactions of animals to stimuli, their behavior, in a word, are grouped into reflex behavior or reflexes, instinctive behavior or instincts, and intelligent behavior or action from reason. To distinguish sharply between reflexes and instincts on the one hand, and instincts and reason on the other is impossible. Reflexes may be defined to be local responses of congenital type (that is, not acquired by experience, imitation, or teaching) which usually involve, in higher animals, only a particular organ or definite group of muscles, and which are initiated by more or less specialized external stimuli. Instincts may be defined as complex groups of coordinated acts which are, on their first occurrence, independent of experience; which tend to the well-being and preservation of the race; which are due to the cooperation of external and internal stimuli; which are similarly performed by all the members of the same more or less restricted group of animals; but which are subject to variation, and to subsequent modification under the guidance of experience. Intelligent behavior may be distinguished roughly from instinctive behavior by being the outcome and product of experience; by involving usually the element of choice among a number of possible responses; by revealing a capacity to act with special reference or adaptation to new circumstances, and by revealing an individuality in dealing with the complex conditions of a variable environment.. In reflex and instinctive behavior the animal acts like a piece of well-made and adequately wound clockwork; in intelligent behavior the clockwork seems protean; it is a plastic machine capable of swift adaptation to external needs.

In the brief discussion of insect behavior constituting this chapter, I shall assume a general acceptance of the above definitions of and distinctions among reflex, instincts, and intelligence—these definitions being substantially in the words of C. L. Morgan, the thorough-going Darwinian student of animal behavior; and I shall consider the particular illustrations of insect behavior taken up in the light of the classification established by the definitions. It is needless to say that the actual character and conditions of the behavior in each case are the essential things to keep in mind in any analytical discussion of the subject, and not the uncertain, if more or less convenient, attempt to classify the cases.

From Loeb's point of view all animal responses differ only in degree, not at all in kind, and are all, from simplest to most complex, rigidly mechanical reactions to actual physico-chemical stimuli. From the anthropomorphic naturalists' point of view on the contrary, a mystic capacity, incident only to living matter, of reason and psychical functioning reveals itself in almost all animal behavior, and the sluggish movements of the starfish toward the water or around its prey are due to appreciation and likes and that intelligent determination familiar as factors in human action. Finally, from the point of view of the churchman naturalist the distinction between the springs of human behavior and "animal" behavior is as sharp as the assumed distinction between the possession of soul and spiritual existence on the part of man and the absence of these attributes in the lower animals. Our point of view will be, however, as stated; that fairly safe one between the rigid mechanicalism of the tropism believers and the mysticism of the believers in a divinely endowed creature of *psyche* as contrasted with a long series of unfortunate soulless brutes.

While the interested observation and recognition of insect habits and behavior has long occupied naturalists and poets, the careful, thoroughly checked and guarded study of this behavior has been curiously wanting. And only in very recent years has anything like experimental investigation of insect behavior been undertaken. The truth is that insects are all highly specialized animals, and by that fact, offer themselves as thoroughly interesting but extremely difficult subjects for the student of animal behavior. It seems at first sight impossible in the face of the well-developed nervous system and highly specialized and complex character of the behavior of insects to expect to analyze successfully this behavior into its separate component reactions with their stimuli; to recognize among insects simple rigidly mechanical reflexes of the nature of direct inevitable response to external physico-chemical stimuli as light, temperature, humidity, gravitation, contact, etc. Yet recent studies have shown that this can in certain cases be done. It has been done, in fact. And a few examples of this work and its results are given in the following paragraphs.

*Reflexes and Tropisms.* The first considerable piece of careful experimental study of insect reflexes was probably that of Loeb on the heliotropism of caterpillars, moths, fly larvæ, flies, plant-lice, and ants; the results of which were published in 1899. This original and able experimenter obtained positive results from this work and from them was led to conclude that light controls or causes certain movements or behavior of these insects in a very definite mechanical way; that it is the direction of the light rays that is the chief controlling factor in the influence exerted by the light on the insects, and finally that "the conditions which control the movements of the animals toward light are identical, point for point, with those which have been shown to be of paramount influence in plants." Therefore Loeb maintains that these phenomena of insect orientation and movement in the presence of light cannot depend upon specific characteristics of the central nervous system, that is, are not manifestations of intelligence or instinct (in the common understanding of the term), but are phenomena much more like those rigidly mechanical ones of iron filings in a field of magnetic force, or of sunflowers turning toward the sun.

Since Loeb's epoch-making work numerous observations and experiments have been made which have revealed other similar reflex phenomena among insects. These phenomena are commonly called "tropisms" and include whatever movements or special behavior can be explained as the immediate rigorously controlled reaction in response to localized external physico-chemical stimuli, such as heliotropism or phototropism, reactions to light; geotropism, responses to gravitation; chemotropism, behavior dependent on the influence of chemical stimuli affecting the organs of taste, smell, etc.; stereotropism or thigmotropism, movement or cessation of movement produced by the stimulus of contact with solid substance; hydrotropism, reactions to the stimulus of moisture or water; anemotropism, response to the stimulus of air-currents; thermotropism, behavior controlled by temperature, etc., etc. Thus Davenport has ascertained the movements of certain small simple insects (Poduridæ) which he found living in the sand beaches of Long Island to be determined as follows:

"I. General movements.
  A. Running: oxygen, lack of (?).
  B. Springing: currents of air, or jarring of substratum.
II. Special locomotive movements.
  1. Whirling: touch, water.
  2. Descent into the sand: touch, water, gravity.
  3. Rising from sand: water, gravity.
  4. Running up stones: gravity, light.
  5. Moving toward wind: current of air.
  6. Leaping into air: gravity, currents, oxygen-need."

Most insect behavior is likely to be due to several or many stimuli acting at once so that the behavior itself is the complexly formed resultant of various reactions. And in most cases it is difficult or impossible to analyze it into its component parts. Insects are really very complexly organized animals and their physiology and psychology is a synthesis of many elements. But occasionally an insect species may be found which lends itself fairly readily to the analytical study, by experimental methods, of its behavior. Or other species may be found which reveal at one or another stage in their life a period when some one reaction or reflex is all-dominant and its relation to its special stimulus is plainly revealed. Two examples of the determination of tropismic behavior on the part of highly specialized insect species which have come under my own observation may be described.

In the course of some experiments on the sense reactions of honey-bees, I have kept a small community of Italian bees in a glass-sided, narrow, high observation hive, so made that any particular bee, marked, which it is desired to observe constantly, cannot escape this observation. The hive contains but two frames, one above the other, and is made wholly of glass, except for the wooden frame. It is kept covered, except during observation periods, by a black cloth jacket. The bees live contentedly and normally in this small hive, needing only occasional feeding at times when so many cells are given up for brood that there are not enough left for sufficient stored food-supplies. One spring at the normal swarming time, while standing near the jacketed hive, I heard the excited hum of the beginning swarm and noted the first issuers rushing pellmell from the entrance. Interested to see the behavior of the community in the hive during such an ecstatic condition as that of swarming, I lifted the cloth jacket, when the excited mass of bees which was pushing frantically down to the small exit in the lower corner of the hive turned with one accord about face and rushed directly upward away from the opening toward and to the top of the hive. Here the bees jammed, struggling violently. I slipped the jacket partly on;

the ones covered turned down; the ones below stood undecided; I dropped the jacket completely; the mass began issuing from the exit again; I pulled off the jacket, and again the whole community of excited bees flowed—that is the word for it, so perfectly aligned and so evenly moving were all the individuals of the bee current—up to the closed top of the hive. Leaving the jacket off permanently, I prevented the issuing of the swarm until the ecstasy was passed and the usual quietly busy life of the hive was resumed. About three hours later there was a similar performance and failure to issue from the quickly unjacketed hive. On the next day another attempt to swarm was made, and after nearly an hour of struggling and moving up and down, depending on my manipulation of the black jacket, most of the bees got out of the hive's opening and the swarming came off on a weed bunch near the laboratory. That the issuance from the hive at swarming time depends upon a sudden extra-development of positive heliotropism seems obvious. The ecstasy comes and the bees crowd for the one spot of light in the normal hive, namely, the entrance opening. But when the covering jacket is lifted and the light comes strongly in from above—my hive was under a skylight—they rush toward the top, that is, toward the light. Jacket on and light shut off from above, down they rush; jacket off and light stronger from above than below and they respond like iron filings in front of an electromagnet which has its current suddenly turned on. What produces the sudden strong heliotropism just as the swarming ecstasy comes on? That is beyond my observation.

The other example is as follows: Silkworm moths (*Bombyx mori*) are sexually mature and eager to mate immediately on issuing from the pupal cocoon. They take no food (their mouth-parts are atrophied), they do not fly, they are unresponsive to light; their whole behavior, in fact, is determined by their response to the mating and egg-laying instincts. We have thus an animal of considerable complexity of organization, belonging to a group of organisms well advanced in the animal scale, in a most simple state for experimentation.

The female moth, nearly immobile, protrudes a paired scent-organ from the hindmost abdominal segment, and the male, walking nervously about and fluttering its useless wings, soon finds the female by virtue of its chemotactic response to the emanating odor. Males find the females exclusively by this response.

A male with antennæ intact, but with eyes blackened, finds females immediately and with just as much precision as those with eyes unblackened. A male with antennæ off and eyes unblackened does not find females unless by accident in its aimless moving about. But if a male with antennæ off does come into contact, by chance, with a female it always (or nearly so) readily and immediately mates. The male is not excited before touching the female, but is immediately and strongly so after coming in contact with her. Males with antennæ on become strongly excited when a female is brought within several inches of them.

The protruded scent-glands of the female are withdrawn into the body immediately on her being touched by a male. If the scent-glands are cut off and put wholly apart from the female, males are as strongly attracted to these isolated scent-glands as they are to unmutilated females; on the contrary they are not at all attracted to the mutilated females. If the cut-out scent-glands are put by the side of and but a little apart from the female from which they are taken, the males always neglect the near-by live female and go directly to the scent-glands. Males attracted to the isolated scent-glands remain by them persistently, moving excitedly around and around them and over and over them with the external genitalia vainly trying to seize them.

The behavior of males with the antenna of only one side removed is striking. A male with left antenna off when within three or four inches of a female (with protruded scent-glands) becomes strongly excited and moves energetically around in repeated circles to the right, or rather in a flat spiral, thus getting (usually) gradually nearer and nearer the female and finally coming into contact with her. A male with right antenna off circles or spirals to the left. It is a curious sight to see two males with right and left antenna off, respectively, circling violently about in opposite directions when the immobile female a few inches removed protrudes her scent-glands. This behavior is quite in accordance with Loeb's explanation of the forward movement of bilaterally symmetrical animals.

The results of all the experiments tried show how rigorously the male moths are controlled by the scent attraction (chemotropism) and how absolutely dependent mating (the one adult performance of the males) is on this reaction. If we can find specialized animals in a condition where response to all attractions and repulsions (stimuli) but one are eliminated, we may readily perceive the rigorous control exercised by this remaining one. We are, unfortunately, in the general circumstances of animal life too much limited to the use of very simply organized animals for reaction and reflex experimentation. This tends to make it difficult to carry over to the behavior of complexly organized animals the physico-chemical interpretation which is steadily gaining ground as the key to the understanding of the springs and character of the behavior of the simplest organisms. But where the complex stimuli and reactions that determine the behavior of complexly organized forms can be isolated and studied, the inevitableness of much of this behavior can be recognized.

*Instincts.* Examples and accounts of instincts are scattered all through this book. Complex and elaborate behavior in connection with egg-laying, care of young, food-getting, defense, offense, nest-making, parasitic, commensal and communal life, and various other specialized phases of insect life, is described often in considerable detail. So that reference to these accounts may suffice in this place in lieu of repeating these descriptions or of adding new ones. For miscellaneous examples of insect instincts, or behavior satisfying our definition of instinct, the reader may refer to the accounts of the egg-laying of bot-flies on p. 337, of the ham-fly on p. 348, of the bee-moth on p. 379, of the monarch butterfly on p. 452, of the California oak-moth on p. 407, of the fig Blastophaga on p. 487, of Tremex and Thalessa on pp. 467 and 483, of gall-flies and their guests on p. 468, of the lace-wing fly on p. 228, of Mantispa on p. 234, of the blister-beetles on p. 290; accounts of the building of protecting larval cases or tents by caddis-flies on p. 240, by leaf-rollers on p. 375, by bag-worms on p. 385, and by tent-caterpillars on p. 415; the account on p. 230 of the ant-lion and its pit, on p. 396 of the "going stiff" of the inch-worms, on p. 394 of the threatening of the puss-moth larva, on p. 107 of the tunnel-building of the termites, on p. 352 of the wing-removing of Lipoptena; the accounts of mrymecophily on p. 552, of the elaborate economy of solitary bees and wasps on pp. 490 and 510; and of the complex communal life of the social bees, wasps, and ants.

With these or some of them well in mind the reader is ready to take part in a consideration of some of the pertinent questions and problems which such behavior, such long, highly coordinated series of actions, such complex apparently psychic manifestations, inevitably bring up to the student of animal life. On what sort or degree of organization of nervous system does this complexity and high and effective coordination of behavior depend? Is the behavior thoroughly adaptive? How rigid or invariable is the behavior; that is, is there any apparent capacity to modify the behavior to suit special cases or suddenly appearing new conditions? Is there any element of reason, any intelligent choice of action, in the behavior? Or on the other hand in how far can complex instincts be analyzed into simple rigorous tropismic or reflex actions?

There is space here to consider but one or two of these problems, and we may select those which are perhaps of most interest. Let us select the matter of the degree of rigorousness or invariability of behavior manifest in insect instinct, and the matter of the possession by insects of any degree of intelligence or reason; that is, the question of whether or not insect behavior is exclusively reflexive and instinctive or is chiefly instinctive but tempered by some degree of intelligence.

This particular problem has been considered and discussed most perhaps in connection with the elaborate and highly specialized behavior of the solitary and social Hymenoptera (wasps, bees, and ants). And there are strong champions for both points of view. Three observers and students of insect life are preeminently conspicuous by virtue of their detailed and long pursued studies of the habits of the solitary wasps. These observers are J. H. Fabre (France) and G. W. and E. G. Peckham (husband and wife, Wisconsin). Now while Fabre holds positively and consistently the belief that this behavior is exclusively instinctive, the Peckhams hold as certainly that it is the result of instinct tempered with and modified by reason. And on this side also stands C. L. Morgan, the great English student of animal behavior in general.

In the first of Fabre's nine fascinating volumes entitled "*Souvenirs Entomologiques*," there are two chapters entitled respectively the Science of Instinct and the Ignorance of Instinct. In one of these is pictured the marvelous precision, coordination, and certainty of the nest-making and the catching, paralyzing, and storing of the living food by the solitary wasp, for its young. As an example of this behavior, but of this behavior observed without any such illuminating experimental treatment as that with which Fabre accompanies his observations, my account of the behavior of the Ammophila of the Palo Alto salt marshes (see p. 493 of this book) may be referred to. In the second of Fabre's chapters, the one on the "ignorance of instinct," there is pointed out on the other hand the definite limitations of the wasp's behavior. I quote from a translation of this chapter.

"The Sphex has just shown us with what infallible, transcendent art she acts, guided by the unconscious inspiration of instinct: she will now show how poor she is in resources, how limited in intelligence, and even illogical in cases somewhat out of her usual line. By a strange contradiction, characteristic of the instinctive faculties, with deep science is associated ignorance not less deep. Nothing is impossible to instinct, however great be the difficulty. In constructing her hexagonal cells with their floor of three lozenge-shaped pieces, the bee resolves, with absolute precision, the arduous problems of maximum and minimum, to solve which man would need a powerful mathematical mind. Hymenoptera, whose larvæ live on prey, have methods in their murderous art hardly equalled by those of man versed in the most delicate mysteries of anatomy and physiology. Nothing is difficult to instinct so long as the action moves in the unchanging groove allotted to the animal, but, again, nothing is easy to instinct if the action deviates from it. The very insect which amazes us and alarms us by its high intelligence, will, a moment later, astonish us by its stupidity before some fact extremely simple, but strange to its usual habits. The Sphex will offer an example.

"Let us follow her dragging home an ephippiger. If fortune favors us, we may be present at a little scene which I will describe. On entering the shelter under a rock where the burrow is made, the Sphex finds, perched on a blade of grass, a carnivorous insect which, under a most sanctimonious aspect, hides the morals of a cannibal. The danger threatened by this bandit in ambush on her path must be known to the Sphex, for she leaves her game and runs bravely at the Mantis to administer some sharp blows and dislodge, or at all events, alarm and inspire it with respect. It does not move, but closes its deadly weapons—the two terrible saws of the arm and forearm. The Sphex returns to her prey, harnesses herself to the antennæ, and passes audaciously under the blade of grass where the Mantis sits. From the direction of her head one can see that she is on her guard, and is holding the enemy motionless under her threatening eyes. Such courage is duly rewarded; the prey is stored without further misadventure."

The author introduces a digression here and then proceeds: "We return to the Sphex, with whose burrow we must make acquaintance before going further. It is made of fine sand, or rather in the fine dust at the bottom of a natural shelter. Its passage is very short—an inch or two without a turn, leading into a single spacious oval chamber, and all is a rude, hastily made den, rather than a dwelling hollowed with art and leisure. I have already said that the captured prey, left for a brief moment or two where it was hunted, is the cause of the simplicity of this abode and of there being but one chamber or cell to each hollow. For who can say whither the chances of the day's hunt may lead? The dwelling must be near the heavy prey, and to-day's abode, too far off to admit of carrying the second ephippiger there, cannot be used to-morrow. Thus each time prey is caught there must be new digging out—a new burrow with its one cell, now here, now there. Now let us try some experiments to see how the insect behaves amid circumstances new to it.

"First experiment.—A Sphex, dragging her prey, is at a few inches from her burrow. Without disturbing her I cut the antennæ of the ephippiger, which we already know serve as harnesses. Having recovered from her astonishment at the sudden lightening of her load, the Sphex returns and unhesitatingly seizes the base of the antennæ, the short stumps not cut off. Very short they are—hardly a millimetre long; no matter, they suffice for the Sphex, who grips what remains of her ropes and drags anew. With many precautions not to hurt her, I cut off the two stumps, now level with the skull. Finding nothing to seize at the parts familiar to her, she takes hold on one side of one of the long palpi of her victim, and drags it, not at all put out by this modification in her style of harnessing herself. I leave her alone. The prey is got home and placed with its head to the mouth of the burrow. The Sphex enters to make a short inspection of the interior before proceeding to store provisions. Her tactics recall those of *S. flavipennis* in like circumstances. I profit by this brief moment to take the abandoned prey, deprive it of all its palpi, and place it a little farther off—a pace from the burrow. The Sphex reappears and goes straight to her game, which she saw from her threshold. She seeks above the head, she seeks below, on one side, and finds nothing to seize. A desperate attempt is made; opening wide her mandibles she tries to grasp the ephippiger by the head, but her pincers cannot surround anything so large, and slip off the round, polished skull. She tries several times in vain; at length, convinced of the futility of her efforts, she draws back, and seems to renounce further attempts. S..e appears discouraged—at least she smooths her wings with her hind feet, while with her front tarsi, first passing them through her mouth, she washes her eyes, a sign among Hymenoptera, as I believe, that they give a thing up.

"Yet there were points by which the ephippiger might be seized and dragged as easily as by the antennæ and palpi. There are the six feet, there is the ovipositor—all organs slender enough to be thoroughly grasped and used as traction ropes. I own that the easiest way of getting the prey into the storehouse is to introduce it head first by the antennæ; yet, drawn by one foot, especially a front one, it would enter almost as easily, for the orifice is wide and the passage short, even if there be one. How came it then that the Sphex never once tried to seize one of the six tarsi or the point of the ovipositor, while she did make the impossible, absurd attempt to grip with the mandibles far too short the huge head of her prey? Perhaps the idea did not occur to her. Let us try to suggest it. I place under her mandibles first a foot, then the end of the abdominal sabre. She refuses obstinately to bite; my repeated solicitations come to nothing. A very odd kind of hunter this to be so embarrassed by her game and unable to think of seizing it by a foot if it cannot be taken by the horns! Perhaps my presence and all these unusual events may have troubled her faculties; let us leave her to herself, with her burrow and ephippiger, and give her time to consider and to imagine in the calm of solitude some means of managing the business. I walked away and returned in a couple of hours to find the Sphex gone, the burrow open, and the ephippiger where I had laid it. The conclusion is that the Sphex tried nothing, but departed, abandoning home, game—everything, when to utilize them all that was needed would have been to take the prey by one foot. Thus this rival of Flourens, who just now startled us by her science when pressing the brain to induce lethargy, is invariably dull when the least unusual event occurs. The Sphex, which knows so well how to reach the thoracic ganglia of a victim with her sting, and those of the brain with her mandibles, and which makes such judicious difference between a poisoned sting that would destroy the vital influence of the nerves, and compression causing only momentary torpor, cannot seize her prey in a new way. To understand that a foot may be taken instead of the antennæ is impossible; nothing will do but the antennæ or another filament of the head or one of the palpi. For want of these ropes her whole race would perish, unable to surmount this trifling difficulty.

"Second experiment.—The Sphex is busy closing her burrow where the prey is stored and the egg laid. With her fore tarsi she sweeps backward before her door, and launches from the entrance a spurt of dust, which passes beneath her, and springs up behind in a parabolic curve as continuous as if it were a slender stream of some liquid, so rapidly does she sweep. From time to time she chooses some sand grains with her mandibles, strengthening materials inserted singly in the dusty mass. To consolidate this she beats it with her head, and heaps it with her mandibles. Walled up by this masonry, the entrance rapidly disappears. In the midst of the work I intervene. Having put the Sphex aside I clear out the short gallery carefully with the blade of a knife, take away the materials which block it, and entirely restore the communication of the cell with the outer air. Then, without injuring the edifice, I draw the ephippiger out of the cell where it is lying with its head to the far end, and its ovipositor to the entrance. The egg is as usual on its breast, near the base of one of the hind legs—a proof that the Sphex had given her last touch to the burrow, and would never return. These dispositions made and the ephippiger placed safely in a box, I gave up my place to the Sphex, who had been watching while her domicile was rifled. Finding the entrance open, she entered and remained some moments, then came forth and took up her work where I interrupted it, beginning to stop the entrance conscientiously, sweeping the dust backward, and transporting sand grains to build them with minute care, as if doing a useful work. The orifice being again thoroughly blocked, she brushed herself, seemed to give a glance of satisfaction at her work, and finally flew off.

"Yet she must have known that the burrow was empty, since she had gone inside, and made prolonged stay, but yet after this visit to the plundered dwelling, she set to work to close it with as much care as if nothing had happened. Did she propose to turn it later to account, returning with a fresh prey, laying a new egg? In that case the burrow was closed to defend it from indiscreet visitors while the Sphex was away. Or it was a measure of prudence against other miners who might covet a ready-made chamber, or a wise precaution against internal wear and tear, and, in fact, some predatory Hymenoptera are careful when obliged to suspend work to defend the mouth of their burrow by closing it up temporarily. I have seen certain Ammophilæ, whose burrow is a vertical well, close the entrance with a little flat stone when the insect goes a-hunting, or stops mining when the hour to leave off work comes at sunset. But in that case the stoppage is slight—a mere slab set on the top of the well. It takes but a moment when the insect comes to displace the little flat stone, and the door is open. But what we have just seen the Sphex construct is a solid barrier—strong masonry, where layers of alternate dust and gravel occupy the whole passage. It is definitive, and no temporary work, as is sufficiently shown by the careful way in which it is constructed. Besides, as I think I have already proved, it is very doubtful, considering the manner in which she acted, whether the Sphex would return to use the dwelling which she had prepared. A new ephippiger will be caught elsewhere, and elsewhere too will the storehouse destined for it be hollowed. As, however, these are but conclusions drawn by reasoning, let us consult experiment, more conclusive here than logic. I let nearly a week pass in order to allow the Sphex to return to the burrow so methodically closed, and use it if she liked for her nest-laying. Events answered to the logical deduction; the burrow was just as I had left it, well closed, but without food, egg, or larva. The demonstration was decisive; the Sphex had not returned.

"Thus we see the plundered Sphex go into her house, pay a leisurely visit to the empty chamber, and the next moment behave as if she had not perceived the absence of the big prey which a little while before had encumbered the cell. Did she not realize the absence of food and egg? Was she really so dull—she, so clear-sighted when playing the murderer—that the cell was empty? I dare not accuse her of such stupidity. She did perceive it. But why then that other piece of stupidity which made her close, and very conscientiously too, an empty chamber which she did not mean to store? It was useless—downright absurd—to do this, and yet she worked with as much zeal as if the future of the larva depended on it. The various instinctive actions of insects are then necessarily connected; since one thing has been done, such another must inevitably follow to complete the first, or prepare the way for the next, and the two acts are so necessarily linked that the first must cause the second, even when by some chance this last has become not only superfluous, but sometimes contrary to the creature's interest. What object could there be in stopping a burrow now useless, since it no longer contained prey and egg, and which will remain useless, since the Sphex will not return to it? One can only explain this irrational proceeding by regarding it as the necessary consequence of preceding actions. In the normal state of things the Sphex hunts her prey, lays an egg, and closes the hole. The prey has been caught, the egg laid, and now comes the closing of the burrow, and the insect closes it without reflecting at all, or guessing the fruitlessness of her labor.

"Third experiment.—To know all and nothing, according as the conditions are normal or otherwise, is the strange antithesis presented by the insect. Other examples drawn from the Sphegidæ will confirm us in this proposition. *Sphex albisecta* attacks middle-sized Acridians, the various species scattered in the neighborhood of her burrow all furnishing a tribute. From the abundance of these Acrididæ the chase is carried on near at hand. When the vertical well-like burrow is ready, the Sphex merely flies over the ground near, and espies an Acridian feeding in the sunshine. To pounce and sting while it struggles is done in a moment.   After some fluttering of the wings, which unfold like carmine or azure fans, some moving of feet up and down, the victim becomes motionless.   Next it must be got home by the Sphex on foot.   She performs this toilsome operation as do her kindred, dragging her game between her feet, and holding one of the antennæ in her mandibles. If a grass thicket has to be traversed, she hops and flutters from blade to blade, keeping firm hold of her prey.   When within a few feet of her dwelling, she executes the same manœuvre as does *S. occitanica*, but without attaching the same importance to it, for sometimes she neglects it.   The game is left on the road, and though no apparent danger threatens the dwelling, she hurries toward its mouth, and puts in her head repeatedly, or even partly enters, then returns to the Acridian, brings it nearer, and again leaves it to revisit her burrow, and so on several times, always with eager haste.

"These repeated visits have sometimes annoying results.   The victim, rashly abandoned on a slope, rolls to the bottom, and when the Sphex returns and does not find it where she left it, she must hunt for it, sometimes in vain. If found, there will be a difficult climb, which, however, does not prevent her leaving it once more on the perilous slope.   The first of these repeated visits to her cell is easily explained.   Before bringing her heavy load she is anxious to make sure that the entrance is clear, and that nothing will hinder her carrying in the prey.   But what is the use of her other visits, repeated so speedily one after another?   Are the Sphex's ideas so unstable that she forgets the one just made, and hurries back a moment later, only to forget that she has done so, and so on?   It would indeed be a slippery memory where impressions vanished as soon as made.   Let us leave this too obscure question.

"At length the game is brought to the edge of the well, its antennæ hanging into the mouth, and there is an exact repetition of the method used by *S. flavipennis* and, though in less striking conditions, by *S. occitanica*.   She enters alone, reappears at the entrance, seizes the antennæ, and drags in the Acridian.   While she was within I have pushed the prey rather farther off, and have always obtained precisely the same result as in the case of the huntress of crickets.   In both Sphegidæ there was the same persistence in plunging into their burrows before dragging down their prey.   We must recollect that *S. flavipennis* does not always allow herself to be duped by my trick or withdrawing the insect.   There are elect tribes among them,— strong-minded families,—who after a while find out the tricks of the experimenter, and know how to baffle them.   But these revolutionaries capable of progress are the few; the rest, rigid conservatives in manner and customs, are the majority, the crowd.   I cannot say whether the hunters of Acrididæ show more or less cunning in different districts.

"But the most remarkable thing, and the one to which I want specially to come, is this: After withdrawing the prey of *S. albisecta* several times from the mouth of the hole, and obliging her to fetch it back, I profited by her descent to the bottom of her den to seize and put the prey where she could not find it. She came up, sought about for a long time, and, when quite convinced that it was not to be found, went down again. A few moments later she reappeared. Was it to return to the chase? Not the least in the world; she began to close the hole, and with no temporary cover, such as a small flat stone to mark the orifice, but with a solid mass of carefully collected dust and gravel swept into the passage until it was quite filled. *S. albisecta* makes only a single cell at the bottom of her well, and puts in but one victim. This one specimen had been caught and dragged to the edge of the hole, and if it was not stored, that was my fault, not her's. The Sphex worked by an inflexible rule, and according to that rule she completed the work by stopping up the hole even if empty. Here we have an exact repetition of the useless labor of *S. occitanica*, whose dwelling I rifled.

"Fourth experiment.—It is almost impossible to be certain whether *S. flavipennis*, which makes several cells at the bottom of the same passage, and heaps several grasshoppers in each, commits the same irrational mistakes when accidentally disturbed. A cell may be closed, although empty or imperfectly stored, and yet the Sphex will return to the same burrow to make others. Yet I have reason to believe that this Sphex is subject to the same aberrations as her two relations. The facts on which I base my belief are these: When the work is completed, there are generally four grasshoppers in each cell, but it is not uncommon to find three or only two. Four appears to me the usual number—first, because it is the most frequent, and secondly, when I have brought up young larvæ dug up when eating their first grasshopper, I found that all, even those provided with only two or three, easily finished those offered, up to four, but after that they hardly touched the fifth ration. If four grasshoppers are required by the larva to develop fully, why is it sometimes provided with only three or even only two? Why this immense difference in the amount of food? It cannot be from any difference in the joints served up, since all are unmistakably of the same size, but must come from losing prey on the road. In fact, one finds at the foot of the slopes whose upper parts are occupied by Sphegidæ, grasshoppers killed, and then lost down the incline, when, for some reason or other, the Sphex has momentarily left them. These grasshoppers become the prey of ants and flies, and the Sphex who finds them takes good care not to pick them up, as they would take enemies into the burrow.

"These facts seem to demonstrate that if *S. flavipennis* can compute exactly how many victims to catch, she cannot attain to counting how many reach their destination, as if the creature had no other guide as to number than an irresistible impulse leading her to seek game a fixed number of times.

When this number of journeys has been made,—when the Sphex has done all that is possible to store the captured prey,—her work is done, and the cell is closed, whether completely provisioned or not. Nature has endowed her with only those faculties called for under ordinary circumstances by the interests of the larva, and these blind faculties, unmdiofied by experience, being sufficient for the preservation of the race, the animal cannot go farther.

"I end then as I began: instinct knows everything in the unchanging paths laid out for it; beyond them it is entirely ignorant. The sublime inspirations of science, the astonishing inconsistencies of stupidity, are both its portion, according as the creature acts under normal conditions or under accidental ones."

Now for the other side. I quote from the concluding chapter in the Peckhams' book on the Solitary Wasps:

"Our study of the activities of wasps has satisfied us that it is impracticable to classify them in any simple way. The old notion that the acts of bees, wasps, and ants were all varying forms of instinct is no longer tenable and must give way to a more philosophical view. It would appear to be quite certain that there are not only instinctive acts but acts of intelligence as well, and a third variety also—acts that are probably due to imitation, although whether much or little intelligence accompanies this imitation, is admittedly difficult to determine. Again, acts that are instinctive in one species may be intelligent in another, and we may even assert that there is a considerable variation in the amount of intelligence displayed by different individuals of the same species. We have met with such difficulty in our attempt to arrange the activities of wasps in different groups that we are forced to the conclusion that any scheme of classification is merely a convenience, useful for purposes of study or generalization, but not to be taken for an absolutely true expression of all the facts. This kind of perplexity is well understood and allowed for in all morphological work, but it has never been fully realized in the study of habits. The explanation is not far to seek. The habits of but few animals have been studied in sufficient detail to bring out the evidence that there is as much variation on the psychological as on the morphological side."

In a recent account of observations made on twenty-eight species of solitary wasps in Texas, Carl Hartman also takes strong ground for the variability of instincts. He has in his own mind, as a result of his long series of observations, no doubt of this variability. And he notes also the interesting point that this "variability in mental traits and dispositions as reflected in the wasps' actions seems to be proportionate to the physical variability. At any rate, *Bembex beljrægi*, the species of Bembidula, and *Microbembex monodonta*, for example, are all very variable species in size and coloration as well as in the demeanor of different individuals."

The Peckhams arrange the activities of the wasps they have studied into two groups, instincts and acts of intelligence, "it being understood that these classes pass by insensible stages into each other, and that acts that are purely instinctive when performed for the first time are probably in some degree modified by individual experience." In the category instinct they place "all complex acts that are performed previous to experience and in a similar manner by all members of the same sex and race, leaving out as non-essential, at this time, the question of whether they are or are not accompanied by consciousness." Under intelligence they place those "conscious actions which are more or less modified by experience." With these definitions in mind they group the activities of solitary wasps under the two heads as follows:

"*Instinct.*—With the Pelopæus wasps we were present on several occasions when the young emerged from the pupa case and gnawed their way out of the mud cell. They were limp and their wings had not perfectly hardened, and yet when we touched them they tried to attack us, thrusting out the sting and moving the abdomen about in various directions. These movements were well directed, and, so far as we could observe, quite as perfect as in the adult wasp. Stinging, then, is an instinctive act.

"The particular method of attack and capture practiced by each species in securing its prey is instinctive. Ammophila pricks a number of ganglia along the ventral face of the caterpillar; Pelopæus, we believe, stabs the spider in the cephalothorax, and probably the several species of Pompilus do the same. *Astata bicolor* adopts the same tactics in capturing her bugs, while it is said of the fly-catchers that they commonly overcome their victims without using the sting. It is by instinct, too, that these wasps take their proper food-supply, one worms, another spiders, a third flies or beetles. So strong and deeply seated is the preference that no fly-robber ever takes spiders, nor will the ravisher of the spiders change to beetles or bugs.

"The mode of carrying their booty is a true instinct. Pompilus takes hold of her spider anywhere, but always drags it over the ground, walking backward; Oxybelus clasps her fly with the hind legs, while Bembex uses the second pair to hold hers tightly against the under side of her thorax. Each works after her own fashion and in a way that is uniform for each species.

"The capturing of the victim before the hole is made, as in the case of *P. quinquenotatus*, or the reverse method pursued by Astata, Ammophila, Bembex, and others of preparing the nest before the food-supply is secured is certainly instinctive; as is also the way in which some of these wasps act after bringing the prey to the nest. For example *S. ichneumonea* places her grasshopper just at the entrance to the excavation and then enters to see that all is right before dragging it in. In experimenting with a French

Sphex which has the same habit, Fabre moved the creature a little way off; the wasp came out, brought it to the opening as before, and went within a second time.   This was repeated again and again until the patience of the naturalist was exhausted, and the persistent wasp took her booty in after her appropriate fashion.   She must place the grasshopper just so close to the doorway, she must then descend and examine the nest, and after that must come out and drag it down.   Nothing less than the performance of these acts in a certain order satisfies her impulse.   There must be no disturbance of the regular method or she refuses to proceed.   Again, we see Oxybelus scratching open her nest while on the wing and entering at once with the fly held tightly in her legs.   Each way is characteristic of the species and would be an important part of any definition of the animal based upon its habits.

"The general style of the nest depends upon instinct.   Trypoxylon uses hollow passages in trees, posts, straws, or brick walls; *Diodontus americanus*, a member of the same family, always burrows in the ground, as do Bembex, Ammophila, and Sphex.   In the case of Trypoxylon the passage may be ready for use or may require more or less preparation; the instinctive part is the impulse that impels the insect to use a certain kind of habitation.   Any one familiar with *T. rubrocinctum* would never look for their nests in standing stems or under stones; to use Mr. Morgan's test, he would be willing to bet on the general style of the dwelling-place.   All of these acts are similarly performed by individuals of the same sex and race, not in circumstantial detail but quite in the same way in a broad sense.   Variation is always present, but the tendency to depart from a certain type is not excessive.   In the drawing of the nest of *Cerceris nigrescens* the burrow is seen to be tortuous, this style of work being common to many species in the genus and very characteristic.   No Sphex nor Ammophila constructs any such tunnel.   The adherence of all the members of a species to a certain style of architecture is, then, due to instinct.

"The spinning of the cocoon, in those species in which the larva is protected in this manner, and its shape, are instinctive.   We find that closely allied species in the same genus make very different cocoons, as is seen in *T. rubrocinctum* and *T. bidentatum*.   Some wasps never cover themselves with a cocoon, as in the Australian species *Alastor eriurgus* and *Abispa splendida*.   It is a well-known fact that silkworms sometimes omit the spinning of a cocoon; but this does not affect the argument, since the descendants of these individuals make the characteristic covering.   Such cases are probably due to individual variation or perhaps to atavism, this throwing back being not uncommon among forms that are well known.

"Not all of the instinctive facts here enumerated are displayed by each species studied, although as a general proposition they are common to most of them. We have doubtless overlooked some activities that should come under this head, as we have not made a thorough study of any sufficient number of species to make a final settlement of the matter. For convenience we give the eight primary instincts that we have enumerated in tabular form:

### INSTINCTS

1. Stinging.
2. Taking a particular kind of food.
3. Method of attacking and capturing prey.
4. Method of carrying prey.
5. Preparing nest and then capturing prey, or the reverse.
6. The mode of taking prey into nest.
7. The general style or locality of nest.
8. The spinning or not spinning of a cocoon, and its specific form when one is made.

"*Intelligence.*—It is obviously more difficult to distinguish actions of this class than of the other. One must be familiar with the normal conditions of the insects in question before he is able to note those slight changes in the environment that offer some opportunity for an adaptation of means to ends, or before he is competent to devise experiments which will test their powers in this direction.

"We find two classes of intelligent actions among the Hymenoptera which are sufficiently distinct to be considered separately, although, like all natural groups, they grade into each other. The first of these includes those actions that are performed by large numbers in a similar fashion under like conditions, while in the second class each act is an individual affair, as where a single wasp, uninfluenced in any way by the example of those about it, displays unusual intelligence in grappling with the affairs of life. Examples of the first class are found in such modifications of instinct as are shown by Pelopæus and other wasps in the character of their habitations. Pelopæus, instead of building in hollow trees or under shelving rocks, as was the ancient custom of the race, now nests in chimneys, or under the eaves of buildings. We have found *T. rubrocinctum* taking advantage of the face of a straw stack that had been cut off smoothly as the cattle were fed through the winter. The same power of adaptation is shown by Fabre's experiment with Osmia, in which he took two dozen nests in shells from a quarry, where the bees had been nesting for centuries, and placed them in his study along with some empty shells and some hollow stems. When the bees came out, in the spring, nearly all of them selected the stalks to build in as being better suited to their use than the shells. All of these changes are intelligent adaptations to new modes of life, serving to keep the species in harmony with its surroundings.    The same thing may be seen when a number of social wasps work together to replace the roof of their nest when it has been torn off.

"An instance of the second class is seen in one of our examples of *Pompilus marginatus*.  This species, while searching for a nesting-place, leaves its spider lying on the ground or hides it under a lump of earth, in either of which positions the booty is subject to the attacks of ants; the wasp in question improved upon the custom of her tribe by carrying the spider up into a plant and hanging it there.  We have now and then seen a queen of *Polistes fusca* occupy a comb of the previous year instead of building a new one for herself, showing a better mental equipment than her sisters who were not strong-minded enough to change their ways and so built new nests alongside of unoccupied old ones which were in good condition.  In Bembex society it is good form to close the door on leaving home, but sometimes a wasp will save time by leaving the entrance open.  This, however, is a doubtful case, as the advantage would, perhaps, be more than balanced by the exposure of the nest to parasites.  The most conspicuous example that we have seen of intelligence among wasps was in that individual of Ammophila that rose above her fellows by using a stone to pound down the earth over her nest.

"The general impression that remains with us as a result of our study of these activities is that their complexity and perfection have been greatly over-estimated.  We have found them in all stages of development and are convinced that they have passed through many degrees, from the simple to the complex, by the action of natural selection.  Indeed, we find in them beautiful examples of the survival of the fittest."

In a short note published after the issuance of their book, the Peckhams describe an experiment with a Sphex whose results to their minds plainly show the tempering of the Sphex instinct by a certain degree of intelligence.  Fabre once experimented on a Sphex, taking advantage of the moment that the wasp was out of sight below to remove her prey to a little distance with the result that when the wasp came up she brought her cricket to the same spot and left it as before, while she visited the interior of the nest.  Since he repeated this experiment about forty times, and always with the same result, it seemed fair, says the Peckhams, to draw the conclusion that nothing less than the performance of a certain series of acts in a certain order would satisfy her impulse.  She must place her prey just so close to the doorway; she must then descend and examine the nest, and after that must at once drag it down, any disturbance of this routine causing her to refuse to proceed.

"We recently found a *Sphex ichneumonea* at work storing her nest," continue the Peckhams, "and thought it would be interesting to pursue Fabre's method and find out whether she were equally persistent in following her regular routine. We allowed her to carry in one grasshopper to establish her normal method of procedure, and found that, bringing it on the wing, she dropped it about six inches away, ran into the nest, out again, and over to the grasshopper, which she straddled and carried by the head to the entrance. She then ran down head first, turned around, came up, and, seizing it by the head, pulled it within. On the following day, when she had brought the grasshopper to the entrance of the nest, and while she was below, we moved it back five or six inches. When she came out she carried it to the same spot and went down as before. We removed it again with the same result, and the performance was repeated a third and a fourth time; but the fifth time that she found her prey where we had placed it, she seized it by the head and, going backward, dragged it down into the nest without pausing. On the next day the experiment was repeated. After we had moved the grasshopper away four times, she straddled it and carried it down into the nest, going head foremost. On the fourth and last day of our experiment she replaced the grasshopper at the door of the nest and ran inside seven times, but then seized it and dragged it, going backward into the nest.

"How shall this change in a long-established custom be explained except by saying that her reason led her to adapt herself to circumstances? She was enough of a conservative to prefer the old way, but was not such a slave to custom as to be unable to vary it."

Morgan believes that a fair weighing of the evidence put forward by Fabre and the Peckhams leads one to conclude that "among the solitary wasps and mason bees the behavior, though founded on instinct, is in large degree modified by intelligence." In the behavior of the Ammophilas observed by Williston in Kansas and the Peckhams in Wisconsin, which used a small stone to tamp down and level off the soil filling the nest hole, Morgan sees "an intelligent behavior rising to the level to which some would apply the term rational. For the act may be held to afford evidence of the perception of the relation of the means employed to an end to be attained, and some general conception of purpose."

After all, to attempt to make sharp distinctions between reflexes and instincts and between instincts and intelligence is bound to lead to more or less verbal quibbling. I believe that the distinctions will be more and more effaced with increasing knowledge of animal behavior on our part. And on the whole it seems to me quite fair to say that our present point of view, in the light of the increasing evidence for mechanical or physico-chemical explanations of insect actions, should be that of the believer in the simpler and less anthropomorphic explanations of behavior, i.e., the explanation of tropisms and reflexes, and complex and coordinated series of them, which may be termed instincts.

# APPENDIX

## COLLECTING AND REARING INSECTS

THE simpler the equipment the better for the beginning collector of insects. A net, collecting-bottle, box for pinning specimens, papers for "papered" ones, a few empty vials and pill-boxes, and a few vials containing 85 per cent. alcohol—this is outfit enough for general work. For special visits to ponds and brooks, a water- or dredging-net, and a jar or tin pail for carrying home living specimens, are needed. A large-bladed jack-knife for digging and prying under stones, cutting into logs and stumps, and splitting canes and galls is always useful. A pair of forceps, for handling stinging specimens, and very small or delicate ones, is convenient.

The net (Fig. 799) should be of some strong non-tearing cloth netting—bobinet is excellent—12 to 14 inches in diameter at the mouth and about 24 inches deep, tapering to a rounded bottom about 4 to 6 inches in diameter. The handle should be light and about $3\frac{1}{2}$ feet long. The wire ring supporting the net should be strong—No. 3 galvanized iron

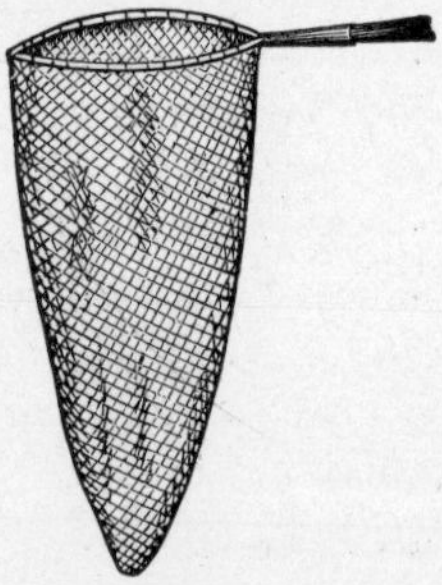

FIG. 799.

FIG. 800.

FIG. 799.—Collecting-net. (After Packard.)

FIG. 800.—Insect-killing bottle; cyanide of potassium at bottom covered with plaster of Paris. (After Jenkins and Kellogg.)

wire is good—and firmly fixed in the handle. For a water-net the meshes should be coarse and the handle, wire, and netting all extra strong.

The killing-bottle (Fig. 800) is prepared by putting a few small lumps (about a teaspoonful) of cyanide of potassium into the bottom of a wide-

656

mouthed bottle from three to six inches high (a quinine or quassia bottle is good) and covering this with wet plaster of Paris. When the plaster sets it will hold the cyanide in place, and allow the fumes given off by its gradual volatilization to fill the bottle. Or the cyanide may be covered with damp sawdust over which is placed a cardboard disk cut so as to fit tightly into the bottle. The advantage of the sawdust covering instead of plaster of Paris is that it allows one to clean out the bottle after the cyanide is used up and to recharge it. The plaster of Paris is broken out of a used-up bottle only with difficulty. The disadvantage of the sawdust and cardboard cover is that it is likely to be loosened if the bottle is jarred often. Insects dropped into a cyanide bottle will be killed in from two to six or seven minutes. Keep a little tissue-paper in the bottle to soak up moisture and to prevent the specimens from rubbing. Also keep the bottle well corked. Label it "poison," and do not breathe the fumes (hydrocyanic gas). Insects may be left in it overnight without injury to them.

Butterflies or dragon-flies too large to drop into the killing-bottle may be killed by dropping a little chloroform or benzine on a piece of cotton, to be placed in a tight box with them. Larvæ (caterpillars, grubs, etc.) and pupæ (chrysalids) should be dropped into the vials of alcohol.

When the collected insects are killed they may be "pinned up" or "papered" in the field; or if not many have been taken, may be brought home in the killing-bottle and cared for after arriving.

To "paper" specimens—and only insects with large wings, as butterflies, moths, dragon-flies, etc., are papered—they should have the wings folded over the back and the specimen then laid on one side on a rectangular piece of smooth paper, not too soft, which is then folded so as to form a triangle with the margins narrowly folded over to prevent its opening. A very success-ful professional collector of my acquaintance "papers," in a sense, small insects in the following way: In the bottom of a small tin, wooden, or paste-board box he puts a thin layer of glazed cotton; over it he lays a sheet of paper, and on this a layer of small insects just as they are poured out of the cyanide bottle; then a covering sheet of paper, and over this a layer of cotton, another sheet of paper, a layer of insects, and so on. In this way he rapidly cares for hundreds or thousands of specimens in the field. When these specimens are brought home he either pins them up immediately while fresh and flexible, or stores them away to be worked over and pinned up at leisure. Before dried insects can be pinned, however, they must be re-laxed. This may be effected by steaming them, or simply by putting them for a day or two into a closed glass jar with a soaked sponge. In my lab-oratory we keep one or two jars with a layer of wet sand in the bottom; into these relaxing jars dried insects can be put at any time, and made ready for pinning.

To "pin up" specimens special insect pins are used. These pins can be bought of any dealer in naturalists' supplies at from ten to fifteen cents a hundred. Order Klaeger pins No. 3 or Carlsbaeder pins No. 5. These are the most useful sizes. For larger pins order Klaeger No. 5 (Carlsbaeder No. 8); for smaller order Klaeger No. 1 (Carlsbaeder No. 2). Pin each insect straight down through the thorax (Fig. 801) (except beetles, which pin through the right wing-cover near the middle of the body (Fig. 802)). On each pin below the insect place a small label with date and locality of capture. If many specimens are going to be collected in one locality, small

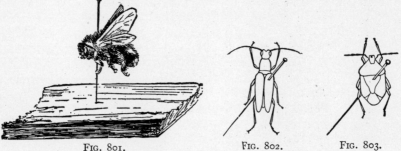

Fig. 801.          Fig. 802.          Fig. 803.

Fig. 801.—Insect properly pinned up.  (After Jenkins and Kellogg.)
Fig. 802.—Mode of pinning beetle.  (After Packard.)
Fig. 803.—Pinning a bug.  (After Packard.)

"locality and date" labels printed in diamond or agate type on paper not too stiff for the pin and yet not so thin and weak as to fold on the pin should be got. The following is the kind of label in use by the students in my laboratory: StanU Cal Jun190  For each specimen the day of the month and year is filled in. We have such labels for each month in the year. Insects too small to be pinned may be gummed on to small slips of cardboard, which should be then pinned up.

The box for pinned specimens which is to be carried on the collecting trip should be small: a cigar-box with its bottom covered with sheet cork or compressed cork is excellent. Corn pith can be used; on the Pacific coast the pith of the flowering stalk of the century-plant is much used, under the name of pita-wood, and is unusually good for the purpose. For containing the specimens permanently cigar-boxes are only to be used when more carefully made boxes cannot be afforded. Certain small insects, especially beetles of the family Dermestidæ, have a particular liking for dried insects and work their way into any but the tightest of specimen boxes. If cigar-boxes have to be used, a small naphthaline cone fastened on a pin should be kept in each box. It will be much safer to obtain tight boxes or trays, either of the glass-topped sort used for display collections, or of the book-shaped sort, used by the National Museum and many other museums and collectors. These boxes may be bought of dealers in naturalists' supplies.

Butterflies, dragon-flies, and other larger and beautiful-winged insects should be "spread," that is, should be allowed to dry with wings expanded. To do this spreading—or setting—boards (Figs. 804 and 805) are necessary.

Such a board consists of two strips of wood fastened a short distance apart so as to leave between them a groove for the body of the insect, and upon which the wings are held in position until the insect is dry. A narrow strip of pith or cork should be fastened to the lower side of the two strips of wood, closing the groove below. Into this cork is thrust the pin on which the insect is mounted. Another strip of wood is fastened to the lower sides of the cleats to which the two strips are nailed. This serves as a bottom and protects the points of the pins which project through the piece of cork. The wings are held down, after having been outspread with the hinder

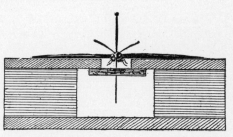

FIG. 804.                    FIG. 805.

FIG. 804.—Setting-board with butterflies properly spread. (After Comstock.)
FIG. 805.—Setting-board in cross-section to show construction. (After Comstock.)

margins of the fore wings about at right angles to the body, by strips of paper pinned down over them.

"Soft specimens," such as insect larvæ, myriapods, and spiders, should be preserved in bottles of alcohol (85 per cent.). Specimens which the collector may desire to preserve in condition fit for future dissecting should be killed in boiling water, into which they should be dropped and allowed to remain for a minute or two until thoroughly stiffened, and then removed to 50 per cent. alcohol for six hours, and finally to 85 per cent. alcohol for preservation. Nests, galls, stems, and leaves partly eaten by insects, and other dry specimens can be kept in small pasteboard boxes.

**Where and how to collect.**—The principal points about where and how to collect will be obvious even to the veriest novice. Go where the insects chiefly congregate, and collect them in the most effective way. But some of the insect haunts may not be known to the beginner nor at first catch his eye, and there are little tricks about collecting in the most effective way. "The most advantageous places for collecting are gardens and farms, the borders of woods, and the banks of streams and ponds. The deep, dense forests and open, treeless tracts are less prolific in insect life. In winter and early spring the moss on the trunks of trees, when carefully shaken over a newspaper or white cloth, reveals many beetles and Hymenoptera. In the late summer and autumn, toadstools and various fungi and rotten fruits attract many insects; and in early spring, when the sap is running, we have taken rare insects from the stumps of freshly cut hard-wood trees. Wollaston says: 'Dead animals, partially dried bones, as well as the skins of moles and other vermin which are ordinarily hung up in fields, are magnificent traps for Coleoptera; and if any of these be placed around orchards and inclosures near at home, and be examined every morning, various species of Nitidulæ, Silphidæ, and other insects of similar habits, are certain to be enticed and captured.'

"Planks and chippings of wood may be likewise employed as successful agents in alluring a vast number of species which might otherwise escape our notice; and if these be laid down in grassy places, and carefully inverted every now and then with as little violence as possible, many insects will be found adhering beneath them, especially after dewy nights and in showery weather. Nor must we omit to urge the importance of examining the under sides of stones in the vicinity of ants' nests, in which position, during the spring and summer months, many of the rarest of our native Coleoptera may be occasionally procured. Excrementitious matter always contains many interesting forms in various stages of growth.

"The trunks of fallen and decaying trees offer a rich harvest for many wood-boring larvæ, especially the Longicorn beetles; and weevils can be found in the spring, in all stages. Numerous carnivorous coleopterous and dipterous larvæ dwell within them, and other larvæ which eat the dust made by the borers. The inside of pithy plants, like the elder, raspberry, blackberry, and

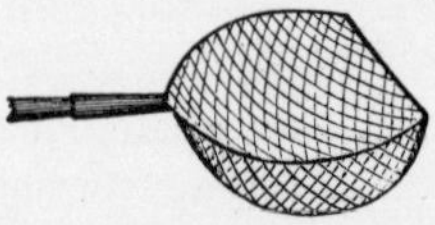

FIG. 806.—Water - net. (After Packard.)

syringa, is inhabited by many of the wild bees, Osmia, Ceratina, and the wood-wasps, Crabro, Stigmus, etc., the habits of which, with those of their Chalcid and Ichneumon parasites, offer endless amusement and material for study.

"Ponds and streams shelter a vast throng of insects, and should be diligently dredged with the water-net, and stones and pebbles should be overturned for aquatic beetles, Hemiptera, and Dipterous larvæ."

Much collecting may be done at night. Many nocturnal moths and beetles are attracted by bright lights: the city's lamp-posts or your own brilliant bicycle-lamp of acetylene gas may be relied on. "Sugaring" for moths on warm nights, a favorite trick of moth-collectors, consists of smearing a mixture of stale beer and sirup in patches a foot square on the trunks of various trees, and then making repeated rounds of these trees with a dark lantern. Throw the light on the smeared spot and any feeding moth there will tarry long enough to be covered with a wide-mouthed bottle or swooped up with the net.

Numerous small insects may be found in galls, in rolled-up leaves, and in bored canes. Where a plant shows leaves ragged or full of holes, there look for the hole-makers. In this kind of insect-hunting one is likely to get the immature stages of insects rather than the adult. So much the better. A collection should not be limited to grown-up insects alone, but should include eggs, larvæ, chrysalids, cocoons, nests, and specimens of insect architecture and industry, and specimens showing the character of the injuries to plants caused by insects. Any specimen which illustrates anything of the life, the biology, of insects should go into the collection. And everything should be labeled, accurately and fully. Locality and date, notes telling of such evanescent conditions as color or of such ecologic relations as character of the surroundings should be put on the specimen, or written into a "collections" book under a number corresponding with one on the specimen. The collecting of immature stages of insects leads naturally to attempts to rear these caterpillars, etc., at home or in the schoolroom or laboratory.

**Rearing insects.**—While in ordinary collecting the insects are killed immediately after being caught, the collector going afield to obtain specimens to keep alive and rear must bring back his trophies unharmed. It is necessary that he modify his field equipment somewhat. He needs empty boxes and little jars, more than killing-bottles and cork-lined pinning-boxes. Do not trouble to punch air-holes in box-lids; enough air will get in through cracks and loose-fitting covers. Aquatic specimens, however, are easily suffocated by filling the water-jar too full and then screwing a tight cover on to prevent splashing. The jars and pails should be carried uncovered if possible, and they should be broad and shallow rather than narrow and deep. Do not try to bring too many water-insects back in one jar; crowding is always fatal to them. With log-burrowing grubs and larvæ bring in some chips and dust of the home log; with underground larvæ bring in some soil. Simply because you find such larvæ in a certain place is sufficient proof that their surroundings are of the right sort for them.

When brought home the live specimens must be transferred to "cages" or rearing-boxes or jars in which proper food is kept and which enables the insect to live as nearly as possible in its normal way. We want our caterpillars not merely to provide us with fine "unrubbed" fresh moths and butterflies for our collection, but want them to go through under our eyes their usual life-history: we wish to see them eat and crawl and moult and spin and transform. We wish to get acquainted with the details of their living; to watch them grow and develop; and to see them display

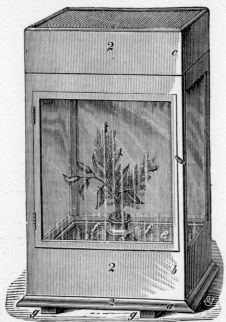

FIG. 807.—Breeding-cage.   (After Packard.)

their instincts and insect wits. We may go so far in our scientific curiosity as to be led to experimenting with them: to note how they react or behave toward light and darkness, toward moisture or dryness, heat or cold; to see if they may be induced to modify their inherited instincts to the extent of doing new and unusual things, or old things in new ways; to see if their life is pure mechanism or in a simpler and more generalized way something like ours, in which consciousness and memory and choice play so important a part.

Particularly available and interesting kinds of insects to rear in home cages and aquaria are the larvæ (caterpillars) of moths and butterflies, various leaf-eating, wood-boring, and ground-burrowing beetle larvæ, honey-bees and ants, and many still-water insects, as water-beetles and bugs, mosquitoes, May-flies, dragon-flies, etc. For these various kinds of insects with their various kinds of habitat and habit several different kinds of cages are necessary.

For moths and butterfly larvæ very simple cages are sufficient. It is only necessary that they admit light and air, that they keep the insects in, and that food, green leaves of the favorite food-plant, may be kept fresh in them, or readily repeatedly supplied. For small, or a few, caterpillars an excellent rearing-cage is shown in Fig. 808. It is made by combining a flower-pot and a lamp-chimney or lantern-globe. When practicable, the food-plant of the insects to be bred is planted in the flower-pot; in other cases a bottle or tin can filled with wet sand is sunk into the soil in the flower-pot, and the stems of the plant are stuck into this wet sand. The top of the lantern-globe is covered with Swiss muslin. These breeding-cages are inexpensive, and especially so when the pots and globes are bought in considerable quantities.

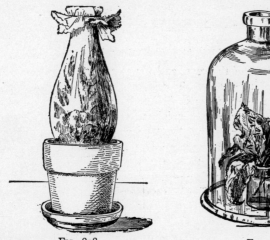

FIG. 808.       FIG. 809.

FIG. 808.—Lamp-chimney and floor of breeding-cage. (After Jenkins and Kellogg.)
FIG. 809.—Bell-jar live-cage.

In our laboratory we have made much use of bell-jars of the kind with a hole in the top for a cork, which can be closed with netting instead of a cork, so that the air may enter (Fig. 809). Small branches of the food-plant are kept in glass bottles of water, whose mouth is closed around the branches by loose cotton so as to prevent the caterpillars from getting in and drowning. For larger, airier cages in which many caterpillars or transforming pupæ can be kept we make much use of common wire-screened meat-safes (Fig. 810), which can be got at the grocer's for about a dollar apiece. Comstock describes a good home-made cage built by fitting a pane of glass into one side of an empty soap-box. A board, three or four inches wide, should be fastened below the glass so as to admit of a layer of soil being

FIG. 810.—Meat-safe live-cage.

placed in the lower part of the cage, and the glass can be made to slide, so as to serve as a door (Fig. 811). The glass should fit closely when shut, to prevent the escape of the insects.

We have even made use in our laboratory of pasteboard shoe-boxes with the middle part of the cover cut out (leaving but an inch or so around the edges), and mosquito netting pasted over the hole. Into such a box fresh leaves must be put often, but beyond the trouble it serves very well. Specially made rearing-cages (Fig. 807) of various kinds can be bought of dealers in naturalist's supplies, but they are mostly rather expensive.

FIG. 811.—Soap-box breeding-cage. (After Comstock.)

For larvæ that live underground cages with soil in must be provided. The principal difficulty of rearing such insects is to keep the right degree of moisture in the soil. If too damp, fungi grow and envelop the insects; if too dry, the larvæ soon die. For the study of insects that live on the roots of live plants Comstock has devised a special form of breeding-cage known as the root-cage. "In its simplest form this cage consists of a frame holding two plates of glass in a vertical position and only a short distance apart. The space between the plates of glass is filled with soil in which seeds are planted or small plants set. The width of the space between the plates of glass depends on the width of two strips of wood placed between them, one at each end, and should be only wide enough to allow the insects under observation to move freely through the soil. If it is too wide, the insects will be able to conceal themselves. Immediately outside of each glass there is a piece of blackened zinc which slips into grooves in the ends of the cage, and which can be easily removed when it is desired to observe the insects in the soil."

Many caterpillars and other larvæ which live above ground in the larval stage when ready to pupate crawl down to the ground and burrow into it. For these soil must be provided in the rearing-cages, or the larvæ when ready to pupate must be removed from the meat-safe and bell-jar cages to boxes containing soil. This soil must not be allowed to dry out entirely, nor yet must it be too moist. Experience is the only teacher that will determine for the novice the "just right" condition.

It may be necessary to keep pupæ, in cocoons or in underground cells, over winter, for many insects, especially in the eastern and northern states, pass the winter in the pupal stage. "Hibernating pupæ may be left in the breeding-cages or removed and packed in moss in small boxes. Great care should be taken to keep moist the soil in the breeding-cages, or the moss if that be used. The cages or boxes containing the pupæ should be stored in a cool cellar, or in an unheated room, or in a large box placed out of doors where the sun cannot strike it. Low temperature is not so much to be feared as great and frequent changes of temperature. Hibernating pupæ can be kept in a warm room if care be taken to keep them moist, but under such treatment the mature insects are apt to emerge in midwinter." Eggs of insects, laid in the fall, may also be kept over winter, but one must be careful to preserve them in a cold place—as an unheated attic or cellar.

Directions for making and maintaining observation beehives and formicaries (artificial ant's nests) are given on pp. 532 et seq. and pp. 548 et seq. of this book.

**Aquarium.**—Many accounts of how to make and keep up aquaria have been published. The following directions have been written by Miss Isabel McCracken, an assistant in my laboratory, who has made and successfully maintained many small aquaria in schools:

To make the aquarium get a board 17×13×1½ inches thick, grooved all around about 1 inch from the edge with a half-inch groove, and painted white. This is for the base. Get two pieces of double-thick glass 15×9 inches for sides and two pieces 11×9 inches for ends. Set the glass into the grooves of the wooden base, bind the corners where the edges of the glass come together with strips of coarse muslin or cambric glued on the outside. (Bicycle-tape is good.)  Place an oblong strip of glass $8\frac{1}{2} \times 1$ inch across the inside of each corner.  Fill the space, thus formed, with cement.

FIG. 812.—Battery-jar aquarium.  (After Jenkins and Kellogg.)

Fill in the grooves of the bottom board with cement before pressing down the panes of glass.  Where the glass sides join the bottom board use cement carefully both inside and out, filling all the cracks.

The cement should be made according to the following formula:

| | |
|---|---|
| White sand. ............................... | 1 part. |
| Plaster of Paris. ......................... | 1 " |
| Litharge. ................................. | 1 " |
| Powdered resin. .......................... | $\frac{1}{3}$ " |

Make into a stiff paste with boiled linseed-oil.  Use as little oil as possible and take proper care in mixing.  Leave for several days to harden the cement.  Then fill slowly and pour off the water several times before using.

Place an inch and a half of sand on the bottom of the box.  This sand should be previously baked or boiled to rid it of bacteria.  Its main purpose is as an anchorage for growing plants.  Over this place a layer of variously sized pebbles treated in the same way.  These form hiding-places for the aquatic fauna.  Fill with water to the depth of five or six inches.  Stock with water-plants, the streams or ponds of the neighborhood to determine the kind.  Watercress, water-crowfoot, Potamogeton, Chara, and eel-grass are good kinds.  Parrot's-feather can usually be obtained at nurseries.

Tradescantia (wandering-jew or inch-plant) is also useful. Avoid the use of algæ (pond-scum). The function of the plants is chiefly to oxygenate the water. The roots of cress will furnish food for some vegetable-feeding animals.

An aquarium, to be in good condition, must be kept aerated, must be kept clean, and its temperature must not be suddenly changed. Sufficient air is sometimes maintained by plant-life alone. Unless this proves to be so, shown by the healthy condition of both plants and animals, dip up a few cups of water every day and let it fall back into the aquarium. All uneaten food, dead animals, or decaying leaves must be removed at once. An apparatus for removing such is described in a later paragraph.

The aquarium should be in the light to enable the plants to produce oxygen, but not in direct sunlight. If it stands in a sunny window, it should be screened from the sun. Water lost by evaporation must be replaced, but the fresh water must not differ materially in temperature from that in the aquarium. If a film appears on the surface of the water, it is due to bacteria and dust. It prevents absorption of air at the surface of the water. It may be removed by absorbent paper (newspaper or blotting-paper). It may be prevented by thorough cleanliness and by using a coarse cheese-cloth cover when not under observation. Never give more food than is eaten.

Implements for use in connection with the aquarium are the following: A small dip-net made by twisting a wire about a bottle for the ring and the ends about each other for a handle,—the net to be made of coarse cheese-cloth or bobinet, used for removing certain objects; a piece of flannel wrapped about a stick for cleaning the sides of algæ, which are bound to accumulate. For removing small particles from the bottom, a $\frac{1}{4}$-inch glass tube long enough to reach to the bottom is useful. Close the upper end with the finger, hold the other end over the object to be removed, lift the finger, and the water will rush up the tube, carrying out the object. Replace the finger on the upper end and lift the tube out of the water. For removing a quantity of sediment, a long narrow chimney tightly fitted at each end with a cork is required. Insert through the center of the corks a short piece of glass tubing, and use as described for the simple glass tube.

To stock the aquarium choose animals that are adapted to life in still water, and keep cannibals by themselves. A wire netting will keep in flying insects.

Of the insects that may be kept in an aquarium some spend their entire life in the water, while others are aquatic during one stage of existence only. Among the insects easily kept in aquaria are the predaceous diving-beetles, the young of which are known as water-tigers and feed on small earthworms and other insects, as mosquito-wrigglers, May-fly nymphs, etc.; the water-scavenger beetles; back-swimmers; water-boatmen; dragon-fly and May-fly nymphs; mosquito larvæ, etc.

Other animals may of course be kept in the aquarium.  Common pond-snails will live easily, feeding on green slime, roots of water-plants, bits of cabbage, etc.; minnows will eat bits of fresh meat, and also the insects; quarrelsome little sticklebacks will eat the pond-snail eggs and small crusta-ceans, as cyclops, etc.; frog and salamander larvæ feed at first on vegetable matter, later on bits of meat, tiny earthworms, mosquito larvæ, etc.

Remember that an aquarium needs daily care to keep it in good condition.

The foregoing account of collecting, preserving, and rearing insects has been made short and only a general course of procedure indicated, with the hope in mind of avoiding the confusion to the beginner likely to result from a longer account, including many "specialties" and refinements in collect-ing methods.  Numerous excellent extended directions for collecting, pre-serving, and rearing have been published.  Two such accounts are those by Comstock in "Insect Life" (Appletons), pp. 284–335, and by Packard in "Entomology for Beginners" (Holt & Co.), pp. 224–288.

# INDEX

Illustrations are indicated by an asterisk. Page references in black face type are to definitions of technical terms. Etymologies are given for the order, suborder, superfamily, and family names. In etymologies of names derived from the Greek, the Greek is followed by the transliteration (in italics) of the Greek letters into Latin letters, and that by the English meaning; in those derived from the Latin, the Latin (in italics) and the English meaning are given; in those derived from other languages, the nativity of each word is specifically indicated. Each of the family names has been derived by adding -idæ (having the force of a patronymic) to the name of the type-genus, which, in the index, immediately follows the family name. The family termination is not repeated throughout the etymologies and should be supplied by the reader.

# THE AMERICAN NATURE SERIES

In the hope of doing something toward furnishing a series where the nature-lover can surely find a readable book of high authority, the publishers of the American Science Series have begun the publication of the American Nature Series. It is the intention that in its own way, the new series shall stand on a par with its famous predecessor.

The primary object of the new series is to answer questions—those (outside of the domain of philosophy) which the contemplation of Nature is constantly arousing in the mind of the unscientific intelligent person. But a collateral object will be to give some intelligent notion of the "causes of things."

The books will be under the guarantee of American experts, and from the American point of view; and where material crowds space, preference will be given to American facts over others of not more than equal interest.

The series will be in six divisions :

## I. CLASSIFICATION OF NATURE

This division will consist of three sections.

**Section A. A large popular Natural History** in several volumes, with the topics treated in due proportion, by authors of unquestioned authority.

The books so far publisht in this section are :

**FISHES,** by DAVID STARR JORDAN, President of the Leland Stanford Junior University. $6.00 net; carriage, 50 cents.

**AMERICAN INSECTS,** by VERNON L. KELLOGG, Professor in the Leland Stanford Junior University. $5.00 net; carriage, 50 cents.

**NORTH AMERICAN TREES,** by N. L. BRITTON, Director of the New York Botanical Garden.

Arranged for are:

**SEEDLESS PLANTS,** by GEORGE T. MOORE, Head of Department of Botany, Marine Biological Laboratory, assisted by other specialists.

**WILD MAMMALS OF NORTH AMERICA,** by C. HART MERRIAM, Chief of the United States Biological Survey.

**BIRDS OF THE WORLD.** A popular account by FRANK H. KNOWLTON, M.S., Ph.D., Member American Ornithologists Union, President Biological Society of Washington, etc., etc., with Chapter on Anatomy of Birds by FREDERICK A. LUCAS, Chief Curator Brooklyn Academy Arts and Sciences, and edited by ROBERT RIDGWAY, Curator of Birds, U. S. National Museum.

**Section B. A Shorter Natural History** by the Authors of Section A, preserving its popular character, its proportional treatment and its authority so far as that can be preserved without its fullness.

**Section C. Identification Books**—"How to Know," brief and in portable shape. By the authors of the larger treatises.

## II. FUNCTIONS OF NATURE

These books will treat of the relation of facts to causes and effects—of heredity in organic Nature, and of the environment in all Nature.

Already publisht:

**THE BIRD: ITS FORM AND FUNCTION,** by C. W. Beebe, Curator of Birds in the New York Zoological Park. 8vo, 496 pp. $3.50 net; by mail, $3.80.

Arranged for:

**THE INSECT: ITS FORM AND FUNCTION,** by Vernon L. Kellogg, Professor in the Leland Stanford Junior University.

**THE FISH: ITS FORM AND FUNCTION,** by H. M. Smith, of the U. S. Bureau of Fisheries.

## III. REALMS OF NATURE

Detailed treatment of various departments in a literary and popular way.

Already publisht:

**FERNS,** by Campbell E. Waters, of Johns Hopkins University. 8vo, pp. xi+362. Price $3.00 net; by mail, $3.30.

## IV. WORKING WITH NATURE

How to propagate, develop and care for the plants and animals.

Already publisht:

**NATURE AND HEALTH,** by Edward Curtis, Professor Emeritus in the College of Physicians and Surgeons. 12mo, $1.25 net; by mail, $1.37.

Arranged for:

**THE SHELLFISH INDUSTRIES,** by James L. Kellogg, Professor in Williams College.

**CHEMISTRY OF DAILY LIFE,** by Henry P. Talbot, Professor of Chemistry in the Massachusetts Institute of Technology.

**DOMESTIC ANIMALS,** by William H. Brewer, Professor Emeritus in Yale University.

**THE CARE OF TREES IN LAWN, STREET AND PARK,** by B. E. Fernow, Late Head of the Cornell School of Forestry.

## V. DIVERSIONS FROM NATURE

This division will include a wide range of writings not rigidly systematic or formal, but written only by authorities of standing.

**FISH STORIES,** by David Starr Jordan and Charles F. Holder.

**HORSE TALK,** by William H. Brewer.

**BIRD NOTES,** by C. W. Beebe.

**INSECT STORIES,** by Vernon L. Kellogg.

## VI. MAN IN NATURE AND EVOLUTION

A Series of volumes by President Jordan, of Stanford University, and Professors Brooks of Johns Hopkins, Thomson of Aberdeen, Przibram of Austria, zur Strassen of Germany, and others. Edited by Professor Kellogg of Leland Stanford.

HENRY HOLT AND COMPANY, New York

010-5